THE LIFE OF
WILLIAM HARVEY

William Harvey *c.* 1627, artist unknown. *National Portrait Gallery*

THE LIFE OF
William Harvey

BY

GEOFFREY KEYNES, Kt.

OXFORD

At the Clarendon Press

1978

Oxford University Press, Walton Street, Oxford OX2 6DP

OXFORD LONDON GLASGOW
NEW YORK TORONTO MELBOURNE WELLINGTON
KUALA LUMPUR SINGAPORE JAKARTA HONG KONG TOKYO
DELHI BOMBAY CALCUTTA MADRAS KARACHI
IBADAN NAIROBI DAR ES SALAAM CAPE TOWN

ISBN 0 19 858119 X

First published 1966
Re-issued 1978 with minor corrections

Printed in Great Britain
at the University Press, Oxford
by Vivian Ridler
Printer to the University

DEDICATED
TO THE MEMORY OF
JOHN FARQUHAR FULTON
PHYSIOLOGIST, MEDICAL HISTORIAN
AND FRIEND

PREFACE

MEDICAL historians have been accustomed for many years to remark how little is known of the life of William Harvey and thereby to imply that little can be known. Even Sir Wilmot Herringham, himself one of the most fruitful writers on the subject, complained in *Annals of Medical History* in 1932 that Harvey was an elusive character and seemed to think that he would ever so remain; yet in the present book I have tried to demonstrate that in fact a fairly complete picture of Harvey in his own environment can be formed, if the scattered threads are gathered. In 1957 Dr. Louis Chauvois published a sympathetic study of Harvey in French and English. It is a matter for astonishment that apart from this no serious attempt to reconstruct the picture has been made since 1897, when an excellent short biography was published by Sir D'Arcy Power, my old friend and predecessor on the surgical staff of St. Bartholomew's Hospital. When Power died in 1942 his library was thrown on the market and much of it was sold in parcels and stacks, giving me the opportunity to acquire many of the source books for Harvey's life, now so difficult to obtain. This provided an incentive to bring nearer to completion the task so well begun by Sir D'Arcy.

It must be admitted that in one respect Harvey's figure is still obscure. Of his wife and home surroundings we know virtually nothing beyond the fact that his wife possessed a tame parrot and it seems unlikely that further research will reveal anything of value. The Harveys remained childless and it seems to me that domestic details, if we had them, would not give any important light on Harvey's work or character. The pages of this book will, I hope, show that it is now possible to see him as a living figure in his relations with his colleagues, patients, and friends, in his work at St. Bartholomew's, in his position at the courts of King James and King Charles, in his travels, and in his sufferings during the social turmoils that disturbed his later years. Much that was previously known necessarily has to be repeated, but much that is new is added to the story. No previous writer seems to have made full use of the Annals of the College of Physicians, and here particularly Harvey's position can be more clearly defined. I have also had the inestimable advantage of being able to use the full and scholarly texts of Harvey's extant writings in manuscript newly edited by Dr. Gweneth Whitteridge. No satisfactory account of Harvey's life could, indeed, have been written until this work had been done, so that in a way Dr. Whitteridge bears a share of the responsibility for this book.

Many volumes have been written on Harvey's scientific work and I have not attempted to provide any last word on this subject. I have only examined his three printed books in so far as they are related to the general story of his passage through this world, hoping that I have brought out the remarkable contrast between the precision and modernity of his work on the circulation of the blood and the confusion of much of his, nevertheless, highly interesting attempt to unravel the mysteries of generation. Harvey was an acute and dedicated 'scientist', but his achievement, great as it was, suffered from the inevitable limitations of the techniques at his disposal.

The most satisfactory assessment of Harvey the scientist yet written was published by Dr. Kenneth D. Keele in August 1965[1] while my biography was still going slowly through the press. Though we were both bred in Harvey's hospital Dr. Keele and I did not pool our resources, for we have always known that our aims did not conflict. Our books are complementary and I can only wish that mine may be found as good as his.

The information given in this narrative is fully documented in the footnotes. I have tried not to leave any doubt in the reader's mind as to what is fact and what conjecture. John Aubrey's confused account of Harvey is a source of great importance and is frequently quoted; it is printed in full in an appendix exactly as he wrote it. The Wills of Thomas, John, and William Harvey are printed in other appendixes, since they will elucidate many relevant names and family references. All the prescriptions attributable to Harvey have been gathered in another appendix. In yet another are listed the references to Harvey's work on the circulation of the blood printed in his lifetime. This is based by permission on the preliminary work of the late Dr. Ernst Weil; although I have made many additions to his list, it is probable that other obscure references still remain to be discovered. Nearly all Harvey's extant letters are quoted in full, transcribed whenever possible from original manuscripts or photostatic copies. At the last moment a letter hitherto unknown has been added in a final appendix.

[1] Kenneth D. Keele, M.D., F.R.C.P., *William Harvey the Man, the physician, and the scientist*, London, Nelson, 1965 ('British Men of Science', general editor Sir Gavin de Beer, F.R.S.).

ACKNOWLEDGEMENTS

I HAVE received help from so many quarters through personal acquaintance or correspondence that it is impossible to acknowledge all individually. Reference has already been made to Dr. Gweneth Whitteridge for her work on Harvey's manuscripts. She has shared with me her deep knowledge of Harveian affairs and I shall always be grateful to her for her generosity. I am under large obligations to the Librarians of the Royal Colleges of Physicians and Surgeons—to Mr. L. M. Payne for his patience in verifying references and his kindness in lending literary material; to Mr. William LeFanu for much helpful advice and more particularly for making many renderings from Latin texts for my enlightenment—his name will be found recurring in the footnotes. I am deeply indebted to the Registrar of the Royal College of Physicians for allowing me to borrow and keep for several years one of the typescript copies of the Annals of the College. It is most generous of the President and Fellows of the College to have contributed the cost of making a coloured reproduction of a page from Harvey's Padua diploma for the degree of M.D. I am grateful to two distinguished historians for their help—to Miss C. V. Wedgwood for her approval of my account of the Battle of Edgehill and permission to make quotations from her work, and to Sir George Clark for correction of some details of fact and interpretation; Sir George's recent *History of the College of Physicians* has naturally been an additional advantage in writing of Harvey. Dr. E. Ashworth Underwood has assisted me in describing the Anatomy Theatre at Padua and has lent an illustrative block from a photograph of his scale model of the Theatre now in the Wellcome Historical Medical Museum. Dr. John Cule has also helped with his knowledge of the Theatre and of Harvey's *stemma* as they are seen at Padua today. Dr. William Urry, Archivist to Canterbury Cathedral, has given me useful information about Harvey's ancestry and relatives. Professor Kenneth Franklin's work is well known and I am grateful for his permission to quote passages from his translations. My wife has read the whole book and her criticisms have been of great value. Many other friends will know that I am not forgetful of their active assistance or their criticism. Lastly I acknowledge my obligations to all those other workers on Harvey's life and writings whose names will be found recorded in the text or in the relevant footnotes.

I am under further obligations for the numerous reproductions which illustrate my book. I am indebted to the Trustees of the British Museum and of the National Portrait Galleries in London and Edinburgh and to the Treasurer of the Royal College of Physicians for permission to reproduce pictures in their custody. Special acknowledgements are due to the Trustees of the Chatsworth Settlement for allowing me to reproduce four drawings by Hollar from their collections and to Mr. Thomas Wragge, Keeper at Chatsworth, for his help in obtaining photographs. I am grateful to Sir Edmund Bacon for allowing me to use his portrait of King James; to Dr. Nellie Kerling, Archivist to St. Bartholomew's Hospital, for photographs and to the Governors for permission to use them; to the Librarian of Sidney Sussex College, Cambridge, for photographs of the petrified skull and of Harvey's letter to Dr. Ward; to Dr. Hollander of the Guildhall Library, London, for help in obtaining a photograph of part of Agas's map of London and of other documents; and to Mrs. Haylock for access to the photograph of a drawing of the Harvey house at Hempstead. Mr. Nicholas Turner has provided a photograph of the Harvey home at Dane Farm near Folkestone and had an important part in making a reproduction of the brass commemorating Harvey's maternal grandparents in the church at Hastingleigh.

CONTENTS

APPENDIXES

LIST OF ILLUSTRATIONS

HARVEY'S FAMILY, BOYHOOD, AND EDUCATION, 1578–1600

DR. WILLIAM HARVEY, the greatest of England's early experimental scientists, is believed to have come from obscure origins in Kent. It has been conjectured that the Harveys stemmed from Sir Walter Hervey, a merchant of the City of London, a member of the ancient guild of Pepperers (afterwards the Grocers), and made Mayor of London by popular demand when King Henry III was lying on his death-bed. Probably the conjecture is based on the fact that William Harvey quartered his family arms with those of Sir Walter Hervey, though other members of the family did not follow his example. In former times arms were commonly assumed without official warrant or even evidence, and genealogists have failed to find any proof of so distinguished an origin for Thomas Harvey, William's father. Another conjectural source of the family is from the Harveys of Thurlby, near Bourne in Lincolnshire, who were descended from the Norman line of Sir Bryan de Hardeby of Evedon.[1] William Harvey's family certainly had connexions with Lincolnshire people, but no proof of descent from that quarter is yet forthcoming.

In the sixteenth century and later there were many families named Harvey in Kent, and genealogical research is thereby made correspondingly difficult and inconclusive. Confusion has also arisen from the proximity of a family or families named Harry, which has sometimes been misread in early documents as Harvey.[2]

William Harvey's father, Thomas (1549–1623), certainly did possess at the time of his death properties at Newington near Folkestone, at the neighbouring hamlet of Arpinge, or Erpinge, and at West Dane Farm. Harvey's friend Sir Charles Scarburgh in his Harveian Oration of 1662 spoke of properties in Kent inherited by Harvey from his grandparents and great-grandparents, implying that the family had lived in that area for several generations. This statement is confirmed by the existence of

---

[1] This is under investigation by Dr. Arthur Jamieson of Barnach, who is persuaded that this is the probable origin of the forebears of Thomas Harvey of Kent.

[2] e.g. in Hasted's *History of Kent*, 1790, iii. 397, where the will of Thomas Harvey of Newington dated 1478 is quoted; the name is in fact Harry.

relevant Wills in the Archdeaconry Court of Canterbury. Thomas Hervy (or Harvye), who died about 1527, left property at Newington and West Dane to his sons John and Thomas; to his wife he bequeathed 'six kine of my best, four oxen, my wanes, carts, ploughs and horse beasts and eight hogs and forty wethers, forty ewes and all poultry'.[1] In the next generation John Harvey left the same properties to his sons Thomas and Richard.[2] Earlier Harveys can be found in the same area near Folkestone in the latter part of the fourteenth century. There are also suggestive references in manorial documents to rents paid by John Hervie, or Harvie, of Newington Bartram, Erpinge, and of Newington Belhouse, Erpinge, in 1558 and 1553–4.[3]

It therefore seems reasonable to believe that William Harvey's forebears had indeed lived as people of substance for several generations in the chalk uplands overlooking the lower coastal area of Newington, Cheriton, and Folkestone in East Kent. They no doubt worked chiefly as sheep farmers, since that was the main use for these steep chalk hillocks and deep valleys reached, even today, only by very narrow lanes. Dane Farm, a short way to the east of Arpinge and very close to an ancient track[4] leading towards Canterbury at the edge of the escarpment, is still there, represented by a small brick-and-timber house of the sixteenth century, which seems likely to have been part of the home of Thomas Harvey before he moved into the neighbouring town of Folkestone.

It may also be remarked at this point that the Wills already quoted show that Thomas Harvye in 1527 bequeathed a lamb to Juliane Hempstede and that John Harvey in 1554 left a sum of money to his daughter Elizabeth Hempsted, thus suggesting an early family connexion between the Harveys and Hempstead in Essex, later to be the burial place of William Harvey and many of his relations.

The five towns, Hastings, Sandwich, Dover, Romney, and Hythe on the coast of Kent, still known as the Cinque Ports, had formed from early times a great and powerful Corporation, which from the reign of Henry II was charged with the defence of the English coast. Its ships constituted the earliest form of a Royal Navy, and it controlled the herring

[1] Register, vol. A 17, f. 168.
[2] Act Book, vol. 15, f. 54. Both identified by the late Dr. Tom Hare.
[3] See Kent County Archives, U270, M258, 259. Communicated by the Archivist, Mr. Felix Hull.
[4] This is marked on most maps as 'Pilgrims' Way', presumably part of the route from Winchester to Canterbury. C. G. Crump (*History*, 1937, xxi. 22–33) has shown that there is no reason for believing that this route was ever used by pilgrims.

PLATE I

Vir petijt fociam, nati tres vnaq; nata
Matrem, nutricem famuli, famula q; magelq;
Mors rapuit, Coniux annis opibulq; repletus,
Vir natis natus, numerofa prole beatus,
Vt genuit rapitur Subterit corpora marmor
Amborum hoc anim Chrifti pia gaudia gaudet.

Iohannes Halke obijt 28	Amia vxor eius obijt 16.
die Mar: A° Dnj 1604.	die feb: A° Dnj 1596.
A° q; ætatis 83.	A° q; ætatis 70,

BRASS COMMEMORATING JOHN AND AMY HALKE IN HASTING-
LEIGH CHURCH, KENT (p. 3)

DANE FARM, NEAR NEWINGTON, KENT
as it is today (p. 2)

fishery, a staple source of food. The power of the Cinque Ports was doomed to ultimate extinction as the harbours were gradually filled by drifts of sand and shingle and rendered almost useless. Only Dover was saved as an important port by the efforts of the Tudor sovereigns, who constructed fortifications and other artificial works.

So Folkestone, a corporate member of the Cinque Ports attached to Dover, also achieved a certain degree of importance, having a castle, monastic institutions, a prosperous population of fishermen, and a minor industry in the cultivation of vines. The town was administered, like the main Ports, by a mayor, twelve jurats, or aldermen, and a council of twenty-four. In the early part of Queen Elizabeth's reign there were 120 houses and the same number of active male citizens, of whom seventy were fishermen. They possessed twenty-five ships and boats. Through the twelfth and thirteenth centuries there had been a good harbour; by the sixteenth century this was becoming spoiled by encroachment of the sea and the castle was destroyed, but the people joined with the Cinque Ports at the threat of the Spanish Armada in a supreme effort to help to build up England's sea power. Together in 1588 they raised £43,000 to equip thirteen vessels, constructed materials for fire-ships, and supplied from Dover the ship which decoyed one of the great Spanish galleasses to destruction at Calais.

By this date Thomas Harvey seems to have prospered through good management of his inherited properties, in spite of political disturbance and the rapidly declining importance of the whole district of East Kent. He was born in 1549, and in 1575, at the age of 26, married his first wife, Juliana, elder daughter of William Jenkin of Folkestone and Mary Juliana Halke. Juliana Harvey died in 1576, probably in childbed, leaving a daughter who lived to marry Thomas Cullen of Dover. Early in the following year, on 21 January 1576/7, Thomas married his second wife, Joan, also named Halke (sometimes spelled Haulke or Hawke), and probably a cousin of Juliana. She came from Hastingleigh, a village on the high land ten miles north-west of Folkestone.

The Halkes of Hastingleigh and Canterbury were a numerous family. Joan's parents, John and Amy, are commemorated by a brass in the nave of Hastingleigh Church, John having been a churchwarden. He was predeceased by his wife in 1596 aged 70, and died himself in 1604 at the age of 83. They were evidently people of good standing, who, though they did not bear arms, adopted the Hawk as their rebus, or emblem, as shown on their brass at Hastingleigh. Juliana Halke's brother, Thomas, became a prosperous *Mercator*, or general merchant, and was a leading citizen of Canterbury. He served as Alderman and Sheriff, and was Mayor in 1610–11. When he married his first wife in 1576/7 his bondsman was John Halke of Hastingleigh, and for his second marriage with Pheanna Finch in 1587 one of his two bondsmen was Richard Halke of the same place. He is also to be identified with Corporal Halke, commander of no. 2 detachment of archers in the Canterbury train-band of 1588. John Marlowe, shoemaker and father of Christopher Marlowe, served in the same detachment.[1]

When Queen Elizabeth came to the throne in 1558 Thomas Harvey was a boy of only 9 with doubtful prospects, but during his adolescence greater prosperity came to Dover, and consequently to Folkestone and Faversham. He proved to be a shrewd man of business and, in addition to his farming activities, is thought to have developed, with two others, a carrying trade between Folkestone, Canterbury, and London, with, at the same time, a coastal and cross-Channel business to France. One partner is said to have been his first father-in-law, William Jenkin, and the other his brother-in-law, Thomas Halke.[2] Thomas Harvey was presumably living mainly at his farmstead of West Dane, which could provide a convenient centre for the horses used in the carrying trade, but he had also leased, according to tradition, a business centre in Folkestone. This may have been the 'faire-built stone house', which John Aubrey[3] stated was the birthplace of all the Harvey children, and was called in Aubrey's time 'the post-house', this name having perhaps given rise to the idea that Thomas Harvey engaged in the carrying trade.

The 'post-house' had become Thomas Harvey's property and, according to Aubrey, passed, to the envy of his brothers, to William, who gave it in due course to Caius College, Cambridge, with some neighbouring lands. Aubrey said that this clause was in his Will, but in this he was wrong.[4] The building is no longer to be seen and its site is uncertain, but

---

[1] Information supplied by Dr. William Urry, F.S.A. See also an article by Andrea Duncan, *Kentish Gazette and Canterbury Press*, 12 July 1963, 'Some Fresh Light on Dr. William Harvey and his Kinsfolk'.

[2] See Tom Hare, 'Harvey's Boyhood', in *Circulation*, ed. J. MacMichael, Oxford, 1958, p. 32; no documentation is given.

[3] For this and all subsequent references to Aubrey's account of Harvey see Appendix I, giving a fresh transcription from the manuscripts in the Bodleian Library. A printed version is also in *Brief Lives*, ed. Andrew Clark, Oxford, 1898, i. 295–305.

[4] Caius College records show that Aubrey's statement was untrue. It has also been stated by various authorities that Harvey in 1617 gave the College the sum of £100 to found a scholarship, but this is also an error. The truth is that Henry Hervey, LL.D., of Trinity Hall left Caius £100 by his Will of 1585. In 1617 it was decreed that lands should be bought to provide for the maintenance of a scholar, but owing to various irregularities the money was

it is believed to have been at the junction of Rendezvous and Church Streets in the centre of the town. There was an official courier and postal service from London by Dover to France, but by 1580 the Merchant Adventurers were finding this inadequate for their needs, and they may have turned to Thomas Harvey's alternative service (if this conjecture is correct) from Folkestone, greatly to his advantage.

Thomas, as we see him in his portrait, painted by a not very skilful hand in 1613, ten years before his death, has the aspect of a rather hard, though intelligent, man. He was undoubtedly fortunate in business, and with his wife through good sense and good management was unusually successful in bringing up a large family at a time when a very high proportion of children died in infancy. He also had the means to launch his sons successfully in the world, having become a leading citizen in Folkestone, where he was appointed a jurat and served as Mayor in the years 1586, 1599, 1601, and 1611. His wife, Joan, died in November 1605, and after some years he moved to Hackney, near London, where he died in June 1623, being buried, according to the local register, on the 17th of the month.

The family born in the 'fair-built stone house' and so successfully reared consisted, as Thomas Fuller said, 'of a week of sons' and two daughters. Of these seven sons five became prosperous merchants, and must have respected their father's business acumen, for, if Fuller is to be believed, 'they got great estates and made their Father the Treasurer thereof, who being as skilful to purchase Land as they to gain Money, kept, employed, and improved their gainings to their great advantage; so that he survived to see the meanest of them, of far greater estate than himself'.[1]

Joan Harvey must also have been a most estimable character and a good mother. At her death a brass tablet was fixed to the wall of the parish church to commemorate her qualities:

A.D. 1605, Nov. 8th dyed in ye 50th yeere of her age,
JOAN, Wife of THO: HARVEY. Mother of 7 Sones and 2 daughters.
A Godly harmless Woman: A chaste loveing Wife:
A charitable quiet Neighbour: A comfortable friendly Matron:

not actually paid to the College until 1628, when lands were bought at Bassingbourne and a scholarship endowed from the rents. (See Venn's *Biographical History of Gonville and Caius College*, Cambridge, 1901, iii. 231. Venn himself started the confusion of names in his *Annals of Gonville and Caius*, Cambridge, 1904, by not distinguishing the 'Dr. Harvey' mentioned on pp. 262 and 340 from his namesake.)

[1] Fuller's *Worthies*, 1662, Kent, p. 79.

A provident diligent Huswyfe: A careful tender-harted Mother:
Deere to her Husband: Reverensed of her Children:
  Beloved of her Neighbours: Elected of God.
Whose Soule rest in Heaven: her body in this Grave:
To her a Happy Advantage: to hers an Unhappy Loss.

Thomas and Joan Harvey's eldest son, William, was born on 1 April 1578, and was baptized on 6 April. There is no contemporary proof of the date of Harvey's birth, but 1 April was the date given on his M.D. diploma at Padua in 1602, and no one other than Harvey himself could have supplied the information. The date of his baptism, on the other hand, is found in the Canterbury Cathedral Register Book where the parish records were copied, so this at least is certain. There is a local tradition that the baptism took place at Hastingleigh, though it actually took place at Folkestone, at the Church of St. Mary and St. Eanswith.

The second of the Harveys' children was a daughter, Sarah, born on 5 May 1580; she died at the age of 11 on 18 June 1591. There followed John on 12 November 1582, Thomas on 17 January 1584/5, Daniel on 31 May 1587, Eliab on 26 February 1589/90, and then twins, Michael and Matthew, on 25 September 1593. The last child of all was a daughter, Amy, born on 26 December 1596.

Of William Harvey's six brothers none can be dismissed as nonentities. Their lives were bound up with his and some account of them will be given on later pages of this narrative. They all left Folkestone and pursued careers at Court or in business in London.

During Harvey's boyhood there was no regular school in Folkestone,[1] the only opportunities for education being provided by itinerant schoolmasters, who practised with or without a licence from the churchwardens. Presumably Harvey received the rudiments of his education in this way, absorbing enough learning to secure his admission to the King's School, Canterbury. It has been conjectured that he was an interested witness of the urgent activity in Folkestone when, in July 1588, the small town was called upon to take its part in helping the Corporation of the Cinque

---

[1] This was remedied shortly after William's death in 1657 by his brother Eliab, who joined with his eldest son Eliab (afterwards Sir Eliab, 1635–99) and a London merchant, John Prestwood, in buying a small estate, Combe Farm, in the neighbouring village of Lympne. The rent of the farm was to form the nucleus of an endowment for a school and to this was added the sum of £200 bequeathed by William Harvey to the poor of Folkestone. In 1671 the Harveys bought premises in Rendezvous Street to form a site for the school. This was actually started in 1674 as the 'Free School'. They also endowed the 'Tanlade', or Tanhouse on another site where the fishermen could tan their nets. The school flourished under the guidance of Trustees and is today known as the 'Harvey Grammar School'. See J. H. Brown's *History of the Harvey Grammar School*, Folkestone, 1962.

Ports to provide ships and materials to repel the Spanish Armada. Certainly his father as a senior jurat must have been deeply concerned in this; the boy, however, was probably by then at school in Canterbury.

There is no documentary evidence at Canterbury of the date of Harvey's admission to the school or of his leaving. The evidence is indirect, notably the inscription recorded by Aubrey as having been over the portrait in the great parlour of the Physicians' College at Amen Corner. This began: *Gul. Harveus, an. aetat. 10, in Schola Cantuar. primis doctrinæ rudimentis imbutus.* There is no reason for doubting the accuracy of this. The earliest age for admission to the school was 9 and the leaving age was 15. Harvey had reached the age of 10 by 1 April 1588, and so is likely to have been at Canterbury before July of that year. The record of his entry at Cambridge confirms that he was educated at Canterbury.

The King's School, Canterbury,[1] and the Cathedral School at York claim that they are the two oldest schools in England. At its foundation and through the Middle Ages the boys admitted to the King's School would be chiefly those intending to become novitiates in the monastery. At the Reformation the Cathedral Priory of Christ Church was surrendered to King Henry VIII in March 1540. A reformed Canterbury Cathedral, with a secular school attached, henceforth known as the King's School, was established in its place, under the King's Great Seal, on 8 April 1541. The constitution of the school provided for fifty King's Scholars, elected as sons either of gentlemen or of parents unable to pay for their education, the only condition being that they should be 'apt for learning'. There were also a small number of choristers and an undetermined number of Commoners. The Scholars were not allowed to vegetate, the Statutes laying down the rule 'that if any of the boys be remarkable for extraordinary slowness and dullness or for a disposition repugnant to learning, we will that after much trial by the Dean, or in his absence by the Vice-Dean, he be expelled and another substituted, that he may not like a drone devour the honey of the bees'. The time to be spent in the school was ordinarily four years, sometimes stretched to five, 'until they have obtained a moderate acquaintance with the Latin grammar and have learned to speak and write in Latin'. Further, no boy was to be admitted to the school who did not know by heart the Lord's Prayer, the Angelus, the Apostles' Creed, and the Ten Commandments. Once a week the Headmaster was to examine the whole school and to

---

[1] The standard works on the King's School are: J. S. Sidebotham, *Memorials of the King's School*, 1865; C. E. Woodruff, *Schola Regia Cantuariensis*, 1908; and D. L. Edwards, *A History of the King's School*, 1957.

promote suitable boys from form to form, of which there were five or
six, three times a year. The chief form of recreation was football, and,
according to the Statutes, 'When leave to play is given they shall play
together and sport together, lest, wandering about here and there, they
incur some loss of character and gradually alienate their minds from
learning by the desire of other things. And they shall not practise any
games which are not of a gentlemanly character and free from all lowness.'

Young Harvey must have been among the Commoners, since the only
extant list of the fifty Scholars in the school during his period is for the
year 1590 and it does not contain his name. He could certainly not have
claimed a place on grounds of poverty and there is no reason for supposing that he was at any time a chorister. While at school he may have
been a boarder or have lived with some relation of his mother in the city.

The Headmaster of the King's School at the time of Harvey's entry
was Anthony Shorte, a Bachelor of Civil Law, formerly a Fellow of All
Souls College, Oxford. During his reign the school was not always in
good repute. In 1584 the Cathedral Chapter granted him five marks 'to
encourage him in his diligence and his paynestaking in teaching, and
for the relief of his charges in his late sycknes'; but at the end of 1588
he was admonished 'to have a greater care and to be more diligent than
he hath byn that the scholars of the schole may better profit in learning,
as well as in good manners and civility than late they have done'. This
reproof had its effect and in 1590 he received a bonus of 53s. 4d. for the
diligence with which he fulfilled his duties. This improvement must
have taken place in spite of his bad health, for he died in October 1591
and was succeeded by Roger Raven, M.A., of Clare Hall, Cambridge.
Raven was a good schoolmaster and remained in office for the next
twenty-four years.

If Harvey was a boarder at the school he is not likely to have had comfortable quarters, and discipline tended to be severe, but he would have
been well fed. Documentary evidence shows that Commoners, who paid
$\frac{1}{2}d.$ to $1\frac{1}{2}d.$ a week for their board, were each given half a pound of beef
or mutton on five days of the week, with milk, eggs, and butter, and
plenty of beer. The fare was more meagre, however, during Lent, though
fresh fish would have been easily obtainable from Folkestone or Dover.

There is good reason, however, for thinking that Harvey was not a
boarder at the School. As already mentioned, a prosperous citizen in
Canterbury, Thomas Halke, was his step-uncle, being a brother of
Juliana, Thomas Harvey's first wife, and it would have been natural for
young William to live in his house while attending the King's School as

a day-boy. It is worth noticing also that another probable relative, Robert Halke, living in the house next to that occupied by Christopher Marlowe and his family, was an apothecary.[1] Is it possible that the boy's interest in medicine was aroused by this first contact with an important branch of the profession?

The instruction at a Cathedral School must have been preponderantly religious and classical, and Harvey no doubt obtained a good grounding in Latin with, perhaps, a little Greek.

We can only guess at Harvey's own inclinations when he was a school-boy. He would have had no instruction in the natural sciences at Canter-bury, but he was a country-born youth and undoubtedly observant, so that he is very likely to have had a spontaneous interest in the animal life on the farm at West Dane and in the wild life of the surrounding woods of Kent, certainly then, as now, exceptionally prolific in interest-ing plants and insects, being ecologically on the 'continental fringe' of southern England. When the time came for him to leave school his father sent him to Gonville and Caius College, Cambridge. The influence of his second headmaster might have directed him to Clare Hall, so that the choice of Caius (as it is usually called) suggests that this was made to suit his particular scientific bent. Gonville Hall had been re-founded as Gonville and Caius College by Dr. John Caius in 1567, and he was its Master from 1559 almost till his death in 1573.[2] He was a truly eminent scholar, physician, and anatomist. Educated at Gonville Hall, Cambridge, and at Padua, he had studied medicine under Giambattista da Monte (Montanus), and anatomy with Andreas Vesalius. He and Vesalius had even shared a lodging and it might be thought that from this great master of anatomy he would have acquired and spread the new scientific learning that was published to the world in *De humani corporis fabrica* in 1543. Caius was not, however, a man who readily accepted innovations, and, although he is regarded as the founder of the study of anatomy in England, he remained a convinced Galenist. His association with Vesalius ended in disagreement, since he preferred the ancient errors of Galen to ocular demonstration of the truth. He even prepared an edition of some of Galen's anatomical writings, pub-lished in 1544.[3]

---

[1] Information supplied by Dr. William Urry.

[2] He resigned on 27 January 1572/3 and died on 29 July 1573.

[3] In this book Caius mentions his discussion of a passage in Galen with Vesalius: 'All the copies we have used have these words, and Galen seems to have meant it. ... Andreas Vesalius, when we used once to share the same house and discuss our anatomical studies with one another, thought these words ought to be deleted, as he was advised from certain manuscripts

At Padua, where he took his M.D. degree in 1541, Caius lectured, according to his own statement, on Aristotle. Later he travelled widely in Europe and on his return to London realized the unsatisfactory state of anatomical teaching in England. The Barbers and the Surgeons, having been united as one Company by Act of Parliament (32 Hen. VIII, cap. 42),[1] were granted each year the bodies of four criminals for dissection, but owing to lack of surgeons interested in anatomy these remained unclaimed. This state of affairs Caius sought to remedy by giving lectures and demonstrations in the Barber-Surgeons' Hall during the years 1544 to 1564. There were no facilities for such lectures at the College of Physicians, who still occupied the small premises in Knightrider Street provided by their founder, Thomas Linacre, in 1518. It was probably Caius who obtained from Queen Elizabeth in 1565 a Charter of Anatomies, and from this time each Fellow in turn was expected to give lectures and was liable to pay fines if he did not do so. Caius had been elected a Fellow in 1547 and was President on nine occasions between 1555 and 1572; his eminence also secured his appointment as physician to King Edward VI and to Queen Mary.

The influence of Caius on the Cambridge College he had refounded must have been profound and its reputation as a place where medical studies were encouraged widely known. A significant innovation made by Caius at Cambridge was to obtain another charter from the Queen enabling the Master and Fellows of his College to have each year for dissection the bodies of two criminals executed in Cambridge or in its Castle. These were to be obtained without charge and without any official interference, for the benefit of medical knowledge and the health of the Queen's subjects.[2] This suggests that the College would have great attractions for a youth with scientific or medical leanings.

There has been some confusion as to Harvey's exact age when he was admitted to Caius. Aubrey's record of the inscription in the College of Physicians already mentioned gives *14 Col. Gonvil. et Caii alumnus*, but

---

which had certain insertions from a very old book. But I do not know whether this had been written on the authority of the book or by the opinion of the transcriber, who repeatedly was wont to insert not what the book had, but what he himself thought.' See *Galen, Libri aliquot Graeci, per Ioannem Caium*, Basel, Froben, 1544, p. 286, note for p. 27, l. 17. Translation by W. R. LeFanu.

[1] Sidney Young, *Annals of the Barber-Surgeons*, 1890, pp. 78–80.

[2] At a dinner held in Caius in 1893 celebrating the tercentenary of Harvey's admission to the College Sir George Paget mentioned in his speech that the remains of the dissected subjects 'were interred with great reverence, the Master and Fellows attending the funeral'. (the *Standard*, 22 June 1893.)

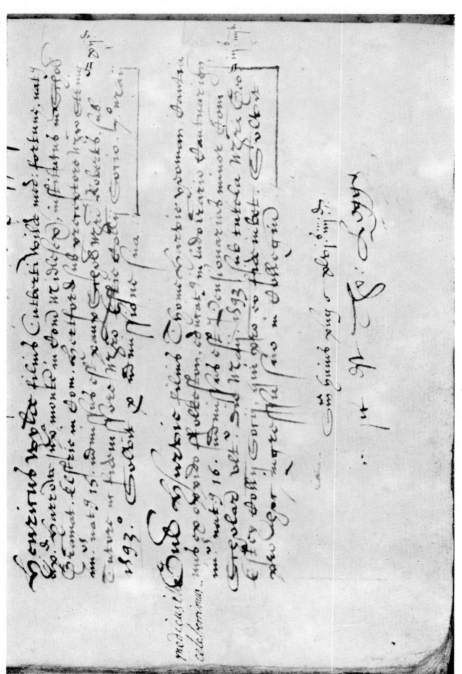

PLATE II

THE ENTRY OF HARVEY'S MATRICULATION AT CAIUS COLLEGE, CAMBRIDGE (p. 11)

in fact he was in his sixteenth year. The entry in the College books is as follows:

Gul. Harvey, Filius Thomae Harvey Yeoman, Cantianus ex oppido Folkeston, educatus in Ludo Literario Cantuar. annos natus 16, admissus est Pensionarius minor [in] Com[meatum] scholar[ium], ultimo die Maii 1593 sub tutela Mgri. Geo. Estey, Collegii Socii, qui pro eo fide jubet. Solvit pro hoc ingressu suo in Collegium iijs. iiijd.

or in English:

Wil. Harvey, son of Thomas Harvey yeoman, from the town of Folkestone in the county of Kent, educated at Canterbury School, in his sixteenth year, has been admitted as *Pensionarius minor* to the Scholars' mess on the last day of May 1593, under the tutorship of Master Geo. Estey, Fellow of the College, who goes surety for him. He pays for this his entrance into the College 3 shillings and 4 pence.

His tutor, George Estey, was a clergyman and a lecturer in Hebrew. Another Fellow of the College in Harvey's time was Thomas Grimston, M.D., an anatomist who probably performed the dissection of the bodies granted to the College.[1] Whether this demonstration was carried out regularly during Harvey's years at Cambridge there is no means of knowing, but many years later in his anatomical lectures in London he referred to the small liver and spleen that he had seen in a corpse in Cambridge, and he is not known to have to returned to the University after going down at the end of 1599.

The student hierarchy of which Harvey had become a member was divided into four grades. The *Pensionarii majores* were Fellow Commoners drawn from the wealthier classes and they seldom studied seriously enough to take degrees. The *Pensionarii minores* consisted of three divisions —the Bachelors of Arts, the Scholars with stipends, and Commoners without stipends; finally there were Sizars who usually carried out some menial duties. Harvey would at first have been one of the third class of minors, but a few months later he rose to the second class, when at Michaelmas 1593 he was awarded a Matthew Parker scholarship.

Parker, born at Norwich in 1504, was a graduate of Corpus Christi College, Cambridge, and became an eminent theologian and preacher. In 1544 he was appointed Master of his College, and, although a reformer by nature, did much to avert spoliation of the University properties by

[1] It is known from the College *Annals* that Grimston did in fact carry out a public dissection with 'great credit to him and to the utmost edification of his audience' two years after Harvey's departure from Cambridge.

Henry VIII. Under Edward VI he was appointed to the important and lucrative Deanery of Lincoln, but in Queen Mary's reign he was forced to retire into obscurity owing to his having been a supporter of the claims of Lady Jane Grey. He was able to emerge again when Elizabeth came to the throne and returned to Cambridge, where his chief interests lay, but at the Queen's desire he was persuaded to accept the see of Canterbury, and he was consecrated Archbishop at Lambeth on 17 December 1559. Though Parker was a generous and enlightened man, he had to take part in seeing that Romish practices were not carried on within his jurisdiction; in 1565 proceedings had to be taken against various evidences of 'superstition' still remaining in Cambridge, and in particular against the Master of Caius, who was justifiably suspected of having inclinations towards Rome.[1] The Archbishop consequently became unpopular in Cambridge, though this did not impair his devotion to the University, and among his many benefactions the manuscripts bequeathed to his College form one of the most splendid. His relevance to the story of Harvey's life may be unexpected, but it is none the less important. Although he had had to censure Dr. Caius on religious grounds he certainly remained his friend and it was perhaps at the suggestion of Caius that in 1571 he founded a medical scholarship at Caius College. Dr. Caius had himself founded twenty scholarships, each with a stipend of £2. 13s. 4d. Archbishop Parker for his single foundation gave £61. 13s. 4d., providing a yearly stipend of £3. 0s. 8d.; it was, however, a 'tied' scholarship, to be held only by a boy born in Kent and educated at the King's School, Canterbury.[2] Knowledge of this benefaction was no doubt an extra inducement to Thomas Harvey to send his son to Caius, knowing that the boy was qualified to hold it, not only by virtue of his origin, but also owing to his character as 'able, learned and worthy', these qualities being required by the terms of the foundation. Although Parker does not seem to have had any special interest in medicine, he did make a remarkable gesture in creating the first medical scholarship in England.

In 1524 Linacre had founded medical lectureships in Oxford and Cambridge, and in the reign of Edward VI a commission had been sent to Cambridge, in 1548, with a view to converting one of the existing Colleges into a medical school, but no definite action had been taken. Parker

---

[1] See John Strype, *The Life of Matthew Parker*, Oxford, 1711, i. 399–400.

[2] For the record of the foundation see John Caius, *Annals of Gonville and Caius College*, ed. John Venn, Cambridge, 1904, pp. 176–7: *De Scholari Archiepiscopi Cantuariensis et aliis ejus donis.*

may have remembered this, though it was surely not by chance that he chose Caius as his scholar's College. There had already been three holders of the Parker scholarship and the third did not complete his tenure until the summer of his sixth year. Consequently Harvey could not receive his stipend immediately on admission; he had to wait until the Michaelmas term and pocketed his first payment in December 1593. His tenure could have lasted until Lady Day, that is 25 March, 1600.

Gonville Hall before the time of Caius was a small College. He doubled its size, and the Annals of the College, for which he was chiefly responsible, record the loving care which he lavished on the details of the construction. He laid the foundation stone himself at 10 o'clock in the morning of 5 May 1565. The appearance of the buildings, with Caius Court on the south side of the older Gonville Court, can be best seen in David Loggan's engraving made about 1688,[1] though some new features had by then been made and others had disappeared. Harvey would have entered the College from High Street (now Trinity Street) through the stone-built Gate of Humility, and have walked westwards along an avenue of trees between walls to the Gate of Virtue; this led into a range of buildings and through the doorway, sometimes known as the Gate of Wisdom,[2] and so into the court where the students were housed. On the south side of this court was the elaborate and beautiful Gate of Honour leading to the Schools. These Gates, or stone doorways, were intended by Caius to remind his students of their proper attitudes to learning, though the Gate of Honour, designed by Caius himself, was not built until after he had died. In its present restored state it opens on to Senate House Passage and so to the Senate House itself, built in the eighteenth century, where degrees are conferred.

In the middle of Caius Court was a stone column surmounted by a block 'wrought with wondrous skill, containing 60 sundials. It was the work of Theodore Haveus of Cleves, a skilful artificer and eminent architect.' The students living near it would thus have no excuse, at any rate in fine weather, for not knowing the time of day. The sundials had disappeared by Loggan's time. The gates were all closed at the dinner hour and at twilight, not to be opened again until next morning. The Hall where meals were eaten was in the older Gonville Court to the north, and this court housed the Fellows. The Master's Lodge and the Chapel were in a building separating the two courts. In the years after

---

[1] Plate xix in David Loggan's *Cantabrigia Illustrata*, Cambridge, *c.* 1690.
[2] The name, not authorized by Caius, was derived from the inscription on its frieze: CAIUS POSUIT SAPIENTIA, this having been copied from the foundation-stone.

Harvey's admission the buildings had become too small for the increased number of students and Fellows, and a block of tenements on the north side of the entrance avenue, bought from Trinity College, was added to the accommodation and was known as the Pensionary; it may have been here that Harvey lodged in 1594. Other buildings had taken the place of the Pensionary before Loggan made his drawing.

The Hall was small, 24 feet wide by 48 feet long; it had an open timbered roof with collar-beams and arched braces. The butteries and cellars were underneath the floor, which was raised 5 feet above the level of the court, giving them a total height of 7 feet. There was no heating in the Hall until 1565, when a fund was left by Dr. Humphrey Busbye to provide firing on Sundays and feast-days between All Saints and Purification, or even on common days when the cold was excessive. Anyone who was late for grace at mealtimes was not allowed to come near the fire, so that there was some inducement to the students to remember to be punctual.

Harvey's three subjects of preliminary study during his residence at Cambridge were the classics (with which he was already well acquainted), rhetoric, and philosophy. It is doubtful whether there would have been any instruction in mathematics. Sir Charles Scarburgh, a close friend of Harvey's later years, said in his Harveian Oration at the College of Physicians in 1662 that at Cambridge 'he drank in philosophy and medicine, and from the purest and richest spring of all, if there be such another dedicated to Apollo in the British Isles'.[1] Scarburgh strengthened this claim by relating how he was once called to a consultation over a very ill patient in company with six other physicians, Harvey being the chief. It was found that every one of the seven had been an undergraduate at Caius College. Clearly, therefore, opportunities for a medical education were exceptionally good there, and since Harvey, as we shall see, spent little more than two years at Padua before graduating as M.D., he must have had a good grounding in medicine at Cambridge—though in another passage Scarburgh asserted that Harvey's final decision to excel in medicine was not made until he went to Padua. Even then he might not have absorbed much knowledge during his early weeks at Padua, since (as Bayon observed)[2] he would have had some difficulty at first in understanding Latin as pronounced in Italy.

There do not appear to have been any formal medical lectures at

[1] Bodleian Library, MS. Rawl. D 815. First identified by L. M. Payne, *Journal of the History of Medicine* (1957), xii. 158–64. Here quoted from a translation by W. R. LeFanu.
[2] H. P. Bayon, ibid. (1947), ii. 51–56.

PLATE III

GONVILLE AND CAIUS COLLEGE, CAMBRIDGE

On the extreme right is the Gate of Humility opening on to the street. In the foreground is the Gate of Honour. Behind this are Caius Court and Gonville Court. After an engraving by Loggan, *c.* 1690

Cambridge, though some informal discourses were occasionally given. Dr. Timothie Bright, a predecessor of Harvey on the staff of St. Bartholomew's Hospital, had certainly given such lectures before 1582. This is evident from the preface to his book, *Hygeina id est de sanitate tuenda*, written in Cambridge, where he mentions that he had given lectures and that his hearers had urged him to print the notes from which he spoke.[1] The two books, *Hygeina*, 1582, and *Therapeutica de sanitate restituenda*, 1583, were the result. If Bright gave such lectures, there may have been others of which there is no record. Instruction in the University was limited to medical readings and disputations on subjects such as pulses, urines, and drugs, Galen's writings, and the *Aphorisms* of Hippocrates. A Regius Professorship of Physic had been founded in 1540, but the only duties were anatomical demonstrations in the winter months, since there were no means of preserving the dissected cadavers. This instruction, as we have seen, would probably have been reinforced by special demonstrations at Caius.

The vogue of scholasticism persisting into the seventeenth century decreed that undergraduate studies should comprise rhetoric, logic, and ethics; rhetoric including knowledge of classical authors, ethics being coloured by the teachings of Aristotle. Harvey would have had little or no opportunity of studying anatomy or medicine until he had taken his B.A. degree. As a Bachelor he would be able to study 'physics', this being a strange mixture of astronomy, chemistry, biology, psychology, physics, anatomy, meteorology, and even geology.[2] Astronomy was considered to be a necessary adjunct to medicine, and perhaps even some astrology, which was still often accepted. The width of Harvey's learning is illustrated in a question asked by Aubrey in 1655. In that year, he stated:

I desired Dr. W. Harvey to tell me how flints were generated. He sayd to me that the black of the flint is but a natural vitrification of the chalke: and added that the medicine of the flint is excellent for the stone, and I thinke he said for the greene sickness; and that in some flints are stones in next degree to a diamond. The doctor had his arms and his wife's cutt in such a one, which was bigger than the nail of my little finger, found at Folkestone in Kent, where he told me he was born.[3]

[1] See Geoffrey Keynes, *Dr. Timothie Bright, 1550–1615: A Survey of his Life*, London, 1962, p. 5.
[2] W. T. Costello, S.J., *The Scholastic Curriculum at Early Seventeenth-Century Cambridge*, Harvard University Press, 1958.
[3] Aubrey, *The Natural History of Wiltshire*, ed. J. Britton, London, 1847, p. 43.

Although medical education was good at Caius, it is certain that the teaching of anatomy was never properly organized. The letters of another student, Joseph Mede, of Christ's College, written a few years later, demonstrate the haphazard methods then pursued:

March 15 1627/8: We had an anatomy lecture upon a boy of some 18 years old, Monday, Tuesday, Wednesday, twise a day the last two dayes. I was once there, but saw it so ill accommodated that I came no more; for it was in the regent house upon a table, when onlye halfe a skore doctors could come to see anything, standing close by the table, and so hindering others seeing, which was the chiefe; for I can read as good as they could heare, and with more ease. It will be next time I hope better, for our new doctor will have one every yeare. We heare talke that the body was begged before any was condemned, which if true was very absurd.

The room in the Regent House where this took place was afterwards the Catalogue Room in the old University Library, and is now used as a common-room for members of the Regent House. Mede wrote again on 16 April 1631:

Going on Wednesday from Jesus College pensionary with Dr. Ward to his Colledge through the closes and gardens and espying a garden open I entred and saw there a hideous sight of the skull and all other bones of a man with ligaments and tendons hanging and drying in the sun by strings upon trees, etc., I asked what it meant. They told me it was the pedler they anatomised this Lent and that when his bones were dry they were to be sett together againe as they did naturally and so reserved in a chest or coffin for their use who desired such an inspection.[1]

All forms of learning were gradually falling into decay at Cambridge during the sixteenth century, but however disorganized medical teaching may have been in Harvey's time, we may be sure that with his native drive and determination to spend his time profitably he would have found the means of studying to greater purpose than did most of his contemporaries. The comparatively short time that he spent at Padua for his later studies argues that he had acquired more knowledge at Cambridge than is usually believed.

Fourteen years later, in 1616, when he was setting down notes for his lectures on anatomy, he recalled many medical observations made during his time at Padua or afterwards in London, a number of his patients being mentioned by name. Thoughts of Cambridge, however,

---

[1] These letters are in the British Museum, Harleian MSS., and are quoted in Professor A. Macalister's *History of the Study of Anatomy in Cambridge*, Cambridge, 1891.

aroused very few useful memories. Speaking of gluttony he recalled as an instance, 'Wilkinson of Cambridge [ate] a pig off the spit.' The individual thus immortalized has not been identified, though he was no doubt notorious at the time.[1] The only other recollections of Cambridge relate to two tragedies which may have taken place in Harvey's own College. Writing of the abdominal viscera, he remarked: 'I saw in a timorous man hanged in a staircase at Cambridge a spleen cleft into great lobes and the liver small', suggesting that he was allowed to witness a post-mortem examination. Then, in his discussion of respiration he wrote: 'And so inspired air which is not suitable suffocates as is evident in the case of those who die from blazing coals WH a scholar of Cambridge.'[2] The symbol WH emphasizes that this was a personal observation. Perhaps the victim was a fellow undergraduate trying to keep warm in an austere college attic with the help of a charcoal brazier. Or it may be that both individuals were unhappy students seeking relief from their problems in suicide.

Our knowledge of how Harvey occupied his time in Cambridge can only be guessed from these rather uncertain indications. The College *Exiit Book and Acta Collegii* (the volume for 1592–1618) shows that his absences were not longer than normal during his earlier years, but that in 1598 and 1599 he was away for longer periods owing to illness. The actual entries[3] in the *Exiit Book* are as follows:

1596 *Harvie. Exiit 6to Julii, rediturus ultimo Septembris. Harvie rediit 7 Oct.*

1597 *D. Harvie exiit 4 Julij, rediturus 30 Septembris. Rediit 27 Sept.*

1598 *D. Harvy exiit 15 Martii rediturus 16 Aprilis. Rediit 30 Martii.*
    Ds. Harvie. Exiit 19 Sept., rediturus 1° Novemb. Petiit absentiam ad Natalitia Christi.

1599 *D. Harvey conceditur in absentia ut aegrotanti ad 13^m Januarii. Rediit eodem die. Exiit 20 Jan., rediturus 24° eiusdem. Rediit 22 Janu.*
    Exiit 3 Feb., rediturus 5 eiusdem. Rediit eodem.
    D. Harvie. Exiit 4to Julii. rediturus 30 Septembris.
    Ds. Harvey 12° Octob. significavit per litteras se morbo graviori laborare eoque absentiam petiit usque dum convaleverit. Rediit 27° Octob.
    Exiit 30 Octob., rediturus 30 Januarii.

---

[1] It is possible that he was the ex-Fellow of Trinity who preceded Harvey on the staff of St. Bartholomew's Hospital. See p. 52.

[2] *Prelectiones*, ed. Gweneth Whitteridge, Edinburgh, 1964, pp. 121, 133, 293.

[3] Kindly supplied by Dr. Philip Grierson of Gonville and Caius College.

It is evident that in the second half of 1599 his illness was serious, since he was away from 4 July to 27 October. Even then he had not recovered and left again three days later, never to return.

Harvey had taken his B.A. degree in the summer of 1597. The actual admissions for that year are not recorded, but the supplicats for the year 1596/7, preserved in the University archives, include Harvey's :[1]

Coll:
Gon: Cays
> *Supplicat reverentiis vestris Gulielmus Harvey ut duodecim termini completi in quibus ordinarias lectiones audiverit (licet non omnino secundum formam statuti) una cum oppositionibus et responsionibus ceterisque exercitiis per regis statuta requisitis sufficiant ei ad respondendum questioni*

Ad.
> Math: Stokys *praelect.*

Coll:
Gon: Caius
Admitted
> William Harvey makes supplication to your reverences that the twelve terms which he has completed and in which he has heard the ordinary lectures (albeit not entirely in accordance with the form of the statute) together with the contrary arguments and replies and other exercises required by royal statute may suffice for him as a reply to the question
>
> Math: Stokys prelector

The clause in the supplicat concerning 'the form of the statute' might suggest that the wording was peculiar to Harvey. All the others submitted at the same time are, however, in identical terms, showing that the regulations about attendance at lectures were not too rigidly applied.

It seems that Harvey resigned his Matthew Parker scholarship at Christmas of that year. He then received the last payment of his stipend, and his name in the *Exiit Book* is replaced on 20 December 1599 by that of his successor, Richard Plumely. The letter written by Harvey to the College authorities in October is not extant and we have no direct clue as to the nature of his serious illness. In later life he suffered severely from gout, but it is unlikely that he was incapacitated by this as a youth —though this was seriously put forward by Sir Thomas Barlow in his Harveian Oration of 1916[2] as the probable cause of his absence. It seems much more likely that Harvey was suffering from a severe infection by the malaria parasite, which was particularly prevalent in the fen country around Cambridge as well as in Kent. In his lecture notes of 1616 he wrote in his description of 'the lower belly', or abdomen: *Iecur magis*

---

[1] Transcribed and translated by Dr. Gweneth Whitteridge.

[2] Sir Thomas Barlow, 'Harvey the Man and the Physician', *Brit. Med. Journ.* (1916), ii. 577; reprinted ibid. (1957), i. 1264–71.

dextra, X *totum. Vide venam umbilicalem, vide conexum lieni.* ♄ *tumorem meum quartana;* that is, 'The Liver is situated chiefly on the right side, X [i.e. *not*] entirely. Observe the umbilical vein, observe the connexion with the spleen. ♄ I had a tumour there when I had a quartan ague.'[1] This reference proves that Harvey had at some earlier time suffered from a serious attack of malaria, since enlargement of the liver and spleen, particularly the latter, are evidence of malarial anaemia and cachexia. Cinchona, or 'Peruvian bark', yielding quinine, was not imported into Europe until 1639, so that when Harvey was a young man he would not have been able to obtain any quickly effective treatment. Illness from this cause for several months would easily explain his prolonged absence during 1599.

The life of a University student or 'undergraduate' (the term was in use by Archbishop Laud as early as 1630) in the late sixteenth century was not without hardships. The day started at five o'clock with a compulsory attendance in chapel. Lectures began at ten minutes past six, lasting for four hours, with a break for refreshments consisting of bread and beer. Dinner was at ten or eleven, meat and broth being served with salt and oatmeal. This régime was described by Dr. Lever, Master of St. John's, in 1550, and he continued: 'After thys slender dinner they be either teachynge or learnynge untyll v. of the clocke in the evenynge, when as they have a supper not much better than theyr dyner. Immedyatelye after the whyche, they go eyther to reasonyng in problemes or unto some other studye untyll it be nyne or tenne of the clocke, and there beyng without fyre are fayne to walk or runne up and downe halfe an houre, to get a heate on their feete whan they go to bed.'[2] There was little privacy, the unheated rooms usually being shared by three or four youths.

The entries in the College books show that Harvey's yearly stipend of £3. 0s. 8d. would almost cover the cost of his commons, but any further expenses would have to be paid out of whatever allowance his father gave him. The tenor of his life after leaving Cambridge suggests that he was always a serious student and is unlikely to have indulged in the more expensive forms of sport, such as falconry or coursing with greyhounds. Horse-riding would have been a necessity rather than an amusement. Football was a favourite relaxation, though it was found that intercollegiate matches led to disorder and the authorities tried to confine the game to the College premises. Bathing was another pastime that was more rigorously suppressed. In 1571 a decree was issued 'That

---

[1] *Prelectiones,* pp. 72–73.   [2] *Sermons,* ed. Arber, 1895, p. 122.

no one do go into the water'; if the order was disobeyed the offender was publicly whipped, and for a second offence was liable to be expelled. The probable reason for this severity was that nudity was an offence against public decency, added to which was the risk of death by drowning, the weedy river Cam in the reaches along the Grantchester Meadows being then (as now) dangerous for inexperienced swimmers.

Another source of trouble was the many scuffles or more serious disorders between the students and the townspeople. Often these were due in the first place to the high-handed actions of the University Proctors, who had considerable powers in the regulation of commercial dealings in the town, so that feuds were started and were then exacerbated by the violent behaviour of the students. In November 1596, among a series of complaints, it was said that 'the maior goinge about to represse misdemeanors offered by divers younge men of the Universitye and to see the Quenes peace kept, was assalted and evel intreated by three or fower Schollers, and his gowne rent and spoiled, and some used lewde speaches to the Maior, and he putt in danger of his lyf. And the Scollers beinge complayned upon, Answer was made by some Universitye officers that they could not amend it, for soe it hathe been and soe wil be still.'[1] If Harvey's temperament was 'choleric', as it was afterwards called by Aubrey, he may sometimes have been a participator in these quarrels, but upon this he remained silent. He never referred to his Cambridge career in any of his writings nor gave any sign that he was particularly grateful for what he had gained from his Alma Mater.

It is notorious that the students in Tudor times were greatly addicted to play-acting. Strolling players had given trouble in 1593, and in July of that year the Vice-Chancellor and Heads of Colleges appealed to the Chancellor, Lord Burghley, to prohibit 'publicke showes and commen plaies', partly because of their being 'of lewd example', but still more because they were thought to be a source of danger in spreading infection of the plague, from which Cambridge had been mercifully free. The young men were therefore thrown upon their own resources and they derived much amusement from performing plays and interludes of their own invention.

A statute of 1558 at Harvey's College, recognizing that the medical instruction available at Cambridge was not adequate for full training as a doctor, allowed Bachelors of Arts wishing to pursue a medical career to leave the University and to go to Padua, Bologna, Montpellier, or Paris. Harvey, following the footsteps of both Linacre and Caius, chose

[1] Cooper's *Annals of Cambridge*, 1843, ii. 560.

to go to Padua, then at the zenith of its fame as a school of medicine. It was, indeed, one of the two or three leading Universities of Europe, with a medical school famous both for its anatomical and clinical teaching. In anatomy the sequence of Vesalius, Columbus, Falloppius, and Fabricius in the professorial chair had given it a quite dazzling distinction. Beginning under the influence of a physician, Montanus, the Clinical School of Padua had also for more than half a century provided a form of teaching unique in Europe until Leyden followed suit. Harvey, therefore, not only had the opportunity of studying anatomy under the most favourable conditions, but was also able to acquire clinical knowledge and bedside experience in the hospitals.[1]

Until the year 1916, when Sir Thomas Barlow gave his Harveian Oration, it was assumed that Harvey had left Cambridge after taking his B.A. degree in 1597. Dr. John Venn's investigation of the Caius College books then showed that Harvey was still in residence during several months of 1598 and 1599, and was receiving his stipend as Matthew Parker scholar until Christmas 1599; it thus became evident that he could not have matriculated at Padua until the beginning of the year 1600. It must, therefore, now be accepted that Harvey arrived in Padua early in 1600, and this agrees with the fact that the first document proving his presence records his name:[2]

D. Gulielmus Arveius Anglus

as heading the list of the English students in the University for the year 1600–1. It was customary at Padua for the record of entry to mention a visible scar or some other physical peculiarity to help in identification of a student, but for Harvey this is lacking.

We have no knowledge of how Harvey travelled to Padua. Sir Charles Scarburgh, in his Oration delivered sixty years later, said that Harvey, wishing to see all countries where he might gain knowledge, 'visited France, Germany, Italy, and there in particular that most flourishing University of Padua'. If, as we believe, he matriculated at Padua early in 1600, it seems probable that he did not in fact spend long on his journey, but travelled without undue delay to his chosen seat of learning.

---

[1] See Professor A. Dalla Volta, 'Harvey at Padua', in *Circulation*, Oxford, 1958, p. 44.

[2] The name was published in Andrich's *De natione Anglica et Scota*, Padua, 1892, p. 46, as *Ameus*. This was critically re-examined for Sir D'Arcy Power and found to have been misread, as recorded in Power's *William Harvey*, London, 1897, p. 18.

TRAINING AT PADUA, 1600–1602

THE University of Padua[1] started its existence as an offshoot of the University of Bologna. As it grew in size and fame it attracted students from other countries, and small separate colleges began to be founded for the different nationalities, the English College being instituted in 1446. In its early days Padua depended for its prosperity to some extent on the political troubles of Bologna, since these deflected students to enter elsewhere, and so in the early fourteenth century, as Bologna's reputation declined, Padua's steadily rose until it took its independent place as Italy's foremost University and School of Medicine. Padua profited also by its proximity to the Republic of Venice, being officially adopted as its university quarter. While the cosmopolitanism of medieval days was passing away elsewhere, Padua's broadminded outlook proved particularly attractive to students from England and other Protestant countries. Artists, scientists, and liberal-minded people came to work there in an atmosphere of civil and academic freedom such as could be found hardly anywhere outside the domains of Venice.

At Cambridge Harvey had been a member of a Magistral University, ruled, like those of Oxford and Paris, by its Masters of Arts and senior dons. He had now moved to a Student University, where the undergraduates themselves exercised control over their courses of instruction and elected their own teachers. As a crowd they were cosmopolitan, but inside the University each national College or 'Nation' elected one representative or *Consiliarius*, or sometimes two, and these, with the Rectors, constituted the executive body of the whole. Moreover there was in Padua a division into two sub-universities; on the one hand the Jurists, who were of higher rank and greater material wealth, and on the other the smaller and poorer university of Arts, including the faculties of divinity, medicine, and philosophy. In early times the Arts division was entirely subordinate to the Jurists, representatives of Canon and Civil Law, to whom fees were paid. In 1399 the Jurists agreed to renounce this unnatural supremacy, though they kept their right of appeal to the

---

[1] The standard work on Padua is Hastings Rashdall's *The Universities of Europe in the Middle Ages*, ed. Powicke and Emden, 1936. See also J. H. Randall, jr., 'The development of scientific method in the School of Padua', *Journal of the History of Ideas* (1940), i. 177–206.

junior Rector in the event of a dispute. When Harvey entered the University he would naturally be a member of the Arts division, but there seems to have been no Englishman of good enough standing to represent the Jurists, so that they chose him from among the Arts students to be at the head of their list. He was accordingly elected *Consiliarius* for the English Nation on 1 August 1600 and, as the documents show, again in the next two years—a remarkable tribute to Harvey's outstanding personality early in his career.

It was customary to commemorate councillors or other distinguished resident doctors or professors by the erection of a *stemma*, that is a tablet bearing a coat of arms or a symbol, in the Great Hall or nearby. In 1892 a search was made by Professor George Darwin, F.R.S., Plumian Professor of Astronomy at Cambridge, for any such tablets put up in honour of Englishmen who had studied at Padua.[1] He found among others tablets for Richard Willoughby, a Fellow of Corpus Christi in 1569, and for the two well-known doctors of a later date, Sir John Finch and Sir Thomas Baines, but he failed to find one for Harvey. The search was continued on his behalf by Professor Ferrari of Padua, who in 1893 was able to report that he had found two symbolic tablets commemorating Harvey. Both were in the cloisters of the courtyard adjoining the Hall and were above the capitals of columns in the concavity of the roof. One situated opposite the great gate of the Palace court was very much decayed. The other was in better condition, with some of its original colour remaining. The symbol on each tablet, presumably chosen by Harvey himself, was a white-sleeved arm holding, against a red background, a lighted candle entwined by two green serpents. If the serpents are to be regarded as the symbols of Æsculapius, then the lighted candle seems prophetic of Harvey's achievement in illuminating medical art with the truths of scientific discovery. This highly suggestive *stemma* was emblazoned on the back of the first sheet of the illuminated diploma received by Harvey when he was granted his degree as Doctor. Above the symbol on the tablet was inscribed: ANGLICA, and below it: GULIELMUS HAR/VEUS ANGLUS. Both tablets, after their rediscovery, were restored at the charges of the Master and Fellows of Caius.

As a *consiliarius* Harvey would have taken part in the ceremony of installation of a Rector; this took place every two years and was held in the Cathedral—a scene of great magnificence, with the whole University in attendance; but the general living conditions seem to have been no better than Harvey had already experienced at Cambridge and there

[1] G. H. Darwin, *Proceedings of the Cambridge Antiquarian Society* (1895), viii. 337.

was even less opportunity for relaxation and amusement. We are told that

the medical session began on St. Luke's Day (18 October) in each year, when there was an oration in praise of medicine followed by High Mass and the Litany of the Holy Ghost. The session lasted until the Feast of the Assumption, on 15 August, and in this time the whole human body was twice dissected in public by the Professor of Anatomy. The greater part of the work in the University was done between six and eight in the morning, and some of the lectures were given at daybreak, though Fabricius lectured at the more reasonable hour *hora tres de mane*, which corresponded with nine o'clock before noon.[1]

It is said that the tranquil atmosphere proper to the academic scene was not infrequently broken by fights between rival gangs of students from different Nations, and sometimes by more serious disturbances occasioned by bitter antagonism between the more liberal-minded cosmopolitan students of the University and those attending a rival institution in Padua kept under strict surveillance by Pope Gregory VIII and members of the Society of Jesus. In 1600 these feelings were aroused in the strongest degree when Giordano Bruno, a former professor at the University and greatly revered as a philosopher and humanitarian, was burned at the stake in Rome. As an ex-Dominican he had incurred the displeasure of the Inquisition, whose servants, having kidnapped him by an ambush, delivered him up for condemnation.

Aubrey, writing many years later, reported that Harvey 'was, as all the rest of the brothers, very cholerique; and in his young days wore a dagger . . ., but this Dr. would be to[o] apt to draw out his dagger upon every slight occasion'. Dr. Louis Chauvois[2] has attributed this habit of wearing a dagger to the disturbed conditions of his life in Padua, and implies that carrying a weapon, as well as 'his trick of fingering the pommel while he talked', persisted into his later life. Aubrey, however, deliberately relates this to 'his young days', and it seems improbable that, even at Padua, Harvey would have been markedly quarrelsome. As *consiliarius* for his Nation almost from the start he would be careful to control his passions, though it was probably safer to wear a dagger if only for self-defence.

It has often been conjectured, no doubt rightly, that Harvey had been attracted to Padua by the celebrity of the medical school and the excellence of the teaching provided. As already mentioned, Caius had worked

[1] D'A. Power, *William Harvey*, 1897, pp. 22–23.
[2] Louis Chauvois, *William Harvey, his Life and Times*, London, 1957, p. 66.

PLATE IV

THE UNIVERSITY OF PADUA, CENTRAL BLOCK, IN 1654
After Thomasini

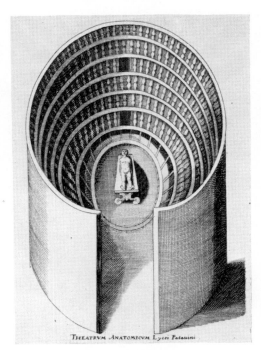

THE ANATOMY THEATRE OF FABRICIUS
Semidiagrammatic view, after Tomasini

PLATE V

THE ANATOMY THEATRE OF FABRICIUS

Scale model by Dr. E. Ashworth Underwood seen from above

there as a fellow-student with Vesalius, whose great textbook of anatomy published in 1543 had first established the subject as a scientific discipline by describing exactly what was to be seen by careful dissection, usually regardless of former opinions. By Harvey's time the teaching of anatomy was in the hands of Girolamo Fabrizi d'Acquapendente, more often known by the latinized form of his name, Fabricius, and his fame was sufficient to have decided Harvey's choice; there can, indeed, be no doubt that Fabricius had more influence on the trend of Harvey's thought than any other teacher that he is likely to have met at Padua or elsewhere.

Fabricius was born about 1533 at Acquapendente, near the Umbrian town of Orvieto. His forebears belonged to the minor nobility and, when he went to Padua in 1550, he had entry to the houses of the Venetian nobles. After a thorough general education, he studied medicine under Gabriele Falloppio (1523–62), whose name was well known throughout Europe, and became his friend. He took his doctorate of Philosophy and Medicine about 1559 and soon afterwards began to give private lessons in anatomy, until, in 1565, he was appointed Professor of Surgery and Anatomy. His pre-eminence both as doctor and as anatomist ensured his reappointment on successive occasions, until in 1609 the chairs of Anatomy and Surgery were separated. He retired from the chair of Anatomy in 1613 and died at the age of about 86 in 1619.

Fabricius continually sought to improve the teaching of his subjects and thereby attracted more and more students to his classes. In 1584 he constructed a special theatre adapted for the first time for anatomical demonstrations, but this was a temporary wooden structure capable of being dismantled and re-erected in different positions outside the main buildings of the University or in the courtyard. Later he put his theatre inside the central university block, occupying the two upper floors between the second and third windows from the left in the contemporary view of the façade of the building. This led to an improved design as a permanent feature within doors. It was constructed in 1594[1] and is the celebrated Anatomy Theatre still to be seen in a somewhat altered form.

It is approached through the room where disputants for degrees defended their theses seated on a chair placed centrally within a horse-shoe-shaped table at which sat the examiners. The wooden theatre itself is made in the form of an oval measuring about 24 by 20 feet at the bottom. On the outside is a spiral staircase leading up to small landings giving access to the five concentric galleries where the spectators stood. There were no seats, the space between the front and back of each

[1] See J. P. Tomasini, *Gymnasium Patavinum*, Utini, 1654, p. 77.

gallery being only eighteen inches, but each is 3 feet above the one below, so that a student leaning on the rail in front of him in the steeply rising auditorium would be able to see over the heads of the men below. The galleries rise at so steep an angle that the audience looked, as it were, down into a funnel and saw the demonstrator with the dissected body on a table at the bottom. Beneath the floor of the theatre at the present time is a small stone chamber for the preparation of the body, which could then be placed on a slab and raised through a hole to the level of the table. In Harvey's time the dissection took place in the stone chamber itself, so that even the spectators in the first gallery, reserved for other professors and doctors, were looking down into the dissecting pit. The size of the table would allow room around it for a very few favoured persons, such as senior officials of the University and other notabilities, but the galleries are estimated to have been able to hold up to 240 people. The theatre was lighted only by two candelabra each with three or four candles, but this was insufficient to provide proper light at the bottom of the pit and was supplemented by eight lamps held by students. A spectator in the top gallery was only about 25 feet away from the demonstrator.

An illustration made in 1654[1] (plate IV) gives a semi-diagrammatic view of the theatre; a more realistic idea is conveyed by a photograph taken almost vertically above a scale model made by Dr. E. Ashworth Underwood for the Wellcome Medical Historical Museum.[2] This shows figures occupying the galleries and the openings by which they entered (pl. V).

This, then, was the scene where Harvey began to absorb anatomical knowledge in a form more acceptable to his clear analytical mind than it had been hitherto—although even here he soon began to question and to criticize.

Although Fabricius was a brilliant anatomist and is to be regarded as the creator of the science of comparative anatomy, he seems to have been in his later days by no means an ideal teacher.[3] Although he was attentive to the needs of individual students and to their general welfare, he did not really like teaching. He is described as having been a good lecturer when genuinely interested, but ready to avail himself of any excuse for shortening or even cancelling his course. He may, however, have had good reasons for this. At one time he was greatly irritated by

---

[1] Tomasini, loc. cit., p. 74.

[2] See E. Ashworth Underwood, 'The Early Teaching of Anatomy at Padua', *Annals of Science* (1963), xix. 1–26.

[3] See K. J. Franklin, '*De venarum ostiolis*' *of Fabricius*, Springfield and Baltimore, 1933.

the bad manners of the German students, who created disturbances during his demonstrations, and he did not improve matters when he abused them and ridiculed by imitating their bad Italian accent. Probably, in fact, he was better equipped for research than for routine teaching; and he may have annoyed his students by dwelling, as they thought, unnecessarily on the comparative anatomy of the numerous animals he dissected alongside his human subjects, when their aim was to learn only human anatomy in order to pass their examinations as soon as possible. He was in great demand as physician and surgeon by many important patients, was of a litigious turn of mind, which involved him in many lawsuits, and a voluminous writer on many different medical and anatomical subjects. All these extramural activities must have made great demands on his time. Fabricius was specially honoured by his University, being given the privilege of wearing the same robe of purple and gold as was worn by a Rector, and, when he resigned his office, was granted the title of Doctor for life and presented with the Golden Collar of the Order of St. Mark. He was given precedence over all other professors and drew a large annual pension.

It is plain that Fabricius had a forceful personality and a vigorous creative mind, which could not fail to impress and inspire a pupil, such as Harvey, who had an equally distinguished personality and mind-in-the-making, ready, however, to criticize creatively and, by sounder reasoning, to transcend his master.

It has always been assumed by his biographers that Harvey's relationship with Fabricius was close and Scarburgh said so in his Oration of 1662. Sir D'Arcy Power wrote that 'Fabricius was more than a teacher to Harvey, for a fast friendship seems to have sprung up between master and pupil',[1] and others have repeated this with variations. It must be admitted, however, that these statements are founded on probability rather than on fact, for there is no clear evidence that it was so. It certainly seems unlikely that Fabricius could have failed to notice that this particular pupil was much above the average in ability, and it may well be that he engaged his master's close attention soon after his admission. He may even have assisted him with his dissections and have enjoyed his friendship and hospitality at Bugazzi, four miles from Padua, where, about 1596, he had built a country house with pleasure gardens. But Harvey was undemonstrative and reticent. He referred to Fabricius in his writings nearly thirty years later with respect and called him 'the celebrated Girolamo Fabrizi d'Acquapendente a most skilful anatomist

---

[1] Power, loc. cit., p. 24.

and venerable old man',[1] but usually his references were made in order to demolish Fabricius's opinions with unanswerable arguments. Nowhere can any expressions of particular gratitude or affection be detected. It will be seen that Harvey's debt to Fabricius was considerable, but it was as much for his having aroused constructive opposition as for acceptable teaching. His example in the wide range of his investigations may also have had a profound effect on Harvey's thinking and methods of work, so that his influence on this remarkable pupil cannot with justice be belittled.

When Robert Boyle, the great chemist and one of the founders of the Royal Society,

asked our famous *Harvey*, in the only Discourse I had with him, (which was but a while before he dyed) What were the things that had induc'd him to think of a *Circulation of the Blood*? He answer'd me, that when he took notice that the Valves in the Veins of so many several parts of the Body, were so plac'd that they gave free passage to the Blood Towards the Heart, but oppos'd the passage of the Venal Blood the Contrary way : He was invited to imagine, that so Provident a Cause as Nature had not so Plac'd so many Valves without Design: and no Design seem'd more probable, than That, since the Blood could not well, because of the interposing Valves, be Sent by the Veins to the Limbs; it should be Sent through the Arteries, and Return through the Veins, whose Valves did not oppose its course that way.[2]

Harvey's answer immediately suggests a reference back to find out what was his direct debt to Fabricius. Before his arrival in Padua in 1600 Fabricius had published a book on the plague (*Dissertatio de lue pestifera*, 1585) and another on surgery (*Pentateuchos chirurgicam*, 1592). Between 1600 and 1619, during his retirement, he produced a series of works on a variety of subjects, such as speech and hearing, embryology, medical consultations, and the surgery of wounds. With one of these we are particularly concerned, since it was a treatise on the valves of veins, *De venarum ostiolis*, a slim folio published in Padua in 1603.[3]

This tract (for it is no more than that) was dedicated, in spite of their earlier bad behaviour, to the students of the German Nation. Among his opening remarks Fabricius wrote (in Professor Franklin's translation): 'A discussion of these valves must be preceded by an expression of

[1] *Movement of the Heart and Blood*, Translated by K. J. Franklin, Oxford, 1957, p. 81.

[2] Boyle's *A Disquisition about the Final Causes of Natural Things*, 1688, p. 157.

[3] The sheets of this tract are usually found bound up with other tracts by Fabricius under a general title page, *Opera anatomica*, Padua, 1625, but Franklin (loc. cit.) has shown that it was undoubtedly first issued as an independent work, though few copies have survived in this form.

wonder at the way in which they have hitherto escaped the notice of Anatomists, both of our own and of earlier generations; so much so that not only have they never been mentioned, but no one even set eye on them till 1574, when to my great delight I saw them in the course of my dissection.' Since Fabricius first noticed these structures in 1574 we may be sure that they were demonstrated to Harvey in the University theatre during the first year of his residence in Padua. Professor Franklin has wondered whether 'valve' is the correct translation of Fabricius's *'ostiolum'*, the name which he says he gave the little membranous pockets found in pairs at the openings of certain veins, particularly those of the lower limbs, when he first saw them. Properly *ostiolum* means 'little door', and it may be doubted whether it is justifiable to give the word any other meaning in Fabricius's context, for it is plain that he completely misunderstood their function. He was quite aware that they opened upwards and could see that two of them when filled might meet and occlude the lumen of the vein, but the accepted function of veins was to afford passage of blood to the extremities. Fabricius had no notion that the blood might be moving in the opposite direction, towards the heart. To him, as he explains in his tract, the *ostiola* were placed where he found them in order to delay the passage of blood downwards (in the lower limb) and not to act as valves preventing it. In his mind, therefore, they would be 'little doors', only partly open in order to perform their function. Incidentally, as Professor Franklin has pointed out, Fabricius's claim to be the first observer of *ostiola* was not justified. They had been demonstrated in the *azygos* and renal veins by Giambattista Canano[1] about 1536 and shown to Vesalius at Ferrara when he visited there in 1545; but Canano understood their function no better than Fabricius and did not publish his observations. Claims have also been made for Charles Estienne and Jacques Dubois (Sylvius), but their observations were too meagre to be seriously considered. More serious are the claims made for the theologian, Pietro Paolo Sarpi (or Father Paul), who is stated by his biographer to have discovered the valves in veins by dissection and to have demonstrated them to Fabricius. This will be mentioned again later in another context (see p. 173).

Harvey in *De motu cordis*, 1628, at the beginning of chapter 13 referred to the discovery of the 'valves' by Fabricius, and it is of interest to note that he designated them by the Latin word *valvula* and proceeded to point out that 'the discoverer of the valves did not understand their real function, and others went no further'. It is tempting to speculate at what

[1] See H. Cushing & E. C. Streeter, *Monumenta Medica*, Florence, 1925, iv, 29.

point the conformation of the valves first suggested to Harvey 'that they gave free passage to the Blood Towards the Heart, but opposed the passage of the Venal Blood the contrary way', as he told Boyle. Did he take the point as he witnessed the demonstration by Fabricius? And did he dare to question his master's interpretation there or in private discussion afterwards? The answer almost certainly is that he did not, for the evidence of his lecture notes composed in 1616 suggests that he did not even then fully realize the implications of the venous valves. Fabricius's demonstration is unlikely to have been the turning-point directing Harvey's mind to the ultimate perception of the great truth that he afterwards established.

Nor does his own account of how he came first to entertain the idea of a circular motion of the blood accord with Boyle's story. In chapter 8 of *De motu cordis* Harvey wrote:

Truly when I had often and seriously considered with myself, what great abundance there was, both by the dissection of living things, for experiment's sake, and the opening of arteries, and many ways of searching, and from the Symetrie and magnitude of the ventricles of the heart and of the vessels which go into it, and go out from it (since Nature making nothing in vain, did not allot that greatness proportionably to no purpose, to those vessels) as likewise from the continued and carefull artifice of the doores and fibers, and the rest of the fabrick, and from many other things; and when I had a long time considered with myself how great abundance of blood was passed through, and in how short a time that transmission was done, whether or no the juice of the nourishment which we receive could furnish this or no: at last I perceived that the veins should be quite emptied, and the arteries on the other side be burst with too much intrusion of blood, unless the blood did pass back again by some way out of the veins into the arteries and return into the right ventricle of the heart.

I began to bethink my self if it might not have a circular motion, which afterwards I found true.[1]

Dr. Louis Chauvois, in a delightful chapter[2] of deliberate fantasy, has attempted to reconstruct the way in which Harvey's mind may have worked shortly before he left Padua. He figures Harvey setting out on a solitary walk towards Venice soon after his capping as Doctor of Medicine on 25 April 1602, and meditating as he goes on the movements in a circle seen in nature; he wonders whether the same might not occur

[1] *The Anatomical Exercises*, ed. Geoffrey Keynes, London, 1928, pp. 57–58.
[2] Loc. cit., pp. 88–97.

as a result of the movement of the heart. In this connexion Dr. Chauvois points out that Galileo was at that very time teaching in Padua, having come there from Pisa in 1589 at the age of 25. By 1600 he was 36 and at the zenith of his fame, and Harvey, aged 22, would have had many opportunities of hearing and meeting him. In the eighth chapter of *De motu cordis* Harvey does indeed refer to the motion of the blood in a circle, and compares the heart to the sun as the centre of our microcosm. Harvey could not, however, have supposed that the heart revolved and so must have accepted the Copernican view, as did Galileo, that the planets revolved around a stationary sun. From this point, continues Dr. Chauvois, Harvey's mind, during his day of solitude and meditation, reasons from the anatomical facts that he knows, including particularly the structure of the valves of the heart, and almost comes to seize the central idea of a circulation from arteries to veins, to lungs and so back to the heart again. This is all to be tested by further observation and experiment when he returns home, and while he is reflecting on how much of his thought is in opposition to what he has been taught at Padua he suddenly finds himself walking into the marshes of the Venetian lagoons and that it is already night. In the early morning he makes his way back to Padua in a market-gardener's cart and wonders as he goes if Fabricius, in the lecture that he is about to give on the veins, is really going to fail to realize the implications of his discovery. This he finds it hard to believe. Yet, as we have seen, it is clear from the tract by Fabricius, published in the year after Harvey's departure from Padua, that he did fail, and it was left to Harvey to demonstrate the truth in his book published twenty-five years later. Dr. Chauvois, for the purposes of his narrative, has certainly greatly accelerated the progress of Harvey's ideas on the circulation, but the main outline of his fantasy is a useful and interesting approximation to what, in all probability, over a very much longer period, did actually happen.

It is, perhaps, not unnatural to think of Harvey as having devoted his attention largely to anatomy at Padua, but this is to lose a sense of proportion. Sir Charles Scarburgh in 1662 characterized him as 'one not to be held bound by the laws of a single discipline'. He was certainly studying medicine in its widest meaning and gathering professional knowledge from experience in hospital wards and autopsy chambers as well as in lecture theatres. In his own lecture notes of 1616, writing of abscess of the liver, he remarked: 'These things I have examined both in the Hospital [of St. Bartholomew] and in the Italian hospitals with much nausea and loathing and stench and I remember them, but many I have forgotten.'[1] This can only refer to the hospitals of Padua or in other centres, such as Bologna, which he may have had opportunities to visit, since he had not returned to Italy after 1602. He also recalled in his notes several individual patients seen in Padua, such as a courtezan 'who had moles [probably syphilitic ulcers] which had eaten into her stomach';[2] a boy[3] whose genital organs had been injured by the bite of a dog; and a man who was not incapacitated for coitus even after his *glans penis* had been removed.[4] Harvey was, in fact, busily developing his capacity for observation of everything that concerned him as a doctor.

Harvey received his degree as Doctor of Medicine at Padua on 25 April 1602. By a happy chance his Diploma has survived to the present day; it came somehow into the possession of the Revd. Osmund Beauvoir, former Fellow of St. John's, Cambridge, and Headmaster of the King's School, Canterbury, who gave it to the College of Physicians of London on 7 July 1764 by request of Sir William Browne, President of the College in 1765. In 1908 a facsimile reproduction was made and issued, together with a pamphlet by Dr. J. F. Payne, Harveian Librarian, giving an English translation of the text.[5] Diplomas given at Padua, like those at some other universities, were elaborately illuminated documents on vellum, pompously worded in Latin. Some of these had a portrait of the new Doctor or his coat of arms; Harvey's shows on the inside of the first leaf only his *stemma* beneath the legend: IN/CHRISTI/NOMINE/AMEN. Surrounding the *stemma* is an elaborate decorative pattern incorporating three small landscapes. The wording of the text, if taken literally, would show Harvey to have been a student of quite extraordinary brilliance. So, indeed, he may have been, but the terms used were conventional, and in fact convey nothing except that he had been judged by the examiners to be worthy of the degree. After this extravagant eulogy of the candidate, the ceremony of capping by Johannes Thomas Minadous of Rovigo, Professor of Medicine, is briefly described as follows (in Dr. Payne's translation):

Johannes Thomas Minadous did then solemnly decorate and adorn the same noble William Harvey (who in a most perspicuous oration asked for and accepted them) with the accustomed Insignia and ornaments belonging to a Doctor: For he delivered to him certain books of Philosophy and of Medicine, first closed and then, a little while after,

---

[1] *Prelectiones*, p. 149.   [2] Ibid., p. 117.   [3] Ibid., p. 209.
[4] Ibid., p. 213.
[5] *Notes to accompany a Facsimile Reproduction of the Diploma . . ., with a translation by J. F. Payne*, M.D., F.R.C.P., London: Privately printed at the Chiswick Press, 1908.

PLATE VI

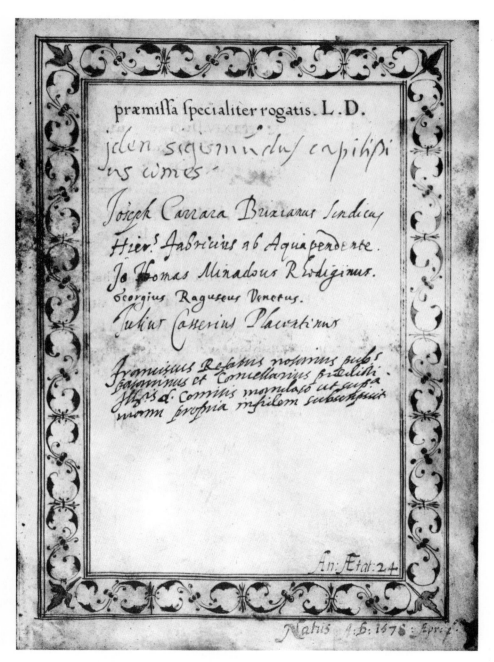

HARVEY'S DIPLOMA FOR THE DEGREE OF M.D., PADUA

The last page with signatures of Fabricius and other officials. Below is Harvey's age and date of birth

open; he put a golden ring on his finger, he placed on his head the cap of a Doctor, as an emblem of the Crown of Virtue, and bestowed on him the Kiss of Peace with the Magistral Benediction.

Harvey had himself appeared as *Consiliarius Nationis Angliæ* to witness the degree conferred on T. Heron [Thomas Hearne] on 19 March,[1] preceding his own ceremony. This was witnessed by a number of local notables, with several members of the English Nation, whose names are given as Antony Fortescue, Richard Willeby [Willoughby], Matthew Lister, Peter Munsel, Simeon Fox, and Robert Darcey. Harvey's document was signed by Minadous, together with Sigismund, Count of Capilisti; Joseph Carrara, Syndic, of Brescia; Hieronymus Fabricius of Acquapendente, Professor of Anatomy and Surgery; Georgius Raguseus of Venice, Professor of Philosophy; Julius Casserius of Piacenza, teacher of Anatomy, Physic, and Surgery; and Franciscus Refatus, Notary Public of Padua and Chancellor of the Lord Count. Finally it was inscribed at the bottom: *An. Ætat. 24 Natus A.D. 1578 Apr. 1°*, thus fixing the date of Harvey's birth, of which this is the only documentary evidence.

Sigismund de Capilisti, Count Palatine, who granted the diploma, was nominated as a non-ecclesiastical Procurator by the Venetian Senate because the usual diploma, given in the name of the Pope, could be granted only to those of the Catholic faith. Padua, with its tolerant and liberal outlook, could by this means grant degrees to Protestants, Jews, or those of any other faith.[2]

Harvey left Padua soon after taking his degree and returned to England. There is no evidence to show that he visited any other medical centre in Europe, and we know nothing of his journeys to and from Padua. He might have travelled there either by Antwerp, Brussels, Lille, Strasbourg, and Basel, or by Paris, Troyes, Geneva, and Milan. Perhaps the second route is the more likely, since his father's presumed knowledge of transport from Folkestone or Dover to France would provide a convenient starting-point. Another medical student, Felix Platter of Basel, has left an extremely interesting account of his journey to Montpellier, undertaken a few years earlier than Harvey's to Padua, and of his experiences at the medical school there.[3] European travel was not easy

[1] See British Museum, MS. Sloane 3450, f. 6. This is a diploma differing from Harvey's only in detail.

[2] See note by J. O. Leibowitz in *The Journal of the History of Medicine* (1957), xii. 264, quoting Castiglioni, *A History of Medicine*, translated by E. B. Krumbhaar, New York, 1947.

[3] *Beloved Son Felix: The Journal of Felix Platter*, translated and edited by Sean Jennett, London, 1961. Harvey refers frequently in his lecture notes to Platter's book, *De corporis humani structura*, Basel, 1583.

in the late-sixteenth century and medical students were an unruly lot, so that we may be sure that Harvey's adventures would have been worth recording, but unfortunately he remained silent.

To what extent Harvey maintained relations with his friends at the University of Padua is unknown. There is an entry in the records of the University under the year 1629:

MDCXXIX–XXX

D. Gulielmus Heruy anglus

die xx Augusti cons. anglicae electus[1]

It is most improbable, however, that Harvey revisited Padua at that time, and it must be supposed that the entry refers to another person of the same name. Harvey had a nephew, William, son of Eliab Harvey, but he was only 14½ in August 1629.

3

ADMISSION TO THE COLLEGE OF PHYSICIANS, 1603–1607

It is assumed that Harvey returned to England in 1602, not earlier than June, and settled in London with a view to obtaining the Fellowship of the College of Physicians. It has been widely believed that no one could be admitted to the Fellowship unless he had the M.D. degree of Oxford or Cambridge. There was no clause, however, in the Statutes making this condition. The notion may have arisen from a discussion which took place at the College Comitia on 23 October 1585. Attention was then drawn to the fact that there were 'very many who have left their own universities before the end of their courses to go abroad, where, in a shorter time and at less expense, they take the doctorate degree'. It was then resolved that all such 'shall pay to the College officers three times the normal fee paid by those who have been created doctors in our universities'. It was also decided that 'anyone who has taken a degree as doctor in any university other than the one in which he was before for seven years with an arts degree, or even longer for one in medicine, that man shall pay twice the usual fee'. A Statute of 1601 had laid down

---

[1] Andrich, *De Natione Anglica et Scota*, Padua, 1892, p. 54.

that a candidate must be a doctor of medicine and an Englishman who had already practised his profession for four years. It was not until 1696 that it was additionally required that he should have the M.D. degree of Oxford or Cambridge.

Whatever the reason may be, it has been wrongly stated by Anthony Wood[1] and all later biographers that Harvey, soon after returning to England, took his M.D. degree at Cambridge by incorporation. It is now clear that he did not do so. The relevant Grace Book in the University Archives, the Supplicats, and other records, none of which is defective,[2] have been searched and no evidence has been found that he took this degree in 1602 or at any later date. It seems that he was content with his diploma from Padua, and rightly regarded any further degree, for which he would have to pay another fee, as unnecessary. It appears doubtful whether the increased fees recommended in 1585 at the College of Physicians were afterwards enforced. In Harvey's time a Candidate had to pay on admission the sum of £11. 3s. 4d., with a subscription of £4 in the first year and £2 a year thereafter. On election to the Fellowship he would have to pay £5. 11s. 8d. and to provide wine and sweetmeats for the Fellows present.

So uncertain and inconsistent was the College practice that it is perhaps not surprising that when Harvey was incorporated M.D. at Oxford on 7 December 1642 he was described as: *Guil. Harvey Cant. incorporatus*.[3] His incorporation at Cambridge was assumed to have taken

---

[1] Anthony Wood, *Athenæ Oxonienses*, ed. 2, 1721, vol. ii, Fasti 6. A source from which Wood may have obtained his erroneous information has recently been found by Dr. Gweneth Whitteridge. In the British Museum, Sloane MS. 1765, is a transcript of degrees given at Cambridge from 1499 to 1658, written in a seventeenth-century hand. This records that in the year 1607 two medical Doctorates were given, the entry on f. 202 being:

Doctores   { —Harvey
Medici   { —Ridgley

A further search of the Grace Book has shown that most of the names in the transcription are correctly given, but that the name transcribed as *Harvey* is in fact Harris. The transcriber's hand has not been identified, but the list is obviously one to which Wood may have had access. Later biographers found their justification for the statement in the evidence provided by good authorities. It is found in Bayle's *Dictionary*, 1738, in Venn's *Gonville and Caius College Biographical History*, vol. i, Cambridge, 1897, and in his *Alumni Cantabrigienses*, vol. ii, Cambridge, 1922—but not in his comprehensive *Book of Matriculations and Degrees*, Cambridge, 1913, where Harvey is correctly credited with the B.A. degree only. When he was elected Fellow of the College of Physicians in 1607 (see p. 42), there was no mention of his incorporation at Cambridge.

[2] With the expert assistance of the archivists, Miss Helen Peake and Miss Raven, I have searched the Grace Books 1602–42, the Transcripts of Degrees, the Supplicats and the Royal Letters and Mandates of James I without result.

[3] Oxford University Archives Register Q 16 (1634–47), Congregation Register, f. 191. Examined by Dr. Gweneth Whitteridge, 1963.

place, and if Harvey noticed this he did not trouble himself to contradict it. This uncertainty can be illustrated from the Annals of the College by a number of passages relating both to permission to practise and to admission to the Fellowship. Frequently pressure had to be resisted when admission of a Fellow by patronage was sought, even when the patron was the King himself. Sometimes, however, patronage was successful, as when Dr. Leonard Poe was admitted a Fellow in 1609 by request of Lords Salisbury, Suffolk, Southampton, and Worcester. On 26 June he had been reminded that, by the College Statutes, 'every Fellow is required to be deeply studied and soundly learned in physic, that he be well read in Galen and Hippocrates, that he be able to read a lecture in Anatomy and able to examine such who shall present themselves to the College, *Which knowledge we are assured Dr. Poe will not challenge unto himself*'. Nevertheless, on 7 July he was admitted by secret ballot and 'he was asked to intercede with the noblemen to become reconciled with each of the Fellows'. The pressure had been too great. Dr. Poe had also a mandate[1] from the King to be created M.D. at Cambridge, but there is no evidence that he actually took the degree.

On 8 September 1615 Dr. Paul de Laune, M.A. (Cantab.) in 1610 and M.D. (Padua) in 1614, showed his diploma and asked for a licence to practise. He was told that he should first be incorporated at Cambridge. This he did in the next year and was duly approved. Yet on 14 January following, Dr. John Hawkins, who presented himself with a letter from Padua, after being told that no one might practise unless a graduate of Oxford or Cambridge and being urged to incorporate, nevertheless was examined and approved. In the same year it was agreed that a royal physician in ordinary for the person of the King, of whatever country, might be admitted a Fellow, and Theodore de Mayerne was at once elected. On 11 January 1621/2 Dr. Robert Giffard and Dr. Peter Chamberlen showed 'their splendid diplomas from Padua' and were at once given licences to practise without any mention of incorporation. On 8 June 1632 Dr. William Goddard, M.D. of Padua, was told he must first be incorporated. When he came again three days later, Harvey himself spoke in his favour, promising that he should be incorporated within a year. On 30 September 1642 the opinion was expressed that incorporation was necessary, and after much discussion it was decided that candidates could be admitted, provided that they signed a bond promising to be incorporated within two years. In 1644 so few doctors were being incorporated at Cambridge that the University protested that they were

---

[1] Now in the University Archives.

PLATE VII

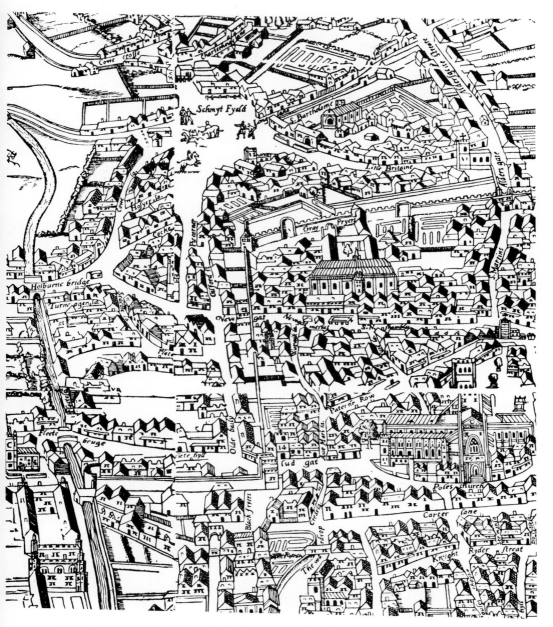

HARVEY'S LONDON: PART OF THE MAP BY RALPH AGAS, 1560–70

Near the top is *Schmyt Fyeld* (Smithfield) with St. Bartholomew's Priory Church on the right and St. Bartholomew's the Less with the Hospital buildings below. In the lower part is *Lud gat* (Ludgate) marking the position of Harvey's house in the precincts of St. Martin's Church. Below this to the right is *Knyght Ryder Streat*, in which was the College of Physicians

being slighted by the College, though by this date political factors were probably coming into play.

Having settled in London, Harvey soon found a wife, and we know from his marriage licence that he was living in 1604 in a house near St. Martin's Church, very close to Ludgate; this was just inside the area demarcated by the Roman Wall, not far from St. Paul's Cathedral and the Old Bailey. There is other documentary evidence[1] that he was living in the Old Bailey quarter about this time, in the form of a list of the names of twenty-two taxpayers with their assessments. Harvey's payment was assessed at iiij^d, but none of the others at more than ij^d, suggesting that he was living in one of the better houses. On the other hand, another document[2] of the same period represents him as a young man of small resources, resisting the imposition of a forced loan to the King.

To the Right Honourable Sir Thomas Knight

Whereas it hath pleased His Majesty to direct his privy seal to William Harvey doctor of physic for to borrow of him six pounds and thirteen shillings and four-pence we whose names are underwritten do certify unto you that the said Doctor Harvey is a young man whose father is yet living and that being to begin the world and to live by his profession his means and abilities are such as in our judgment he is unfit to lend.

Robert Shawe	Joseph Fenton
Richard Finns	Richard Cooper
Ric. Mapes	Edw. Grayne Churchwarden
Adam [*illegible*]	

Of these signatories two, Fenton and Mapes, were surgeons on the staff of St. Bartholomew's Hospital; the others were no doubt living in the neighbourhood, and were familiar with Harvey's circumstances.

There is no certain evidence of how long Harvey kept his residence in the parish of St. Martin's. Later references to 'Blackfriars' do not necessarily indicate a move to a neighbouring parish, the area known as Blackfriars being so close to St. Martin's as to make the names virtually interchangeable; it is probable that he stayed there at any rate until, as royal physician, he was given quarters in Whitehall Palace in 1639.

In theory Harvey's magnificently worded diploma from Padua enabled him to practise medicine anywhere in Europe, but in fact it was necessary to obtain entry to the London College of Physicians before any doctor qualified elsewhere was at liberty to practise his profession in the metropolis. Harvey knew well enough that any unlicensed stranger,

[1] British Museum, Sloane MS. 395B, f. 1.
[2] Ibid., Add. MS. 36767, f. 49.

English or foreign, who attempted to practise within the jurisdiction of the College, would be in trouble as soon as he was detected. In 1511, the third year of his reign, King Henry VIII had tried to eliminate the untrained doctors and 'empiricks', or quacks, who had become so numerous that they were to be regarded as a public danger. He made an Act forbidding anyone to practise in the City of London or within seven miles without having been examined and approved by the Bishop of London or the Dean of St. Paul's, aided by the opinion of four physicians and others with knowledge of surgery. In the country the licensing authority was the Bishop of each diocese, helped by such medical men as he chose to appoint. Fines could be exacted if anyone was caught practising without a licence. After some years' trial the King's Act proved ineffectual, and in the year 1518 he granted a Charter to Cardinal Wolsey and six trusted physicians, three of whom were in attendance on the King's person, to form a College of Physicians of London. The chief of these was Thomas Linacre, who, with his five colleagues, was to choose two others, this body of eight being known as *Elects*; they were appointed for life, and each year were to elect a President from among their number and to fill vacancies, as they occurred, by co-option. They were given the powers originally vested in the Bishops to license practitioners and to fine those who had offended by unlicensed practice. Queen Mary, still unsatisfied with the results, gave the College greater powers; fines were increased to a maximum of £20 and imprisonment was allowed in default of payment. If a prisoner escaped, the College could sue the keeper of the gaol for double the amount of the fine. It was clear, however, that so small a body could never enforce its jurisdiction in the country at large, and the College records show that even in the London area unlicensed practitioners could successfully defy the authority of the College if they enjoyed the protection of a powerful courtier or nobleman. Fines often remained unpaid and prison sentences were ignored, if only because an Earl's retainers were more numerous than any the College could command. Even so distinguished a stranger from Flanders as Baldwin Hamey the Elder ultimately had to conform. He had trained at Leyden and was appointed physician to Fedor Ivanovitch, Czar of Russia, in 1594. After Fedor's death four years later Hamey was invited to attend his successor, the Czar Boris, but by then he was in London and had decided to stay there for various reasons, one being that he wished to educate his son, Baldwin the Younger (later to become Harvey's close friend), in England.[1] Hamey recognized from

[1] John Keevil, *Hamey the Stranger*, London, 1952.

the fate of other foreigners that it would be unwise to attempt unlicensed practice for an unlimited period, though the process of obtaining a licence might be difficult and protracted. The Censors were not to be satisfied by a single examination and Hamey was to feel thoroughly humiliated before he was approved as a Candidate for the Fellowship at his fifth appearance on 12 January 1609/10. At his third attendance on 6 October 1609 he had to face a large body of College officers and Fellows, among them Dr. Harvey, ten years his junior.

Even Harvey, with his diploma from Padua, did not have a specially easy passage. The premises occupied by the College were still in the rather small stone house in Knightrider Street, close to Ludgate, bequeathed to the Fellows by Linacre. Harvey attended there for the first time on 4 May 1603, when he was the only candidate, and the entry in the College Annals records that 'Mr. Harvey, a doctor of medicine in the University of Padua, came to this Comitia and presented himself for examination. His replies to all questions were entirely satisfactory when he was examined. Nevertheless he was put off until another time, with our tacit permission to practise.' Harvey was, therefore, immediately put in a better position than Hamey, who had been forbidden to practise and fined when he ignored the interdiction. Harvey had first attended at the College only six weeks after the death of Queen Elizabeth, and during a specially bad epidemic of the plague in London. Only the President and three Censors, Dr. Edward Lister, Dr. John Argent, and Dr. John Giffard, were present at this Comitia, and the thin attendance may have been due to a general exodus, including the doctors, to the country.

Harvey's second attendance at the College was nearly a year later, on 2 April 1604. It was then recorded that 'Dr. Harvey was examined for the second time for a Candidateship and his reply was approved.'[1] Things now moved somewhat faster. On 11 May 'Dr. Harvey was examined for the third time and approved.'[2] On 7 August 'Dr. Harvey

---

[1] Harvey's fellow examinees were John Craige, Physician to the King in Scotland and afterwards in London; Thomas Hearne (or Heron) of Brasenose College, Oxford, and M.D. of Padua; Thomas Lodge of Trinity College, Oxford, who failed to pass; and Thomas Rawlins of Clare Hall, Cambridge.

[2] On this occasion Harvey was examined with Rawlins and Edward Elwin of Corpus Christi College, Cambridge, Physician to the royal household in 1609, together with three others, who, as noted by Sir Norman Moore, 'besides practising medicine achieved fame in poetry: Matthew Gwin, the epilogue of whose comedy of *Vertumnus* [1607] seems to have suggested to Shakespeare the salutations of the witches in *Macbeth*, Thomas Lodge, whose story of *Rosalynde* [1590] is the source of the plot of *As You Like It*, and Raphael Thorius, whose *Hymnus Tabaci* [1626] and other Latin poems were much admired while such verses were in fashion' (*History of St. Bartholomew's Hospital*, London, 1918, ii. 457).

was examined for a Candidateship. He was approved and elected on condition that he paid the usual amounts due to the College.' Finally on 5 October, 'Dr. Elwin and Dr. Harvey on this day took the oath as Candidates according to the form in the Statutes.' He was now a *Permissus*, or, as sometimes designated, a *Licentiatus*, and was free to practise within the jurisdiction of the College.

We do not know what questions were put to Harvey; although the examinations were entirely oral, the details were usually not recorded in the Annals of the College. References are found to the 'Book of Examinations', and, if this were extant, it would have given much interesting information, but it was destroyed by fire in 1666. When details occur in the Annals, it was because the candidate was suspected of malpractice or because he was particularly ignorant. Some idea of the procedure can, however, be gained from these.

On 4 November 1614 a Dr. Eyre, who had been practising in London without permission, 'making use of a language very like Latin, promised to do his best' under examination. The President then made clear to him that he must be examined and reply in Latin. 'Then the first Censor asked the number of natural things forming part of ourselves. The doctor replied that he had read about these things today, but now indeed they were forgotten; but he was engaged in subjects relating to women (although he was a bachelor). The Censor enumerated seven [natural things]—elements, temperaments, parts, humours, spirits, actions, and experiences, but to these the doctor added nothing further. The Censor asked what was an element. The doctor replied that it had no substance. By no means, the Censor began to say, for there was substance from them and it was that least part of that which it constituted. The second Censor asked how a disease and a fever differed. The doctor replied that a fever is not a disease, to which the Censor said, that if he treated a disease that was not a disease, then he must therefore often treat a fever as if it were a disease. At this the doctor muttered. Then the Censor asked the number of temperaments. The doctor said that he had read that today, but now he did not remember.' After further questions the candidate lost his temper and refused to answer any more 'because of his lapse of memory'. A decision on his competence was postponed until another meeting.

On another occasion (23 November 1624) the Duchess of Richmond sought to obtain by patronage a licence for a man named Theodore Naileman to practise. This candidate hoped to excuse his lack of Latin by pleading that a fractured skull had caused him to forget it. When asked why he had lost his Latin rather than his English, he said 'by want of using it'. The President asked what books he had read of Hippocrates; he replied 'the aphorisms in English and Dutch'. Sir William Paddy asked what were the three faculties. He answered 'phantasy, imagination, reason, memory'. Dr. Winston asked what disease he had cured in the Duchess's family. He replied, the yellow jaundice, which was, he said, 'the overflowing of the gall; this went to the mawe [stomach], the place of the first decoction'. From there it went by the *vena cava* to the body. Asked how he would diagnose jaundice by the urine, he replied 'by colouring of a cloth'. Other signs were given by yellowness of the skin and eyes, by faintness, and by the stools. When asked how many elements there were, he said four—air, fire, water, and earth. An element, he said, was a beginning, and was that which, by its equal proportions, kept a man in health. Elements were equally in the body by weight. The candidate was judged insufficient, but, to please the Duchess, was told to attend again.

On 3 December of the same year another man called Eyre, who practised medicine without authority, said he understood Latin, but could not speak it. He had not studied in any university, but had gained his knowledge by travel, his father being a surgeon and a merchant. In answer to questions he said gout was 'a weakness of the nerves'; there were four types—sciatica, gout in the hand, gout in the foot, and gout in the knee. These came not all from the same humour, but 'now from the bile, and now from the blood'. Epilepsy he said was a humidity of the body; the patients fell. Asked what is colic, he said he did not know, neither did he attend to it, but gave the best medicaments. Clearly another insufficient candidate!

On 11 June 1632 a Dr. Boet senior was examined in Harvey's presence. Asked whether he had read Galen's *De inequali intemperie*[1] he said that he had, but, being asked what was variable madness, it was clear from his answers that he had not understood it. Asked where the humours were engendered, he said in the stomach. When reminded about the liver he agreed. The examiner continued that the liver was a univocal subject, and this might produce a univocal effect; the humours, however, are not univocal. Dr. Boet 'did not have the wherewithal to reply to the subject'. Nor did he have any idea how the bones were joined. Further questions, about phlegm in the stomach, producing unsatisfactory replies, he was rejected and advised to apply himself to studying for some years

[1] *De temperamentis et de inaequali intemperie, libri tres. T. Linacro Anglo interprete*, Cambridge, 1521.

yet and then to present himself before the College. Meanwhile he was warned to abstain from practice entirely. He withdrew full of indignation.

In contrast to these insufficient candidates was Peter Salmon of King's College, Cambridge, a doctor of medicine of Padua and incorporated at Oxford, who was approved on 8 April 1639. He was questioned regarding the nature of fevers, about the blood, about the distinction between the plague and pestilential fevers, about the types of heads and the paroxysms of fevers. Dr. Salmon was appearing for the fifth time and was now unanimously elected a Candidate, a grade implying that election to the Fellowship would follow later. The unfamiliar medical jargon of the period used in these examinations perhaps makes some of the questions now seem rather more difficult than they really were.

This last example was more on normal lines than the others mentioned above. In 1676 Dr. Charles Goodall, in his book *The College of Physicians Vindicated*, summarized the three examinations to be held before the President and the four Censors. The first was to inquire into the candidate's knowledge of 'the rudiments of physic', that is, of physiology and anatomy. At the second, questions were to be asked about 'the pathological part of physic', that is, concerning the causes, differences, symptoms, and signs of disease, the doctrine of fevers, and details about the pulse and the urine. At the third, inquiries were made about treatment of disease, this to include diet, the management of acute disorders, and the uses of purging, vomiting, bleeding, and opiates. This systematic form of examination may have been varied since Harvey's candidature, but no doubt it covered substantially the questions that he was expected to answer.

Harvey had to wait a further two and a half years before he attained the dignity of the Fellowship. Then, on 16 May 1607, was 'Dr. Harvey elected Fellow'; he was formally admitted on 5 June, and so had achieved his main ambition within five years of leaving Padua. Sir Norman Moore has painted a vivid, and not too fanciful, picture of the proceedings at the College when Harvey was admitted:

While waiting in the outer room, before coming in to take the oath and to shake hands with all the Fellows, Harvey was in company with two other physicians who were admitted on that day. One, Matthew Lister, had been at Padua with him, and was a witness of his degree, and afterwards became physician to Anne of Denmark, Queen of James I. The other physician was a senior of Harvey's at Cambridge, Dr. William Clement of Trinity, afterwards registrar of the College. His only surviving works are two Latin verses in praise of Winterton's metrical version of the aphorisms of Hippocrates [1567]. Dr. Henry Atkins was President at Harvey's admission and fourteen other Fellows, of whom one, Dr. Ralph Wilkinson, [was] physician to St. Bartholomew's, and another, Dr. Thomas Fryer, lived within its precincts and had a large garden there, at the foot of which was the city ditch.

The three new Fellows took their seats at the table, and some business was transacted: Dr. Mark Ridley was elected a Censor; Dr. Edward Elwin was appointed to entertain the Fellows at a feast on the first Tuesday in July; Dr. Lister was to make preparations for the demonstrations in anatomy; everyone was desired to obtain information as to where a Dr. Bonham had practised; Dr. Thomas Davis was elected Lumleian Lecturer in succession to Dr. William Dun. The President took up the caduceus and the meeting was at an end.[1]

4

MARRIAGE, 1604

AUTHENTIC details of Harvey's activities during these years before his Fellowship cannot be recovered, but at least we know that, late in 1604, soon after he had been admitted a Candidate at the College, he had married, the ceremony taking place at the Church of St. Sepulchre, very close to St. Bartholomew's Hospital. The Church Register of this date has been lost, but the marriage licence, issued by Sir Edward Stanhope (1546?–1608), Chancellor of the diocese of London, is still extant:[2]

24° Novembris 1604

This daie appeared personally before Sir Edward Stainhope knighte William Harvie Doctor of Phisicke a batcheler aged xxvj[ty] yeres or there abowts of the parishe of St Martins by Ludgate alledgeth that he intendeth to maray with one Elizabeth Browne mayden of the parishe of St Sepulchers withowte Newgate London aged xxiiij[ty] yeres or there abowts the naturall and lawfull dawghter of Lancelott Browne alsoe doctor of Phisicke of the parishe of St Sepulchers aforesaid Att which tyme appeared alsoe personally before the Judge Lancelott Browne Doctor of Phisicke of St Sepulchers aforesaid the naturall father unto the said Elizabeth Browne and giveth his expresse consente hereunto and offereth to make faieth that to their knowledges there is no lawfull lett

---

[1] Loc. cit., p. 458.

[2] Guildhall Library, MS. 10091/2. See also *Publications of the Harleian Society*, vol. xxv, 'Allegations for Marriage Licences issued by the Bishop of London, 1520 to 1610', London, 1887, for an abbreviated extract.

or impedimente to hinder this their intended marriage wherefe [wherof] he the said William Harvie Doctor of Phisicke desiereth license of the Judge of this Courte to be married in the parishe Church of St Sepulchers withowt Newgate And then appeared Thomas Harvye one of the jurats of the Towne of Folston in Kent the naturall father unto the said William Harvie and giveth his consent to this intended marriage

Will Harvey
Lancelot Browne
Thomas Harvy

Endorsed: fiat 24 novemb 1604
      E Stainhope

Harvey's father-in-law, Dr. Lancelot Browne, born at York about 1545, had been at St. John's College, Cambridge, and was afterwards a Fellow of Pembroke Hall. He was licensed to practise physic in 1570, took his M.D. degree in 1576, and then moved to London, where he was elected a Fellow of the College of Physicians. He filled the office of Censor, that is, an examiner, of whom there were four, was made an Elect in 1599, and served on the Council in 1604–5. He was of sufficient eminence to be appointed physician to Queen Elizabeth and later to King James and his Queen,[1] and was thus in a favourable position for trying to advance the career of his clever son-in-law. An opportunity arose in July 1605, when there was a prospect of obtaining for him a court post as Physician to the Tower of London. Had Harvey been successful he would have met there some interesting prisoners. Sir Walter Raleigh, Henry Brooke, Lord Cobham, and Thomas, Lord Grey of Wilton, were all three suffering King James's cat-and-mouse manœuvres for supposed complicity in the Bye Plot; Guy Fawkes arrived there on 5 November for torture and ultimate execution, and Sir Henry Percy, ninth Earl of Northumberland, joined him on 27 November. Dr. Browne, knowing that the Physician to the Tower, Dr. Elvine, might soon be succeeding to a post held by Dr. Marbecke[2] at Court, wrote to Robert Cecil, Earl of Salisbury, asking whether his son-in-law could have Dr. Elvine's position:

[1] In the Public Record Office, E 304/2363, Annuities, &c., are four entries of quarterly payments of £25 each, 1600–1, to Dr. Lancelot Browne as one of the Queen's physicians. Noted by John Keevil.

[2] Roger Marbeck, M.D. (Oxon.), Provost of Oriel in 1564. Fellow of the College of Physicians about 1578. First Registrar of the College, Censor and Councillor. Physician to Queen Elizabeth. Accompanied Raleigh and Howard on the expedition against Cadiz, of which he wrote an account. Died July 1605 (Munk's *Roll*, 1861, pp. 73–74).

To the Right Honorable, his singular good Lorde, the Earle of Salisbury
  his Maties principall Secretary of Estate give these wth speede. At Courte.
My most hd. good Lorde

Although by your owne expresse commandement I am for a while
barde from accesse unto you, yet I beseeche yor good Lordship to stand
my honorable frend and Lord in a suite for my Sonne in Law Dr. Harvie.
Dr. Marbecke is very sicke and in great daunger, and I fear me will not
last longe though he should escape this brunte. Yf he departe I under-
stande by yor honorable favour to Dr. Elvine that he is to enjoye his
place in Courte wch I shalbe very glad (yf the other man die) of, because
he is a very kind and honest man, which place if he have he must thereby
be bounde to follow the Courte, and so can not perform the service
required by his charge in the Tower. I therefore humbly desyre that
my sonne Dr. Harvey may succeede Dr. Elvine in that place. I dare
assure you, that he is every way fitte for performaunce of as greate a
charge as that is. I did never in my lyfe know any man any thinge near
his yeares that was any way matche with him in all pointes of good
learninge, but especially in his profession of Physician wherein beinge
examined in the Colledge three several tymes, he did answere so readily
and fully wthall, as the whole company did both admire him, and took
very singulare lyking unto him. Besides yf any doubtfull matter of
momente in physik should occur in his practice there, he should have me
alwayes readie to resolve him therein fully I trust; now for his Loyall
and faithfull performance of the trust that I repose in him I wilbe bound
with him and for him body for bodie, as the phrase goes. He is both him
selfe of that discreate and honest caryage and his parents and friends are
so honest people, as I dare (and that withoute daringe) venter lyfe and
lymme for him. He is now in Kent with his father at Folkestone, but if
need shalbe here of his presence, I can and will send for him presently.
So dooinge yr Lp shall bynd both him and me alwayes to be readie at
yr commaundement to do you all the service we both can. And so with
my most humble dewty I take my leave committinge yr Lp unto the
Almighties protection.

Yor Lp most bounden in all dewty
LANCELOT BROWNE

London this xvij of July 1605.[1]

Dr. Browne's recommendation seems by its terms to have been genuine
and not mere nepotism; five days later he renewed his efforts for Harvey:

To the Right Hon my Singulare good Lord, the Earle of Salisbury geve
  these at the Courte wth speede.

I beseech your Honoure to beare with my boldnes in renewinge my
suite unto you for my sonne Dr Harvie. Dr Marbecke departed yesterday

----

[1] Hatfield House Library. Cecil Papers, vol. 111/125.

a little fore vj a clock at eveninge. This morninge by advise of a good frend of myne I mooved my L. Treasourer for him who very honorably answered that yf he had not past his promise to Dr Gwinne (brother to my L. Admirals Apothecary, and reader of the Physike lecture in London) my sonne should have had all the good furtherance he could therein. Since noone I went to my Lord Lieftenant of the Tower, and mooved him for my sonne, and told him that I had written to yor Honour about my suite alreadye and told him withall what answere I had from my L. Treasourer, who answered that he hoped my L. Treasourer wold not doe him wronge in choosinge of the physician for the Tower, and that in the appointinge of one he would wholly depend and be ruled by yor Honour, and willed me againe to crave your Lp. favour herein. I humbly therefor request yor Lordships good favour herein for my sonne in all dewtifull service to show or thankefulness therfor. If I may understand your Lp. pleasure herein, I will send for my sonne out of the country to attende in Dr Gwin's place in the Tower untill his returne. And so most humbly I take my leave, wishinge from my suite unto yor Lp all honour and prosperitie. ffrom an Apothecary's shop in ffanchurch streete in all hast this xxij th of July 1605.

> Yor honours most bounden
> in all dewtiful service
> LANCELOT BROWNE[1]

Dr. Matthew Gwinne, a much older man than Harvey, had been chosen in 1598 as first Professor of Physic at Gresham College and was by 1605 a well-known member of his profession. Harvey, by comparison, was unknown and it is not surprising that Dr. Gwinne was appointed. Presumably Harvey was not recalled from Folkestone. His parents were still living in the town and it may be conjectured that, as a good son, he had gone there to attend his mother in an illness. She was in her fiftieth year and died on 8 November, so that Harvey probably paid more than one other visit to Folkestone in the latter half of that year. Dr. Lancelot Browne also died in 1605, it is believed at the beginning of December.[2] Although of some eminence as a doctor, he appeared in print only as the author of a conventionally phrased commendatory letter prefixed to John Gerard's *Herbal*, 1597. Some of his books passed to his son-in-law, one of the very few of Harvey's books to be saved from the burning of the College in 1666 being the *Opera omnia* of Falloppius, Frankfort, 1584, with Browne's signature on the title-page and Harvey's annotations in the margins.[3]

[1] Hatfield House Library. Cecil Papers, vol. 101/86.
[2] Munk's *Roll of the Royal College of Physicians*, 1861, i. 79.
[3] Another volume from Browne's library in the British Museum is Galen's *Libri aliquot Græci per I. Caium*, Basel, 1544.

Harvey's wife, Elizabeth, remains a very shadowy figure. The baptismal Registers[1] of the parish of St. Martin's, in which they lived, contain no entry under their name and as far as we know they never had any children. Harvey had no occasion to mention his wife in his writings, except for the well-known anecdote which found its place in *De generatione animalium*, 1651. The passage is taken from the anonymous translation of 1653, and has the unusual light relief of a quotation from Virgil:

My wife had an excellent, and a well instructed Parrat, which was long her delight; which was now grown so familiar, that he was permitted to walk at liberty through the whole house: where he missed his Mistresse, he would search her out, and when he had found her, he would court her with a cheerful congratulation. If she had called him, he would make answer, and flying to her, he would grasp her garments with his claws, and bill, till by degrees he had scaled her shoulder; whence he descending by her arm, did constantly seat himself upon her hand. If she bad him talk or sing, were it night, and never so darke, he would obey her. Many times when he was sportive and wanton, he would sit in her lap, where he loved to have her scratch his head, and stroke his back, and then testifie his contentment, by kinde mutterings, and shaking of his wings. I still interpreted all this to proceed from his customary familiarity and obsequiousness, for I alwaies thought him to be a Cock-parrat, by his notable excellence in singing and talking. For amongst birds, the females seldom sing, or provoke to discourse; but the males onely charm the females by the pleasant musick of their voice, and allure them to pay their homage to Venus. And therefore Aristotle saith, *If Partridge-hennes stand over against the cocks, and the winde blow from whence the cocks are, they conceive and grow big and for the most part, they teem even by the voice of the cock, if they be at that time wanton and lustfull: and this also may fall out from the cocks flying over them: namely if the cock do transmit a fructifying spirit into the Hen.* And this happens chiefly in the springtime; whence the poet:

> *Vere tument terræ & genitalia semina poscunt.*
> *Tum Pater Omnipotens fœcundis imbribus æther.*
> *Conjugis in gremium lætæ descendit, & omnes*
> *Magnus alit, magno commistus corpore, fœtus.*
> *Avia tum resonant avibus virgulta sonoris,*
> *Et Venerem certis repetunt armenta diebus.*[2]

> Earth swells in Spring, and fertile seed requires,
> Descending Æther with her voice conspires,
> And fruitful showrs cheer his glad consorts hart,

---

[1] Guildhall Library, MS. 10213.   [2] *Georgicon.* II. 324–9.

Which do to all her Issues growth impart.
The Desart woods are then the shrill Birds Quire,
And all Beasts are inflam'd with Venus fire.

But not long after these kinde dalliances, the Parrat, which had lived many years sound and healthy, grew sick, and being much oppressed by many convulsive motions, did at length deposite his much lamented spirit in his Mistresses bosom, where he had so often sported. When dissecting his carkase, (to finde out the cause of his death) I found in the womb an egge almost completed, but, for want of a Cocke, corrupted. Which many times befalleth those Birds, that are immured in Cages, when they covet the society of the Cock.[1]

Poor Mrs. Harvey's pet may have been a comfort to her in her childless state; apart from this anecdote nothing is known of her character, and it can only be assumed that she proved to be a good and faithful wife to her busy husband.[2] He mentioned her in his Will as 'my dear deceased loving wife' in carrying out a distribution of money 'to Mr. Samuel Fenton's children', as she had directed. She was still alive in 1645 when her brother-in-law, John Harvey, left her a legacy of £100, so that she must have died between that date and 1652, when her husband first drew up his Will. She had a brother named Galen, clearly destined by his father for the medical profession. He did in fact become an 'extra licentiate' of the College on 24 August 1629, twenty-four years after taking his M.A. degree at Cambridge.[3] Harvey, with his usual generosity directed in his Will 'that the twenty pounds which I yearly allow him my brother Galen Browne' was to be carried on 'as a legacy from his sister during his natural life'. Evidently Galen Browne did not make a great success of his career. This completes our meagre knowledge of Harvey's wife and her family.

[1] *Anatomical Exercitations, Concerning the Generation of Living Creatures*, London, 1653, pp. 24–25.
[2] A portrait of Mrs. Harvey with her parrot hung for many years in the house of the Finch family at Burley-on-the-hill, Rutland, but unfortunately it was destroyed together with a portrait of Harvey when part of the house was burnt in 1907. It had never been photographed.
[3] Munk's *Roll*, 1861, i. 183.

5

PRACTICE IN LONDON * APPOINTMENT TO
ST. BARTHOLOMEW'S HOSPITAL, 1609

DR. LANCELOT BROWNE had done his best to help his son-in-law to a lucrative post at Court, but had failed. Another three and a half years were to pass before Harvey obtained any medical appointment of which we are aware. We can only be sure that, having been given permission to practise medicine in the London area in May 1603, he would have exercised that privilege. In the course of his practice he must have come to know many of his fellow practitioners and gradually, as his sphere of practice enlarged, he would mix with more and more members of the relatively small Jacobean society centring round the Court. If a medical man with any ambition stayed to practise in London, it must always have been with an eye to attracting notice in Court circles, since all advancement came that way. This was not an unworthy aim; it was the custom of the time, and Harvey would not have been likely to make his mark in the world unless he had conformed. How exactly he set about it we cannot know. When his father-in-law died in 1605 he had lost his closest connexion with the Court, and it can only be supposed that ability and personality together brought him the notice that he needed —conceivably reinforced, as we shall see, by help from the member of the Harvey family next to him in age, his brother John. His time in Padua and his work under Fabricius had inspired him with a passion for 'research'—though that was a concept as applied to the natural sciences that grew only gradually during the seventeenth century. Fabricius had taught him the pleasures of discovering new facts by the dissection of human bodies and the intellectual satisfaction of identifying anatomical and biological parallels through the investigation of the bodies of other animals. If his time in these early years was not fully occupied by a slowly growing medical practice, then we may be certain that Harvey was accumulating notes and thinking over the problems ultimately to be crystallized in his first published work on the circulation of the blood. Unfortunately we possess no documentary relic of his scientific work and no means of knowing where he could have carried it out. The Barber-Surgeons' Hall and the College of Physicians were the official centres for the study of human anatomy, which was forbidden anywhere else in

London. A heavy fine could be inflicted for disobeying this rule. No other form of anatomical work was countenanced or would have aroused much interest in most of Harvey's acquaintances. Perhaps it was in his own home that he conducted most of his biological research.

As soon as he attained the dignity of the Fellowship of the College of Physicians in 1607 he would certainly have begun to look around for an appointment which would bring him increase of clinical experience and some modest emolument. At that date there were (apart from the leper hospitals) only two institutions in London for the general care of the needy and the sick poor—St. Bartholomew's in Smithfield, just outside the City walls, and St. Thomas's in Southwark, across the river Thames. St. Bartholomew's was conveniently situated within a short distance of his house at Ludgate and would naturally attract his attention. Although this Hospital had been founded by Rahere, an Augustinian monk, in 1123, as an independent institution on ground granted by King Henry I, it had been closely associated with the neighbouring Priory of St. Bartholomew, and was administered by a Master, who was a priest, with eight Brethren and four Sisters. It possessed its own parish Church of St. Bartholomew the Less. At the Reformation the Hospital was in great danger of being suppressed together with the Priory, and in fact its property and revenues were appropriated by the Crown. The Priory was surrendered to the King on 25 October 1539. By that time the Hospital was almost empty and unable properly to perform its function of care for the sick poor, on which the people had depended for over 400 years. The Lord Mayor, Sir Thomas Gresham, with the Aldermen and citizens of London, then petitioned the King for restoration of the revenues, to alleviate the growing scandal of sick people lying in the streets, their wants unattended. King Henry listened, but was slow to act, and it was not until nearly six years later, in 1544, that he granted part of the Lord Mayor's requests. The Hospital had never closed its doors, but its income was still inadequate and in 1546 letters patent were granted restoring its revenues. A Royal Charter laid down in 1547 a constitution on which the administration of the Hospital has been based until the present day.

The Hospital was to be supervised by a Court of Governors with the Lord Mayor as President. From the members of this Court a smaller body of Almoners was appointed with the Treasurer as the executive officer. The patients, to the number of about a hundred, were to be attended by a Matron and twelve nursing Sisters, and there were three salaried Surgeons, who were charged 'faithfully and truly to the uttermost of your knowledge and cunning to help to cure the griefes and diseases of the poor of this Hospitall, setting aside all favour, affection, gain, or lucre, and that as well to the poorest destitute of all friends and succour, as to such as shall peradventure be better friended, yee shall with all favour and friendship procure the speedy recovery of their health'.[1] The surgeons were to admit no patient to the wards whose disease was incurable, and to reject none that was curable—a distinction that must sometimes have been difficult to make. No physician was at first appointed, nor was there any mention of an apothecary or supply of drugs and applications.

Harvey appears to have established some connexion with the Court of King James by the beginning of 1609, possibly through the influence of his younger brother, John, who had secured a position as 'foot-man' to the King. There is some doubt as to what this title implies, but it cannot have been so menial as it sounds today. So, in February, Dr. Harvey presented a letter of recommendation from the King to the Treasurer and Almoners, applying for the post of Physician to the Hospital 'in reversion', that is, on the departure of the holder of the post. This method of appointment was usual at the Hospital, Dr. Wilkinson, whom Harvey hoped to succeed, having himself followed Dr. Thomas Doyley on the same terms. It was convenient at times, the individual appointed in reversion being expected to carry out the duties of the holder when he was absent.

The first Physician to St. Bartholomew's was Dr. Roderigo Lopez, appointed in 1561. He held the office until 1581 and became Physician to Queen Elizabeth in 1586, but in 1594 was executed on suspicion of complicity in a plot to poison the Queen. Dr. Peter Turner was the second physician, succeeding Lopez in 1581, but only four years later he resigned in order to become member of parliament for Bridport. Dr. Timothie Bright was the third physician and officiated for six years, though with indifferent success. He had too many interests, including the invention of modern shorthand, and before the end of 1590 the Court of Governors was complaining that he did not properly carry out his duties. In spite of this he continued to neglect his patients, and was finally dismissed in September 1591. Bright was succeeded by Dr. Thomas Doyley, and he, in 1603, by Dr. Ralph Wilkinson, a distinguished Fellow of the College of Physicians, who continued in office until he died in the autumn of 1609. In February his resignation or death was foreseen and Harvey presented himself with letters from King James to support his suit:

[1] *Orders and ordinances, for The better government of the Hospitall of Bartholomew the lesse,* London, 1652, p. 23.

Curia tent. Sabti xxv° die Februarii A° Dni 1608|9

In presence of Sr. John Spencer, Psydent
[and 12 other Governors]

MR. DR. HARVEY

This day Mr. William Harvey Doctor of Phisycke made sute for the rev'cion of the office of the Physicion of this howse when the same shalbe nexte voyd, and brought the King's Matie his l'res [letters] directed to the Gov'nors of this howse in his behalfe, and showed forthe a Testimony of his sufficiency for the same place under the hande of Mr. Doct^r Adkynson presydent of the Colledge of the phisytions and div'se others doctors of the auncientest of the said Colledge. It is graunted at the contemplacion of his Maties l'res that the said Mr. Harvey shall have the said office nexte after the decease or other dep'ture of Mr. Doctor Wilkenson whoe nowe holdeth the same wth the y'ly ffee & dewtyes therunto belonginge, Soe that then he be not founde to be otherwyse imployed, that may lett & Hynder the chardge of the same office, which belongeth thereunto.

Harvey was thus in the position of assistant to Dr. Wilkinson, who was failing in health and probably delegated most of his work to him. His feelings towards Wilkinson were, perhaps, not entirely respectful, if he was the person mentioned in the lecture-notes as an example of a notorious glutton, at any rate during his time as a Fellow of Trinity College, Cambridge.[1] Harvey appeared again before the Court of Governors on 28 August, after Dr. Wilkinson's death, and agreed to perform the duties of physician to the Hospital without pay until he was formally appointed:

xxviii° die Augusti A° Dni 1609

Mr. Gayus Newman [and five other Governors]

DR. HARVEY

Mr. Willm. Harvey Doctor of Physick came before the Gov'nors beforenamed and is contented to execute the office of the physicion of this howse untill mych'as next, w'h out any recompence for his paynes herein; which office Mr. Doctor Wilkenson late deceased held. And Mr. Dr. Harvey beinge asked whether he is not otherwyse imployed in any other place which may lett or hynder the execucion of the office of the physicion towarde the poore of this hospitall; hath answered that he is not, whearfore yt is thought fytt by the sayd Gov'nors that he supply the same office untill the nexte Court, And then Mr. Dr. Harvey to be a

---

[1] *Prelectiones*, p. 120. 'WH Wilkinson of Cambridge. pigg of ye spitt.' The identification is conjectural.

sutor for his admyttance to the said place accordinge to a graunt thereof to him heartofore made.

At last, on 14 October, he was admitted to the office of Physician, being sixth in the succession, and received his 'charge' from the President the Lord Mayor:

Cur. tent. Sabti xiiii die Octob[r] *1609*

In presence of S[r] John Spencer Knight, President
[and fifteen other Governors]

DR. HARVEY

This day Mr. Willyam Harvey Doctor of Phisick is admytted to the offyce of the Physicion of this Hosp[ll], which Mr. Dr. Wilkenson deceased late helde according to a form[r] graunt to him made and the chardge of the sayd office hath bene redd unto him.

Harvey's 'charge' must be given in full, as it enables us to see something of him in the performance of his duties. A similar charge is still given by the Treasurer to every officer appointed to the staff of the Hospital.

14° October 1609

The Chardge of the Phisicion af St. Bartholomewes Hospitall

PHISICION:

You are here elected and admitted to be the Phisicion for the Poore of this hospitall, to p'forme the chardge followinge, That is to say, one day in the weeke at the leaste thorough the yeare, or oftner as neede shall requyer you shall come to this Hospitall, and cause the Hospitler, Matron, or Porter, to call before you in the hall of this hospitall such and soe many of the poore harboured in this hospitall, as shall neede the counsell & advise of the phisicion. And you are here requyred & desyred by us, in God his most holly name, that you endevour yourselfe to doe the beste of your knowledge in the profession of phisicke to the poore then p'sente, or any other of the poore at any tyme in the weeke w[ch] shalbe sent home unto you by the Hospitler or Matron for your counsell,[1] wrytinge in a booke appoynted for that purpose, such medicines with theire compoundes and necessaries as apperteyneth to the apothecary of this house, to be provyded and made reddy for to be ministred unto the poore, every one in p'ticular, according to his disease. You shall not for favour, lucre or gaine, appoynte or write any thing for the poore, but such good and wholesome things as you shall thinke wth your best advise will doe the poore good, without any affection or respecte to be

---

[1] It was assumed that Harvey would live within the hospital precincts, as others had done, but, as will be seen, he did not choose to do so.

had to the apothecary. And you shall take noe gifte or reward of any of the poore of this house for your counsell. This you will promise to doe as you shall answere before God, and as it becometh a faithful phisicion, whom you cheifly ought to serve in this vocation, is by God called unto, and for your negligence herein, if you faile you shall render accompte, And soe we requyre you faithfully to promise in God his most holly name, to p'forme this your chardge in the hearinge of us, with your beste endevour as God shall enable you soe long as you shalbe phisicion to the poore of this hospitall: [*added later in another hand*: Provided alwaies that if any patient now admitted or hereafter to bee admitted shalbe soe infirme of body, that hee, shee, or they canot p'sonally come into the hall without p'judice to their healthes That then att all tymes in such cases haveing notice you shall goe into such ward or wards in this howse to p'scribe for their deseases.]

Harvey was to receive an annual salary of £25 for his services, and the Hospital ledgers record that he was also given 40*s*. each year until 1627 for his livery.

It is clear from the charge that the physician was only expected to go to the wards to see the patients if they were too ill to come to him. At least once a week most of them would come to be seen in the Great Hall of the Hospital. He would then prescribe medicines to be made up by the apothecary. The surgeons, on the other hand, would go to the wards, but as to whether they operated actually in the wards or in a special chamber at St. Bartholomew's there is no record. Probably the idea of an 'operating theatre' was still in the distant future, though illustrations of sixteenth-century surgeons at work sometimes show evidence of their being to some extent segregated for the purpose. The charge given in 1609 did not, however, define precisely the relation of the physician to the surgeons. This was made clear by Harvey himself at a later date (see p. 69). The surgeon's status was inferior and he had to operate under the supervision of the physician. Harvey in his lecture notes of 1616 gave warning of the dangers attending surgical measures such as paracentesis to remove fluid from the abdomen[1] or to draw fluid or pus from the thoracic cavity. Of the latter he said: 'Everywhere by injections it is possible to cause harm both with regard to the cough and to the place in which they are put in the body, therefore avoid the veins and arteries, &c., and tap on the top of the rib or as Nature directs.'[2] He also recommended his hearers to 'be cautious in trepanning one side [of the diplöe] being through before the other, wherefore it is not to be undertaken

---

[1] *Prelectiones*, p. 67.   [2] Ibid., p. 221.

PLATE VIII

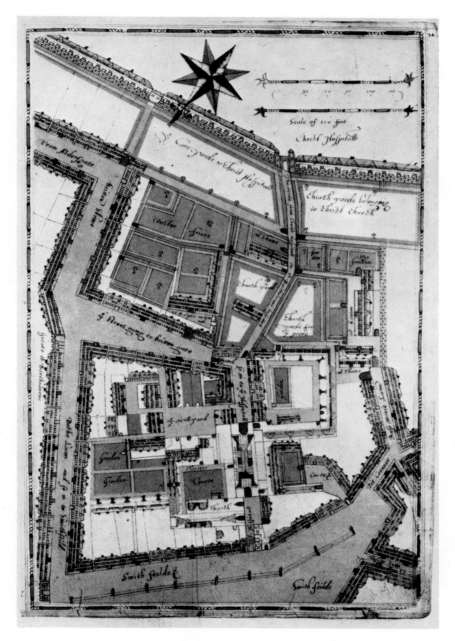

PLAN OF ST. BARTHOLOMEW'S HOSPITAL IN 1617

Smithfield is to the north. The Cloister is seen close to the east end of the Church. The City
Wall bounds the Hospital grounds to the south

PLATE IX

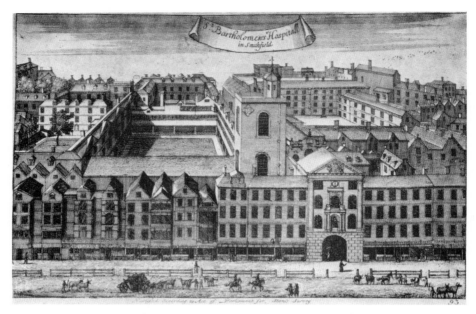

ST. BARTHOLOMEW'S HOSPITAL IN 1720
The Cloister is seen to the right of the church tower. Smithfield is in the foreground

MARTIN BOND'S PEWTER STANDISH (p. 57)

when the brain swells or when the patient coughs'.[1] He was full of practical wisdom and well able to direct his surgical colleagues.

The chief source of knowledge about St. Bartholomew's and its affairs in Harvey's time is contained in the two books of records known respectively as the Repertory Book and the Journal. The Repertory Book contains, with some early records, a number of later maps and plans, one of which (a portion is reproduced on Pl. VIII) gives a good idea of how the Hospital buildings lay in relation to the whole site, bounded to the south by Christ's Hospital and the great Church of Greyfriars; to the north by Smithfield and its markets; to the east by Britten Street and Docke, or Duck, Lane (now combined as Little Britain); to the west by Rosemarie Lane and the area now occupied by the General Post Office. The perimeter of the area was fringed, except on the south, by small houses. It appears from this plan that barely a third of the whole precinct was occupied by the Hospital. Even so a large part of the area was taken up by the Great Cloister on the west, the parish church of St. Bartholomew's the Less with its vicarage on the north, and a number of yards and gardens scattered among the buildings. A structure near the Smithfield entrance and facing the Church is believed to have been the Great Hall, where, according to his charge, Harvey saw those of his in-patients who were able to walk and also a small number of out-patients. The plan does not distinguish the identities of the various small buildings, which seem to have been placed without any settled design.

When Harvey was appointed there were twelve wards, and two more, named Katherine and Mary Magdalene, were built in 1629. There were over 190 bedsteads listed in an inventory of 1590, and many more must have been added by Harvey's time. The bedsteads, then as now, had curtains giving some degree of privacy, and there was adequate provision of mattresses and bolsters, both feather and flock, with sheets, coverlets, and blankets of various colours. In at least one ward there was a settle beside the fireplace, and others had stools and benches. Medicines prescribed by Harvey were made up and dispensed by the Apothecary, for whom a special building, the first Dispensary, was put up in 1614.[2]

Recent excavations (1963) have disclosed the chalk foundations of the medieval cloisters lying beyond the west end of the tower of St. Bartholomew's the Less; the north part of the cloister abutted on the church.[3] In the seventeenth century on each Monday morning the patients who

[1] *Prelectiones*, p. 305.
[2] M. V. Stokes, *St. Bartholomew's Hospital Journal* (1957), lxi. 168.
[3] Nelly J. M. Kerling, Archivist, ibid. (1964), lxviii. 19-31.

were to be dismissed assembled in the cloister for examination, and an equal number of new patients were then admitted if approved by the physicians. This custom continued until the middle of the eighteenth century.

The southern part of the area between St. Bartholomew's and Christ's Hospital was occupied mainly by gentlemen's houses with their gardens and by the Hospital graveyards. Dr. John Caius had lived there for many years, and after his death at Cambridge in 1573 his viscera were brought to St. Bartholomew's to be buried in the church—a rather macabre form of piety. His epitaph at Caius stated laconically: *Fui Caius*. The largest house when Harvey came to the Hospital had been occupied since 1597 by Sir Thomas Bodley, who remained there (when he was not in Oxford seeing about his library) until his death. Lady Bodley had died there in 1610 and was buried in St. Bartholomew's the Less, where the memorial tablet put up by her husband is still to be seen. Bodley himself became ill in the summer of 1612 and was visibly failing, as an observer, John Chamberlain, wrote to the Secretary of State, Sir Ralph Winwood. In July he had, according to Chamberlain, 'the advice and consultations of all the best physitians about this town',[1] Harvey no doubt being one of them. Soon afterwards Bodley died and was buried at Merton College, Oxford. About the same time Harvey had been in attendance upon the Lord Treasurer, Robert Cecil, as is apparent from a passage in a letter written on 25 March 1612 by Chamberlain to the diplomatist Sir Dudley Carleton (afterwards Viscount Dorchester), another distinguished resident in St. Bartholomew's Close.

In my last I wrote you of my Lord Treasurers amendment, which goes on still though fayre and softly, by reason of the weakness of his body and the uncertainty of his disease not fully discovered till very lately, and yet he wants not a whole college of phisicians that consult upon him every day, among whom Turquet [de Mayerne] takes upon him, and is very confident, though he have fayled as often in judgement as any of the rest. His letting bloud is generally disallowed as well by reason as by experience in this case, and in Sir William Cornwallis whom by that meanes he dispatched very presently. Within this fortnight my Lords disease hath varied (at leastwise in name or opinion) twise or thrise, for first yt was held the scorbut, then the dropsie, and now yt hath got another Greeke name that I have forgotten, but yt imports as much as *malus habitus*, wherein he hath found most goode from the phisicians and surgeons of the hospitall, and specially of Fenton.[2]

[1] *Letters of John Chamberlain*, ed. McClure, 1939, i. 367.
[2] Ibid. i. 341–2.

Harvey and his surgical colleague, Joseph Fenton, had therefore scored some credit in competition with the most eminent rivals.

The next tenant of the big house, then known as Mordant House,[1] was Sir Ralph Winwood, who, as a great state official, entertained there lavishly. In April 1617 he invited Sir Francis Bacon, just appointed Lord Keeper of the Great Seal, to dine with him. Bacon enjoyed his dinner so much that he afterwards asked his host to lend him his cooks.[2] It seems likely that Harvey may sometimes have shared this hospitality, and by so doing have enlarged his acquaintance among people of consequence. Winwood died in Mordant House in the same year and was buried in the church.

More important, perhaps, to Harvey than these neighbours in high places was Martin Bond, Treasurer of the Hospital from 1619 until 1636, he having been a Governor since 1607. He had acquired wealth as a Merchant Adventurer and was an open-handed character. His portrait, now in the committee-room of the Hospital, shows him with a staff in his right hand and a playing-card in his left, with an ace of hearts exposed on top of a pack lying on the table beside him—implying, perhaps, that he had played his cards well in life. On his election to the office of Treasurer he gave the Hospital a large standish, or pewter inkstand with its appurtenances, inscribed with his name and coat of arms. This is still to be seen in the committee-room, and it is traditionally believed (with some degree of probability) that Harvey used it whenever he signed official documents in the administrative quarters. Near Bond's portrait can be seen another of Sir Nicholas Rainton, Lord Mayor and President of the Hospital during the latter part of Harvey's time.

That Harvey never lived within the Hospital precincts is made certain by a series of entries in the Journal book. The first of these shows that in 1614 the Governors proposed that he should have premises contingently upon the death of a former occupant's widow:

Cur. tent. Jovis xxviii° die Julii A° Dni 1614

In presence of Sir Thomas Lowe President [and others]

DR. HARVEY

It is thought meate by this court That Mr. Dr. Harvey or his successor Phisicion for this hospitall, shall have the howses nowe or late in the tenures of M^ris Gardner & Dr. Bonham, with a p'cell of the garden nowe in the tenure of Willm Allen in West Smythfield after the expiracion of the lease sometyme graunted to Rob'te Chidley gent, which the said Willm

---

[1] *Chamberlain*, loc. cit., p. 10.   [2] Ibid., p. 73.

Allen now holdeth. And the same then to be devyded and layed forth at the discrecion of the Gov'nors of this howse, for so longe tyme as he shalbe Doctor to this howse, for such y'ly rent and uppon such condicions as this court shall thinck fytt.

Allen's widow did not die until March 1626, and Harvey was then invited to consider whether he would accept the tenure of the houses:

Cur. tent. ultimo die Marcii Anno Dni 1626

In presence of S\r Thomas Bennett Knight Presedent [and others]

DOCT\R HARVY.

This day Mr. Doctor Harvy physicion to this hospitall made suite to have the howse in West Smithfeild late in the tenure of Widowe Allen deceased accordinge to a former graunt. It is ordered that if he will sufficiently repaire the same in all manner of replacions to the contentment of the Gov'nors, and give the yerely rent of xiii\ld vi\s viii\d, Or otherwise pay the yerely rent of xx\ld, & the said howse to be repaired at the charge of this hospitall, Then he to holde the same soe longe as he shalbe Doctor to this hospitall and shall inhabitt the same, & shall give his psonall attendance for the vsitacion of the poore of this hospitall, And Mr. Tre'r Mr. Palmer Mr. Hill Mr. Strangways & such other of the Gov'nors as shall meete on Monday next to conferr w'h him accordingly.

Harvey had still not made up his mind in June, so the matter was again raised and he was given ten days in which to decide:

Cur. tent. Ven'is nono die Junii Anno Dni 1626

In presence of S\r Thomas Bennett Knight Presedent
[and others]

MR. DOCTOR HARVY

It is further ordered that forasmuch as Mr. Doctor Harvy phisicion of this hospitall hath bine warned to this court to give his aunswer whether he will accepte of the offer made to him at the last court of a Messuage or Tenement in Smithfeild late in the tenure of Sara Allen widowe deceased, accordinge to an order then set downe, whoe hath refused to take the same accordingly It is therefore thought good for the benefitt of the poore of this hospitall that if he shall not accepte thereof before the 19th day of this instant moneth, Then it is graunted that John Meredith Skynner shall have a lease of the same ten'te for 31 yeares if he and Elizabeth his nowe wife shall soe longe live, for the ffyne of c\ld to be paid at the sealing and the yerly rente of ffower pounds and he to bestowe in & uppon the same ten'te in needful reparcions within one yere nexte followinge the some of c\l and to be bound to all repar'cions.

By the next meeting of the Court he had decided to relinquish any claim, and was given an increased stipend in compensation:

Cur. tent. Veneris septimo die July Anno Dni 1626

In presence of Sr Thomas Bennett Knight Presedent

[and others]

DOCTOR HARVY

It is graunted that Mr. Doctor Harvy Physicion shall have his stipend beinge xxv^{ld} p. ann' augmented to the some of 33^{ld} 06^s 08^d in consideracion that he doe relinquishe all his claime of any form^r graunt of a howse in Smithfeild late in the tenure of Widowe Allen wch was ordered for him whoe hath refused to take the same uppon such condicions as this court hath thought fitt.

In 1846 Sir James Paget, afterwards Surgeon to St. Bartholomew's, drew attention in his *Records of Harvey* to the fact that in the Charter of 1547 it was agreed that the City Corporation should find one physician and one surgeon at an annual salary of £20 each. Yet in 1548, when appointments were first made, three surgeons were named, each receiving £18 annually, but no physician was mentioned. Paget suggested that this deficiency was compensated by the presence of Thomas Vicary as a resident superintendent of the general affairs of the Hospital, including some care of patients. Vicary is reputed to have been Sergeant-surgeon to Henry VIII and his three successors, and is so described on the title-pages of some editions of a book, *The Englishman's Treasure, with the True Anatomy of Man's Body,* first published in 1586 and several times reprinted. It is now doubted whether Vicary in fact wrote any part of the book, which is really a compilation from the works of earlier writers. The hospital records indicate that Vicary never worked as a surgeon there, and it is significant that soon after the disappearance of his name from the Journal Dr. Lopez was appointed as the first physician. It was probably intended by the Governors that the physician should be resident, as Vicary had been, and Lopez did live in the Hospital during his earlier years; so did his successors, Drs. Turner, Bright, and Doyley. It is uncertain whether Dr. Wilkinson did so, and Harvey, as has been shown, certainly did not, but his house was so near the Hospital that his refusal could be overlooked. It was not until after Harvey's retirement in 1643 that a second, or assistant, physician was appointed.

When Harvey became physician his surgical colleagues were Joseph Fenton, Richard Mapes, and John Collston; Roger Gwynne was Apothecary, having been appointed in 1588. None of these men was of any special distinction, but when Mapes retired John Woodall was appointed in his place on 19 June 1616. Woodall was a far from negligible character, and his relation to Harvey will be defined later, when we reach the point where the physician was asserting his ascendancy over the other members of the staff. Several 'specialists', as they would now be called, were also employed as needed, such as one who could cut for the stone, and others to set broken bones, couch for cataracts, or cure ruptures. These practitioners worked also at St. Thomas's Hospital on the same terms, being paid for individual operations.

Patients admitted to the wards were gathered in the City by Hospital officers known as Beadles, eight or ten of whom scoured the streets for suitable people. The Charter directed that the Hospital should care not only for the sick, but also for the destitute, so that some of the occupants of the wards needed food and lodging rather than medical care. The physician was responsible for writing prescriptions and for seeing that these were duly made up by the Apothecary and administered to the patients. Dr. Bright had been in trouble because he was too casual to attend properly to these duties. Harvey was more punctilious and was never called upon to answer for any negligence during his thirty-five years at St. Bartholomew's. There is no evidence that he performed any surgical operations or practised any midwifery in the Hospital, though he seems to have done so outside.

Eight months after Harvey took up his appointment a curious financial transaction came to light and was recorded in the Journal under the date 21 October 1609. It appears that Marten Lewellen, Steward to the Hospital, was in debt to Harvey's brother John, 'one of his Majesty's footmen', in the sum of £52. 10s. John Harvey had petitioned the Court of Exchequer for payment and their Lordships referred the matter to the Lord Mayor and Aldermen of the City, who in turn passed it on to the Governors of the Hospital, Lewellen being one of their officers. The Governors found that Lewellen was 'bound by his obligation to Dr. William Harvey' for repayment of the debt. Lewellen was receiving £10 yearly as Steward and it was ordered that 50s. of his stipend each quarter should be paid instead to Dr. Harvey until the debt was discharged—it would have taken over five years at £10 a year. Nothing more was heard of the matter, so presumably some of the money was paid, but it is difficult to understand exactly what position Dr. Harvey occupied in the transaction. The Steward was an important official in the Hospital hierarchy and it looks as if the physician, in the kindness of his heart, acted as intermediary between his brother and the debtor, assuming some of

PLATE X

JOHN HARVEY
wearing the uniform of Yeoman of the Bedchamber to James I about 1620

the financial responsibility. Harvey's confidence in the Steward was, it is to be feared, misplaced. It is evident from the hospital records that a few years later he was again in debt, and when the sheriff's officers came to arrest him they were attacked and beaten by two of the Sisters, while Lewellen made his escape.

John Harvey's position in the King's household must have been at this time a comparatively humble one, and it is surprising that he should have been able to lend Lewellen so large a sum as £52. 10s. There were a number of men called 'footmen' among the King's attendants, but most of them were not close to his person. It is recorded that after the King's death, when his body was brought from Theobald's to Denmark (afterwards Somerset) House for the funeral, most of the servants rode, but 'the Footmen in black suites and velvet cappes and coates down to the knee ran all the way about the body, not ranked, but in such manner as they do when the King removes.'[1] In 1609, however, John Harvey was only 27 years of age, and, after starting his career in this humble capacity, he succeeded later in improving his position. A portrait of him, probably painted about 1620, and afterwards preserved at Rolls Park, one of Eliab Harvey's country seats, shows him dressed in a falling ruff and a doublet gorgeously embroidered with the royal emblems of a Tudor rose surmounted by a crown. This splendid livery indicates that he had attained the position of 'Yeoman of the Bedchamber', and so was in a privileged position close to the King's person. The proof of this is found among entries in the Wardrobe Accounts of the Royal Household dated 1556–7,[2] showing that the Yeomen of the Bedchamber wore the livery embroidered with these emblems both back and front. On 6 July 1620 John Harvey was given a pension of £50 a year on resigning his place to Toby Johnson,[3] and in 1625 he was described as 'Sergeant-in-ordinary to the King', when, with his brother William, he was admitted a member of Gray's Inn. For William this meant little, but John may have gone further and have obtained some legal status, for in 1626 he was appointed Receiver General of Crown Property in Lincolnshire, jointly with his brother Daniel.[4]

In 1623 John Harvey inherited his father's property at Newington and Arpinge near Folkestone, and in 1640 became member of parliament for Hythe. In 1643 he took the National Oath and Covenant, thus breaking

[1] John Nichols, *The Progresses &c. of King James the First*, 4 vols., London, 1828, iv. 1037.

[2] Public Record Office, Wardrobe Accounts, 21 June 1556 (E. 101.427/16, no. 11), and Account Book of Sir Edward Waldegrave, Master of the Wardrobe (E.101.428/5). Personal communication from Mr. J. L. Nevinson.

[3] *Domestic State Papers*, London, 1859, cxvi. 161.   [4] Ibid. clxxxv. 499.

with the royalist sympathies of the rest of his family. He died unmarried in 1645, leaving, as already mentioned, a legacy to his sister-in-law, Elizabeth Harvey, though most of his property went to his parliamentary friend Sir Harbottle Grimston, and so was lost to his relations.

6

THE COLLEGE OF PHYSICIANS AND THE
BARBER-SURGEONS * JOHN WOODALL

FROM 1609 onwards William Harvey's time was divided between his hospital duties, his private practice, his anatomical and physiological research, and his various duties at the College of Physicians. In the College he was very active and was intensely loyal to its dignities and status for the remainder of his life. He was first appointed a Censor in ·1613, being reappointed in 1625, 1626, and 1629. He was named Elect on 3 December 1627 and appointed Treasurer in 1628. He was given this office again in the next year, but had to resign in December when the King commanded him to attend the Duke of Lennox in his travels abroad. During these twenty years Harvey's name constantly recurs in the Annals of the College as attending the meetings at which the ordinary business was transacted, when candidates were examined, or when cases of infringement of the College prerogatives were to be judged.

It proved to be a constant struggle to control effectually the activities of the untrained practitioners and to maintain the College monopoly of practice in the London area. There was much jealousy between the College and the members of the Barber-Surgeons Company. On the one hand, physicians were expected to call in a surgeon to a 'viewing' of any patient thought to be suffering from a surgical lesion, and, on the other, only a physician was allowed to prescribe internal medicines for administration by a surgeon. There was, however, no reciprocity, for a physician was permitted by the Statutes of the College to perform such surgical operations as he might think necessary.[1] Every effort was made to keep the surgeons in a subordinate position, and this was naturally resented. The inequality arose in the first place from the inferior education of the surgeons, who could not, as a rule understand Latin, the

---

[1] C. Goodall, *The Royal College of Physicians Founded*, London, 1684, p. 20.

accepted medium for the communication of medical learning. Nearly all books on medicine were printed in Latin, an essential condition for the dissemination of knowledge in the various countries of Europe. In France during the sixteenth century the same jealousies had smouldered between the Faculty of Physicians, the surgeons, who belonged to the College of St. Cosmas, or St. Côme, and the inferior caste of barber-surgeons. Even Ambroise Paré, one of the greatest surgeons of all time, having started his career as a barber-surgeon, was persistently persecuted by the two other bodies, who tried to prevent him from publishing his books because he did not know Latin. Paré defied his opponents and won his battle by sheer force of character and professional competence, his surgical works written in the vernacular being far the best published in Europe during the second half of the century. These quarrels were repeated in London, though on a lesser scale because the physicians were never faced with an adversary of the calibre of Paré, and Harvey played his part in maintaining the ascendancy of the College of Physicians.

Some of the prosecutions instituted by the College seem to have been brought on rather petty grounds. On 12 July 1605, just before Harvey's time, a surgeon, Walter Priest, appeared at the College 'on a charge of practising medicine. He confessed that he had given a purgative potion to a certain man on the advice of Dr. Brown [probably Harvey's father-in-law], but he had done nothing on his own responsibility.' On this occasion the charge was dismissed, but no doubt even so trivial an offence was regarded as the thin end of the wedge, the thick end including many charges of blatant quackery and even magic.

On 19 July of the same year John Lumkin appeared and was asked about the illness of a patient named Hill. 'He was asked to reply in Latin, but, confessing his ignorance, refused. On account of his bad practice, his unbecoming behaviour, and his abusive language, which was not to be borne, he was imprisoned with a fine of twenty pounds.' Lumkin had evidently given serious offence, yet the College was thwarted in its efforts to discipline him—he had to be released at the instance of the Earl of Northumberland.

Soon after Harvey's admission to the Fellowship an extremely troublesome practitioner was brought before the President and Censors. This was a Licentiate, Stephen Bredwell, son of a Licentiate of repute and grandson of John Banister, a distinguished surgeon who had successfully defied the authority of the College in 1587. On 7 August Bredwell was accused by another practitioner of offensive behaviour, and several other Fellows complained of his 'insolence and obstinacy'. He was admonished and advised in a friendly manner 'to behave more moderately'. On 4 September there was another complaint and he was summoned to the next meeting. He did not appear and nothing further was heard of him for three years, but on 2 April 1610 he came before the full Comitia, including Harvey, and 'behaved himself in a very impudent fashion'. He was told to come again 'in a more reasonable frame of mind'. He attended again on 25 June, Harvey again being present, and was arraigned for publication of a pamphlet, or *libellus*, containing unfair statements against the College and repeating the erroneous opinions of Sambucus Hispanus[1] published in a book pretending to disprove opinions of Hippocrates, Galen, and many others. He had also 'said he would make up medicaments in his own home and sell them and engage apothecaries'. He acknowledged his faults and made a formal 'confession'; a fine of £4 was imposed, yet he appeared on several later occasions and was admonished for contumacy. Eventually he took the oath of fealty to the sovereign on 11 January 1610/11. Bredwell is only one example of the great difficulty experienced by Harvey and his colleagues in curbing unorthodoxy and insolence to the College.

On 19 October 1613, in Harvey's presence, a surgeon, Edward Clarke, was arraigned for having administered mercury pills on various occasions; also other pills, dietetic purges, and sudorifics. It was decided that the accused should be fined £8 and imprisoned. On this occasion Harvey was inclined to be merciful and delivered his opinion that, though it had been ill practice, the fine might be remitted if Clarke submitted to imprisonment. If, on the other hand, he paid his fine, the imprisonment might be forgiven. Harvey even guaranteed that Clarke would present himself when he was summoned, or that he would pay the fine, or that he would submit to the will of the Censors.

On 12 December John Turner, a surgeon, was accused of having given two pills. 'Where did he obtain them? From Thomas Collins, a surgeon. He had made them himself, so he confessed, from eight grains of a precipitate with rose water. He gave them to some one suffering from a wound in the head and to another with an ulcer in the mouth. He had taken away overgrowing flesh. By what means? By mercury water.'

On 8 September 1615 'Mrs. Bryers, an aged quack with a long face, confessed to the charge namely that she had given to many people

---

[1] Oliva Sabuco de Nantes Barrera, *Nova philosophia de hominis natura*, Madrid, 1587, &c., purporting to be by the author's daughter. See Sir George Clark, *History of the Royal College of Physicians*, 1964, i. 201 n.

sudorifics to cure the French pox, ointments, plaster, potions, extreme unction, both on her own authority and that of other surgeons'.

An instance of frank magic occurred on 11 June 1623. It was charged that one Robert Booker had given physic to John Parker lying in St. Martin's Lane. 'He annointed him with certaine oiles from the neck to the foote, using at the same time of anointing this charme: *Three biters have bitt him, hart, tongue and eye. Three better shall help him presently, God the Father, God the Sonne, and God the holy spirit*; and that also the next day he gave him a drinke which he then dranke, and more he did not to the sick patient, making him believe that he was bewitched and that he would discover who had bewitched him.'

On occasion reprisals were attempted by the other side, and in one of these Harvey was implicated. It is recorded in the Minute Book of the Company of Barber-Surgeons that on 17 November 1635,

This daye Wᵐ Kellett being called here in Court for not makeing presentation of one of Mr. Kinnersley's Maides that died in his charge, he saied here in Court that Mr. Doctor Harvye being called to the patient did upon his vew of the patient saie, that by the meanes of a boulster [poultice] the tumour on the temporall muskle would be discussed [dispersed] and his opinion was, that there was noe fracture, but the vomiting came by reason of the foulenesse of the stomacke, and to that purpose prescribed physick by Briscoe the Apothecarye, soe the patient died by ill practice, the fracture being neglected & the Companie not called to the vew'[1]

Harvey could doubtless afford to ignore this imputation of neglect. He had, it seems, made a mistake in diagnosis such as any practitioner may do in difficult circumstances, and, as for his accuser, an earlier entry in the Company's Minute Book reveals the character of William Kellett. Under the date 15 February 1626 it is stated that 'At this Courte it is ordered that William Kellett do bring in his fine of vjˢ viijᵈ at the next Courte for his unseemly carriage and vile language to Walter Preist being contrary to the ordinance and good government of this house, which fine the said William Kellett here in Courte refused and said he would not paye it.' Priest did in fact owe Kellett £3, which he was ordered to pay. But on 8 June Kellett, not having paid his fine, was ordered to be dismissed out of the livery. On 26 October he was repentant, paid his fine and was readmitted.[2] It may also be suspected that Kellett was wishing to pay off some old scores, for it was recorded in

[1] *Annals of the Barber-Surgeons*, compiled by Sidney Young, London, 1890, p. 336.
[2] Ibid., p. 209.

the Annals of the College twenty years earlier, on 11 February 1613/14, that William Kellett was summoned before Comitia and examined 'regarding medical treatment of Alice Robinson, which he forthwith denied', but, it was added, 'Dr. Harvey will prove it'. Details were recorded in the Book of Examinations, but unfortunately this is no longer extant.

John Woodall has already been mentioned as appointed to the staff of St. Bartholomew's in June 1616 in succession to Richard Mapes. He thus became a colleague of Harvey on the surgical side and was not, perhaps, a very easy one. He was a much older man, born about 1556, and was an experienced naval and military surgeon. He had seen service in France under Lord Willoughby de Eresby, had lived in Poland, France, and Holland, and in 1613 had been appointed first Surgeon-General to the East India Company. He had filled several offices in the Barber-Surgeons' Company and was Master in 1633. His two books *The Surgeon's Mate*, 1617, and *Viaticum, being the pathway to the surgeon's Chest*, 1628, were important textbooks, the first one remarkable for giving one of the earliest accounts of treating scurvy with lemon-juice. Woodall published his collected writings as *The Surgeon's Mate, or Military and Domestic Surgery* in 1639, with his portrait introduced as part of an elaborate engraved title-page. Passages in this book testify to the wide extent of his surgical experience, much of it gained in the wards of St. Bartholomew's Hospital. Writing of the many patients that died in former times by sheer loss of blood during amputations Woodall claimed:

I may to God's glory, and so justly doe I affirme for a truth, that for the space of nere 24 yeares I have been a Surgeon in the Hospitall of Saint Bartholomewes, where I have taken off, and holpen to take off many more than one hundred of legges and armes, besides very many hands, and fingers, amongst all of which, not one of them all hath dyed in the time of their dismembring, nor afterwards, through the exceeding effusion of blood, in the operation that ever I could gather or conceive, and further-more, I affirme that not above foure of each twenty dismembred, but lived to have beene healed, and have beene delivered whole out of the Hospitall.[1]

As an example of this success in amputations he related

A History or a relation of a remarkeable example of an amputation by me performed upon a woman in Saint Bartholomewes Hospitall, of both her legges, and part of seaven of her fingers in one morning together

---

[1] *The Surgeon's Mate*, 1639, p. 388.

all taken off in the mortified part, without paine or losse of blood or spirits at all, and the woman was living at the writing hereof, and the patient was a certaine poore maid or woman servant in London, named Ellen French, of whom there were made Bookes and Ballads, that were sung about the streets of her, namely, that whereas the said maid or servant, was given to pilfering, and being accused thereof by her master and mistresse, used to curse and sweare, and with words of execration to wish, that if shee had committed the crime shee stood accused of, that then her legges and hands, might rot off, the which thing accordingly no doubt by the Providence of God, came to passe, as a judgement upon her, namely, that both her legs almost to the gartering place, with parts of seaven of her fingers did rot off, the which wretched woman neverthe-lesse, being referred to me in Saint Bartholomewes Hospitall to be cured, by God's mercy and permission, I healed her perfectly, by cutting off both the Sphacelated [gangrenous] legges in the mortified parts with also part of her seaven fingers, as is said, all in one morning without paine, terrour or of any losse of blood unto her, in the taking them off, and made her perfectly whole in a very short time, namely, within three moneths, so mercifull is our God unto us vile creatures, when wee are most unworthy of such his mercies. She is at the instant writing hereof, also living.[1]

The old naval surgeon did not cultivate any parsimony of words in the telling of his tale.

In 1621, not long after his appointment to the Hospital, Woodall joined with his three colleagues, William Clowes, Richard Mapes, and Joseph Fenton, and eight other surgeons in presenting to the House of Commons a petition protesting against the monopoly of medical prac-tice in London possessed by the College of Physicians and of their power over the surgeons. They complained, with some justice, that the College thereby 'do not only take unto themselves the arts of Physition, Chirurgion and Apothecary, but do likewise go about to restraine your petitioners from using unto their greved and wounded patients such wound-drinkes, potions, and other inward remedies as they by their long practice, study and tryed experience have found most necessary for the recovery of their patients'. Of these petitioners, Clowes was not the least distin-guished; he was the son of a former well-known surgeon to St. Bartho-lomew's and became afterwards surgeon to Charles II. This petition occasioned a considerable flutter in the College dovecots. In October 1617 a new Royal Charter had been shown at Comitia and the Registrar had read out selected passages. The Charter was then locked up in

---

[1] Ibid., pp. 398–9.

the College chest by the President. The confirmation of this Charter seems to have been neglected, for on 12 December 1620 Comitia agreed that, under the leadership of the President, Dr. Atkins, four other Fellows should take counsel with a view to pursuing the matter in Parliament and that they should promote by every means its extension according to the promise of the King. The matter was brought up again on 1 February 1620/1, together with a consideration of what action was to be taken against the surgeons' petition to Parliament. At a later meeting it was decided that the Fellows should be asked to visit as soon as possible those friends whom they had among the burgesses of Parliament and to win them over to their side, particularly those burgesses representing the Universities. On 17 February Dr. Goulston and Dr. Baskerville were asked to visit the members for Oxford University; Dr. Harvey, Dr. Clement, and Dr. Wilson to visit those of Cambridge. Dr. Clement was also to call on de Mayerne, the Court physician, to seek his advice.

The two representatives of Cambridge University in 1621 were Dr. Barrabas Goche, LL.D., Master of Magdalene, and Sir Robert Naunton, formerly a scholar of Trinity and later a Fellow of Trinity Hall.[1] Naunton was a highly influential person. He had first entered parliament in 1606 and was later a successful politician and diplomatist. Through his friendship with the Duke of Buckingham he was promoted to the office of Secretary of State in January 1617/18, and represented his university in parliament in 1621, 1624, and 1625. Harvey's mission on behalf of the College was clearly an important one and he discharged it with great promptitude, for on 21 February, four days after being briefed, he brought back a reply from the Cambridge burgesses. He reported that they raised various complaints against the College, one being that 'we admitted more doctors from other universities than from our own; this was denied, nor due to a claim to that exclusive right'. Exception was also taken 'to the form of examination as being unworthy of doctors'. Harvey's mission has sometimes been taken to indicate that he visited Cambridge in order to obtain the support of the University, but it is clear from the rapidity with which he brought the reply that he had only had to see the two members in London. The complaints, however, had struck home. The President forthwith proposed that the College should, for the future, not admit any unless from Oxford or Cambridge or incorporated in one or the other, though no action to include this in the statutes was taken until many years later. A proposed change in the examinations was ruled out, but it was decided that a copy of the new Royal Charter should be

[1] *The Historical Register of the University of Cambridge*, ed. Tanner, Cambridge, 1917, p. 30.

PLATE XI

SIR CHARLES SCARBURGH
conducting an anatomy assisted by Edward Arris, 1651 (p. 87)

JOHN WOODALL
Surgeon to St. Bartholomew's Hospital, 1616

taken to the university representatives, and it was noted that the College had 'their most complete agreement against the surgeons'. At the next Comitia in April, 'with regard to the controversy and intrigues of the surgeons against the College', it was ordered that the surgeons' petition should be copied in the Annals with the names of the petitioners. In fact the surgeons' protest had failed for the time being and no more was heard of it until at the Comitia of 3 May 1624 it was decided to request Dr. Atkins to 'speak before the Commissioners regarding the occasion of the Royal Charter and the need for an oath. Sir William Paddy was to open the case and oppose the petition of the surgeons.' In June Harvey and six others were deputed to draw up the arguments against the surgeons. The ratification of the new Royal Charter proceeded very slowly, and on 15 February 1624/5 no account was given in Comitia about the related action taken concerning the opposing surgeons and apothecaries because it was secret. The argument dragged on for another two and a half years until finally the matter was settled against the surgeons. On 28 August 1627 the President of the College, with Doctors Harvey and Goulston, formally thanked the Lord Keeper, Sir Thomas Coventry,[1] for his support against the surgeons' demand for a licence to practice. The physicians had thus successfully defended their monopoly, and, at a later date, Harvey asserted their authority in his capacity as sole physician to St. Bartholomew's Hospital. It must have been extremely galling to the self-respect of Woodall and the other surgeons when Harvey, in 1633, drew up a set of rules, at a time when he was expecting to be away from London in attendance on King Charles, leaving a deputy, Dr. Richard Andrews, in his place. He now proposed to the Governors on 15 October 1633 the following very harsh regulations for the governance of practice in the Hospital.

Decimo quinto die Octobr Anno Dni 1633

Doc[r] Harvey Phisicion to this hospitall presented to this court c'taine orders or articles by him thought fitt to be obs'ved and putt in practize —viz—

1. That none be taken into the hospitall but such as be curable or but a c'taine number of such as are incurable.

2. That those that shalbe taken in for a c'taine tyme be discharged at that tyme by the hospitler, unless they obtayne a longer tyme; And to be discharged at th'end of that tyme alsoe.

3. That all such as are c'tefied by the do[r] uncurable & scandelous or infeccous shalbe putt out of the said howse, or be sent to an out-howse;

[1] Created Lord Coventry, 1628.

And in case of suddaine inconvenience this be done by the do^r or apothecary.

4. That none be taken into any outhowse on the charge of this hospitall, but such as are sent from hence.

5. That no chirurgion, to save himselfe labour, take in or p'sent for the do^r; otherwise the charge shopp wilbe soe greate, & the successe soe little as it wilbe scandelous to the howse.

6. That none lurke here for releife only or for slight causes.

7. That if any refuse to take theire phisick they may be discharged by the do^r or apothecary or punished by some order.

8. That the chirurgions in all difficult cases, or where inward phisick may be necessary shall consult with the Do^r at the tymes he sitteth once in the weeke, & then the M^r himselfe relate to the Do^r what he conceaveth of the cure & what he hath done therein, And in a decent & orderly manner p'ceed by the do^{rs} dirreccions for the good of the poore and creditt of the howse.

9. That no chirurgion or his man doe trepan the head, peirce the body, dismember or doe any greate oper'cion on the body of any but wth th'app'bacon & by the direcion of the Do^r (when conveniently it may be hadd) & the chirurgions shall thincke it needfull to require.

10. That no Chirurgion or his man practize by givinge inward phisick to the poore, w'hout th' App'bacion of the Do^r.

11. That noe Chirurgion be suffered to p'forme the cures in this howse by his Boy or s'rvant w'hout his owne ov'sight or care.

12. That ev'ry chirurgion shall shewe & declare unto the Do^r, whensoev^r he shall in the p'sence of the patient require him what he findeth & what he useth to ev'ry external malady; that soe the Do^r beinge informed may better w^h judgm^t order his p'scrpts.

13. That ev'ry Chirurgion shall followe the direcions of the Do^r in outward oper'cions for inward causes, for recov'y of ev'y patient under theire sev'all cures, & to this end shall once in the weeke attend the Do^r, at the sett howre he sitteth to give dirrecions for the poore.

14. That the Apothecary Matron & Sisters doe attend the Do^r when he sitteth to give direccons & pr'scripts, that they may fully conceave his direccions & what is to be done.

15. That the Matron & Sisters shall signifie & complaine to the Do^r or Apothecary in the do^{rs} absence if any poore lurke in the howse, & come not before the Do^r when he sitteth or taketh not his phisick but caste it away & abuse it.

16. That the Apothecary keepe secrett & doe not disclose what the Do^r pr'scribeth nor the p'scripts he useth but to such as in the Do^{rs} absence may supply his place & that wth the Doctors approbacion.

This transcript gives the fair copy of the regulations as agreed by the

Treasurer, Martin Bond, and the Governors under the Presidency of the Lord Mayor, Sir Robert Ducie.

The 'outhouses' mentioned in clause 4 refer to the small hospitals founded in medieval times as Lazar-houses for the lepers. There were two: the Lock in Kent Street, Southwark, for women, and the Spital in Kingsland for men. Each had about thirty beds, and they were administered from St. Bartholomew's. After Harvey's time they were used for venereal diseases and other conditions thought to be contagious and therefore unsuitable for the main Hospital, the beds being reserved for patients sent from Smithfield.

An addition to clause 6, that none were to be taken from St. Thomas's Hospital unless 'they bring a certificate [that] they have not been there certified cured', had been struck out. Clause 9, limiting the freedom of the surgeons to operate without instruction from the physician, was repeating a regulation included by the College of Physicians in the previous year, in a petition to the King designed to muzzle the apothecaries in their encroachments on the privileges of the physicians (see p. 78). This was greatly resented by the surgeons, who in 1635 made a counter-petition to King Charles resulting, despite Harvey's influence in that quarter, in the annulment of the regulation.[1]

Woodall's feelings in 1633 may be imagined at this reassertion of the complete ascendancy of the physicians over the surgeons, who were restrained not only from operating without the physician's approval, but also from administering any internal medicines; they were not even allowed to know the ingredients of the prescriptions given to their patients, whereas the composition of every external application used by them was to be known to all. There is no indication in the hospital records that serious quarrels resulted from this action by Harvey. Many years later, in his book *De generatione animalium*, 1651, Harvey quoted Woodall as the authority for a most remarkable observation made by him in Borneo:

A certain Chirurgion of my acquaintance, an honest man, being returned from the East-Indies, told me upon his credit, that in the Island called Borneo, in the Inland and Hilly parts of it, there are a race of men born with Tails, (as Pausanias writes of another place) and that he saw a Virgin of that flock, whom they had much ado to catch, (for they are wilde) who had a fleshy thick tail, a span long, reflected between her leggs, to conceale her modesty: such care hath nature to hide those parts.[2]

[1] J. F. South, *Memorials of the Craft of Surgery in England*, London, 1886, p. 216.
[2] *Anatomical Exercitations*, 1653, p. 18.

Harvey's friend Baldwin Hamey the younger annotated his copy[1] of *De generatione animalium* and, noting the story of the men with tails, appears to have accepted it, adding several quotations from *Purchase his Pilgrimage* in confirmation. Neither did Harvey give any hint of disbelief in Woodall's faulty observation, and clearly they remained on very good terms, though Harvey seems to have been determined to maintain the authority of the physicians more strictly within the Hospital than the College could hope to do outside. His character as a rigid disciplinarian is, however, brought too sharply into focus by this episode. Owing to his duties at Court he was no longer able to give so much time to hospital duties as formerly and was now about to leave a younger colleague in charge. Probably he felt that his deputy's hand needed some strengthening if he was to keep control of so forceful a character as John Woodall, one of the most distinguished military surgeons of the day and Master of the Barber-Surgeons' Company. It was this feeling rather than any insubordination on the part of his surgical colleagues that prompted Harvey's action; he has nevertheless incurred some sharp criticism on this score.

7

HELKIAH CROOKE'S *ANATOMY* (1614) AND HARVEY'S ATTITUDE TO SURGERY

IN 1614 the College was seriously disturbed by doubts about the propriety of describing the human generative organs in an anatomical treatise. The author of the work in question entitled Μικροκοσμογραφία, *A Description of the Body of Man, collected and translated out of all the best authors of antiquity*, was Dr. Helkiah Crooke, an anatomist of repute, who had taken his M.D. degree at Cambridge in 1604. At a Comitia held on 11 November 1614 the President, Dr. Thomas Moundeford, and sixteen Fellows (not including Harvey) considered the question.

There was some discussion regarding the partly released English anatomy of Dr Crooke and whether it was fitting that it should be published. Not a few considered that nothing of this kind should be published in English; several thought that a few subjects and more

---

[1] Cambridge University Library (Adv. *c.* 33. 1), bound in contemporary black morocco, with Hamey's signature and extensive annotations on the fly-leaves and margins.

indecent illustrations should be removed, and other points ought to be corrected, while many considered that book four with the pictures of the generative organs should be destroyed and that he should be enjoined to confess that it was a translation, that is of many subjects from Laurentius and of summaries and illustrations of Bauhin. Finally it was decided that the President, Sir William Paddy and Dr Lister should wait upon the Bishop of London (who had sent us a copy) to agree that he should not publish the book, which ought to be suppressed, and that under his authority something should be paid to the printer towards the cost: but, however, if he did not do that, then they should insist on the need at the very least to delete book four first.

Dr. Crooke had been admitted a Candidate of the College on 25 June 1613, but he had not attended when subsequently summoned and had not paid his fees. On 22 December he was again summoned to appear, Harvey being present on this occasion, but he was late.

When Dr. Crooke arrived he was asked by the President why he had delayed so long: he replied, not because of his own business: why then? because he was called away by another's: thus, and by chance to another. Then the Treasurer said to him, 'As you have not paid the sums due to the College, we do not recognize you as a candidate: but if you are, why do you not attend when you have sworn to do so?' ' I am here,' he said, 'surely it is not a matter of great importance if the time has slipped by,' He was warned to come more promptly and to pay the money due to the College.

Dr. Crooke was guilty of disrespect to the College, but probably a greater cause of offence was his infringement of the accepted custom of writing about anatomy and other professional mysteries in Latin. Though he knew Latin well enough, he was in league with his publisher, William Jaggard, to make the innovation of writing in the vernacular, and accordingly on 3 April 1615 the President, in the presence of sixteen Fellows, 'informed the wife of Jaggard the printer with regard to Dr. Crooke's book on anatomy and written in English, that the volume was completely condemned, and that if the fourth book were published in its present form, he would burn it wherever he might find it. Finally it was decided that Dr. Giffard and Dr. Clement should amend book four and book five, and the books were handed over to them. Each promised to read through and correct twenty-four folios.' Harvey was again not present on this occasion and it is difficult to believe that, if he had been there, he would have assented to the mixture of prudery and obscurantism displayed by his colleagues though it was in accordance with the traditional attitude. The President's threats proved, however, to be but an empty form of words, and the Bishop of London was not in agreement, for the whole book was duly published in the same year. A second enlarged edition appeared in 1631 with all the illustrations unchanged.

Three years after the publication of his book, on 21 April 1618, Helkiah Crooke's name was proposed for election to the Fellowship, Harvey being among the twenty-one Fellows present. Sir William Paddy objected to Dr. Crooke because he had prefixed to his *Anatomy* a letter to King James stating 'that they themselves in public dissections exhibited the human body of either sex to be seen and touched and that they cut up indecent parts and explained each separately in the vernacular; from which it seemed that he had brought discredit to the College and our anatomy lectures'. Crooke denied that he had written this against the College, adding that he had seen these dissections done by Pavius at Leyden. In fact he had written about the dissections at Surgeons' Hall. Nevertheless, he was rejected by a majority in a ballot. A few weeks later, however, he wrote a letter of apology in high-flown language, which seems to have satisfied the Comitia held on 3 July, and he was then duly elected into the next vacant place as a Fellow by a majority of seventeen votes to two. Harvey was present and was surely not one of the two dissentients. Crooke was admitted a Fellow in 1620 and was afterwards appointed Censor on five occasions, so that his dangerous innovation seems to have been forgiven and forgotten. His *Anatomy*, published in 1615, being a compilation from earlier authorities, contains no reference to Harvey's work, but in the address to King Charles added to the second edition of 1631 he paid a tribute to Harvey, one of the earliest to appear in print. Crooke had summarized the progress made in various branches of medicine—pharmacy, the practice of medicine, and anatomy—concluding:

Pars Anatomica illustrata quidem est a me isthoc opere, sed penitius ab Harveyo tuo, viro ingeniosissimo juxta & oculatissimo culta & locupletata: Sola Chirurgia Idiomate nostro inculta adhuc jacet.

The anatomical part has indeed been elucidated by me in this very work, but more deeply cultivated and enriched by your Harvey, a man alike most gifted and observant. Surgery alone is still uncultivated in our language.

In 1615 there is likely to have been some element of medical politics behind the objections made by the physicians on the score of decency, for the Barber-Surgeons took a very different view. Their minutes record that on 7 May 1616, 'At this Court is given unto Mr. Dr. Crooke the sum of £5 for that he did dedicate a book unto this Company and gave one of them to this house.'[1] Crooke's address to the Company, dated May 1615, contains much admirable sense. It states quite clearly his debt to other authors, more particularly the anatomists, Laurentius and Bauhin, and defines the proper relation of anatomy to surgery and of physician to surgeon. Of the latter relation he wrote: 'Neither yet doe I thinke it fit, that the Physitian should be ignorant in the Chirurgical part, but be able to guide the Chyrurgeon that is not able to guide himself, to assist and confirme him that is, and to amend a fault when it is committed: but for the worke of the hand, I take it to be more lawfull for him then expedient, more honourable to bee able and not to doe it, then profitable to do it though he bee never so well able.' Harvey would assuredly have assented to the principles laid down by Crooke, whose tribute to him was plainly sincere. Harvey, during his years of service as physician to St. Bartholomew's Hospital, had assisted his surgical colleagues, in Crooke's sense, at scores of operations. He had a wide knowledge of surgery acquired by observation, as is shown by his writings, but it is very improbable that he transgressed the proper limits of his professional status by performing major operations himself.

It had been expressly laid down by Henry VIII in his Act of 1541 'for Physicians and their Privileges' that physicians might operate if they chose. 'Forasmuch as the science of Physick doth comprehend, include and contain the knowledge of Surgery, as a special member and part of the same, Therefore be it enacted, That any of the said Company or Fellowship of Physicians, being able, chosen and admitted by the said President and Fellowship of Physicians, may from time to time, as well within the City of London, as elsewhere within this Realm, practise and exercise the said science of Physick in all and every his members and parts; any Act, Statute or Provision made to the contrary notwithstanding.'[2] Hence physicians were authorized to perform operations if they wished, but the lower status of surgeons ensured that they did not often or willingly soil their hands by exercising the privilege.

Certain phrases used by Harvey in *De motu cordis* have given rise to the belief that he often did perform major operations himself. Thus he wrote in chapter 9: 'In the amputations of limbs or the excision of tumours, I have sometimes found a rapid occurrence of the same end-

[1] Barber-Surgeons Company, Court Minute Book, MS. 5257, vol. 4 (1607–21), f. 289. Noted by Dr. Gweneth Whitteridge.
[2] Goodall, loc. cit., p. 20.

effect [i.e. emptying of the circulatory system].'[1] The implication is that he had noticed this when attending at operations done by his surgical colleagues. Similarly in chapter 11, describing the effect of tight ligatures, Harvey wrote: 'Such a ligature we use in the excision of parts when we anticipate haemorrhage. Such, again, they use in the castration of animals and the removal of tumours; it completely interrupts the forward flow of nutriment and of heat, and we see the testicles and huge fleshy tumours decline and die and later drop off.'[2] It must not be assumed that Harvey had himself removed large sarcomatous tumours in this way. Aubrey stated that towards the end of his life he was reluctant to see patients unless they were special friends, 'e.g. my Lady Howland, who had a cancer in her breast, which he did cut off and seared, but at last she dyed of it', but here we may be sure that Aubrey was loosely reporting what Harvey had told him, or what he knew only by hearsay, about a consultation resulting in an operation by a surgeon.

It is well known that Harvey included in his will a clause by which he bequeathed to Sir Charles Scarburgh 'all my little silver instruments of surgery'. It would be illuminating to have a list of these instruments, but there are no details. A collection of surgical and obstetrical instruments was given to the College of Physicians by Dr. Thomas Prujean on his admission as a candidate in 1653 (presumably because as a physician he would have no further use for them), but they are all large, rather clumsy, steel tools, and clearly quite different from Harvey's bequest, which most likely were silver sounds, probes, catheters and dilators, silver-mounted lancets, and other instruments for diagnosis and minor surgery only. Under minor surgery would come certain gynaecological operations, such as dilatation of the *cervix uteri* and injection of medicaments into the uterus, which Harvey describes in the obstetrical section of *De generatione animalium*. Some guide to the nature of Harvey's instruments is suggested by a set deposited in the Hunterian Museum at the Royal College of Surgeons in 1965. This consists of nine small objects contained in a silver-mounted shagreen case and comprising: a tongue depressor (with hall-mark probably of 1614), a sinus forceps, scissors, a scoop with a long handle, a dental scraper, an ointment spatula, a director with a stone extractor at one end, a director with ring handle, and a caustic holder. All are of silver with steel blades for the sinus forceps, scissors, and scraper.

[1] Franklin, loc. cit., p. 64.   [2] Ibid., p. 71.

8

THE COLLEGE OF PHYSICIANS AND
THE APOTHECARIES

DIFFERENCES with the Barber-Surgeons were not the only cause of medico-political disputes facing the Fellows of the College of Physicians. The Apothecaries were another chronic source of trouble.[1] In 1614 King James was considering the advisability of granting a Charter to them to practise pharmacy as a Livery Company independent of the Grocers, with whom they were until that date incorporated. They received no medical training, but many of them nevertheless presumed to treat patients as if they were doctors, by this presumption earning the name of 'empirics'. Both the King and Sir Francis Bacon, as we shall see, tended to favour these untrained practitioners and many noblemen kept an apothecary as a member of their households from whom they could get medical advice at any time. An example of the harm done by these men came before the College Comitia on 18 April 1614. The Annals record that

The President made a report, confirmed by Dr. Goulston, with regard to the *Aurum Potabile* of Dr. Anthony given to the theologian Dr. Sanderson[2] deceased. When he was about to die, he had himself complained that he was being killed by it, that it had incurably inflamed his throat and that he had first paid twenty shillings for it and then forty shillings for the essence of gold. This affair among others ought to be remembered against him [Anthony]. There was some discussion about the others, whether in taking a firm stand against empirics it would be preferable to approach the King, the most important Councillors and Judges of the Kingdom, or to present a petition to Parliament which had already assembled according to custom. It was decided in a matter of such importance that they should take counsel and that the President, Sir William Paddy, Dr. Atkins, Dr. Lister, Dr. Argent, Dr. Harvey, Dr. Clement, and Dr. Goulston should pursue the matter as soon as they could.

[1] These affairs are fully described in Wall, Cameron, and Underwood's *History of the Society of Apothecaries*, Volume I, 1963. The brief account given here is based mainly on an independent examination of the Annals of the College of Physicians, Harvey's part in them being emphasized.

[2] Perhaps Dr. Thomas Sanderson, Archdeacon of Rochester.

On 23 May the Fellows, including Harvey, decided that it was desirable to separate the Apothecaries from the Grocers, and three representatives were appointed to take further counsel in the matter. As a result, on 3 June a letter was addressed to the King praying him to consider most strongly the errors of the Apothecaries and to proceed in the way in which he had already most conscientiously started. In consultation with his Law Officers the King accepted the advice to make the separation and issued a warrant for the drafting of a suitable Bill and Charter. The physicians made a number of recommendations as to clauses to be included in this Charter, one of the most important from their point of view being to lay down that every member of the new Company must take an oath that he would limit his practice to dispensing drugs prescribed by the physicians and would never, except in emergency, treat patients independently. Although the College hoped to have powers enabling them to fine and even imprison individuals proved to have contravened this regulation, they would have found it very difficult to enforce their authority over the large number of persons carrying on illicit practice. There were about 150 Apothecaries in London, but only 30 Fellows of the College with whom, in theory, they could work. The exaction of the oath was not in the end allowed.

The Charter granted by King James is dated 30 May 1616. It gives the names of 116 apothecaries who were to be freemen at the first incorporation of the Society, including that of Richard Glover, pharmacist to St. Bartholomew's Hospital. The Society was to have a Master, two Wardens, and twenty-one Assistants to conduct its affairs. In future no Grocer was to be allowed to keep an apothecary's shop, and no one else might keep such a shop until he had served a seven years' apprenticeship. No apprentice was to be made free until he had been examined and approved by the President of the College of Physicians or by other physicians deputed by him. The Master and Wardens of the Apothecaries were given the power to search shops and houses and to destroy any unwholesome or hurtful medicines that they might discover. The College of Physicians was to have the same powers of search and might call in the Master and Wardens of the Apothecaries to assist.[1]

The Apothecaries, having thus obtained some degree of independence by separation from the Grocers, continually sought to establish a right to practise their profession as pharmacists and to treat patients without reference to the Fellows of the College of Physicians, thereby seriously infringing the monopoly of medical practice in London enjoyed by the

[1] See Goodall, loc. cit., pp. 119–46.

College, and the Fellows naturally felt that it was necessary to combat this infringement by any means within their power.

A few individuals were particularly troublesome to the College, among them being Thomas Bonham, about whom inquiries were being made at the meeting when Harvey was admitted as a Fellow on 5 June 1607. Later Bonham was arrested and in 1609 brought an action against the College for false imprisonment. At the hearing Sir Edward Coke[1] ruled that, as a medical graduate of Cambridge, Bonham could be imprisoned only for malpraxis, and that he could be fined only if it had been proved that he had practised for at least a month. Bonham's name frequently recurs in the Annals of the College and it is clear that his defiance of authority was not unsuccessful.

Another person whose activities helped to bring matters to a head was John Buggs, admitted to the freedom of the Company of Apothecaries in 1620. He belonged to the company of players patronized by the Queen of Bohemia, daughter of the King. In 1630 he was practising in London and is mentioned in a petition addressed by the College to the Lord Chamberlain on 11 February 1630/1:

That wheras ther are divers Empericks which contrarye to Lawe and Conscience presume to practise Phisicke in and about the Cittye of London, as one Butler a Glover, Trigg a Last maker, Bugges one of the Queen of Bohemia's Players, sometimes ane Apothecary, one Hill, one Blayden, one Blank a pewterer, and one Sir Saunder Duncombe a pentioner to his majestie with divers others, against whom the Colledge cannot take the benefitt of their Charter and his majesties Lawes, by reason that they shrowd themselves under the colour of beeing his majesties servaunts.

The Lord Chamberlain allowed this petition and the College consequently resorted to the lawcourts, but without ever getting complete satisfaction. Buggs took his M.D. degree at Leyden in 1633, obtained a licence to practise from Cambridge, and was incorporated M.D. at Oxford in 1635. In spite of this the College repeatedly arraigned him without preventing him from practising, which he continued to do until he died in 1640.

On 11 May 1632 Buggs had been accused of having caused the death of a patient by malpraxis, and a few days later another apothecary, Christopher Mathews, was implicated in an even more serious case of poisoning. It was alleged that a man named Lane had been killed by means of corrosive sublimate administered by his servant, Cromwell.

[1] See Goodall, loc. cit., pp. 170–201.

By command of the King a full inquiry was held by the College, in which Harvey took a conspicuous part. The decision was reached that Lane had indeed been poisoned by sublimate and Sir Theodore de Mayerne was requested to draw up a report to that effect. In this it was further stated that the fatal potion had been obtained by Cromwell from the shop of the apothecary Mathews. At the conclusion of the report the Fellows asked for an edict from the King

to be enacted by law as soon as possible that in future no grocer, apothecary, druggist or any other chemist or person may sell freely (as has generally been done) to any poor woman or the meaner sort of people, arsenic, orpiment, mercury sublimate or precipitate, opium, coloquintida, scammony, hellebore, and other drugs either dangerous or poisonous: but only to those who are willing to give their names and publicly reply regarding the item purchased.

May it also please the royal majesty to prohibit the apothecaries one and all by an edict under the most severe penalties from daring to either compound or administer either to the well or sick any medicament without exception, especially vomits, purges, opiates, soporifics, mercurial or antimonial remedies without the prescription of a living physician: and that they shall be bound to show the prescriptions when asked to do so. Any one doing otherwise shall be punished by law as a public enemy against the life of man.

The report was signed by eighteen Fellows, including Harvey.

The petition from the College was referred to the Privy Council, for which Harvey acted as spokesman on 25 June:

Concerning our petition made to his Majestye concerning Apothecaryes, which is now referred to the Lords, the Colledge is to advise now what they would desire in that behalfe, and Dr. Harvye sayeth that the Lords agreed that poyson should not bee sould, but with Caution to bee had of the buyer.

To prevent the practize of the Apothecaryes it is thought fitt

1. That they should make no medecyne without a livinge Doctor's bill: and if any body shall bringe any dead phisitions receipt to bee made then the partyes hand whoe takes the phisicke is to bee sett therto.

2. That those Clauses presented by Mr. President maye bee inserted into their oathe, and that they shall make all their Medicines according to our dispensatorye.

3. Thirdlye that ther bee a rate sett upon the medecynes of the dispensatorye seeing they sell att divers prizes, wheras the medecyne ought to bee the same.

4. Concerning Chirurgions, that they shall not sett the Trepann nor doe anye other great operation in Chirurgerye without calling a Doctor to Counsell.

It seems from the last clause that the opportunity had been taken to make another dig at the surgeons while the Apothecaries were being brought under control.

A few days later, on 4 July, the matter of the petition was again brought up at Comitia, the Apothecaries having made a complaint concerning Harvey's practice at St. Bartholomew's Hospital:

Upon the petition made to the Kinges Majestye concerninge the Apothecaryes: the Apothecaryes gave out, that if they should not reforme the Doctors bills, much harme might be done: and instance was made by Mr Glover Apothecarye to St. Batholomews hospitall, of a bill given wherin was Colocinthidos ʒj, upon the taking wherof the patient dyed.

This bussines being questioned by Mr. President first, Nathaniell Ridd, servaunte to Mr. Glover being demaunded therof, sayeth that Dr Harvye their Doctor writts him selfe his bills in a booke, and when the booke is full the Doctor hath itt home; yett withall hee acknowledgeth that sometymes his Master writts: and that hee the said Nathaniell writte this bill himselfe and did not shewe itt to the Doctor, after the writing therof.

Hee further sayeth, that the Medecyne given to the mayde about a yeare agoe was colocinthidi ʒj vini albi ʒiiij the bill wherof is forth comming, but hee hath not brought itt with him: and hee heard that the Medecyne wrought excessivelye, and that shee dyed upon the working therof: yett was hee not with her himself att the tyme of her death: the Doctor whoe prescribed the Medicyne hee acknowledgeth to bee a Rationall phisition, but his name he will coenceale: the medicyne was wayed to a grain.

Mr. Richard Glover Apothecarye being called, denyeth that hee ever told the Doctor of the dose of the Medicyne: but hee is sure such a bill ther was, and such a medicyne was given.

And hee further sayeth, that being sent for by the Master and Wardens of his Companye: att a second meetinge, the Clauses propounded by the Colledge to bee inserted into their oathe wear readd, which he denyed to take, as esteeming some of them unlawfull, because phisitions maye mistake; and because one of the best Ranke prescribed a dragme of Coloquintida which medecyne being taken the patient dyed that night.

But itt being objected to him, why hee did not shewe the Doctor the bill he acknowledged that hee had not shewed itt him; and that it was written by his man, whoe hee thincks would not deale dishonestlye by him.

But itt being made knowne, that the partye had taken divers stronge medicines that had not wrought, itt was supposed the Doctor might bee induced to use so great a remedye; and Dr Winston did then averr, that hee had given 15 graynes of Antimonie to a patient.

Hereupon Mr. Glover promised, that his man should never make anye phisicke, till hee had reade the bill to the phisition; and that hee himselfe will cause the Apothecaryes to meet, and make itt knowne to them that they mistooke him.

So the Apothecaries' squib proved to be a damp one; Harvey was exonerated of any blame for the patient's death, the hospital pharmacist not having seen fit to show him the prescription. Though Harvey was present at the inquiry, there is no record in the Annals that he was called upon to give evidence.

The Apothecaries naturally reacted to the various clauses in the Physicians' petition, and replied with much show of indignation; the quarrel gave every sign of becoming embittered and protracted. It was further complicated by complaints made by the Physicians against individual apothecaries who had resisted a search being made of their shops by the Censors of the College even though accompanied by a Warden of their Society. This search was directed to the detection of adulterated drugs, particularly of *lac sulphuris*. During this dispute there seems to have been some attempt to effect a reconciliation, the Master and Wardens of the Apothecaries with several others having come to the College on 4 July 1634 to help at an inquiry about the drugs that had been condemned. At this meeting it was first announced that 'Dr. Harvye hath given the skinn of the man tanned for a monument to bee reserved in the Colledge'. The Annals then give a rather confused account of the discussion, and its conclusion.

Dr. Harvye by the President's direction made a speech to the Apothecaryes, persuading them to Conformitye, and explaining to them the justnes of the demaunds made by the Colledge, wee desyring in our Apothecaryes sufficiencye for the well understanding of their Art: Honestye in the right and well preparing of their medecynes; and conscience in rating them so that they maye not bee burdensome to the poore. And lastly hee declared the opinion of the Colledge concerning Medecynes: that itt was in the discretion of anye doctor for his private use to appoint anye Medecyne to bee made which is not in our dispensatorye, yett so as that the Colledge must bee the judges therof; and that such Medecynes must not bee permitted to bee promiscuouslye sould: and that no other medecyne which is not in our dispensatorye shalbee promiscuouslye sould till itt bee alowed and approved by our Colledge.

On 9 July 1634 Harvey was again present at Comitia when it was decided to address a letter to the Apothecaries referring in particular to *lac sulphuris*, the drug believed to have been adulterated. This was a form of precipitated sulphur in a state of fine division, and was used in the treatment of coughs and other lung complaints, and also for colic, arthritis, and rheumatism. It must have been a drug in very general use, since feelings about it evidently ran high. Harvey was not, however, as far as the Annals tell us, personally implicated, and the matter need not be pursued in further detail.[1]

In spite of all their efforts the Physicians never, in Harvey's lifetime, succeeded in settling their differences with the Apothecaries. Pinpricks were constantly administered by both sides, as for example on 13 October 1637, when the Annals record that

Robert Cooke servant to Weale an apothecary 2 yeares and at this present servant to his father in the same trade where he hath served 2 yeares and a quarter confessed that he had made the *saccharum rosarum* which was given by his father to the Lady Rainy in August last and that he added juyce of Lemons *Coloris gratia* as he said. At his parting from the Table he sawcily putt on his Cap so soone as his back was turned, for which his malapert behaviour Dr Winstone did presently rebuke him; but he had at home the wherewithal to learn.

The Apothecaries won their battle in the end—but not until 1815, when the Society was granted the independent right to issue licences to practise medicine. Circumstances had by then so much altered that the College of Physicians could afford to welcome them as colleagues, and the L.S.A. (Licentiate of the Society of Apothecaries) is still admitted as a qualifying degree.

During the course of his own practice Harvey must have employed a number of apothecaries, whose names have not been recorded. Outside St. Bartholomew's Hospital he was associated, as will be seen, with Adrian Metcalfe, apothecary to Charles I. The only other claimant to the distinction of having served Harvey as his apothecary was 'N.L.', the signatory of a pamphlet[2] advertising at some date after the Restoration a variety of remedies attributed to Gideon De Laune, the celebrated apothecary to Anne of Denmark. De Laune had died at a great age in 1659 and was certainly well known to Harvey. The particular remedy

---

[1] A full account will be found in *The History of the Society of Apothecaries*, pp. 266–303.
[2] *Delaun Reviv'd, viz. a Plain and Short Discourse of that Famous Doctor's Pills, their Use and Virtues. With Choice Receipts for the Cure of Scurvy, Dropsy, Jaundies, Veneral and other Diseases*, 4°. [*c.* 1702] A copy of the pamphlet is in the Wellcome Historical Medical Library.

known as 'Delaun's Pill' was immensely popular and was the prototype of later imitations, such as 'Beecham's Pill' of the nineteenth century. 'N.L.' claimed definitely to have been Harvey's apothecary:

My own knowledge in Physick I acknowledge to Pharmacy, being bred under the great Inquirer into Nature Dr William Harvey, as his Apothecary, who above all Cathartics, having experimented this Pill, commended it to the world, as the most friendly to Nature, and effectually [*sic*] in sweetning the blood, and maintaining its Circulation, whereof (to England's glory) he was the true Author.

The initials N.L. cannot be those of Nicolas Lefebvre, professor of chemistry to Charles II and apothecary in ordinary to the royal household until his death in 1669, since he did not come to England until 1660.

9

ANATOMICAL LECTURES—*PRELECTIONES* (1616)

IN August 1615, although he had held the Fellowship of the College of Physicians for only eight years, Harvey was appointed to the important post of Lumleian Lecturer. According to the Annals[1] this appointment was 'due to the death of Dr. [Thomas] Davies before St. Bartholomew's Day', that is, before 24 August. Harvey was appointed 'within the next week'. Dr. Davies was buried at St. Dunstan's in the West on 20 August, so that Harvey's appointment must have been made about that date.

The Lumleian Lectureship had been founded by John Lumley, sixth Lord Lumley, in 1582, the Indenture being dated 3 July.[2] Lumley had had a distinguished, though chequered, career in court circles, and was High Steward of Oxford University for fifty years. He was imprisoned in the Tower of London from 1569 to 1573 for taking part in a Catholic conspiracy, but a few years after his release, in February 1579/80, he acquired great wealth by becoming sole legatee of his father-in-law, the twelfth Earl of Arundel. Lumley was troubled because abuse of the good name of surgery by quacks and wise-women was still rampant in spite of

---

[1] This entry, dated 4 August, was not made in the Annals of the College until 1617, and the date appears to be inaccurate.

[2] See Francis W. Steer, *Medical History* (1958), ii. 298–305. This article prints a counterpart of Lumley's grant now in the archives at Arundel Castle (MS. J4/16).

PLATE XII

WILLIAM HARVEY *c.* 1627
Artist unknown

King Henry's efforts to suppress them; he therefore sought to raise the repute of both surgery and anatomy by founding, at the suggestion of Dr. Richard Caldwell, a senior Fellow of the College, 'a publicke lecture or lesson in Surgerie', as it is called in Holinshed's *Chronicles*. The lecturer's stipend was to be equal to that awarded in the Universities.

According to Holinshed,[1] the reading was to be given twice a week over a period of six years

to wit, on Wednesdaies and Fridaies, at ten of the clocke till eleven, shall the reader read three quarters of an houre in Latine, and the other quarter in English, wherin that shall be plainlie declared for those that understand not Latine, what was said in Latine. And the first yeare to read Horatius Morus tables,[2] an epitomie or briefe handling of all the whole art of surgerie, that is of swellings or apostems, wounds, ulcers, bonesetting, and healing of bones broken, termed commonlie fractions, and to read Oribasius of knots and Galen of bands, such workes as have beene long hid, and are scarcelie now adaies among the learned knowen, and yet are (as the anatomies) to the first enterers in surgerie and novices in physicke; but amongst the ancient writers and Grecians well knowne. At the end of the yeare in winter to dissect openlie in the reading place all the bodie of man especiallie the inward parts for five daies togither, as well before as after dinner, if the bodies may so last without annoie.

The second yeare to read Tagaultius[3] institutions of Surgerie, and onlie of swellings or apostems, and in the winter to dissect the trunke onelie of the bodie, namelie from the head to the lowest part where the members are, and to handle the muscles especiallie. The third yeare to read of wounds onelie of Tagaultius, and in winter to make publicke dissection of the head onelie. The fourth yeare to read of ulcers onlie the same author, and to anatomize or dissect a leg and arme for the knowledge of muscles, sinewes, arteries, veines, gristles, ligaments, and tendons. The fift year to read the sixt book of Paulus Ægineta,[4] and in winter to make anatomis of a skeleton, and ther withall to shew and declare the use of certeine instruments; as *Scamnum Hippocratis*,[5] and other instruments for setting in of bones. The sixt yeare to read Holerius[6] of the matter of Surgerie, as of medicines for surgians to use.

[1] *Chronicles*, 1808, iv. 496–9.

[2] Horatius Morus of Florence, *Tabulæ universam chirurgiam miro ordine complectens*, London, 1584. English edition, 1585.

[3] Tagaultius of Paris, *Chirurgia institutiones*, Paris, 1543.

[4] Paulus Ægineta, *De re medica*, Paris, 1532.

[5] i.e. the bench for mechanical reduction of dislocations, described by Oribasius in Hippocrates, *Chirurgia*, Paris, 1544.

[6] Jacobus Hollerius, *De morborum curatione, Ejusdem de febribus, de peste, de remediis κατὰ τόπους in Galeni libros de materia chirurgica*, Paris, 1565.

It seems probable that the details of the readings as laid down by the founders were not observed with any exactitude, but were modified by successive lecturers. The first appointed was Dr. Richard Foster, who began his course in the Easter Term of 1588 and continued in the office until December 1602. He was succeeded by Dr. William Dunne, who, by his death in May 1607, gave place to Dr. Thomas Davies. Harvey was therefore the fourth Lumleian Lecturer when he took up his appointment in August 1615; he held the office for the next twenty-eight years.

If the Lumleian Lectures had been given as originally planned, the anatomy demonstrations would have duplicated those already given by the College. It was accordingly decided in 1599 that these should be delivered in alternate years by the Lumleian Lecturer and a Fellow of the College. It appears from Harvey's lecture notes, or *Prelectiones*, that he gave his first lectures on 16–18 April 1616. Dr. Gweneth Whitteridge has noted that the Justice of the City of London condemned two felons to be hanged on Friday, 12 April, so that their bodies would have been available for Harvey's demonstrations on the following Tuesday, Wednesday, and Thursday.

Owing to the decision of 1599 already mentioned, another Fellow of the College must have given the anatomy lectures in 1617. Harvey was instructed to give them in 1618, and his turn would come again in 1620, 1622, 1624, 1626, and so on. We have, indeed, definite evidence that he was lecturing in March 1623/4, when Sir Simonds D'Ewes was a member of his audience (see p. 121).

It seems to be uncertain whether the lectures were delivered in Latin or in English. Probably it would depend on the composition of his audience. Surgeons would understand only English; physicians would wish to assert their superiority by emphasizing their familiarity with Latin. Harvey's notes in the mixed languages do not give any indication one way or the other, since either language would have been equally easy for him. It has been noticed that, at somewhat later dates, Harvey's two friends Dr. Baldwin Hamey the younger and Sir George Ent, wrote their notes in English.

We do not possess any eyewitness account of the delivery of anatomy lectures at the College of Physicians. Queen Elizabeth had granted permission for the College to use each year the bodies of up to four malefactors executed for felonies anywhere in London or Middlesex or within a radius of sixteen miles. A Charter of James I increased the number of bodies available to six.[1] The lectures were delivered at first in the house

[1] In 1641 an Act for enlargement of the privileges of the College of Physicians increased the

given to the College by Linacre in Knightrider Street, but it was small and was later enlarged, a more adequate lecture theatre being built in 1583–4. This was used until the College removed to new premises at Amen Corner in 1614 and it was there that Harvey gave his first anatomy lectures in April 1616. It is possible that he had already given some lectures on surgery, but of this there is no record.

In the absence of any description of the procedure at the College of Physicians we can only depend for an idea of how it was done on knowledge of the probably very similar routine carried out from about the year 1577 by the Company of Barber-Surgeons.[1] The 'mysteries' of both public and private 'anatomies' were held in the Company's Hall, private dissections not being allowed elsewhere under pain of a heavy penalty. Members had to hold a special licence from the Master to bring a body, and the remains had to be reverently buried, as after a public anatomy, 'for the worshippe of the said mysterie'. A skeleton might be prepared on payment of ten pounds. The surgeon undertaking a public dissection would usually do one privately beforehand.

The stewards attending upon the Master were to provide each year a mat by the hearth

that Mr. Docter be made not to take colde upon his feete nor the gentelmen that doe come and marke the Anatomye to learne knowledge. And further that there be ij fyne white rodds appointed for the Doctor to touche the bodye when it shall please him, and a waxe candell to loke into the bodye and that there be alwayes for the Doctor two aprons to be from the sholder downwarde: and two payr of Sleaves for his hole Arme with tapes for chaunge for the sayed Doctor and not occupye one Aporne and one payr of Sleves every day which is unseemly. And the Masters of the Anathomye that be about the bodye to have lyke aprons and sleves every day bothe white and cleane; yf that the Masters of the Anathomye that be about the Doctor doo not see these thinges ordered and that there knyves probes and other instruments be fayer and cleane accordingly with Aprons and sleves: if they doo lacke any of the said things afore rehersed he shall forfayte for a fyne to the hall xl s.

The lecture lasted from five to six o'clock, and when it was over the Doctor pulled off his robes and bonnet and put on a clerk's gown in which to dine, the company then being 'plentifully regaled'. The

number of bodies available to sixty (*Historical Manuscripts Commission, Fourth Report,* 1874, House of Lords, p. 71).

[1] See J. F. South, *Memorials of the Craft of Surgery in England,* edited by D'Arcy Power, London, 1886, pp. 136–42.

procedure was exactly the same on the second and third days. Careful arrangements were made for everyone attending the anatomy to be able to see properly, and an iron framework was put up round the dissecting table so that the body could be decently hidden by curtains before the demonstration began. There was also 'a case of weynscot made with paynter's worke upon it, as semely as may be done for the Skellyton to stand in'.

The routine of public anatomies seems to have continued virtually unchanged through the years until after Harvey's time. Samuel Pepys gives a vivid account of what he saw on a visit to the Barber-Surgeons' Hall in 1662, with asides on the Holbein picture of Henry VIII giving audience to the surgeons and on the technique of judicial hanging. Probably Pepys chose a particular day because, in addition to his delight in any new experience, he had a special interest in the urinary system, having himself been successfully 'cut for the stone' by Thomas Hollyer four years earlier, on 26 March 1658. His Diary entry under the date 27 February runs as follows:

About 11 o'clock, Commissioner Pett and I walked to Chyrurgeon's Hall (we being all invited thither, and promised to dine there); where we were led into the Theatre; and by and by comes the reader, Dr. Tearne, with the Master and Company, in a very handsome manner: and all being settled, he begun his lecture, this being the second upon the kidneys, ureters, &c., which was very fine; and his discourse being ended, we walked into the Hall, and there being great store of company, we had a fine dinner and good learned company, many Doctors of Physique, and we used with extraordinary great respect. Among other observables we drank the King's health out of a gilt cup given by King Henry VIII. to this Company, with bells hanging at it, which every man is to ring by shaking after he hath drunk up the whole cup. There is also a very excellent piece of the King, done by Holbein, stands up in the Hall, with the officers of the Company kneeling to him to receive their Charter. After dinner Dr. Scarborough took some of his friends, and I went along with them, to see the body alone, which we did, which was a lusty fellow, a seaman, that was hanged for a robbery. I did touch the dead body with my bare hand: it felt cold, but methought it was a very unpleasant sight. It seems one Dillon, of a great family, was, after much endeavours to have saved him, hanged with a silken halter this Sessions (of his own preparing), not for honour only, but it seems, it being soft and sleek, it do slip close and kills, that is, strangles presently: whereas, a stiff one do not come so close together, and so the party may live the longer before killed. But all the Doctors at table conclude, that there is no pain at all in hanging, for that it do stop the circulation of the blood; and so stops all sense and motion in an instant. Thence we went into a private room, where I perceive they prepare the bodies, and there were the kidneys, ureters [&c.], upon which he read today, and Dr. Scarborough upon my desire and the company's did show very clearly the manner of the disease of the stone and the cutting and all other questions that I could think of . . . how the water [comes] into the bladder through the three skins or coats just as poor Dr. Jolly has heretofore told me. Thence with great satisfaction to me back to the Company, where I heard good discourse, and so to the afternoon Lecture upon the heart and lungs, &c., and that being done we broke up, took leave, and back to the office, we two, Sir W. Batten, who dined here also, being gone before.

Harvey was certainly familiar with the painting of Henry VIII presenting the Charter to the Company. Four years after Pepys's visit it was very seriously damaged in the Fire of London, but he had not forgotten it, and on 29 August 1668 'after dinner [Harris] and I to Chyrurgeon's-hall, where they are building it new, very fine; and there to see their theatre, which stood all the fire, and, which was our business, their great picture of Holben's, thinking to have bought it, by the help of Mr. Pierce, for a little money: I did think to give £200 for it, it being said to be worth £2,000; but it is so spoiled that I have no mind to it, and it is not a pleasant, though a good picture.' The picture was thereafter re-painted and acquired its present appearance. Harvey is unlikely to have seen the other version, thinly painted over the paper of Holbein's original cartoon made in 1542.[1] King James may have discussed the picture with Harvey, for in January 1617/18 he wrote a letter from New-market to the Company asking to borrow it in order that it might be copied, but it seems that this was never done. The Company was unwilling even to lend the picture without payment of a substantial deposit.[2]

With the help of this description of the scene in a sister institution we may form a mental image of Harvey lecturing at the College of Physicians. His small figure would be, perhaps, rather lost in the volu-minous gown and large round bonnet proper to the occasion, but his bright brown eyes lighting up his face with its olivaster complexion (as Aubrey called it) and small pointed beard, his alert and eager manner, and his precise diction would combine to compensate for any loss of dignity due to a low stature. In his hand he would carry a slender wand

[1] This hung in the Surgeons' Hall in the Old Bailey from 1786 until 1799 and subsequently in the present Royal College of Surgeons of England in Lincoln's Inn Fields.
[2] South, *The Craft of Surgery*, London, 1886, pp. 93–94.

for pointing to the part of the dissected body under scrutiny. A silver-tipped whalebone rod still preserved at the Royal College is traditionally the instrument used by him on these occasions.

According to his notes, Harvey introduced his hearers to the subject by first defining anatomy as 'that branch of learning which teaches the uses and actions of the parts of the body by ocular inspection and by dissection',[1] from which it is at once plain that the lecturer was not concerned with detailed topographical anatomy such as was taught to students until very recently. It was applied anatomy and physiology that he was trying to demonstrate, and it is to Harvey's method that teaching of anatomy at the present time is tending to revert.

This was followed by a philosophical discussion of the nature of the animal body, its divisions and uses, many of Harvey's opinions being traceable to those of Aristotle. He concluded his remarks with a reference to St. Augustine, deducing from a passage in one of his sermons that Nature's principal object is to create beauty, not all our parts being strictly needed, but being made for the sake of beauty only, 'wherefore Nature is more concerned with their adornment than with their necessity because our earthly appetites are consummated by the resurrection'.

Harvey then laid down eleven general rules for conducting an anatomy, and these illustrate so well his approach and actual methods that they must be quoted in full.

GENERAL RULES FOR AN ANATOMY

1. Show as much in one viewing as can be, for instance, from the whole belly or from the whole of some other part, those things which are interesting, and thereafter make division (according to the position and connections of the parts).

2. Point out the peculiarities of the particular body [you are dissecting], and the things that are new or but newly discovered.

3. To supply only by speech what cannot be shown, on your own credit and by authority.

4. Cut up as much as may be in the view of all, that practical skill may be learned together with theoretical knowledge.

5. Review your own and other people's observations in order to consider carefully your own opinion, or, in the strictest form, deal with other animals according to the rule of Socrates where it is fairer written. From this follow observations outside the field of anatomy but relating i. to the causes of diseases—of the greatest use to the physicians, ii. to the verity of Nature—of the greatest use to the philosophers. iii. Observa-

---

[1] *Prelectiones*, p. 5.

tions for the purpose of refuting errors and solving problems and,
iv. for discovering the uses and actions of the parts, their rank and, on
account of this, their classification. For the end of Anatomy is knowledge
of the part, why it exists, for what purpose it is necessary and what is its
use. For philosophers the chief use of Anatomy is to learn what parts
are required in each action and what is of most importance. For the
physicians it is to learn what is the natural constitution of the body, that
is, the general rule, by which means they may single out those who are
sick, and then know what to do in diseases.

6. Not to praise or dispraise, for all did well (as beholden to those who
concluded erroneously for they lacked opportunity).

7. Not to dispute [or] confute other than by visible evidence, for to
do otherwise would need more than three days.

8. Briefly and plainly, yet not letting pass any one thing unspoken of
which is subject to the view.

9. Not to speak anything which without the carcase may be delivered
or read at home.

10. Too eager an enquiry is not suitable in the dissection of each
member and the time does not allow it.

11. To serve in their three courses according to the [hour-]glass:
i. the lower belly, nasty yet recompensed by admirable variety, ii. the
parlour [thorax], iii. the divine banquet of the brain.[1]

The 'rule of Socrates' mentioned in Harvey's fifth rule was the
principle of developing philosophical arguments with the help of analo-
gies. Harvey insisted on this again in a later lecture, saying that it should
be set up 'in great print'.[2] Being true to his principles, Harvey, in his
general account of the divisions of the body, made frequent side glances
at comparable parts in the animal kingdom, pointing out, for instance,
how those creatures that lack hands supply their needs 'either by a long
neck and a beak, or by the tongue as in bees and dogs, or by a proboscis
as in in the elephant and the butterfly, or by the feet as in monkeys and
the parrot. WH I knew one that clasped things with its feet',[3] this last
reference being to the parrot that lived in Harvey's home as his wife's
pet.

Near the end of his general remarks Harvey indicates that he shared the
belief in the shape of the human body having changed since ancient
times. Speaking of the thorax, he mentioned 'the cardiac fossa, where
heart-burn and heart-break are felt; here in ancient times was the heart

---

[1] Dr. Whitteridge, *Prelectiones*, pp. 17, 19, points out that this order had been practised at
least from the time of Mondino in the early fourteenth century, and was advocated by Galen.

[2] *Prelectiones* ,p. 87.   [3] Ibid., p. 27.

and the ignorant still show the heart here; sick at heart'.[1] At the end of these remarks he introduces an original observation by comparing the proportions of the human body to a musical scale: 'The proportion of the chest to the belly is one fourth, as three to four, that is a ratio of 4:3; of the chest to the head 2/3, a fifth; of the chest to the stomach 2/1, a whole octave.'[2]

The pages containing the notes for Harvey's course of lectures have been preserved among the Sloane Manuscripts in the British Museum, and they constitute an invaluable source of information on his views and mental processes. Harvey was not, however, thinking of posterity when he put his notes on paper and the result is a document of almost unimaginable difficulty for modern scholarship to interpret. Only now (1964) have we been given by Dr. Gweneth Whitteridge an authoritative transcription and transliteration into intelligible English.[3] The illegibility of Harvey's informal hand is notorious. Although the lectures were delivered in Latin, he mixed Latin and English in his notes in the most casual way. He was a proficient Latin scholar, but probably he still thought in English, and in making his notes put down whatever came easiest. Aubrey, familiar, as he believed, with Harvey's habit of mind in his last years, stated that 'he understood Greek and Latin pretty well, but was no Critique, and he wrote very bad Latin'. This does not at all agree with scholarly opinion at the present time. It is clear that Harvey knew but little Greek and was quite unused to writing in Greek characters, whereas his Latin 'was no better and no worse than that of many of his contemporaries. It is a perfectly adequate medium for the conveyance of his thoughts.'[4] He may not have been an outstanding Latinist, but suggestions that he used English words in his notes because he did not know the Latin equivalents are quite beside the mark. The badness of Harvey's hand in his notes is made more difficult for us by his use of abbreviations both of words and of sentences, even though they are conventional, and by the inconsistency of his spelling. Harvey was educated at a time when the spelling of English was still not subject to fixed rules; it was settling down during his later years, but he did not, in this respect, move with the times. In spite of these obscurities in his writings, Harvey has left us in no doubt as to which of his opinions he regarded as important or original, marking them with the symbols Δ

---

[1] *Prelectiones*, p. 37.   [2] Ibid.
[3] Gweneth Whitteridge, *The Anatomical Lectures of William Harvey*. Edited with an Introduction, Translation and Notes. Edinburgh and London. 1964. Referred to hereafter as *Prelectiones*.   [4] Ibid., p. xxi.

PLATE XIII

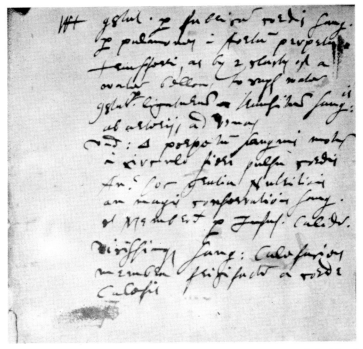

(i) A page of Harvey's manuscript concerning the circulation of the blood added to his lecture notes about 1628 (p. 93)

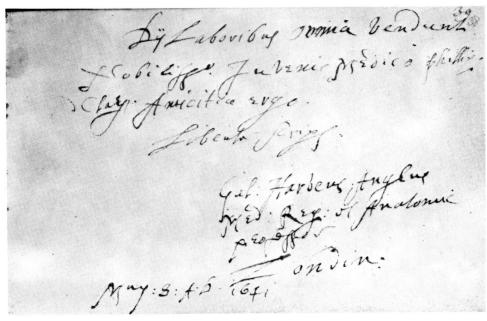

(ii) Harvey's inscription in the autograph album of Philip de Glarges (p. 283)

TWO SPECIMENS OF HARVEY'S HANDWRITING

(D, for *demonstratio*, or 'it can be shewn'), or WH. If he regarded a quoted opinion as wrong, he marked it X.

Harvey's name has been so fixedly associated in our minds with his demonstration of the circulation of the blood that any normal reader of his lecture notes will look first of all for evidence that in these discourses he was delivering to the world the message of his new discovery, that the year 1616 saw the first announcement of a dazzling advance in scientific knowledge and method, and that the lecturer's audiences listened breathlessly to revelations of new truths. Unfortunately no such dramatization of the impact of Harvey's words in his first course of lectures can be allowed. Until recently there seemed to be some justification for taking a dramatic view in the shape of a page in the manuscript (f. 80ᵛ) giving a summary statement of the facts of the circulation, and this passage has become famous. Suspicions have more than once been expressed that the page was written in a slightly different hand from the rest and had been added later. That this is true has now been fully demonstrated by Dr. Whitteridge, who conjectures that the page was added about 1627 or 1628, though admitting that the assignment of a more definite date is not yet possible. It might even have been written after 1628. There are other evidences in the body of the notes that Harvey was not writing them with full knowledge of the circulation of the blood.

When Harvey composed his notes he drew up a title-page in Latin, written in red ink, proudly calling his manuscript 'Lectures on the Whole of Anatomy by me William Harvey, Doctor of London, Professor of Anatomy and Surgery, Anno Domini 1616, aged 37,[1] delivered on April 16 17 18 on the male and female body'. At the top he wrote a line from Virgil's *Eclogues* (III. 60), *Stat Jove principium, Musæ, Jovis omnia plena*[2] (From Jove is the beginning of all things, Muses, with him all things are filled). Below he added a sentence from Aristotle conveying that 'The inner parts of man are uncertain and unknown, wherefore we must consider those parts of other animals which bear any similarity to those of man.'

Harvey was fond of this line from Virgil and used it twice in his book *De generatione animalium*. In Exercise LV of this work he elaborated the idea of the Omnipotent God present in the structure of all living creatures:

Nor can these Attributes appertain to any, but to the Omnipotent

---

[1] Harvey had miscalculated his age; he was in fact a fortnight over 38.
[2] Misquoted according to modern texts; it should be *Ab Jove*.

Maker of all things, under what name soever we cloud and veil him: whether it be *Mens divina*, the divine Mind, with Aristotle, or *Anima mundi*, the soul of the Universe, with Plato; or with others, *Natura Naturans*, Nature of Nature herself; or else Saturnus, or Jupiter, with the Heathen; or rather, as befits us, the Creatour and Father of all things in Heaven and Earth: upon whom all Animals and their births depend: and at whose Beck, or Mandat, all things are created and begotten.

This illustrates, as Sir D'Arcy Power pointed out, how Harvey, like others, exhibited, even at a public lecture, 'a broad spirit of religious charity quite foreign to his environment, but befitting the position he has been called upon to occupy in the history of science.'[1]

Dr. Whitteridge has shown that for descriptive anatomy Harvey followed mainly Caspar Bauhin's *Theatrum anatomicum*, using first the edition of 1605 and later adding references from the second edition of 1621. Sometimes he repeated passages from Bauhin almost verbatim. His reliance on Bauhin may be attributed partly to the excellence of his anatomical descriptions, and partly to the fact that he also had received much of his training at Padua. He was born in 1560, and so was only eighteen years older than Harvey. His family had fled to Basel to avoid religious persecution and it was there that he afterwards taught both anatomy and botany, but his philosophy was Aristotelian and his teaching carried on the Vesalian tradition acquired at Padua. Harvey referred also to many other authorities: Vesalius, Realdus Columbus, Laurentius, Jean Riolan, Fernel—all these can be identified, with occasional allusions to Benivieni, Caius, Erastus, Hollerius, Massa, Peramato, and Felix Platter.[2]

Bauhin's *Theatrum* was not a dissecting manual, but, being an ordered survey of human anatomy, was a sound basis for systematic lectures. Harvey could intersperse original observations as he pleased, and with his remarks on comparative anatomy, clinical illustrations derived from his own practice, memories of things seen in his student days at Cambridge and Padua, and lessons learnt from autopsies conducted even on the bodies of members of his family, all these served to prevent his lectures from being conventional or dull. Occasionally he made points more vivid by references to individuals well known at the time, an example being his mentioning in connexion with disproportionate limbs 'Long Harry',[3] otherwise Henry Savile, a distinguished antiquary of exceptional stature. Similarly unusual conditions were illustrated by reference

---

[1] D'A. Power, *William Harvey*, London, 1897, p. 55.   [2] *Prelectiones*, p. xxxv.
[3] Ibid., p. 29.

to some he had seen in the streets. A hairy mole on the face is thus recalled: 'When the skin is diseased, the hair falls out or grows in strange places: the boy about Holborn Bridge, [who had] a beard on one cheek only.'[1]

Occasionally Harvey's illustrations are slightly facetious; talking of calloused skin he coupled as examples the flanks of hackneys thickened by constant spurring and 'saints' knees'.[2] An even more definite note of humour is found on almost the next page, showing that Harvey's delivery was not always so solemn as the nature of the subject might suggest. Thinking about goose-skin and the rising of the hair, Harvey wrote in his notes: 'Quibusdam motu voluntario, porcupin, hedghog, turkey, coctoo, ruff bird in the ballad. Hominibus: vigiliis, mane lord, how you look! as gamesters; sick leane dog; begger sick, eriguntur pili horridi'; or, as rendered in more sober-looking English: 'In some animals the skin can be moved by a voluntary movement, porcupine, hedgehog, turkey, cockatoo, ruff-bird in the ballad. In men after long vigils, in the morning, Lord! how you look! as gamesters; sick lean dog; beggar sick, the dishevelled hair stands on end.'[3] It has so far not been possible to identify the ballad where the ruff-bird figures, perhaps as the symbol of civic pomposity. Probably the ballad was circulating in the streets as a penny broadsheet and has long since vanished into limbo.

Occasionally a note may catch Harvey glancing at contemporary *mores*. Aristotle had remarked in his *Problemata* (II. 30): 'Those who run naked in the summer have a healthier colour than those who wear garments.' Harvey altered this observation to the form: 'The shape of the skin is the shape of the body, wherefore the best fashion to leap, to run, to do anything [is to] strip to the skin. Fashion is but excess of covering fantastically arranged.'[4]

Harvey's respect for authority was not overdone. Although, as a Fellow of the College, he could not advance ideas directly contrary to the teaching of Galen, he sometimes, as already mentioned, excused differences by saying that the human body had changed since ancient times. Whether he really believed this may be questioned. It was certainly a convenient way to avoid giving offence and having to pay fines to the College for unorthodoxy. Although Aubrey attributed to Harvey a very crude epithet for the 'neoteriques', or modernists, he was not so violent

---

[1] *Prelectiones*, p. 41. It has been suggested, though very improbably, that this refers to the rare condition of a coccygeal growth of hair associated with *spina bifida* (R. A. Hunter and I. Macalpine, *Journ. Med. Hist.* (1960), xv, 295–6).

[2] Ibid., p. 43.   [3] Ibid., p. 45.   [4] Ibid.

in his lectures. Speaking of the lobes of the lungs, he said: 'The neo-
terics criticize Galen X because they have found only four lobes in man
and they say that Galen exercised in apes [which have five lobes] rather
than in man. WH I suspend my censure as in the case of the liver, for
perhaps in Galen's time it was common in man whereas now it is rare. WH
yet indeed I did see five yesterday in a foetus.'[1] Here we see Harvey
vacillating between tact and an impulsive desire to speak the truth. At
other times he could be very plain. Talking of the diaphragm, he wrote:
'There is further great controversy over its action and its uses. It is
unnecessary to relate and discuss the opinions and beliefs of others, I WH
will say what I myself think.'[2] Occasionally he is goaded into using
stronger language: 'The heart has two ventricles, a right and a left. WH
I am amazed at Aristotle who describes three so precisely. Unless he could
possibly have taken the left auricle for a ventricle.'[3] Or again: 'Laurentius
says that they are out of their minds who do not believe that the brain by
its pulsation draws in air, drives out sooty vapours and makes the spirit.
I WH am then out of mine for I say that the pulse is made by the arteries
and by the spirits, and because of this the whole brain seems to pulsate
because it is like a quagmire.'[4]

Occasionally Harvey dropped in a telling phrase, perhaps intending
thereby to catch and stimulate the attention of his audience. Thus he
began a passage on the genitalia in general with the words: 'By the string
tied to eternity', meaning that Nature, having failed to make the individual immortal, ensured the continuity of the species by instituting the
act of generation, an act, Harvey added, 'which is in itself loathsome.
And just as nothing is more pleasing to them which desire to act, so
nothing is more loathsome to them which are past it or come to see it.'[5]

Although Harvey's lectures were intended for delivery as a 'public
anatomy' with a dissected body in front of him, he did not confine
himself to Bauhin's formal scheme. He enriched it with innumerable
references to other members of the animal kingdom.[6] He mentioned in
his notes more than a hundred different kinds, including insects. Sometimes he was quoting Aristotle, for he is unlikely ever to have seen the
bodies of a camel, whale, grampus, or sea-horse (walrus). On the other
hand he had certainly dissected for himself the 'ginneyconey', or guinea-
pig, seals, dogs, cats, moles, and rats. He had also experimented on the
hearts of frogs, eels, various fishes, pigeons, dogs, calves, and deer. He
referred once to 'my monkey', an animal presumably kept as a pet, for he

[1] *Prelectiones*, p. 279.   [2] Ibid., p. 241.   [3] Ibid., p. 259.
[4] Ibid., p. 309.   [5] Ibid., p. 175.   [6] Ibid., p. lx.

did not dissect it until it died of a hectic fever; he then observed the state of its lungs, the appearance of which suggest that it died of tuberculosis.[1]

Occasionally the notes were intended not for the audience, but rather to remind himself of an alternative order of demonstration, as for instance: 'NB NB Enquire whether the renal veins and the vena cava and the aorta and both testicles can be clearly shown, the intestines having been allowed to remain. If not, here should be inserted the discussion of the viscera or together with the pancreas, the root of the coeliac artery and its offshoots, likewise the arteries which are distributed in the mesentery, likewise the two nerves, the first to the liver, gall-bladder and pylorus, the second to the spleen, the fundus of the stomach and the omentum.'[2] On another occasion he interjected: 'NB NB Here should be pointed out following the dissection of the abdomen the dangers of wounds in the gastric and epigastric region.'[3] Often he introduced controversial subjects meant for discussion rather than demonstration, such as the function of the pylorus of the stomach ('B. a shilling stuck which he always carried in his purse'),[4] of the ileocaecal valve and the caecum, which he held to be vestigial ('In man it is merely a token like the nipples'), of the colon and its capacity for passing on foreign bodies such as leaden bullets and 'my own gold ring'[5] (did he swallow this experimentally?), the nature of concoction and the origin of the blood. Clinical references are not so frequent, but he sometimes felt impelled to pass on useful experience, as when he observed that the acute pain of a stone in the bladder could be relieved by counter-irritation in the form of a hot compress applied to the perineum, acting, he suggested, through the prostate gland.[6]

In 1649, when writing his first letter to Jean Riolan of Paris, Harvey stated that he intended to write and publish a work on morbid anatomy, having been stimulated by Riolan's new book.

The example set by so great a man kept demanding a corresponding activity on my part, and determining me to indite and commit to writing in similar fashion my medical anatomy also, that is, my anatomy most closely adapted to medical use. This was not solely, as in Riolan's case, for the purpose of showing from the cadavers of healthy subjects the sites of diseases and of listing what others had thought must be the appearances of diseases in those places. But it was rather so that from many dissections of patients dying of very severe and remarkable complaints I should undertake an account of the ways and manners

[1] Ibid., p. 281. [2] Ibid., p. 93. [3] Ibid., p. 99.
[4] Ibid., p. 123. [5] Ibid., p. 107. [6] Ibid., p. 97.

in which the internal parts change in site, size, constitution, figure, substance and other appreciable variables from the natural form and appearance commonly described by all anatomists, and the various remarkable ways in which they are affected.[1]

Obvious as this now seems, it was then a new conception. Harvey's aim was far more ambitious than Riolan's and would have led to a much greater advance in knowledge. His statement expresses his belief in the importance of morbid anatomy for the understanding of disease, though it does not prove that he ever came to the point of actually collecting his observations and notes in the form of a book. We may, in fact, be certain that he never did. He was too tired and ill a man to be able to undertake it in 1649. We have, however, the lecture notes of 1616 as evidence of the close attention he paid over the years to morbid conditions and the frequency with which he observed post-mortem examinations. He did not always perform these autopsies himself, as appears from a letter to be quoted later (p. 125). Harvey is there described as having 'guided' the examination, that is, overseeing an assistant's actions as he would have done for a surgical operation at the hospital. But on other occasions he was, perhaps, not above using his own hands. In a second letter to Riolan he wrote: 'I have sometimes, in a recently strangled human cadaver within two hours from its hanging, opened up the chest and pericardium (before the redness of the face had disappeared) and demonstrated to many witnesses the right auricle of the heart and the lungs greatly distended and infarcted with blood, but especially the auricle, swelling up to the size of a man's large fist that you would think it would burst.'[2] In the next passage, describing the autopsy on Sir Robert Darcy, a relation by marriage of Dr. Argent, former President of the College, Harvey related how he died of heart disease and of their finding post-mortem a ruptured ventricle with a rent of such a size that 'it easily took one of my fingers'.[3]

This was a finding later than the lecture notes. Harvey's memory for pathological details was good, but his observations on the morbid anatomy of the heart are surprisingly few. In fact he began his remarks by saying: 'The heart suffers scarcely any morbid affection without death intervening', adding, 'I WH have seen scarcely any morbid affection in cadavers'.[4] His interest in the heart must have led him to examine it with more than ordinary care at autopsies, and yet he failed to observe valvular disease, arteriosclerosis in the coronary arteries, or,

---

[1] *The Circulation of the Blood*, translated by K. J. Franklin, Oxford, 1958, pp. 9–10.
[2] Ibid., p. 50.　　　　　[3] Ibid., p. 51.　　　　　[4] *Prelectiones*, p. 251.

it seems, any other gross lesion in the heart muscle. He noted that it tended to shrink in old age, though it did not waste in phthisis, and had once 'found a heart that was very flaccid and pallid', perhaps an example of acute dilatation. Beyond this he could only quote other authors, such as Columbus, who had found tumours in the heart, Vesalius, who had described what was evidently thrombosis in the auricle of a patient with fibrillation, Scolfinus, who had found 'a stone in the heart', and Fabricius, who said he 'found a scabby heart'.[1]

In his lecture notes Harvey frequently gave the patient's name, so that they help to give an idea of the extent of his practice in 1616—and in the following years, for some of the notes were added later. Sir William Rigden, perhaps the husband of Harvey's cousin, Amy Halke, is mentioned several times. He suffered from jaundice due to biliary obstruction by gall stones followed by infection. Sir James Crosby,[2] an unidentified character, was another sufferer from biliary trouble, with a distended and inflamed gall-bladder. Sir Robert Wroth, perhaps the husband of Sir Philip Sidney's niece Lady Mary Sidney, exhibited 'short-lasting horripilations' due to intermittent fever with abscess of the kidney.[3] Another humbler patient, Chirn's wife, also had an infected kidney with a ureter distended with pus to the size of an intestine.[4] Lord Chichester, perhaps Arthur, Lord Chichester who died in 1625, had what Harvey described as 'a double bladder. In shape it is concave, getting narrower and narrower towards the neck. Its use is to collect the urine and to send it forth after opening or discretion.'[5] Sir Thomas Hardy (or Hardes?) had a prostatic caruncle.[6] Lord Clarke, perhaps to be identified with Sir Robert Clarke, a judge and Baron of the Exchequer, appears to have had retraction of the penis to such a degree that he illustrated the belief of some people 'that men can degenerate into hermaphrodites or women'.[7] Sir Robert Clarke, however, died in 1607, so that he may not have been seen by Harvey himself. Sir Robert Shirley (1581–1628, formerly an envoy to the Shah of Persia, if the identification is correct) showed an inflammation of the mammary gland with production of a fluid resembling milk, which Harvey attributed, probably wrongly, to 'an effeminate constitution'.[4] An unidentified Robert Devill had a lung abscess. Cicely Hill walked in her delirium.[8] Mistress Fisher seems to have had a severe fit of choking in the course of whooping cough, though it is not clear whether she came to autopsy from this cause.[9] The young daughter

---

[1] Ibid., pp. 83, 147, 241.
[2] Ibid., p. 91.
[3] Ibid., p. 173.
[4] Ibid., p. 221.
[5] Ibid., p. 197.
[6] Ibid., p. 203.
[7] Ibid., p. 209.
[8] Ibid., p. 287.
[9] Ibid., p. 289.

of Harvey's friend Dr. Argent suffered pain in the head and died from meningitis diagnosed post-mortem.[1] Observations on the morbid anatomy of the liver were illustrated by examination of the bodies of John Bracey, Joan Johnson, and Mr. Benton.[2] Harvey was here attempting to classify liver diseases by tabulating thirteen different kinds of enlargement, grouped according to size, twelve of which Harvey had himself seen.

Another important organ was the spleen. Harvey had himself suffered from splenic enlargement (see p. 19), and he was obviously much interested in this organ. He mentioned a number of examples of big spleens, including his sister's, which he said weighed five pounds. The operation of splenectomy for enlargement cannot often have been successfully accomplished, but Harvey mentioned one such event, when it was 'removed without detriment in the case of Mr. Gillow'.[3]

References will be found on other pages to members of Harvey's own family, though he wisely did not always attend them himself when they were ill. In 1643, when one of his brothers was ill, Dr. Baldwin Hamey the younger was called in, but Hamey was uncertain of the diagnosis—he thought it might be scurvy—and he wrote to Harvey: 'For professional etiquette I now consult you.'[4] Harvey also quoted in his notes pathological observations made by his colleagues Robert Fludd, Theodore Goulston, and John Argent, and by the surgeons at St. Bartholomew's, Richard Mapes and Joseph Fenton. There is one reference also to a barber-surgeon, Philip Kingeman. He referred frequently to records of pathological conditions made by earlier writers. Harvey was sometimes bothered by neurotic patients who did not oblige him by providing an interesting autopsy. One such was Lady Croft, perhaps wife of Sir Herbert Croft (d. 1622): 'Valetudinarians are affected and nice in their food and many of them are always complaining, like Lady Croft.'[5]

Harvey's experience was so wide and his observations were so acute and accurate, that a work by him on morbid anatomy would have been of great historical interest. Dr. K. D. Keele has acclaimed him as 'a pioneer in morbid anatomy', whose fate was to be 'a fore-runner crying in the wilderness', since it was more than a century before Morgagni carried on the study of morbid anatomy to the point of making it a recognized branch of medicine.[6] Harvey had, however, turned it to good

---

[1] *Prelectiones*, p. 307.　　　[2] Ibid., p. 147.　　　[3] Ibid., p. 135.
[4] J. J. Keevil, *The Stranger's Son*, London, 1953, p. 53.　　　[5] *Prelectiones*, p. 83.
[6] K. D. Keele, 'William Harvey as Morbid Anatomist', *Proc. Roy. Soc. Med.* (1962), lv. 677–84.

account in his researches on the circulation of the blood, so that his efforts were by no means wasted.

On the third day of his lectures Harvey came to what he called 'the divine banquet of the brain'. This phrase seems to express his admiration for the complex organization of the central nervous system, but he did not attempt to contribute much that was new. His account leaned heavily on Bauhin's or was derived from Aristotle and Galen; it is of interest as a summary of the current beliefs of his time, though he did not always accept these. Reference has already been made to his contemptuous rejection of a common explanation of the pulsation of the brain as due to its own movements (p. 96). He saw clearly that the apparent movement was simply part of the general pulsation of the arterial system following the systole of the heart.

When Harvey came to describe the brain he found that his loyalties to heart or brain as the more 'honourable' organ were divided.

The brain is set in the topmost part of the body which serves as the safest tower with, as its defences, hair, skin etc. As Nature made no part more greatly defended, so is it deemed the prince of all the parts. However, WH there is no disputing with the heart because its sway is wider, for the heart is seen even in those creatures that want a brain. Perchance the head is more honourable than the heart which for very necessity must exist and is earlier formed, but still more honourable because it is better to exist completely than merely to exist. Wherefore, since all animals have one most perfect part, man has his brain whereby he excels all other animals and by whose means he has dominion over them all, has dominion over the stars. And so the head is the richest member of the body and to swear by the head and eat one's word is profane.[1]

Aristotle had regarded the heart as the centre of sensation, but Harvey recognized that the brain was the more important.

Therefore the action of the brain is sensation and the brain exists for the sake of sensation which constitutes the very definition of an animal. Wherefore, since the brain is the organ of sensation, and since there are diverse sensible objects and diverse kinds of sensation, the brain is divided up as it were and distributed into the nerves. This is why Avicenna says that the nerves are like slips of the brain growing out into the organs of sensation, like WH the fingers of the hand. So the brain itself neither sees nor hears, and so forth, yet it does all these things. Moreover, it can itself experience sensation by reason of the sensations which are brought back to it, and because of this it is called the organ of sensation

[1] *Prelectiones*, p. 311.

in general, which is but one thing and which comprises the brain, the nerves and the special sense organs. And it is necessary that it should be so, that the brain may perceive the oneness of what it is seeing or hearing and so forth, out of many things apprehended one thing comprehended.[1]

Dr. Whitteridge points out that Harvey's predecessors and contemporaries would have attributed this faculty to the soul, not to the brain.

Yet Harvey still retained some curious beliefs concerning the size of the brain: 'At times the brain increases in amount, for instance in the full moon, in shouting, according to Avicenna, and in wet places and times.'[2] He also subscribed to the old ideas that the brain purged itself through the palate and the nostrils, and he became entangled in a discussion of 'vapours' and 'spirits', whereby sleep is induced. But in the end he cut the knot, saying: 'WI with none of them do I agree, for many are questionable and others impossible in the highest degree. WI it is rather a question of blood, for spirit, like flame, is in no wise separated from it. But of these things it is more appropriate to speak when dealing with the anatomy of the nerves.'[3] His description of the cranial nerves followed Bauhin's and repeated what Dr. Whitteridge calls the 'particular seventeenth-century muddle'[4] caused by the failure of the anatomists to make the right connexions in tracing the nerves through the cavernous sinus.

The last point of interest concerning the brain is Harvey's employment of 'the Second Dissection'. This, according to Dr. Whitteridge,[5] was invented by Varolius in 1570 and followed by Bauhin. At the first dissection the top of the skull was removed with the meninges, and the brain was examined from above. At the second dissection all the bones of the skull were removed, leaving the brain, still invested by the meninges, with its appendages, such as eyes and spinal medulla, still attached. It was then turned upside-down and the first order of dissection was reversed. Harvey added to his notes at a later date an 'Appendix WI Of the Nerves as they appear in the course of dissecting'.[6] It is evident from his notes that Harvey gave as clear an exposition of the difficult subject of cerebral anatomy as anyone of his time could have done, but it was not in any way a special field for his researches.

The *Prelectiones* as we have them are not complete. They include no account of the skeleton, with which Harvey said he would deal in its proper place. There is nothing about the special sense organs, the female genital organs, the visceral nerves, or most of the blood vessels. Indeed,

---

[1] *Prelectiones*, p. 315. [2] Ibid., p. 317. [3] Ibid., p. 319.
[4] Ibid., p. 332 n. [5] Ibid., p. 336 n. [6] Ibid., p. 341.

Harvey's account of the veins and arteries of the muscles Dr. Whitteridge characterizes as 'lamentable'.[1] There is no systematic description of the muscles in the *Prelectiones*, but these were dealt with in another manuscript, *De musculis*, until now associated with a preliminary draft of a different book, *De motu locali animalium*. Dr. Whitteridge believes *De musculis*, from the evidence of paper and script, to have been written not earlier than 1618,[2] but it seems to belong to the same category as the *Prelectiones*, that is to say it was prepared for delivery as part of the Lumleian lectures. As before, Harvey used Bauhin's anatomy as his basis, but was more interested in describing the actions of muscles than in their detailed anatomy. He also included some of the nerves and blood vessels. His account of the nerves of the arm he marked 'Δ WH 1627', so that parts of this manuscript represent a later revision. The notes for *De musculis* contain many of Harvey's WH signposts, though there is nothing of outstanding originality. Probably for this reason they had never been transcribed or translated until included by Dr. Whitteridge in her book with the *Prelectiones*; it was obviously desirable to have Harvey's notes in their entirety so that they can be related to a later work of greater interest, *De motu locali animalium*, which will be noticed in its proper place.

In chapter xvii of *De motu cordis*, writing of respiration, Harvey remarked: 'But I will say more about this in my treatise on respiration.' In his last book, *De generatione animalium*, he said again of respiration that he was 'perhaps resolved to discuss the debate more fully in its proper place'.[3] This suggests that the treatise remained in the realm of good intentions, and if he ever prepared a draft nothing of it has survived. The *Prelectiones*, therefore, provide the only clues we possess to his views on this important subject, though they do not disclose any outstanding discoveries. He was aware of the actions of the various muscles concerned in breathing, but was uncertain whether the lungs themselves contributed anything to the movement of the thoracic cage. He knew that the lungs would collapse if the pleura was opened and twice referred to having seen the air expelled from a penetrating wound of the thorax with enough force to blow out a candle,[4] but obviously he was puzzled and uncertain about the problem. Later he became aware of the perforations of the lungs leading into the abdominal cavity found in birds, and mentioned it as his own discovery in *De generatione animalium*,[5] having demonstrated them in the ostrich, turkey, dung-hill cock, and other birds. Boyle afterwards repeated this with a reference to Harvey in his

---

[1] Ibid., p. li.   [2] Ibid., p. xx.   [3] *Anatomical Exercitations*, 1653, p. 484.
[4] *Prelectiones*, pp. 233, 285.   [5] *Anatomical Exercitations*, 1653, p. 8.

New Experiments Touching the Weight and Spring of the Air, 1660 (p. 343);
but Harvey had not found them in man and remained unable to account
for the formation of pus in the pleural cavity unaccompanied by air. His
observations in the *Prelectiones* end rather evasively with the exclamation:
'WH but the works of Nature are to be admired.'[1] More suggestive is the
sentence: 'Why and how air is requisite for all animals that breathe, as also
how air is necessary for a candle and for fire, I WH have seen.'[2] Boyle with
his air-pump had proved this by 1660,[3] but where had Harvey seen
this demonstration? Dr. Whitteridge asks whether he had seen Robert
Fludd perform the experiment on a flame in an inverted glass, and her
question is almost certainly to be answered in the affirmative. Fludd's
folio[4] on metaphysics, physics, and various technical contrivances was
published in 1617. It contains a large number of engravings illustrating
all manner of semi-scientific and mechanical subjects. Among these is a
plate with a drawing of a lighted candle burning within a flask inverted
in a basin of water. This is designed to illustrate the principle: *Ubi aër in
aliquo loco inclusus aut evacuatur aut consumitur, ibi necesse est, ut novum aliquod
corpus illum locum impleat, ne admittatur vacuum. Demonstratur hoc exemplis
sequentibus*, or, in other words, that nature abhors a vacuum, so that if air
is consumed inside a closed vessel something else will enter to take its
place, as, in this example, water. The quenching of the flame at the same
time is not mentioned, but if Fludd had shown Harvey this simple
experiment he would have noticed it as one of the consequences.
Although, therefore, fully aware of the necessity of air for the maintenance of life, he did not attribute the red colour of blood coming from the
lungs to aeration. His explanation was different: 'All incoming nutriment is brought through the liver; through the lungs passes incessantly
all the nutriment of the body and the whole mass of blood, which explains
why arterial blood is redder.'[5] At this time he was also wedded to the idea
that an important function of the lungs was to cool the animal; later
he changed his belief and asserted, in writing of the breathing of the newborn infant, that 'Air is allowed to Animals neither for refrigeration nor
nutrition sake'.[6] His mind in 1616 reached out in an interesting direction
by asking the then unanswerable question whether plants 'need air and
its alteration'. 'Does the scent of plants come from their exhalation?'[7]

---

[1] *Prelectiones*, p. 285.   [2] Ibid., p. 297.   [3] *New Experiments*, 1660, pp. 326–34.

[4] *Utrius cosmi majoris scilicet et minoris metaphysica, physica atque technica historia*, Oppenheim:
Aere Johan de Bry, Typis Hieronymi Galleri, 1617, vol. i, Tract. iii, Lib. iii, p. 471, *De motu
ex quatuor Elementorum naturi generato*.

[5] *Prelectiones*, p. 297.   [6] *Anatomical Exercitations*, 1653, p. 483.

[7] *Prelectiones*, p. 295.

It was not until the eighteenth century that Stephen Hales provided the answer.

Harvey's account of the heart, since it was in the 'middle belly', or thorax, was given on the second day of his course. In his description of its anatomy he began naturally with the pericardium, giving a full account of its relation to the heart itself, of its attachments and its anomalies. He also noted that it always contained some fluid of a yellowish colour, even in fishes such as the sting-ray, and repeated the observation made by Vesalius that the amount was increased in the bodies of those hanged in the sun. In the first edition of *De corporis humani fabrica* Vesalius had ended his observations on the subject by saying that he would go on to the heart itself to avoid falling into the theologians' dispute concerning the statement that when Christ's side was pierced on the Cross by the centurion's lance 'came there out blood and water'.[1] He omitted this altogether in later editions of the *Fabrica*. When, at a later date, Laurentius referred to it, he was accused by Riolan of blasphemy. Harvey nevertheless stepped in boldly and wrote: 'W-I I think it to have been made by Nature to prevent the heart from becoming completely dry. So the wounds of Christ exuded water along with the blood.'[2] Had there been any protest he might have deleted the sentence, but it was allowed to remain. Harvey's particular interest in the heart is reflected in his notes by the amount of space devoted to its anatomy, movements, and function.

Reference has already been made to the erroneous impression created by the statement on the circulation added to his lecture notes many years later than 1616. In the prefatory letter addressed to Dr. Argent and printed with *De motu cordis* in 1628 Harvey wrote:

On several earlier occasions in my anatomical lectures I revealed my new concept of the heart's movement and function of the blood's passage round the body. Having now, however, for more than nine years confirmed it in your presence by numerous ocular demonstrations, and having freed it from the objections of learned and skilfull anatomists, I have yielded to the repeated desire of all and the pressing request of some, and in this small book have published it for all to see.[3]

This might seem to imply that the full evidence regarding the circulation was disclosed from 1619 onwards in Harvey's lectures, but Dr. Whitteridge has marshalled[4] the actual evidence of the lecture notes to show that

---

[1] Gospel of St. John, xix. 34.   [2] *Prelectiones*, pp. 249 and 248 n.
[3] K. J. Franklin, *Movement of the Heart and Blood in Animals*, Oxford, 1957, p. 5.
[4] *Prelectiones*, pp. xxxvi–l.

complete realization of this doctrine was only arrived at by stages during the first twelve years covered by the lectures. There is plenty of evidence to show that he was often making additions to his notes, though it may be that what he actually uttered from the rostrum was in advance of the notes that lay before him. The subject was so much in his mind that he would not need to have written down everything that he intended to say. It is, in fact, impossible to date exactly the first full statement of his doctrine before a London audience. The sequence of Harvey's ideas as they appear in his notes certainly do not substantiate the claim that he fully knew the doctrine of the circulation of the blood in 1616.

It is clear that when he wrote his notes he was in agreement with Realdus Columbus of Padua on the systole and diastole of the heart. Columbus had taught anatomy at Padua and his views could have reached Harvey's ears directly through his two immediate successors, Fallopius and Fabricius, in the chair of anatomy. Columbus had also published his views on the systole and diastole in his book, *De re anatomica*, published in 1559. The common belief was that the apex beat coincided with the diastole, while blood was entering the heart. Vesalius had doubted this, though he did not say so in so many words, as is plain from the contemporary account written by a German student at Bologna in 1540. According to this Vesalius said:

'I shall proceed to the heart, so that you shall see its movement and feel its warmth . . . and here around the ilium feel the pulse with one hand, and with the other the movement of the heart. And, please, tell me what its movement is, whether the arteries are compressed when the heart is dilated, or whether they in the same time also have the same movement as the heart.' I saw how the heart of the dog bounded upwards, and when it no longer moved, the dog instantly died. Those mad Italians pulled the dog at all sides so that nobody could really feel these two movements. But some students asked Vesalius what the true fact about these was, what he himself thought, whether the arteries followed the movement of the heart, or whether they had a movement different from that of the heart. Vesalius answered: 'I do not want to give my opinion, please do feel for yourselves with your own hands and trust them.'[1]

Harvey quoted the accepted opinion from Bauhin and then commented: 'I have observed these things for hours together and I have not been able easily to distinguish between them either by sight or touch.

[1] *Andreas Vesalius' First Public Anatomy at Bologna 1540. An Eyewitness Report by Baldasar Heseler*, ed. R. Erikson, Uppsala and Stockholm, 1959, p. 293.

Wherefore I would now lay them before you that you may see them with your own eyes and judge for yourselves.'[1] The last sentence seems to indicate quite positively that Harvey included in his lecture a demonstration of the heart movements in a live animal with the thorax opened. He then described to his audience, with the organ beating before their eyes, the different movements and the conclusions that he drew from his observations, namely that when the heart 'is erected or contracted it drives out the blood as it were by force from the right ventricle into the lungs, and from the left ventricle into the aorta, and this is the reason for the arterial pulse. . . . Action of the heart: thus relaxed receives blood, contracted scups it over. The whole of the body responds to the artery as my breath in a glove.' His views on the heart movements were decided and defined, with quotations from Columbus,[2] and there was little to add to his later account in the second chapter of *De motu cordis*.

As regards priority in the doctrine of the lesser circulation, it is true that Michael Servetus had formulated it in 1553, but his book was primarily theological in its purpose and it was so effectively suppressed that it cannot have had much, if any, influence on anatomical teaching in its own century. It was Columbus who made the first effective statement about the pulmonary circulation in his book already mentioned, his evidence being derived from direct experiment. He cut the pulmonary vein in a living dog at some distance from the heart, and showed that bright red blood, not air, came out of it. He stated his disbelief in the porosity of the interventricular septum, and declared that the blood passed to the lung by the pulmonary artery and then, with the air from the lungs, by the pulmonary vein to the left ventricle of the heart. Andreas Cæsalpinus of Rome had to some extent restated the views of Columbus in 1593 and first introduced the phrase '*circulation* of the blood across the lungs'. Cæsalpinus had been a pupil of Columbus in Pisa, but he still believed that blood passed through the interventricular septum, and his other statements are somewhat confused, so that, in effect, he added nothing to what was already known to his predecessor. Harvey's notes show that in 1616 he knew and accepted the teaching of Columbus about the lesser circulation. He had reasoned it all out for himself afresh, and so probably did not feel that he need always mention his predecessors. Some value was certainly attached to priorities in Harvey's day, but perhaps not quite so much as is usual at the present time.

What Harvey might have known as a student about the function of valves has already been described (see pp. 29–30). In his notes of 1616 he

---

[1] *Prelectiones*, p. 265.   [2] Ibid., p. 265.

stated that 'a rod inserted into the vena cava reaches as far as the loins',[1] but did not proceed, as he did at some later date, to pass his rod into a more distal vein and find it completely obstructed by the valves, all of which he described in chapter 13 of *De motu cordis*. The only other mention of the valves to be found in the lecture notes gives them a function agreeing with pre-circulatory notions.

The arteries have a thicker coat, and especially in adults whose heart beat is stronger, because the artery sustains the impulse. WH hence a thing which none have mentioned, the pulmonary artery is thicker for it sustains the pulse of the right ventricle in adults and of the artery in the foetus. Hence also, neither the vena cava nor the pulmonary vein is of such a structure because they do not pulsate, but rather they may be said to suffer an attraction and this because the valves set in a contrary direction break off the pulse both in the heart and in the other veins. WH and for this reason the veins have very many valves opposed to the heart, while the arteries have none except in the exit from the heart in contrary fashion.[2]

In 1616, therefore, Harvey seems to have known little more about the true functions of the valves in veins than did his teacher Fabricius, though enlightenment must have followed within a very few years. Elsewhere he spoke of the stomach receiving blood from the splenic branch of the portal vein, and also of blood running back from the liver by the portal vein to the spleen, where it was 'concocted and perfected by means of the abundant heat and loose texture of the part'.[3]

We must believe from Harvey's statement in his letter to Dr. Argent that he did make demonstrations by experiment at the College, but which of the experiments described in *De motu cordis* he may have used we do not know. Apart from the demonstration of the movements of the heart in a dog he does not seem to have used vivisected animals in his public lectures.

Much of the evidence from the lecture notes seems to throw us back to the conclusion that they are of more value in showing how little Harvey knew of the circulation of the blood in 1616 rather than how much. Why, then, do they not contain more numerous additions showing how his knowledge of the true facts extended during the years after 1619? Is it possible that he preferred for some time to express orthodox views in his public lectures while building up contrary views in his own mind and giving private demonstrations to his friends in the College, using

---

[1] *Prelectiones*, p. 263.   [2] Ibid., 273.   [3] Ibid., p. 129.

dogs and other animals for the purpose? In the end we have to admit that there is a serious hiatus in our knowledge of what actually happened between the year 1619 and the publication of *De Motu cordis* in 1628. After that date there must have been an extensive revision of the *Prelectiones*, of which only the passage on f. 80ᵛ now remains. Harvey had convinced most of his colleagues in the College, and his views had been published to the world in his book, so that henceforth he could state his true opinion without equivocation or any fear of the consequences. The *Prelectiones* as they now stand do not truly represent the Lumleian lecture on the heart as delivered after 1628.

Whatever Harvey's private views about the circulation may have been in 1616, it is clear that his mind was also dwelling on other matters of primary significance. The liver was regarded as a very important organ, for here, according to the ancient learning derived from Galen, to which Harvey still largely subscribed, concoction was conducted. This term covered the elaboration of the nutritive juices derived from the food. The first concoction took place in the stomach, the second in the liver, resulting in 'sanguification', or the making of blood, but, said Harvey, the liver 'was only the instrument of the heart and secondarily'. The liver also 'serves to beget the natural spirits', chiefly, it seemed, because it was abundant in 'innate heat'. This warmth he called, in Aristotelian phraseology, 'the tool of tools', adding that 'it is first made in the heart'. After delivering these opinions, Harvey gave an unmistakable hint that he had already embarked fruitfully on his investigation of embryology, though his second great book, *De generatione animalium*, was not to be brought into being until thirty-five years later. For here, in his lecture notes of 1616, before coming to his account of the heart itself, he enunciated a central theme, repeated and developed in his later book. It is given the usual symbol of being worthy of special attention:

W⊣ If I could show what I have seen, it were at an end between physicians and philosophers. For blood is rather the author of the viscera than they of it, because blood is in being before the viscera, nor does it come from the mother into the egg, indeed not one drop. The soul is in the blood. Innate heat is the author of life and where it most abounds there it exists principally and primarily. I have seen, as Dr. Argent will bear witness, a body with all parts perfected yet with a liver unformed; a heart fashioned with auricles but the liver ill-made and a shapeless mass; a heart exceedingly white, its auricles purple and filled with blood.[1]

[1] *Prelectiones*, p. 127.

In *De generatione animalium* Harvey asserted, after describing his observation of the '*Punctum Rubrum saliens*, the Red capering Point', that is, the beginnings of the heart in the chick embryo, that 'I conclude (against Aristotle) that the *blood* is the first Genital Particle, and that the Heart is its instrument designed for its circulation'.[1] This belief is then developed at some length. The embryo, therefore, had already in 1616 revealed to Harvey, as he thought, the important secret of the origin of blood. The question of how it circulated may have been to him at that time of secondary importance.

Perusal of Harvey's lecture notes creates an impression of the lecturer as one who seldom failed to capture the full attention of his audience. He was lively, learned, and interesting, yet none of his hearers has left for posterity any first-hand description of Harvey in the rostrum. The nearest approach to it is found among a set of Latin verses addressed by Dr. Peter Bowne in 1624 to the President and Fellows of the College, in which he sought to characterize a number of the Fellows, devoting to each a few hexameters. Dr. Bowne (1575–1624) published in the year of his death a pamphlet entitled *Pseudo-medicorum anatomia*, containing an attack on the quacks and empirics with the Latin verses appended.[2] He was an Oxford graduate and after being admitted as a Candidate at the College in 1616 was granted the Fellowship in 1620, but his health was bad and he left London in 1624.[3] He could have heard Harvey lecture on many occasions over a period of seven years and the date of his book (1624) ensures that his opinion was not influenced by Harvey's later fame after the publication of *De motu cordis* in 1628. His lines on Harvey are therefore of some interest:

Doctori Harvey

TE dextrè & doctè Anatomen tractare loquuntur:
　Vidi, & dexteritas vix imitanda tua est.
Lectio perdocta est, dissectio mira: quid ergò?
　nùm tua me audacem dextera docta facit?
Fecit, & optarem, nam sic tua facta merentur,
　ut quae *Musa priùs*, post tua dextra secet.

---

[1] *Anatomical Exercitations*, 1653, p. 275.

[2] Bowne's pamphlet is known only in three copies. Two are in London (the British Museum and the Wellcome Historical Medical Library); the third, the only one containing the Latin verses, is in the National Medical Library, Bethesda. See Richard T. Durling, *Medical History*, 1964, viii. 279–80.

[3] *Munk's Roll*, 1861, i. 166.

To Doctor Harvey

They talk of your learnedly and skilfully treating of anatomy.
　I have seen it, and your dexterity is hardly to be matched.
Your reading is most learned, your dissecting marvellous. What then?
　Does your skilled hand make me bold?
It has! and I should wish (for this your deeds deserve)
　That what my Muse does first, your clever hand should then cut up.

10

LORD CAREW AND SHAKESPEARE

AT some time before 1616 Harvey had been a friend of George Carew
(1555–1629), Lord Carew of Clopton, near Stratford, created Earl of
Totnes in 1626. Carew had played an important part in Irish affairs; he
was President of Munster in the years 1600 to 1603 and had ruthlessly
suppressed the King's rebellious subjects. Harvey does not say that he
had attended Carew himself as a patient, but refers in his notes on the
muscles to 'my Lord Totnes's barber Will'[1] as an example of limping
following rupture of a leg muscle, so that he certainly attended his Lordship's household. That he was on fairly familiar terms with Carew is
shown by a somewhat ribald reference in his anatomy lecture notes of
1616, where he was describing the male genitalia. In his usual manner he
reviewed briefly the comparative anatomy of his subject, and added after
his sign WH 'a pretty bauble—Lord Carew—a whale's as big as his
middle'.[2] Carew in his younger days had been on expeditions to Spain
and the Azores and probably had told Harvey of strange things he had
seen. Harvey had also gathered from him 'a memorable relation' of an
unfortunate woman who was delivered of twins during the fighting in
Ireland. The story is recorded in the obstetrical section of *De generatione
animalium* (1651) to illustrate his conviction of the hardiness of country
women compared with 'those that are tenderly brought up and doe lead
a sedentary and lazy life'. Carew told Harvey,

　There was a Woman bigge with Child, which followed her husband,
who was a Souldier in the Army; and the Army being daily in motion,

---

[1] *De motu locali animalium*, ed. Gweneth Whitteridge, Cambridge, 1959, p. 85.
[2] *Prelectiones*, p. 213.

was it seemes forced to make a Halt, by reason of a little River that run cross the place whether they intended to March: whereupon the poor woman finding her labour come upon her, retired to the next thicket, and alone by her self, without any Midwife, or other preparation, brought forth Twins: which she presently carried to the River, and there washed both her self and them; which done, she wrapt her Infants into a course cloath, and tied them to her back, and that very day, marched along with the Army twelve mile together, bare-footed: and was never the worse for the matter.

The next day after, the Deputy of Ireland, the Lord Mountjoy (who was at that time General of the Army against the Spaniards, at the siedge of Kingsale) and the President of Munster, being affected at the strangeness of the story, did both vouchsafe to be God-fathers to the Infants.[1]

Carew was a neighbour and a friend of Shakespeare at Stratford, but this is too tenuous a link to justify the conjecture that Harvey was at any time acquainted with the poet, though it would have been quite possible for them to have met. Harvey would surely have occasionally witnessed some of the plays presented at Court, if nowhere else, but there is no indication of interest in the drama in his writings save for a probable reference to the gait of an actor taking the name part in Marlowe's *Jew of Malta* found in the notes for his treatise on movement already mentioned,[2] written in 1627. The play was revived at Court and at the Cockpit in 1633, and Harvey might have added his note in that year.

Shakespeare had a wide knowledge of doctors and their ways, and all his plays contain references that may be classified as 'medical'.[3] When he wrote *Coriolanus* in about 1608 he knew something of the movement of the blood. Menenius Agrippa, in his famous speech on the prime importance of Belly in the Body Politic, says (Act I, sc. i):

> True it is my Incorporate Friends (quoth he)
> That I receive the generall Food at first
> Which you do live upon; and fit it is,
> Because I am the Store-house, and the Shop
> Of the Whole Body. But if you do remember
> I send it through the Rivers of your blood,
> Even to the Court, the Heart, to th'seate o'th'Braine
> And through the Crankes and Offices of man.

The expression, 'the Rivers of your blood', has been held to show that

---

[1] *Anatomical Exercitations*, 1653, p. 509.   [2] *De motu locali animalium*, p. 53.
[3] See R. R. Simpson, *Shakespeare and Medicine*, Edinburgh, 1959. Dr. Simpson finds 712 medical references in the plays.

Shakespeare had knowledge of the circulation before Harvey had published his doctrine to the world,[1] but this is clearly wrong. It does not imply that the poet had any more knowledge of the movement of the blood than any person with the ordinary education of his time. He died in 1616 in the week following Harvey's first Lumleian Lecture, and so could scarcely have gained any further knowledge even if poet and doctor had been acquainted. Some of Shakespeare's medical lore might have been imparted to him by his son-in-law, Dr. John Hall, who started practising in Stratford in 1600 and married Susanna Shakespeare in 1607. Hall was older than Harvey by three years and had matriculated at Queens' College, Cambridge, in 1589, taking his B.A. degree in 1593–4 and his M.A. in 1597. He afterwards studied medicine abroad. He never took any qualifications in London.[2] He died in 1619. His practice had ranged as far afield as Oxford, and he attended many prominent people. He kept notes of his patients and of the prescriptions used in their treatment: these were published after his death,[3] and include two derived from Harvey, though they provide no evidence that Hall and Harvey ever met. It is nevertheless possible, as with Harvey and Shakespeare, that they might have been acquainted.

I I

PATIENTS (SIR WILLIAM SMITH, JAMES HOWELL, LADY PHILIPPA HOBART), 1620

Although we know a little about many of Harvey's patients, we have full details about only one besides King James. This knowledge is contained in documents now in the Public Record Office[4] and found there by Dr. C. J. Sisson when he was searching for something else. The story is of great interest as shedding light on medical practice in Harvey's time, on Harvey's character, and on the vagaries of human nature. Its veracity is not unquestionable, since it is based on evidence given by possibly biased witnesses nearly three years after the events and obviously

[1] A. Lefranc, *Sous le masque de William Shakespeare*, Paris, 1919, i. 62.

[2] R. R. Simpson, loc. cit.

[3] *Select Observations*, translated by James Cooke, London, 1657; reprinted 1679 and 1683. See Appendix II, pp. 442–3.

[4] P.R.O. C 2 / Jas. I / 19 / 63.

after they had agreed with each other on most of what they were going to say; nevertheless, it can be regarded as an approximation to the truth.

In October 1619 Harvey was consulted by an elderly patient, Sir William Smith, a city merchant of some wealth, who was suffering from a stone in the bladder. He was well enough to be 'pricked by the King' on 13 November as Sheriff for the county of Essex,[1] yet he had been in physical distress for some time and had consulted many doctors at great expense without obtaining any relief. At length he had come to Dr. Harvey. He alone of the consultants had encouraged him to believe that there was a cure—a secret remedy known only to Harvey himself. Sir William was naturally anxious to avoid the dangerous operation of being 'cut for the stone', and signed an agreement with Harvey to pay him in quarterly sums an annuity of £50 as long as he did not have the operation, payment ceasing if, after all, the operation had to be performed. Dr. Sisson[2] says that payment of a retaining fee as a form of health insurance was not uncommon in Elizabethan England, and the principle is familiar in Chinese practice.

For some months Sir William used the secret remedy, but without any improvement in his symptoms, and finally, with Harvey's agreement, the operation was done. The result was reported by John Chamberlain in a letter of 27 July 1620 to Sir Dudley Carleton, Ambassador at the Hague. 'Sir William Smith that more than two months since was cut for the stone in the bladder and a huge stone taken from him, though he seemed to be well healed and held out so long, yet by some other disorder is lately dead.'[3] The operation, skilfully performed, could often be successful, but for Sir William, burdened with a very large calculus of long standing, the prognosis was not likely to be good. So large a stone would inevitably be accompanied by severe urinary infection ascending to the kidneys, and the patient's death two months later would not be a matter for surprise; there the matter might have rested had the patient fully discharged his obligation for the period elapsed before the operation was done, but a quarter's payment (£12. 10s.) was still owing, and Sir William, in angry disappointment at Harvey's failure, had on his deathbed forbidden his son, William, his executor, to make any further payment whatever. In the circumstances Harvey might well have waived this relatively small sum, but, to our regret, he came under the influence

---

[1] Chamberlain, *Letters*, ii. 272.
[2] See 'Shakespeare's Helena and Dr. William Harvey' in *Essays and Studies 1960 collected for the English Association*, London, 1960.
[3] Chamberlain, *Letters*, ii. 313.

of a friend, Christopher Brooke, and his wife, the Lady Jacob. Brooke was a lawyer, best known today as having been the close friend of Dr. John Donne, Dean of St. Paul's, and one of his sponsors when he entered at Lincoln's Inn on 6 May 1592. Brooke was the recipient of verse letters from Donne, was the friend of Selden, Ben Jonson, Michael Drayton, and other poets, and himself wrote poetry, contributing in 1600 to Bodenham's anthology, *England's Helicon*, and to many other volumes. In 1601 Christopher Brooke and his younger brother, Samuel, were parties to Donne's clandestine marriage, Samuel performing the ceremony. All three were thrown into prison when the marriage became known. Christopher had been Donne's chamber-fellow in Lincoln's Inn and they remained friends for life. When Donne made his will in 1630, the elder brother had been dead for nearly three years, but Samuel, then Master of Trinity College, Cambridge, was remembered as 'my ancient friend'.[1] Christopher Brooke had remained a bachelor until December 1619, when he married Mary Jacob. That the couple were somewhat litigious characters is suggested by a passage in a letter from John Chamberlain to Sir Dudley Carleton dated 1 July 1622: 'There is a hot suit commenced in the Starchamber twixt Sir John Davies Lady and the Lady Jacob about womanish brabbes and an uncivil scurrilous letter written by Kit Brooke in his wifes behalf.'[2] We know that Harvey was a friend of Selden, but there is nothing to show what other connexions he may have had with this literary and legal set beyond his being persuaded by the Brookes to bring the rather discreditable action against Sir William Smith's son for a debt of £12. 10s. The evidence indicates that 'womanish brabbes' were again at the bottom of it, for more than one witness stated that Mary Jacob coveted a damask table-cloth belonging to the deceased and had intended to buy it from young Smith at her own valuation of £4. When she was refused, she used words to the effect that now he should 'know the spleen or malice of a woman', and that otherwise the action would not have been brought. It was stated that Mary Jacob was contributing some £6 towards Harvey's legal expenses.

The action is summed up in an entry in the Chancery Order Book[3] dated 14 December 1621. This refers to an order of 30 October last by which an injunction was awarded for stay of the defendant's proceedings at Common Law until the defendant had answered and the Court taken other order to the contrary. The defendant's counsel, Mr. Christopher Brooke, this day informs the Court

[1] Gosse, *Life of Donne*, 1899, ii. 360   [2] Chamberlain, *Letters*, ii. 444.
[3] Chancery Order Book (C. 33/141), p. 257.

that the defendant has put in a perfect answer to the plaintiff's bill setting forth that he being physician to the plaintiff's father and having an annuity of £50 from the said father to be paid quarterly during the life of the said father in respect of the care and pains he took with him in the time of his sickness being troubled with continual infirmities the defendant having had no other fees or consideration in recompense, thereof except the said annuity. And there being £12. 10s. due to the defendant at the death of the said father, the plaintiff refused to pay the same, whereupon the defendant brought the action at Common Law.

It is ordered that if the plaintiff shall not at the next General Seal shew unto the Court good cause to the contrary, the injunction is dissolved.

On 2 March 1621/2 Harvey sought to hasten the proceedings, but in the plaintiff's view the defendant in his answer 'hath in effect in limited and qualified words confessed the substance of the plaintiff's bill, which is a verbal promise made unto the said plaintiff's father not to demand or receive any annuity after the time that the said plaintiff's father should be cut of the stone which if the said plaintiff shall not sufficiently and really prove by depositions he will be ready to pay the annuity and such costs as his Lordship shall assess'.[1] By 29 June the plaintiff had not pursued the matter, and it was ordered that the injunction should be dissolved.[2] The case accordingly came to a hearing in October 1622.

The documents recording the case may be consulted in the Public Record Office,[3] so that only the more interesting points need be extracted here. First, there is a long statement of his case by William Smith, the patient's son and executor, setting out the facts as already more briefly recounted above. Then follows an interrogatory of ten questions to be put to each of the eight witnesses in turn, and from their answers various important points emerge. These witnesses had been present at consultations with Dr. Harvey, for there seems to have been little privacy in the patient's bedroom at this time and they were prepared to repeat what they remembered to have heard three years before, sometimes, perhaps, with involuntary embellishments.

First appeared Katherine Huettson, wife of a victualler dwelling at the upper end of King Street near Westminster Abbey. She had been a servant for several years at Sir William Smith's house, and could confirm the facts about his illness and Dr. Harvey's promise to cure him on the terms stated. She was in the chamber when the doctor 'searched', or examined, the patient and heard him say that either he had no stone at all, or, if there

---

[1] Chancery Order Book (C. 33/141), p. 460.   [2] Ibid., p. 828.
[3] References: C 2 / Jas. I / 19 / 63; C 24 / 493 / 155.

was one, it was very small and could be dissolved. The patient objected that he had been told by many surgeons that it was impossible to dissolve a stone by medical means, but the doctor replied that his secret remedy would be successful. She was also present when an unqualified practitioner named Emerson was unexpectedly found by Dr. Harvey in the patient's room and described a violent scene that followed, Harvey threatening reprisals by the College of Physicians.

The second witness was John Smith, a draper aged 25, living near St. Paul's, who happened to call on Sir William Smith during a visit by Dr. Harvey. On this occasion the doctor had looked at a specimen of Sir William's urine in a urinal and shaken it, remarking, 'Your water is better than it was, and I can keep you at this [stage]', but then seemed to give him encouragement to be cut, saying that in this event he would relinquish the agreement.

The third witness was a grocer, Humphrey Smith, living near London Stone. He gave evidence similar to that of John Smith, adding nothing material.

Katherine Saxie of the City of Westminster, a widow aged 60, followed, and said very much the same as the first witness, confirming that Dr. Harvey had searched the patient and declared that he had no stone at all or a very small one, which could be dissolved by his secret remedy. She was with Sir William Smith about three hours before he died and heard him tell his son not to pay Dr. Harvey any more of the annuity.

The fifth witness, Elenor Smith, aged 35, lodging in Crowne Court, Chancery Lane, confirmed most of what had been already said, but had not heard the doctor affirm absolutely that he would cure Sir William's disease. On the other hand, she remembered the words that had passed on more than one visit by the doctor. About a month or six weeks before Sir William was cut she recalled that he 'was in marvelous great extremities of pain, and took no rest all night long'. When Dr. Harvey came next day, Sir William complained of his bad night and 'told him plainly that he thought (when all was done) that he must be cut for it, because he was not able to be so tortured as he was, and that he found his pains were so great as that they would distract him of his senses'. The doctor then begged him 'to have patience for a month or some such time longer, for that he had a secret which no man in England had but he, and that he would make trial of that and that he did not doubt but it would do him good'. Sir William replied, 'Good doctor, let me have it and let my apothecary make it because he knoweth the state of my body best.' 'No', said Harvey, 'I will make it myself because I will have it known to no man but myself.' When the patient had made trial of the secret remedy for about a month he was no better, but rather the pains were worse. He declared 'that he found he was not cured, but that he must be cut, for that the pain growing and continuing so extremely upon him as it did, it was not possible for him to live or die in his right senses'. Harvey then said, 'Sir William, you were best venture to be cut'; and 'So I will', said Sir William, 'for it is not possible for me to live in this manner as I do'. 'But', said the doctor, 'I think you have not the heart to be cut.' 'No?', said Sir William, 'do you think I have not the heart of a man as other men have?' 'Yes', Harvey replied, 'but I know you are afraid to die.' 'Well', said Sir William, 'seeing I can have no ease, by God's grace I will adventure it.' 'Which do then', said the doctor, and agreed that then the annuity would cease, adding, ''Tis true and if you be cut I do not intend to demand it of you. And I wonder you will move such a matter to me. Do you think me so unreasonable a man as to look for it if you be cut? It is so poor a thing as I regard it not.'

The witness then told how she remembered Mr. Emerson, a minister, coming often to Sir William and giving him medicines for the stone. On one occasion Dr. Harvey came in and, finding Mr. Emerson there, was very angry that he should neglect his profession and come to London like a horse-leech and take upon him to give things to such as were under physician's hands, 'and did withal threaten him to lay him in prison for his meddling in that wherein he had no skill'. Emerson replied that he had given his medicine to many knights, gentlemen, and ladies and had done them good. 'For his own part he did not regard his threatening words and that he would justify or maintain what he had done.' Sir William defended Emerson, saying that he had sent for him, and that he had found more ease in his remedies than in Dr. Harvey's. He prayed Dr. Harvey to be contented, 'for', said he, 'if you imprison any man that shall want to do me good, I will quickly find means to enlarge him again'.

The sixth witness was George Smith, aged 22, a younger son of the patient, who had lived in his home. He was not able to add anything new to the evidence, but said that he had asked Lady Jacob to mediate between the parties and to persuade Dr. Harvey to forbear to seek the payment. Lady Jacob replied that his brother had used her very discourteously and then spoke of the table-cloth that she had wished to buy. She said 'that if he had let her have the table-cloth at her price, nay if he had given it to her, he should have lost nothing thereby, and that the doctor would never have sued him, but now he shall once know the malice of a woman, for he shall be sure to pay the annuity to Dr. Harvey'.

John Emerson of Shoreham in Kent (Dr. Sisson calls him Vicar of Shoreham), the seventh witness, confirmed the main facts, but added one very important point—that he heard Dr. Harvey declare, when he made the search, that 'he felt something hard bear against his finger like a stone'. Harvey had also 'completely assured Sir William that by his viewing of anatomies [dissections] he had found out a way to cure the patient of the stone without cutting'. Emerson had spent some months with Sir William, during which Dr. Harvey often came and 'gave him directions what he thought most meet and necessary to use for his most ease of his pain and for the more speedy cure thereof. And amongst other observations prescribed a very strict and sparing diet, enjoyning him to abstain from flesh, strong beer, fish and other such nourishing meals.' With this the witness did not agree, advising the patient 'that he ought rather to cherish his stomach with all nourishing meals that he could'. At this Dr. Harvey was very angry and made the threatening speeches already reported by Elenor Smith.

Walter Bilmore, aged 34, the eighth and last witness, repeated most of the evidence already given, including the doctor's threats against John Emerson and the story of the damask table-cloth demanded by Lady Jacob. He said she had fallen into a passion against him because he had repeated her words; further, that Mr. Brooke had confessed to him that his wife had laid out £6 or thereabouts on Dr. Harvey's behalf.

The result of the action is not known, the verdict having not yet been found among the Chancery Court records. There can be little doubt, however, that Harvey obtained his verdict, since he was clearly entitled to the money if he chose to demand it. There was a curious conflict of evidence about Harvey's examination of the patient. Most of the witnesses declared that he said that he could find no stone or that it was anyway a very small one. Investigation *per rectum* with a finger was the only means of diagnosis available to him other than the use of a bladder sound, and no small stone could possibly be felt in that way except, perhaps, in a child.[1] On the other hand, the 'huge stone' reported by Chamberlain to have been removed at operation might well have been felt by an experienced finger, and this, said John Emerson, a clergyman and the most credible of the witnesses, was what Harvey had indeed reported. His evidence sounds more honest than that of most of the

[1] Harvey's awareness of the fact that urinary stones could sometimes be felt by a finger in the rectum is proved by a passage in his lecture notes of 1616. In discussing conditions found in the rectum and possible sources of obstruction he wrote: 'Hence too the stone in the bladder can be touched, for example, cutting on the finger.' The last words refer to one recognized method of 'cutting for the stone'.

others, who were clearly doing their best to support William Smith's resistance to making the payment and to denigrate Dr. Harvey. If Harvey knew that so large a stone was present, he would have been unlikely to regard its cure as possible, and, knowing this, may have hoped to alleviate Sir William's symptoms by his remedy and so tide him over the period of suffering before his inevitable death. Our knowledge of Harvey's character suggests that he may have taken this ethically justifiable view and so was resentful of the clergyman's well-meant interference. The medical ethos of the time did not disapprove entirely of 'secret remedies'; indeed, as already demonstrated by the proceedings recorded in the Annals of the College of Physicians, great efforts were made to maintain this secrecy, lest the apothecaries should get to know all their prescriptions and so be able to take much practice out of their hands. Only a demand by the President and Censors of the College could compel disclosure of such secrets. Not for more than a hundred years after Harvey's time was disapproval of secret nostrums expressed by the College, and Harvey cannot be criticized on that score. The parts played by Harvey's counsel, Christopher Brooke, and his wife form, if true, the least creditable side of the story; it must be remembered, however, that we have heard only one side, and that side determined to discredit the apparently unsuccessful physician as far as possible. It is noticeable that four of the eight witnesses were named Smith and may all have been related to the plaintiff. Other doctors' bills were also being resisted by the executors. We know that one of them, Dr. Stephen Higgins, did win his action, being awarded £34. 4s. 11d. with £10 damages.[1]

It seems idle to speculate on the nature of Harvey's secret remedy for the stone. Numerous herbs were credited with properties capable of dissolving stones, many of them being called 'saxifrages' by contemporary botanists. Sir Thomas Browne in 1646 recalled that the blood of a goat had once been thought sovereign for the stone and was commended by many good writers.[2] A few years later Robert Boyle had been told 'by a very ingenious gentleman concerning one of the eminentist of our London physicians, who was wont, as this Confidant of his assured me, as an excellent secret to employ in some of his choice Remedies that peculiar saltpetre which he had drawn out of the Earth digg'd up in Church-yards'.[3]

---

[1] Sisson, loc. cit., p. 16, though the verdict is there erroneously associated with Harvey's action.

[2] *Pseudodoxia Epidemica*, London, 1646, book ii, chapter 5.

[3] *Certain Physiological Essays*, London, 1661, p. 53.

Attention is naturally arrested in this affair by the fact that Harvey's counsel was Christopher Brooke, the old and close friend of the Dean of St. Paul's, and the question arises, did Donne and Harvey know one another? One answer is that the King's chaplain (since 1615) and the King's physician (appointed in 1618) could hardly have failed to meet, and Dr. F. N. L. Poynter[1] has assembled an array of facts tending to support the idea that they were more than chance acquaintances and that Donne is likely to have been in Harvey's audience at one or more of his lectures. It was not unusual for men outside the medical profession to attend anatomy lectures. Sir Simonds D'Ewes, a barrister who entered the Middle Temple in 1623 at the age of 21, illustrated the width of his interests by recording in his autobiography that on 27, 28, and 29 March 1623, 'I was for the most part present at an anatomy lecture read by Doctor Harvey at the Physicians' College near Paternoster Row, by which I gained much profitable knowledge, as I did also by the converse of very able students, who were my ordinary companions in the Middle Temple.'[2]

John Donne had connexions with the medical profession from early in his life. His father having died when he was a child, his mother soon married again, his stepfather being a physician, John Syminges, who was President of the College of Physicians for many years in succession and lived in the precincts of St. Bartholomew's Hospital. This proximity to the scene of Harvey's later labours does not constitute any sort of evidence for acquaintanceship, but it suggests that Donne's inquiring mind had been subjected to medical influences, and there are passages in his poems that indicate familiarity with the trend of Harvey's thoughts on the circulation. *The Second Anniversarie*, a long poem in praise of the young daughter lost by Sir Robert Drury in 1611, contains the lines:

> Know'st thou how blood, which to the heart doth flow,
> Doth from one ventricle to th'other goe?

At least Donne was interested in the movement of the blood. At a later date, on 8 April 1621, he preached a sermon at Whitehall containing the passage:

Hee doth not say yet, lest thou bee satisfied; there is no great feare nay there is no hope of that, that he will be satisfied. We know the receipt,

[1] F. N. L. Poynter, 'John Donne and William Harvey', *Journal of the History of Medicine* (1960), xv. 233–46. See also David H. M. Woollam, 'Donne, Disease and Doctors', *Medical History* (1961), v. 144–53.

[2] *Autobiography*, edited by J. O. Halliwell, 2 vols., London, 1845, i. 230.

the capacity of the ventricle, the stomach of man, how much it can hold; and wee know the receipt of all the receptacles of blood, how much the body can have; so wee doe of all the other conduits and cisterns of the body; But this infinite Hive of honey, this insatiable whirlpoole of the covetous mind, no Anatomy, no dissection hath discovered to us. When I looke into the larders, and cellars, and vaults, into the vessels of our body for drink, for blood, for urine, they are pottles, and gallons; when I looke into the furnaces of our spirits, the ventricles of the heart and of the braine, they are not thimbles; for spirituall things, the things of the next world, we have no room; for temporall things, the things of this world, we have no bounds.[1]

This statement is startling because Harvey's lectures, their substance not yet published to the world, would seem to be the only source from which Donne could have got knowledge of these quantitative measurements of the capacity of the viscera, including the chambers of the heart. No one but Harvey had made such measurements. Even the language of the one is reminiscent of the terms used in his lectures by the other.

When Donne was seriously ill and composing his *Devotions*, published in 1624, he recorded that King James sent his physicians to attend him, and after the consultation he wrote: 'They have seene me and heard me, arraign'd mee in these fetters, and receiv'd the evidence; I have cut up mine Anatomy, dissected my selfe, and they are gone to read upon me.'[2] Donne's illness happened in December 1623, when Sir Theodore de Mayerne was still in England, and it is probable that he was sent to see the patient; but he was not alone. His colleague could have been Harvey, whose friend Dr. Simeon Fox attended Donne in his last illness in 1631 and paid 100 marks (according to Izaak Walton) for the marble effigy of his patient now in St. Paul's Cathedral.

Another patient of Harvey's at this time, better known, though probably less influential than Sir William Smith, was James Howell, author of many works, including the *Epistolæ Ho-Elianæ*, first published in 1645. Howell was a man of great mental and literary activity, who spent much of his life as an adventurer and gatherer of political intelligence. He was a Welshman, born about 1594, one of a large family. After being educated at Hereford Free School and Jesus College, Oxford, he travelled abroad, returning to London early in 1622. In a letter to his father, dated 'London 2 February 1621 [1621/2]', he gave an account of his health and the treatment he had received from Dr. Harvey. Some doubt

---

[1] *Donne's Sermons*, ed. Potter and Simpson, University of California Press, 1951, iii. 235–6.
[2] Donne's *Devotions*, London, 1624, p. 201.

has been cast on the credentials of Howell's letters, but a careful examination by Joseph Jacobs (1890–1) led to the conclusion that the bulk of them are genuine, though extensively edited by the writer, who was apt to make guesses at the dates; there were no dates in the first edition of the *Epistolæ Ho-Elianæ*, but they were added in the second edition of 1647.

Howell had an 'ingenious' mind and was much appreciated by King James, who was greatly interested in Sir Kenelm Digby's claim to have healed with 'the powder of sympathy' some wounds sustained by Howell in trying to separate two duellists. Digby gave a highly coloured account of the incident in his much later *Discourse*[1] on the subject (1658), and claimed that not only the King and the Duke of Buckingham were impressed by the apparent miracle, but that also Sir Theodore de Mayerne was interested in his 'secret'—which in fact consisted of powdered vitriol. Digby's procedure was to ask for some object that had Howell's blood upon it, and he was given a garter which had been used at first as a bandage. Digby then dissolved some of his powder in a basin of water and put the garter in the solution, whereupon Howell, who was unaware of what Digby was doing, suddenly felt an alleviation of the pain in his wounded hand. Digby now advised removal of all plasters, the wound only to be kept clean and cool. Presently, to satisfy the curiosity of the Duke of Buckingham, he took the garter out of the basin and dried it before a fire. Howell's servant then came running to say that the wound was again burning more than ever. The garter was put back in the basin and the pain again departed. It was soon afterwards healed. Harvey's name is not mentioned with de Mayerne's, though he must have known about it; probably his opinion would have agreed with the impression derived from reading Digby's story at the present day—that the healing of a superficial wound, after showing some initial inflammation, took place in the ordinary way.

Howell's letter to his father was written a year or two earlier than the duelling incident:

Sir, It hath pleased God after almost three years peregrination by Land and Sea, to bring me back safely to *London*, but although I am com safely, I am com sickly: for when I landed in Venice, after so long a Sea-voyage from Spain, I was afraid the same defluxion of salt rheum which fell from my Temples into my throat in Oxford, and distilling upon the

---

[1] *A Late Discourse Made in a Solemne Assembly of Nobles and Learned Men at Montpellier Touching the Cure of Wounds by the Powder of Sympathy. Rendered out of French into English*, London. 12° 1658, pp. 6–14.

uvula impeached my utterance a little to this day, had found the same channell again, which caused me to have an Issue made in my left arm for the diversion of the humour. I was well ever after till I came to *Rouen*, and there I fell sick of a pain in the head, which, with the Issue, I have carried with me to *England*. Doctor Harvey who is my Physician, tells mee that it may turn to a Consumption, therfore he hath stopped the Issue, telling me there is no danger at all in it, in regard I have not worn it a full twelvemonth: My Brother I thank him hath been very carefull of me in this my sicknes, and hath come often to visit me; I thank God I have pass'd the brunt of it, and am recovering, and picking up my crums apace. . . .

Lond. 2 *Febr.*   *Your dutifull Son.* J. H.[1]
1621.

The 'issue' on Howell's arm, of which Harvey disapproved as having been open long enough, was an artificial ulcer produced by surgical incision with the idea of causing counter-irritation or with a vague notion that it would cause, as Howell says, some 'diversion of the humour', that is, in modern terms, production of antibodies to bacterial action. Howell pursued his acquaintance with Harvey and his dealings with him thirty years later are recorded on another page.

Evidence of the extent to which Harvey was trusted by people of eminence in the society of his time is found in a letter written by Sir Henry Hobart, Chief Justice of Common Pleas from 1613 to 1625, to Robert Sidney, first Earl of Leicester, in 1620. Leicester's daughter, Lady Philippa Sidney, had married Hobart's son, Sir John, but died at the age of 27, leaving two young children, a boy and a girl. Hobart wrote under the date September 20:

I have receyved your Lordship's Letter, wherin I find all that could be expected; for I finde an entire loving Father in your sorrow. I finde a true Christian in your Patience. And I finde a noble Disposition, in that it pleaseth you to acknowledge the Love, which was repayed to that Christian Soule, in a full Measure; not only by her Husband, but by us, and all that belong to us. . . . But for my Sonne, I must say true, his Sorrow keepes no Boundes, and when it will end I know not, and yet I cannot finde in my Harte to blame it. There are two Thinges, that may much allay our Sorrows: Wee have cause to joy, that she dyed in the Favour of God and Men; for she lived most vertuous, and was in her

---

[1] *Epistolæ Ho-Elianæ. Familiar Letters Domestic and Forren.* The second Edition, enlarged with divers supplements, and the Dates annexed which were wanting in the first. London. 8°. 1650, section ii, p. 1.

Devotions with Zeal to her last Breath: And she lived as long as was possible, for it apeers, by that last Act of her Opening (which was guided by Dr Harvey) that she had been preserved hitherto by Arte and Care, and now all would not serve, and so she was overcomed. For the two Motherless Children, there lyes a Charge upon me (for I will not quit myself from my Parte) to see to them, which I will not neglect.[1]

Harvey's acknowledged skill in conducting a post-mortem examination was able to help in assuaging some of the father's grief.

12

STONEHENGE, 1620

IN the year 1620 Harvey appears to have taken some interest in archaeology, for we find him playing a part in an investigation of the ancient monument on Salisbury Plain known at that time as Stone-Heng, now Stonehenge. In that year King James was visiting the Earl of Pembroke at Wilton, near Salisbury, probably with Harvey in attendance. James no doubt rode over to visit the celebrated antiquity, situated only some seven miles from Wilton, and became so curious about its history and origin that he ordered his architect, Inigo Jones, to investigate the site. Jones, five years Harvey's senior, was primarily artist and architectural designer; the studies he had made in Rome as a young man had no doubt stimulated his interest in classical archaeology, but he had no claim to be a fully instructed archaeologist, and he saw in the great monoliths at Stonehenge only what knowledge of Roman antiquities had taught him to see. He made a careful survey of the stones, drew plans, and conducted some sort of excavation. He recorded what he found in rough notes, but never recast them in an orderly form, though he came to the definite conclusion that the monument was a Roman temple erected by Agricola in the first century A.D. After Jones's death in 1652 his devoted pupil, John Webb, found his notes and worked them up into a book published in 1655 under the title, *The most notable Antiquity of Great Britain, vulgarly called Stoneheng, on Salisburie Plaine, restored by Inigo Jones, Esquire, Architect-Generall to the late King*. It was a thin folio volume containing a

---

[1] *Sir Henry Sidney Letters and Memorials of State*, ed. A. Collins, London, 1746, ii. 352, and *Historical Manuscripts Commission. Sidney Papers*, v, 1962, p. 421.

portrait of Jones engraved by Hollar after van Dyke and a number of engraved plans of the monument. The book was read by an eminent physician, Dr. Walter Charleton, who had been physician to King Charles in company with Harvey at Oxford, and was a prolific writer on a variety of subjects. His perusal of Inigo Jones's book roused him to write a book in opposition to the Roman theory, entitled *Chorea Giganteum, or the most famous Antiquity of Great Britain, Stonehenge, standing in Salisbury Plain, restored to the Danes*, 1663. Charleton claimed to have proved that Stonehenge was a ceremonial site, or Danish Court-Royal for election of kings. This attack on Jones stimulated John Webb to defend his Master in yet another book, published two years later as: *A Vindication of Stone-Heng Restored. In which the Orders and Rules of Architecture observed by the Ancient Romans are discussed, As also a Historical Narrative of the most memorable Actions of the Danes in England*, 1665. The arguments on neither side have any relevance today, since both were wrong, but the last book is of interest in the present context because it was here that Webb brought Harvey into the picture. In his wordy discourse he wrote (p. 122):

But while I recall these matters of Antiquity to memory, I am not to forget Mr Jones, whom this Doctor [Charleton] imagined to have been as weak of constitution as himself, to be transported at every airy bubble. He was of another temper, neither arrogant, nor ambitious, and so far from exulting of this his εὕρηκα, εὕρηκα, as that his notes were not found, much less *Stone-Heng Restored* written, until long after his death; nor should it ever have been published, had not our famous Anatomist Doctor William Harvey, John Selden Esquire, and the best Antiquaries then living overperswaded me to it, lest a work so grateful to his country should utterly be lost; and those great Lovers of Antiquity, the learned Sir Justinian Isham Baronet, and Sir John Penruddok Knight, the Head of that loyal family, with divers others yet surviving can testify what I say is Truth.

Harvey, in common with Selden and the others named, seems to have believed in Jones's theory and so naturally joined with his friends in urging its publication. But that was not all. Another passage in the *Vindication* brings to our mind's eye a vision of Harvey busily excavating the ground within the stone circles in the company of the Duke of Buckingham, who, to please the King, had also developed an interest in field archaeology. Harvey's interest was genuine, because, as will be seen, his knowledge of comparative anatomy could be brought to bear on the problem. Webb wrote as follows (p. 127):

It being then thus, there is no further question to be made, but that those Heads of Bulls, or Oxen, of Harts, and other such Beasts, digged up in or near our Antiquity, were the Reliques of such Beasts as were anciently offered at that place. And should I positively affirm, that they could be of the Sacrifices of no other People than the Romans, I suppose, I might securely enough justifie the same.

He then quoted several authorites to support the belief that whereas the Britons, Saxons, and Danes offered human victims, the Romans immolated only bulls, oxen, and harts to their deities. He disregarded skulls ploughed up in adjacent fields.

Those concern immediately our discovery, that have been found in several parts of the Court surrounding Stone-Heng itself, and near about it; for, besides the abundance of them which were digged up by Dr. Harvey formerly mentiond, Gilbert North Esquire, Brother to the Right Honourable Lord North, Mr. Jones, and divers other persons, at several times, when the Right Noble George, late Duke of Buckingham, out of his real affection to Antiquity, was at the charge in King James his daies, of searching and digging there, great numbers were found also. And as at all the former times, so in like manner at this same time, were great quantities of burnt Coals, or Charcoals digged up likewise here, lying promiscuously together with the Heads, there, in pits by themselves apart, here more, there less.

No record was kept of these haphazard excavations, and they achieved nothing except to spoil the evidence that might have been obtained by the more scientific archaeologists of the eighteenth and nineteenth centuries had the ground been undisturbed.

Charleton's contribution to the controversy is valued today chiefly for the prefixed poem by John Dryden in praise of the author. In this the poet celebrates the names of several of the English scientists, including Harvey's:

> Among th'Assertors of free Reason's claim,
> Th'English are not the least in Worth, or Fame.
> The World to *Bacon* does not onely owe
> Its present Knowledge, but its *future* too.
> Gilbert shall live, till *Load-stones* cease to draw,
> Or *British* Fleets the boundless Ocean awe,
> And noble *Boyle*, not less in *Nature* seen,
> Than his great Brother read in *States* and *Men.*
> The Circling streams, once thought but pools of Blood
> (Whether Life's fewel, or the Bodie's food)

From dark Oblivion *Harvey's* name shall save:
While *Ent* keeps all the honour that he gave.

Sir George Ent was credited by Dryden with having preserved Harvey's honour because of his part in defending the doctrine of the circulation of the blood and in giving to the world Harvey's second treatise on generation to be described in another chapter.

13

HARVEY'S FATHER AND BROTHERS

WHILE Harvey was developing his career in medicine his brothers were making their way to prosperity in commerce, helped in their early years by their father, Thomas Harvey. They had lost their mother in 1605, but their father lived on for some years in Folkestone, being elected mayor for the third time in 1611. At an unknown date after this he left his home town for the north-east outskirts of London and took up residence in the village of Hackney, where he died aged 73 in 1623. Although he had called himself 'yeoman' when he entered William at Cambridge in 1593, it is probable that with the rise of his own fortunes as a landowner and of his sons in commerce, he decided to become a 'gentleman', and to this end acquired a coat of arms. Having established his sons Daniel, Eliab, Michael, Matthew, and Thomas as merchants trading with the Levant and the Far East, and perhaps having taken some part himself in their ventures, he assumed a coat described as: *Or on a chief indented sable 3 crescents Argent*, the crescents being the mark of a Turkey merchant. This was surmounted by a crest—*A dexter hand appaumée proper, over it a crescent inverted argent*. It has always been supposed that the Harvey family did not assume these arms until long after Thomas Harvey's death, but a manuscript[1] now in the British Museum records that they were granted to the Harveys by the Garter king-of-arms, Sir William Segar, who died in 1633. The grant is not dated, but must have been made after January 1606/7, when Segar was confirmed in his office by a patent under the great seal. The manuscript gives a list of Segar's grants

---

[1] *Aspidora Segariana*, or the Grants, confirmations, &c., of Sir William Segar. British Museum, Dept. of MSS., 12225, f. 54. My attention was drawn to this by the late Edward Mars Elmhirst, F.R.C.S.

PLATE XIV

THOMAS HARVEY, SENIOR
Age 64, 1614

and they include the Harvey coat. Some confusion has been caused by the statement that it was confirmed to Thomas Harvey's grandson, Sir Daniel Harvey. This may have been true, but it is also true that Sir William Segar's list was copied and brought up to date by his grandson, Simon Segar, who naturally gave the title to the most distinguished Harvey of the generation contemporary with himself, namely Sir Daniel, fourth son of Daniel Harvey, who became Ambassador to Constantinople in 1668. That the first grant of arms was made to Thomas Harvey before 1623 seems certain from the fact that another manuscript[1] now in the Royal College of Arms, compiled in the shop of an heraldic painter named Philpott, records the provision of a dozen escutcheons of the Harvey coat for the funeral of Thomas Harvey of Hackney in June 1623. There can be little doubt, therefore, that the father of the successful Harvey brothers had risen in the social scale and could claim to be a gentleman before he died. His portrait at the age of 64, painted by an unknown artist in 1614, shows a dignified figure in dark clothes wearing a ruff in the Elizabethan fashion and holding the hilt of a sword in his left hand. He had considerable facial likeness to his eldest son and a look of keen intelligence, albeit perhaps rather hard. No coat of arms is seen on this portrait, and it is probable that Thomas Harvey had then not yet assumed it. As already mentioned, the Harvey family sometimes quartered the coat of crescents with that of Sir Walter Hervey, 'pepperer' and Mayor of London in 1272, this being: *Argent two bars nebulée sable, on a chief of the last three crosses pattée fitchée.*[2] The Guild of Peppers afterwards became the Company of Grocers, but any connexion with Sir Walter's family must have been pure assumption on the part of the Harveys, no genealogical evidence to justify it having been discovered.

Thomas Harvey's Will,[3] proved in the Prerogative Court of Canterbury, 16 July 1623, represents him as a man of substance, though not of great wealth. He named his son William as sole executor and 'commended him and all the rest of them to the blessings of Almighty God, desireing them to live in his fear and unite with one another fast knit together, as they may be evermore an helpe one to another'. He left money to the

---

[1] Reference O.I, f. 23. See Anthony Wagner, *History Heraldry of Britain*, Oxford, 1939.

[2] The coat with the quarterings is dimly seen on the pillar behind William Harvey in the large portrait at the Royal College of Physicians, and clearly on the portrait of uncertain date now belonging to Brigadier Carr at Ditchingham Hall, Norfolk, with Harvey's *stemma* added as a crest. See Keynes, *The Portraiture of William Harvey*, London, 1949, p. 37. The quarterings are to be seen also on Harvey's monument at Hempstead, but are not used on those of his successors in the Harvey Chapel.

[3] Printed in full in Appendix V, p. 456.

poor of the parishes of Newington, Folkestone, and Hackney, to the ministers of the churches he attended in Folkestone and Hackney, and to many members of his family and their children. His 'capitall messuage and Lande in the parishes of Newington and Foulkstone or elsewhere, knowne by the name or names of West Dane or Arpinge' he left to his son John, perhaps because at that date he was the least prosperous of the brothers. As already related, it is certain that this land near Newington, or some of it, had been in the possession of him and his forebears for two or three generations.

Thomas Fuller in his *Worthies of England* said of the Harveys that 'they got great Estates and made their Father the Treasurer thereof, who being as skilful to purchase Land, as they to gain Money, kept, employed, and improved their farmings to their great advantage, so that he survived to see the meanest of them of far greater estate than himself'.[1] Thomas Harvey's advice to his sons to keep 'fast knit together' was observed by them, and there are indications that they were always an harmonious group, but Fuller's claim that they were all wealthy before their father's death was a great exaggeration, as the dates given below will show.

Daniel was apprenticed to Thomas Weston of the Grocers' Company, and was admitted to the Company in 1611 at the age of 24, when he was given a loan of £50 from a benevolent fund to help him to start in business.[2] Eliab, apprenticed to Richard Pigott, was admitted in 1616, and both the brothers served on the Livery. The other brothers were not members of the Grocers' Company, but Daniel and Matthew belonged to a small group of Merchant Adventurers trading with France. There was some trouble in 1628, when they were accused by their fellow traders of acting in fraudulent collusion with the French merchants. They were brought before the Privy Council, but nothing further was heard of the matter and presumably they were acquitted. Thomas and Daniel Harvey were admitted to the Levant Company on 18 November 1616, and it seems likely that this event suggested to their father that the family should adopt the three crescents as their coat of arms. Thomas and Daniel were also at that time partners in a firm as 'farmers of the pre-emption of Tynne', that is, of 'all tin produced in the counties of Devon and Cornwall and elsewhere excepting that guaranteed to the Pewterers for five years'. A fine was due on admission to the Levant Company, and,

---

[1] Fuller's *Worthies*, London, 1662, Kent, p. 79.
[2] These facts concerning the Harvey brothers were established by Sir Wilmot Herringham through researches in the Public Record Office and were published in 'The Life and Times of Dr. William Harvey', *Annals of Medical History* (1932), N.S. iv. 575–89.

Daniel being absent abroad, Thomas paid £25 on the understanding that if one of the partners died the survivor would have to pay a second fine. This became due when Thomas died, aged 38, in February 1623, a few months before his father's death. Daniel refused at first to honour the agreement, but eventually paid in December 1625. Eliab and Michael, who had been apprenticed to Thomas, were admitted to the Levant Company on 27 November 1637, and managed to get part of their fees remitted. Daniel was also a member of the East India Company by June 1624, and the freedom of the Company was granted to Eliab, Matthew, and Michael in 1628, each giving £10 to the poor box. They wished 'to be adventurers in the new subscription for Persia'. The brothers were, as Sir Wilmot Herringham said, 'a somewhat close-fisted set'. When they were given the freedom of the Company they were expected to contribute a fine of £20 each, but they only gave £6, and were made to understand that this was mean. Daniel was certainly accumulating wealth by this time, since he was able to buy £5,300 of East India stock in 1625 and 1626. Evidence of the later prosperity of the brothers will be seen when the distraints made upon them by Cromwell come to be described.

Meanwhile, in 1623, Daniel's refusal to pay his fine to the Levant Company had reacted upon an innocent dependant of the brothers, a Welshman named Lewis Roberts, who had been apprenticed to Thomas. Owing to Daniel's default, Roberts was refused admission to the Company until the fine was paid in 1625. Nevertheless, he bore no grudge, and when he published a book, *The Marchants Mappe of Commerce*, in 1638 he dedicated it to:

Wᵐ Harvey D. of Phys.	John Harvey Esquire
Daniel Harvey Merchant	Eliab Harvey Merchant
Michael Harvey Merchant	Mathew Harvey Merchant

Brethren,
and John Harvey

Merchant, only sonne to Mr. Thomas Harvey Merchant deceased.

This tribute from Roberts shows that he, at any rate, regarded the brothers as a united family. He further explained that 'The Draught of this Map of Commerse was above twenty years past roughly traced out and delineated for the furtherance and helpe of mine own imployment beyond the Seas at the charges and expence of that worthy Merchant your loving Brother and my deceased Master Thomas Harvey, since whose death you were pleased for some years to second what he had thus given a beginning unto. Be pleased to accept of this my thankfulnesse and let [allow] the Worke (as a Child first bred under your Roofe at his and your charges).' Evidently he regarded himself as having been generously treated by the whole family.

When the elder Thomas died in 1623 he was doubtless attended in his illness by William among others, and William also witnessed an autopsy on his father's body, for he added to his lecture notes of 1616 relating to the description of the large intestine a marginal note: 'A vast colon Δ in my father.'[1] He had already performed a similar office for his brother Thomas a few months before, for he added to his notes on the spleen: 'Sorrow Thom: a spleen hanging like a letter V was on the right side, the lower part being more towards the front.'[2] Personal involvement was never allowed to interfere with any opportunity of making an interesting observation in morbid anatomy.

Thomas Harvey the younger was the first of the brothers to die. No hint of any sort of dissension among these seven men, all of them of some strength of character, has come down to us, and the inscription on Thomas's monument[3] in the church of St. Peter-le-Poor in the City of London reflects something of the feeling of unity among the family:

As in a Sheafe of Arrowes
Vis unita fortior

The band of love
The unitor of brethren
Here lyeth the body of *Thomas Harvey*
Of *London*, Merchant
Who departed this life the 2. of Feb.
Anno Dom. 1622

He was a faithful man, and feared God
above many. Ier. 7. 2.

Perhaps the least fortunate of the family was the youngest, Amy, born in 1596. She married a man named William Fowke, or Foulk, of whom nothing is known, and had two children, Mary and William. The boy was mentally defective and Amy's brothers made themselves responsible for his welfare. He became Dr. Harvey's 'ward in lunacy', and an entry[4] in the books of the Court of Wards and Liveries records the payment of

---

[1] *Prelectiones*, p. 107.   [2] Ibid., p. 75.
[3] Stow's *Survey of London*, 1633, p. 868. The correct reference for the text is Nehemiah, vii. 2.
[4] Public Record Office, Wards 9/163. Communicated by Dr. Gweneth Whitteridge.

£2 from William Harvey in July 1637 to the Receiver-General for the whole fine of the custody of the lands of 'William Fowke, alias Fowkes, idiot, of London'. His grandfather, Thomas Harvey, and his uncles John, William, and Matthew also made provision for him in their Wills.

14

DR. ROBERT FLUDD AND
SIR THEODORE DE MAYERNE

BY virtue of his position at the College of Physicians, holding all the important offices between 1607 and 1628 except that of President, Harvey must have been acquainted in lesser or greater degree with all the London physicians of his time. Many of these have already been mentioned or will appear on later pages, but two of the men who were to play some part in Harvey's life may now be described in greater detail, although they have not found a niche in earlier biographies.

One such, an unusual character, was Robert Fludd, or, as he preferred to be known, Robertus de Fluctibus. Like Harvey he was a man of Kent, born four years earlier, in 1574, at Milgate in the parish of Bearsted close to Maidstone.[1] His father, Sir Thomas Fludd, was Treasurer of the Cinque Ports. His family had originated in Wales and it may have been a Celtic strain that directed his mind to mysticism, so that he came to be known as 'the English Rosicrucian'. In 1591 he was admitted at St. John's College, Oxford, where William Laud had preceded him by only two years. He graduated in Arts in 1596–7. Fludd was a faithful member of the Church of England and is reputed to have been of great personal sanctity. As a layman he was not bound by Church authority, and he chose to enlarge his theological studies in the direction of mysticism and many other kinds of esoteric religion. He travelled extensively abroad for nearly six years, ostensibly studying chemistry and medicine, but it was probably during these years that he met with and adopted the tenets of the secret brotherhood of the Rosy Cross. This society was first organized by Cornelius Agrippa, but was later reorganized by Theophrastus Paracelsus and so had an admixture of medicine with mystical theology. A German, Michael Maier, was supposed to have introduced the

[1] See J. B. Craven, *Doctor Robert Fludd. Life and Writings*, Kirkwall, 1902.

Rosicrucian Order into England in 1616, and he was a friend not only of Fludd but also of Sir William Paddy, a distinguished physician at the court of King James, so that the Rosicrucians cannot at that time have been of ill repute. Yet they had their opponents, and Fludd himself published at Leiden in 1616 an *Apologia* for the Brotherhood. They were reputed adepts in Hermetic philosophy and they practised alchemy, astrology, and all kinds of magic, including power over elemental spirits. But they did not, like Faustus, use this power to gain riches and sensual pleasures. They despised money and the founders were all 'bachelors and of avowed virginity'. Fludd himself was never married. They did, however, claim to have powers of healing quite beyond those of orthodox practitioners.

Between the years 1616 and 1637, when he died, Fludd published a series of works, partly medical, partly mystical, and these show that he was interested in everything odd and unorthodox, starting, no doubt, with the view that the Pope was Antichrist. He believed in cure by the 'powder of sympathy' at a distance, a subject later studied by Sir Kenelm Digby, and defended the use of the 'weapon salve', whereby the weapon, being smeared with an ointment compounded of human tissues, blood, and fat, and the wound caused by it being 'kept clean with a linen cloth wet every morning with his urine',[1] then the patient would be cured. Fludd's most interesting book at the present time is his *Anatomiæ Amphitheatrum*, 1623, in which every part of the human body is given its mystical significance. Seven chapters are devoted to the mystic anatomy of the heart, the sun of the microcosm, the seat of the passions. The contraction of the heart is that hardening of the heart which was Pharaoh's doom.

It is tempting to assume that Harvey was himself familiar with this book, since the phraseology of his address to the King at the beginning of *De motu cordis* is oddly reminiscent of Fludd: 'Most Serene King! The animal's heart is the basis of its life, its chief member, the sun of the microcosm; on the heart all its activity depends, from the heart all its liveliness and strength arise. Equally is the King the basis of his kingdoms, the sun of his microcosm, the heart of the state.'

Fludd had attempted entry to the College of Physicians later than Harvey although he was an older man, having been delayed by his travels abroad. He had proceeded M.D. at Oxford on 16 May 1605 and first presented himself at the College on 8 November following: 'On this day Dr. Fludd of Oxford applied for admission as a Licentiate, but when he was examined in both Galenical and spagyrical medicines he was not

---

[1] This was an early demonstration of the healing power of urea when applied to wounds.

satisfactory enough in either. They therefore advised him to apply himself more diligently to his studies.' He was enjoined to 'abstain from practice'. On 7 February 1605/6 he was examined a second time and, being 'considered to be not uneducated', was given permission to practise. This seems to have stimulated him to arrogant behaviour, and on 2 May it was reported at a meeting of the College that 'Dr. Fludd had boasted much about himself and his chemical medicaments and looked down with contempt on Galenical medicines'. He denied this, but was 'warned to think and speak modestly about himself and with respect to the College'. In the following year Fludd's behaviour was even worse. At a meeting on 21 March 1607/8, at which Harvey was present, 'Dr. Robert Fludd behaved himself so insolently that he offended everyone: he was therefore rejected by the President and forbidden to practise.' At length, on 25 June 1608, he was admitted as a candidate and on 20 September 1609 was chosen as a Fellow by secret ballot. His attempts to enter the College had evidently taught him a wholesome lesson, for he was elected Censor four times in later years and practised with distinction in London.

Harvey must have known Fludd very well, though it is unlikely that he was impressed by his mysticism or by his extravagant claims of cures at a distance. Yet this mystic had an open mind and was one of the very first to accept Harvey's doctrine of the circulation in his book, *Pulsus seu nova et arcana pulsuum historia*. This is the fifth volume of *Medicina Catholica*, which is dated 1631 on the title-page, but there is internal evidence that it was written in 1629. On p. 11 Fludd wrote:

Whence, as we see that a single chord with its weight by a whole action, as it were, makes the minutes of the hour on the clock in the motion of one circle or wheel (by its movement first forward and immediately after backward, partly acting, partly recoiling), just so the vital spirit in the function of life is moved in its vessels by the whole action of one spirit and in a circle of wind.

This seems to confirm exactly that notion and opinion of the most grave William Harvey, skilfull physician, distinguished anatomist, and most experienced in the deepest mysteries of philosophy, my dear compatriot and faithful colleague, where (with due consideration and prudence) he clearly teaches the world *in a certain little book of his, entitled Exercitatio anatomica de cordis sanguinisque in animalibus motu*, both with argument drawn from Philosophy's store and with manifold ocular demonstration, that the movement of the blood itself is circular. And why not, you Cynics, when it is certain that the spirit of life retains the impress both of the planetary system and of the zodiac? Thus, as the moon follows her unchanging path, completing her journey in a month, she incites the spirit of the blood, and therefore the blood itself, by virtue of its *astra imperceptibilia* to follow in a cyclical movement. Every seaman is acquainted with the influence of the moon on wind and tide. Why should she not exercise a similar influence in the 'microcosm' of man?

Fludd may, however, have been too ready to accept Harvey's conclusions because they did tend to confirm his own mystical beliefs in the meaning of circular movement, even though his reference to 'manifold ocular demonstration' is reassuring as to his genuine acceptance of Harvey's doctrine. Thomas Fuller rather unkindly suggested that Fludd's high-sounding language was designed simply to fortify the effect of his treatment by creating an 'atmosphere' of mystery: 'His Books written in Latine are great, many and mystical. The last some impute to his Charity, clouding his high matter with dark language, lest otherwise the lustre thereof should dazzle the understanding of the Reader. The same phrases he used to his Patients, and seeing conceit is very contributive to the well working of Physick, their fancy or faith-natural was much advanced by his elevated expressions.'[1] Nevertheless he did succeed in gaining the confidence of even so hard-headed a patient as John Selden.

Fludd died in 1637. His bust is to be seen on his tomb under the tower in the church at Bearsted in Kent.

Sir Theodore Turquet de Mayerne, a very different character from Fludd, was certainly one of the most distinguished physicians of Harvey's time in England—though this was the country of his adoption, not of his birth. He was born in Geneva in 1573 and made his medical studies in Heidelberg and Montpellier. He lectured in Paris on anatomy and pharmacy and became specially interested in chemistry. Like Fludd, he made wide use of chemical remedies, though probably with better judgement. He came to occupy a very distinguished place in the medical life of France in spite of being virulently attacked by the Galenists for his enlightened views of medical science. After being physician to Henry IV of France until 1606, he first came to England as physician to James's Queen, Anne of Denmark, but he did not stay, and was probably in France until 1610, when King Henry was assassinated. It was only in 1611 that he came to live in this country. King James had invited him to come by letters patent under the Great Seal and forthwith appointed him Royal physician. He took a leading part in attending Henry Prince of Wales through his fatal illness in 1612. The Prince's disorder can now be diagnosed as typhoid from the excellent account of

[1] Fuller, *Worthies*, London, 1662, Kent, p. 79.

PLATE XV

SIR THEODORE TURQUET DE MAYERNE
Aged about 57, *c*. 1630, from a water-colour drawing by Rubens

the whole illness drawn up by de Mayerne.[1] Associated with him were three other court physicians, Drs. Hammond, Butler, and Atkins; Harvey was not yet officially attached to the Court.

Although de Mayerne was a foreigner and had given offence to strict Galenists by his interest in chemical drugs such as calomel, the College of Physicians made him welcome and unanimously elected him a Fellow in 1616. Two years later they invited him to write the dedication to the King printed in the first *Pharmacopoeia* published by the College. He was knighted in 1624 and lived for another thirty-one years, dying in 1655, only two years before Harvey. He enjoyed a large medical practice in London and acquired riches with his honours, though he did not always follow the advice that he gave to others. The cause of his death at 82 was thought to have been a carousal with his friends at a tavern in the Strand. The only book de Mayerne published in his lifetime was an *apologia* for his heterodoxy when he was accused by the Faculty of Paris of neglecting the teaching of Hippocrates and Galen. Other writings were published after his death, including a volume giving an account of his methods of treatment edited by his godson, Sir Theodore de Vaux, in 1690. This book has an attractive frontispiece showing de Mayerne as a portly and handsome old gentleman embracing a skull as the emblem of his trade. The Fellows of the London College had themselves solemnly stated in 1608 that 'our Statutes require that every Fellow of the College be deeply studied and soundly learned in physick, that he be well read in Galen and Hippocrates, that he be able to read a lecture in Anatomy'. Perhaps they would not have welcomed the unorthodox de Mayerne with quite such open arms had it not been for his position at Court with the King's favour to recommend him. This enlightened man would have attracted Harvey's approval and friendship, and it is not, perhaps, extravagant to suggest that de Mayerne's influence may have had a part in the appointment of Harvey as Physician Extraordinary to the King. It is not known exactly when this took place, but it must have been before, or early in, 1618; the *Pharmacopoeia Londinensis*, already mentioned as prepared by the College and dedicated to the King, was published on 7 May of that year. Harvey had been a member of the committee responsible for the book and he is named there as *Medicus Regis juratus*, 'sworn physician of the King', showing that his appointment was by then an accomplished fact.

It is difficult to envisage Harvey, so serious, so coolly appraising and self-possessed, finding his proper place in the extravagant, untidy

[1] de Mayerne, *Opera Medica*, ed. by Joseph Browne, London, 1700.

entourage of King James. Was he able to appreciate the King's 'pawky' (because Scottish) wit? Or was he, perhaps, thinking partly of the ungainly Royal buffoon when he told Aubrey in later life that 'man was but a great mischievous baboon'? Of one thing we can be certain, that Harvey was more interested in the King's bodily ills than in any of the intrigues with which he was surrounded. His senior colleague, de Mayerne, was, by any modern standards, an outstanding clinician. His voluminous bedside notes (now among the Sloane manuscripts in the British Museum) bear witness to the extraordinary care with which he observed his patients. Nothing was too trivial to escape his notice; every small disorder, as well as large, was to be attended to and treated. Of particular interest are his notes on the bodily condition of King James, as they give a most vivid picture of Harvey's Royal master in health and illness and some idea of what it must have meant to be attached as physician to a man so beset with minor troubles and so careless of his own well-being. The notes[1] were written by de Mayerne in his own hand in Latin and are very long, so that it will be convenient to give them in the form of Sir Norman Moore's abbreviated version in English:[2]

James the First, King of Great Britain, was born at Edinburgh in the year 1566 on June 19th at half-past eleven in the morning, and is now aged over 57 years. He had a drunken wet-nurse and was suckled for about a year. He has a very steadfast brain, which was never disturbed by the sea, by drinking wine, or by driving in a coach.

He is easily affected by cold and suffers in cold and damp weather. His chest is broad and well formed, and the vital parts contained therein have strong and lively warmth and never are afflicted unless as a result of morbid conditions elsewhere. In this way it happens that his lungs are often attacked by fluxion, the material of which is swiftly thoroughly matured by the power of a very warm heart. The liver naturally good, large, of much blood, warm, liable to obstructions, and inclined to generate much bile. The spleen now easily heaps up melancholic juice, the presence of which is indicated by various symptoms. There is no swelling in either of these viscera and no hardness. Each hypochondrium is soft and never distended, except with wind. The stomach is always ready for the burden of a large quantity of food and is prompt to get rid of any hurtful excess, chiefly by the bowel. He has naturally a good appetite and duly digests a sufficient quantity. He very often thirsts and often swells out with wind, of which imperfect digestion or fermentation is the origin. Bowels uncertain; the discharge soft and fluid. The

[1] British Museum, Sloane MS. 1697, f. 42 ff.
[2] *The History of the Study of Medicine in the British Isles*, Oxford, 1908, pp. 97–106.

mesentery is apt to be obstructed in the wanderings of its vessels. Kidneys warm, disposed to generate sand and gravel. His legs seem not strong enough to sustain the weight of the body. His habit loose and of pervious texture, and he readily heats with dry heat. Skin thin and delicate, so that it itches easily. Fauces narrow, causing difficulty in swallowing, which defect is hereditary from his mother and grandfather, James V of Scotland. Animal and vital faculties blameless. All functions naturally good, but perverted on occasion and most from disturbance of mind. As to non-naturals:

Air—His Majesty bears all changes of air fairly well; in damp weather with a south wind he is attacked by catarrh.

Food—As regards food he does not much amiss except that he eats no bread. He generally takes roast meats. Owing to want of teeth he does not chew his food, but bolts it. Fruit he eats at all hours of day and night.

Drink—In drink he errs as to quality, quantity, frequency, time and order. He promiscuously drinks beer, ale, Spanish wine, sweet French wine, white wine (his normal drink), and Muscatelle wine (whence his diarrhoea) and sometimes Alicant wine. Nevertheless, he does not mind whether wine be strong or no so it be sweet. He has the strongest antipathy to water and all watery drinks.

Exercise and rest—The King used to be given up to most violent exercise in hunting. Now he is quieter and lies or sits more, but that is due to the weakness of his knee-joints.

Sleep and waking—He naturally sleeps ill and restlessly, and often at night he is roused and calls the valets, and sleep does not return unless, as often, it takes him by surprise while the reader is reading aloud to him.

Affections of the mind—His mind is easily moved suddenly. He is very wrathful, but the fit soon passes off. Sometimes he is melancholy from the spleen in the left hypochondrium exciting disorders.

Excreta—He often blows his nose, sneezes very often. Does not spit much unless from catarrh. Stomach easily made sick if he retains undigested food or bile. Vomits with great effort, so that after being sick his face appears for a day or two spotted with red spots. Much wind. Vapours from his stomach precede illness. The alvine discharge is uncertain and depends on the nature of his food, which often produces morbid changes. A tendency to looseness gets rid of a burden produced by what he has eaten.

Urine generally normal and sufficient. Often sandy sediment after a time. Sometimes friable calculi or rather agglutinated grains of sand are sifted out. He sweats easily owing to the thinness of his skin, especially at night, after exercise, after copious meals. He is impatient of sweat as of all things. From the year 1619, after a severe illness, in which leeches were applied, has had a copious haemorrhoidal flow almost daily. If this does not occur the King becomes very irascible, melancholy, jaundiced, glows with heat, and his appetite falls off. When the flow returns all things are changed for the better.

Former illnesses and present aptitude to various morbid conditions—The King to the sixth year of his age was not able to walk, but was carried about, so weak was he from the bad milk of his drunken nurse. Between the second and fifth year he had small-pox and measles. In his fifth year he had suppression of urine, nevertheless no sand or slime was ejected.

Colic—He often has colic; this was worse before he was twenty-four; it afterwards became milder. Fasting, sadness, cold at night produced it. It is relieved by the converse. Cholera often, and when young almost every year he was seized with cholera morbus, with shivering preceding sickness and bilious diarrhoea.

Diarrhoea—He has been liable to diarrhoea all his life; most in spring and autumn, most of all from about the end of August or beginning of September, after eating fruit, sometimes with fever, sometimes without. Before this diarrhoea he almost always has depression of mind, sighing, dread of all things, and other melancholic symptoms. In 1610, at the end of Parliament, after great sadness, diarrhoea for eight days, with watery, bilious, very fetid, and at last black excreta. Cardialgia, palpitation, sighing, sadness, &c. Vomiting recurring twice or thrice a day. The King regained his health after proper remedies.

In 1612, December 4, after the death of his son, a paroxysm of melancholy—an attack of illness ending in diarrhoea lasting a few days. 1619, after the Queen's death, pain in joints and nephritis with thick sand. At Royston continued fever, bilious diarrhoea, watery and profuse throughout the illness. Hiccough for some days. Aphthae all over mouth and fauces, and even the oesophagus. Fermentation of bitter humours boiling in his stomach which, effervescing by froth out of his mouth, led to ulceration of his lips and chin. Fainting, sighing, dread, incredible sadness, intermittent pulse. Nevertheless, it is to be noted as to this intermission of pulse in the King that it was frequent. Nephritis, from which, without any remedy having been administered, he excreted a friable calculus, as was his wont. The force of this, the most dangerous illness which the King ever had, lasted for eight days. Remedies were used with success. After that illness for two years the King was fairly well and free from other, even his usual, affections; afterwards, as was his wont, diarrhoea recurred, but was less severe.

This year 1623, at the end of autumn, it lasted for two or three days, and was excessive. After this arthritis, and after this, after an interval of three weeks, he was able to walk without help, while before for months he had had to sit in a chair and be carried or be helped along by the

PLATE XVI

KING JAMES I IN MIDDLE AGE
By an unknown painter

support of others. The happy effect of the spontaneous evacuation is to be noted.

Our King is easily attacked by catarrh descending from the brain and producing coryza. Most often it attacks the lungs, and a most violent cough follows, but within two or three days maturation occurs and the coughs ceases, and the humour thick and black is rejected from the bronchi.

Fever—He rarely has fever, and if any it is short and ephemeral.

Jaundice—Easily comes on if he is in any way out of sorts, whether in mind or body. Often his eyes grow yellow, but soon it passes off.

Haemorrhoids—Some loss of blood nearly every day, with sometimes prolapse and tenesmus.

Nephritis—Many years ago, after hunting and long riding, he often had turbid urine and red like Alicant wine (which are His Majesty's words), but without pain.

July 12 1613 bloody urine, with red sand, soon faeculent and with thick sediment. Ardor urinae, pain in the left kidney; frequent vomiting and other nephritic symptoms.

The same, but worse, August 17. In 1615, October, the same symptoms. His accustomed flux relieved all these paroxysms. Afterwards the evil often renewed, and in some of the accessions calculi or rather concoctions were ejected, and soft sand adhering together with imperfect cohesion, and then the attack came to an end.

Arthritis—Pains many years since invaded first the right foot, which had an odd twist when walking, and from a wrong habit of steps had a less right position than the other, and grew weaker as he grew older. Afterwards occurred various bruises from knocking against timber, from frequent falls from horseback, from the rubbing greaves and stirrups and other external causes which the King ingeniously discovered, and exactly noted, that he might baffle the accusation of internal disorder on the part of his physicians.

Pain of his right foot used to afflict him most often; not the toes, not the joint of the foot with tibia, but underneath the external malleolus. All the same, I have observed that the whole foot has more often swelled and so much weakness from pain remained, that for several weeks he had to give up usual exercises and was compelled to stay in bed or in a chair. At last, in the year 1616, this weakness continued for more than four months with oedematous swelling of the whole skin and of both feet. In following years it happened that the pain went on to joints of other parts, the great toe of the left foot and the malleoli to both knees and shoulders and hands, more often with swelling. The pain is acute for the first two or three days. By night it rages now worse, now milder; weakness succeeds, which is neither subdued nor disappears till after a long course of days. In winter time the arthritis is much worse, nor are the joints free till the return of the sun and summer warmth restores health to His Majesty.

Thrice in his life he was siezed with most severe pains of the thigh, very recently on October 28 1623, as if by a spasm of the muscles and tendons bending the left leg by a vaporous influence most pertinaciously twitching those parts in the hours of the night. The leanness and so to speak atrophy of his legs were to be noted as due to the intermission of exercise not calling the spirits and nourishment to the lower parts which from childhood were slender and weak.

The King when coming into England from Scotland, falling from his horse, broke his right collar-bone. Another time from a fall he suffered from a bruise of the left scapula. He was completely cured. From that time nevertheless there was descent of humours into his right arm whence arose swollen glands like the phlegmatic excrescences of scrofula, which first swelled with redness and pain, then subsided and at length suppurating, formed ulcers that were healed after a long time.

It is to be noted that from the same humours, or perhaps from arthritic juice descending, a tumour appeared two years later on his right olecranon distended with wind and serum, which happily ceased after proper remedies without breaking the skin. Once having bruised and almost broken his ribs on a fall from his horse, for three days he had slight fever. He recovered without blood-letting.

Another time the fibula of the other leg was squeezed by the weight of a horse with most dangerous bruising and blackening of the whole leg. He was cured without fever. He is of extreme sensitiveness, most impatient of pains; and while they torture him with most violent movements his mind is tossed and bile flows around his praecordia, whence the evil is not relieved, but made worse.

He demands relief and freedom from pain, little considering about the causes of his illness.

As to remedies—The King laughs at medicine and holds it so cheap that he declares physicians to be of very little use and hardly necessary. He asserts the art of medicine to be supported by mere conjectures and useless because uncertain.

15

THE DEATH OF KING JAMES, 1625

EARLY in 1625 King James had gone to his favourite retreat at Theobalds in Hertfordshire. He was unhappy in his relations with his favourite, the Duke of Buckingham, he was crippled with arthritis, and had fallen into a profound melancholy. He had so often been ailing that when he developed feverish attacks at Theobalds no great importance was at first attached to them; but presently his doctors, Harvey among them, became alarmed, and a message about his illness was sent to the Lord Keeper of the Great Seal, Bishop John Williams. It was unusual for a cleric to occupy the important position of Lord Keeper, but Williams, at this time Bishop of Lincoln, had succeeded Sir Francis Bacon in the office and discharged it with distinction. The King respected his abilities and was greatly entertained by his powers of conversation, so that his company was always welcome. In the presence of serious illness he could assist the King with both worldly and spiritual advice, and so, in the words of John Hacket, the garrulous biographer of Williams:

The Lord Keeper on March 22 being Tuesday received a Letter from the Court that it was feared his Majesties Sickness was dangerous unto Death; which Fear was the more confirmed, for he, dispatching away in all haste met with Dr. Harvey in the Road, who told him, That the King used to have a Beneficial Evacuation of Nature, a sweating in his left Arm, as helpful to him as any Fontinel could be; which of late had failed. And that argued, that the former Vigour of Nature was low and spent. This Symptome of the Kings Weakness I never heard from anyone else. Yet I believe it upon so learned a Doctors observation. And this might well cause a Tertian Ague, and a Mortal, when the Spring had Entred so far, able to make a commotion in the Humours of the Body, and not to expel them with accustomed vaporation.[1]

This account of Harvey's words may have been garbled in their passage from his mouth to the pages of Hacket's book. Any fever of uncertain type was apt to be put down to some species of 'ague', or malarial attack. Malaria was common enough in England at this time, but there is no mention of it in de Mayerne's medical history of the King. Harvey's

[1] John Hacket, *Scrinia Reserata. A Memorial offered to the Great Deservings of John Williams D.D.*, London, 1693, pp. 222–3.

opinion at least shows that he was aware of the gravity of the King's condition.

According to Hacket, Williams, having reached Theobalds, remained with the King in order to warn him that his end might be approaching:

I am satisfied, says the sick King, and I pray you assist me to make me ready to go away hence to Christ, whose Mercies I call for and I hope to find them.

His devoted Chaplain stirr'd very little out of the Chamber of Sorrow, both to give an Ear to every Word the King spake in that extream condition, and to give it him again with the Use of some Divine Meditation; as also to Repulse those who crept much about the Chamber. They were of the most addicted to the Church of Rome, whom he controuled for their Sauciness, and commanded them as a Privy Counsellor further off. . . . So being rid of these locusts, he was continually in Prayer, while the King lingered on, and at last shut his Eyes with his own Hand when his Soul departed.[1]

This was on Sunday, 27 March. Bishop Williams had been more concerned with keeping the Church of Rome away from the sick-bed than with medical details, but it is plain that James was a difficult patient, and when he came to die there was serious trouble in determining the cause of death. This gave an opportunity to the enemies of the Duke of Buckingham for accusing him of having at any rate hastened the King's death by administration of an injurious plaster and potion. The postmortem examination of the body had not revealed anything of consequence other than to confirm the history given in de Mayerne's notes concerning recurrent trouble with urinary infection and renal calculi. The autopsy was described by William Neve in a letter to Sir Thomas Holland, dated 5 April 1625:

The King's body was about the 29th of March disbowelled, and his harte was found to be great but soft, his liver fresh as a young man's; one of his kidnys very good, but the other shrunke so littel as they could hardly find yt, wherein there was two stones; his lites and gall blacke, judged to proceed of melancholly; the semyture of his head soe strong as that they could hardly breake it open with a chissell and a sawe, and so full of braynes as they could not, uppon the openninge, keepe them from spillinge, a great marke of his infinite judgement. His bowels were presently put into a leaden vessel and buryed; his body embalmed.[2]

[1] Hacket, loc. cit.
[2] John Nichols, *The Progresses &c. of King James the First*, London, 1838, iv. 1037.

Rumours of foul play continued to circulate and were deliberately fostered by Dr. George Elsingham, who had earlier been for ten years personal physician to King James. In his pamphlet entitled *The Fore-Runner of Revenge*, first published in 1626 and reprinted in 1642, Elsingham accused Buckingham of having poisoned not only the King, but also his trusted adviser, the second Marquess of Hamilton, who died of a malignant fever in March 1624/5. Finally, in April 1626, a year after the King's death, Parliament decided to hold an inquiry into the circumstances. A series of medical witnesses were called to give evidence, and the manuscripts preserved at Lowther Castle include notes quickly taken as the witnesses made their statements.[1] From these notes it can be seen that Harvey was only one of many doctors who attended the bedside of the dying King, none of them sure of the nature of his illness or of how best to treat it. First, on 25 April, Dr. Bedwin was called, a King's 'sworn physician', though he was not a Fellow of the College. He had heard, he said, that plasters and potions were administered, and was told by the King that this was done without the assent of the physicians. 'He heard it acknowledged that Duke told King he had used such plaster and it had done him good.' He had seen a note giving the ingredients, but did not know the contents, although it seems he had been asked whether the plaster or the julep could have done any harm. The plaster smelt of treacle and 'he saw no inconvenience in it'. Dr. Chambers, another 'sworn physician', gave similar evidence and said the doctors murmured because they had not assented to the treatment. He thought Hayes, the King's surgeon, had applied the plaster, and the King had improved for a short time, but had then got progressively worse. He said that Dr. Harvey, who was with the King through the night, told him 'the King was worse that night, and if he had the like could not scape'. The plaster had been applied when the King had a cold fit, and was taken away when he was hot. The King had said, 'They gave me warm drink that makes me burn and roast so.' Chambers deposed further that 'The drink the Duke gave was a posset with a gillyflower', and the King said, 'Will you murder me and slay me?'

Harvey's evidence followed and was recorded in a long note which is far more coherent than the others:

A plaster applied to his side, thinks twice, first his fit worse, secondly done in the afternoon at the beginning his fit, the King desired it; commended by the Duke as good for him, and Earl of Warwick his

---

[1] *Historical Manuscripts Commission. Thirteenth Report*, Stationery Office, 1893. Appendix part vii. Notes in Parliament, 1626.

opinion asked before done; he gave no opinion because the ingredients not known. He gave way to it, the King thinking it easy and could do no harm; he thought it not against his opinion nor consultation, and the King desired it, it being external to work while he by; and it was hot, and at his hot fit they took it off. Lister present at the laying it on. The posset drink the Duke prepared; the King called for it, drank once or twice; because it was commended King desired it; because the medicine Duke and Warwick had used it, King determined to take it. He knows no advice of doctors to take it. Sunday, King heavy, he got him to rise; said better, but found heaviness at his heart on Monday, as in other fits, and he feared that fit would be worse because he had less fit before, which he told physicians, his disease not mending when that done. He first that spoke of King's demise before that fit twice, and he was in fit before next consultation. Lister, Moore came; he thinks Atkins. Lister opposed the posset thinking King called for drink; the night before the ague in his opinion still increased; on Sunday at conference the physicians thought not the King was mending. The day the King died upon, knows Sir William Paddie brought the note: and it was approved and might be used: generally they disliked a plaster, but not this. They said the plaster was a secret of a man of Essex; Hayes laid it on, King liked it as approved and experimented it, and King took divers things whether they would [or] not, undervaluing physicians. He commended the posset.

Dr. Lister said that, although he knew about the plaster, he was not there when it was applied and did not advise about it.

Hayes, the King's surgeon, then confirmed that he had applied the plaster, 'the Lord Duke's folk having brought it in'.

Sir Edward Payton added something about toad's or frog's flesh, but evidently the note-taker did not get the sense of it.

Dr. Moore stated that he had come a week before the King died, and was there every day at all consultations except one. The application of the plaster was not, as far as he knew, approved by the physicians. Harvey, he said, saw it applied, and, not knowing the contents, must be blamed. All the doctors had agreed to send a letter to the maker asking about the contents, and he had replied that 'it was London treacle and juice of citrons', and Hayes added that the drink was 'plain posset with hartshorn in it'. London treacle, or *Theriaca Londinensis*, was included in the official Pharmacopoeia of 1618 and contained thirty-two ingredients including stag-horn and opium.

A further hearing took place on 27 April at which statements were made that both the plaster and the posset drink were given by direction of Buckingham. Also that the King refused another drink when the plaster was taken off because it made him worse; but he admitted that he had taken it because 'he had had it of the Duke'. Elsingham asserted in his pamphlet that: 'The Sunday after his Majesty died, Buckingham desired the Physitians who attended his Majesty, to signe with their hands a writ of testimony that the powder which he gave him, was a good and safe medicine; which they refused.'[1]

The decision after the inquiry was that the Duke's action should be added to the charge against him 'as a transparent presumption of dangerous consequence'. Harvey's is the only consistent statement that emerges from the confused welter of evidence. It seems to be clear that in fact Buckingham's remedies were harmless, though wrong because the physicians did not know the ingredients and so could not be held to have agreed to them. The King's symptoms suggest that he was having rigors and convulsions due to infection and failing function of the kidneys and could not in any case have recovered. It is plain also that he had far too many doctors, of whom Harvey was the only one with a clear idea of the seriousness of the King's plight.

The absence of the great Sir Theodore de Mayerne from the last scenes in the King's life and from the inquiry afterwards is explained by his being abroad. In August 1624 he had composed a letter to his numerous colleagues at the Courts of the King and the Prince of Wales telling them that, as he was to be absent for some time, he thought proper, with the King's approval, to set down for them 'certain forms of prescription and methods of practice, of which his experience had taught him the efficacy in the disorders to which his illustrious patients were most liable'.[2] He had not foreseen the crisis that was impending, and it is improbable that his presence and advice would have saved the King's life, though it might have prevented the wrangling and confusion in which Harvey's professional integrity was unavoidably implicated.

Harvey's devotion to his patient was generously recognized by King Charles a few weeks after the inquiry ended, a special gift of money being conveyed to him by an order dated 28 July 1626: 'Unto Doctor Harvie the sum of 100 l., as of His Majesty's free gift, for his pains and attendance about the person of his Majesty's late dear father, of happy memory, in time of his sickness. By writ, dated 27th of May, 1626 . . . 100.0.0.'[3] A document dated 10 February 1626/7, now in the library of the Royal College of Physicians, shows that the King afterwards granted Harvey a 'general pardon'. The purpose of this is thought to have been

---

[1] *A Fore-Runner of Revenge*, 1642. p. 22.   [2] Munk's *Roll*, 1861, i. 155.
[3] F. Devon, *Issues of the Exchequer*, London, 1836, p. 350.

to ensure that he, as a Royal servant, was not to be held blameworthy for anything that might seem to have incriminated him during the previous reign. Perhaps the part played by Harvey during King James's last illness was to be covered by this pardon, though it is expressed in general terms.

It was widely believed at the time that the King had been poisoned by Buckingham's remedies, but Harvey's evidence, taken with that of the other witnesses and with the King's symptoms from the start of his illness, seems to discount the accusation. Most historians have not believed it, but in a recent and somewhat sensational Life of Buckingham[1] the author argues that he had more to gain than lose by James's death owing to the domination he had achieved over Prince Charles during their expedition to Spain in 1623. He concludes, without bringing forward any medical evidence, that Buckingham's guilt is very probable.

16

COLLEGE AFFAIRS, 1624–1628

WHEN the agitating episode of King James's illness and death was over, Harvey was able to return to his usual avocations. A minor feature of his practice at about this time is illustrated by a document dated 18 November 1624 indicating that a country gentleman was not allowed to remain in London during the winter months unless he could find good reason for doing so. It was addressed by Secretary Conway at Newmarket to Attorney-General Coventry:

MR. ATTORNEY

His Majesty is graciously pleased in regard of the indisposition of health of Sir William Sandis and his Lady and the great danger of their remove into the Country, as appears by the enclosed certificate of Dr. William Harvey, to dispense with their stay in London this winter season, notwithstanding the proclammation. And accordingly requires you to take present order for their indemnity that no charge or trouble come upon them for their stay in London this winter for which they have his Majesty's leave.[2]

---

[1] Hugh Ross Williamson, *George Villiers First Duke of Buckingham. A Study for a Biography*, London, 1940.

[2] *Calendar of Domestic State Papers*, 1623–5, clxxiv. London, 1859, p. 382.

Sir William's health did not improve and in December 1626 he was excusing himself from appearing before 'the Commissioners of the loan at Winchester' on the same score. In January 1627/8 Harvey was again called upon to help him with a certificate.

I do hereby certify of a truth that Sir William Sands is in body infirm and subject to those diseases [which] in the country he cannot receive remedy for, nor undergo and perform that course of physic which is fitting for his recovery.

William Harvey[1]

On 23 May 1627 Harvey had been attending the Lord Treasurer, Sir James Ley, in an attack of urinary calculus.[2]

He was also a constant attendant at the College Comitia. An alarming increase in the deaths from plague had occurred and on 21 April 1625 each Fellow present at Comitia was asked separately who he thought should be deputed to wait upon the Lord Mayor in response to his request for a special report on precautions against the epidemic. The President then named four—Sir William Paddy, Dr. Argent, Dr. Harvey, and Dr. Fox. Their task was to undertake either the prevention or the treatment of the plague when they had devised suitable methods. This was a tall order, since it was already well known that both prevention and cure were wellnigh impossible. The outcome of their deliberations is not recorded, but in November the pestilence was still raging in London and the Elects were summoned to a meeting at Dr. Atkins's house in the country to choose a new President, Dr. Argent being chosen. By the beginning of December so many doctors had left London that no full meetings of Fellows could be called, but Harvey was there on 1 December and was chosen as one of the four Censors, taking the oath on 13 January 1625/6. He was not one of the deserters who left their posts for fear of infection. He was at another meeting on 3 February, when among several applicants for licences to practise was one John Antony, who confessed that he had already practised for two years, but knowing his own imperfections was unwilling to undergo further examinations. On 3 March Antony appeared again before the President, Sir William Paddy, Gwinne, Harvey, Fox, and Goulston. On this occasion 'he brought 8 pounds which he handed over to the President and asked that he might be allowed to practise and connived at: which was granted to him by those present'. No doubt the plague epidemic had

---

[1] Ibid., 1627/8, xlvii. London, 1858, p. 2.

[2] From a letter in the *Calendar of Domestic State Papers*; see D'Arcy Power, *William Harvey* 1897, p. 73. Corrected.

caused a dearth of doctors in London. It is difficult otherwise to account for this serious lapse in the proper conduct of the granting of licences.

On 9 March Harvey and others read over the Apothecaries' Bill then in parliament, but 'they all despised and rejected it'. Harvey was then, as usual, one of five chosen to go immediately to the lawyers. On 29 March the number of those attending Comitia was increasing and Harvey was one of seventeen Fellows who received from the Parliamentary Commission a letter regarding religion and a request for the names of all those practising medicine or pharmacy who were suspected of papacy. Eighteen names were given, including that of Dr. Fludd, who, as a Rosicrucian, was obviously, though quite unjustly, open to suspicion.

Harvey continued to take a prominent part in College affairs for the rest of the year 1626 and during the next year, but nothing of special note occurred until 1 June 1627 when the College was requested by the Privy Council to investigate an alleged nuisance caused by the manufacture of alum in the village of Wapping to the east of London. Wapping was then in so rural a district that on 24 July 1629 King Charles killed a stag in a garden of the village, having hunted it from Wanstead in Essex.[1] The alum factory, a large wooden building, had been put up in 1626 close to the Thames near the Tower of London without, it seems, any thought of its effect on the neighbourhood. The fumes spread over the parishes of St. Katherine's, St. Botolph's, Aldgate, and several others; the effluent poisoned their wells and killed the fish in their ponds and the complainants regarded it as 'an unsufferable and contagious annoyance'. In June, July, and August 1627 a series of petitions signed by a large number of citizens living in Whitechapel and surrounding parishes was addressed to the Justices of Middlesex and, finally, when nothing was done, to the King himself. The proprietors of the works maintained that it was no such nuisance, the complaints being a pretence stirred up by certain persons for their own ends. The College deputed six Fellows, Harvey among them, to make a personal examination of the site. Their report submitted on 23 July said that 'the works standing in that place must necessarily breed great annoyance both to the neere Inhabitants and by spreading vapours from thence issuying to many places more remote; and to all such passengers as ether by land or by water have occasion to frequent those parts, not only by their contynuall noysome savours to make all their habitations grievous and unpleasant, but also by their putrid quality to endanger their healthes'. On the strength of

---

[1] Stow's *Survey of London*, 1633, p. 402a.

this report it was ordered that the factory should be destroyed or removed, but the promoters delayed to do so on the pretext that if they ceased working there would be a shortage of the alum needed for dyeing, leather-making, and other purposes. The factory was still there on 12 December, when a fresh order for its removal was issued by the Privy Council.[1] The nuisance was no doubt abated in the end, for it was not mentioned by John Evelyn in his *Fumifugium*, 1661, as one of the sources of exhalations added to the existing 'Hellish and dismall Cloud of Sea-coal', which he sought to banish from London to improve the health of the people.

On 27 November 1627 an important meeting was held at the College, at which the President explained that owing to the death of Dr. Gwinne there was a vacancy among the Elects. He wished to propose that Sir Theodore de Mayerne should be elected, in spite of the fact that he was a foreigner, because he was one of those 'who could bring strength and dignity to the College'. He had already shown them many kindnesses, and the candour of his disposition and his favour at Court made him capable of rendering them distinguished services. It seems there was no precedent for this step, and the Statute against the election of foreigners had to be 'adapted by an exception', the operative phrase being 'unless he is the principal physician of the King'. This was agreed, and three Fellows were deputed to wait upon Sir Theodore at his house. Their prospective Elect, however, in a most courteous speech declined the great honour he was offered, his ties at Court making it impossible for him to give College affairs the close attention they merited. His intentions, he said, were good, but he was bound to refuse by reason of his more arduous duties.

The place of an Elect was not allowed to be vacant for more than forty days, so another meeting was called for 3 December. Having explained why de Mayerne had excused himself, the President proposed Dr. Harvey for the vacancy and he was unanimously elected. He was in the house at the moment and was at once 'examined according to custom and having been approved by all he took the oath of the College'. Harvey had now risen to the highest position he could attain short of the Presidential chair, and he was calculated to bring, like de Mayerne, 'strength and dignity' to the College. The honour perhaps gave him confidence in his resolution to brave the opinion of the world by presently publishing a book which was bound to give a severe shock to orthodoxy and might recoil on its author in personal enmity and abuse.

[1] Ibid., pp. 462–8.

On 18 December a special meeting was called to consider a letter just received from the King's Council conveying a request for the names of 'such a number of skilfull and learned Physitians' as might be thought necessary to deal with the sick and wounded marines and soldiers recently arrived at Plymouth, Portsmouth, and Southampton. The casualties were those resulting from a second unsuccessful attempt by the Duke of Buckingham to relieve the siege of the Protestant rebels at Rochelle in the Bay of Biscay, already long invested by the army of Louis XIII. Six Fellows were nominated for this service. Later in the day Harvey was among the Fellows who met to consider a letter received from the Bishop of Durham concerning an unqualified practitioner, John Lambe, who had been examined by the Bishop and had claimed that he made 'a poore Living by practise in Phisicke and Chirurgery, whereto by his long experience and practise he holdeth himself sufficient, affirming that he hath done many and great Cures in each kind'. The man's claims had come to the King's notice, and the opinion of the College was requested. This was no ordinary case of malpractice, for Lambe was already notorious. It was stated in the Annals:

The reputation of this man namely John Lambe had been on the lips of everyone for some time, due to his knowledge of magic, astrology and of other mystic sciences. For which reason he was esteemed by not a few women of rank and was supported on a generous scale at their expense. But this most wretched rascal had been known to the College previously on account of tricks and many shameful deeds. When at that very time by the command of some nobles he was held in prison, in order to free himself he pretended to be a physician to the Bishop of Durham, from whom he might have concealed the extent of his charges. Wherefore he was sent by the aforesaid Bishop to the College and as will be seen from the following examination was found to be alien from all erudition, or rather, completely stupid.

His examination was conducted in due form, but in the easiest way that could be thought of, and he was pronounced 'convict and guilty of all manner of insufficience and ignorance in this Faculty'. The actual questions and answers sent to the Bishop are worth reproducing as they give a vivid impression of the kind of problem that Harvey and his colleagues had to face in consequence of public gullibility.

Being asked of his beginning in Phisicke and of the meanes he came by his knowledge and whether his bringing up were that way or no, and required to read a little in a Latin Galen:

He answerereth: that he never had taken to that study, that he makes no profession thereof, but that he lives by making gentlemen merry: nor understandeth Latine.

Being asked by what signes he knowes a disease, and how he Cure it:

He answereth: He knoweth no signes but only as he is told by the party, and for cure that he is not wont to use anything but a few outward thinges and sometimes a little pulvis sanctus; which from the Apothecaries he hath Learned to be a Purge.

Being asked in Astrology what house he looketh into to know a disease, or the event of it, and how the Lord Ascendent should stand thereto:

He answereth: he lookes for the sixt house; which being diagnosed, he sayth he understandes nothing therin but what he hath out of Caliman:[1] and being asked what bookes he hath read in that Art, he saith he hath none but Caliman.

Being asked how he knowes an Apoplexe and how he cures it:

He answereth he knowes nothing unlesse he be told, nor doth use anything for cure but a few oyles and unguents and that for satisfaction only.

Being asked in Chirurgery, What is a Revulsion or Derivation:[2] He answereth he knoweth not the tearmes.

Being charged with the contradiction that in Colledge he confesseth himself ignorant and denyeth practise, whereas in his Examinacion by the Lord Bishop of Durham he made show of Long experience and sufficience and of having done many great cures as by his Lordshipps letters appeareth:

His answeare is that he did not professe any such thing to his Lordshipp and that he craves mercy of the Colledge: and that they would not be the Cause of his undoing.

Being pressed, from the notoriousness of his practise and publique fame that goes of him and the great resort made unto him.

He answereth it is without his desert, that he cannot hinder commers to him and that all he did was trifles, fooleryes, and babbles to gett a little mony.

[1] The name is given thus in the Annals; perhaps Sir Thomas Cadyman is meant. He was a papist practising in London and in 1630 was admitted a Licentiate of the College, being then a physician in ordinary to the Queen. His work, *De signis morborum tractatus*, has remained in manuscript (see Munk's *Roll*, 1861, pp. 185–6). On 24 March 1635/6 the King made a grant of privilege to de Mayerne and Cadyman for fourteen years 'for the sole exercise of a new way of distilling strong waters' and for making vinegar out of cyder, perry, and buck under a rent of £10 to the King. Two years later this venture became incorporated as the Distillers' Company (see Sir John Charles, *Lancet* (1955), ii. 990).

[2] *Revulsion*: 'The action or practice of diminishing a morbid condition in one part of the body by operating or acting upon another.' (*O.E.D.*) The meaning of *derivation* is very much the same.

RELATIONS WITH KING CHARLES

AFTER the death of King James there was certainly no break in Harvey's attendance at Court as the new King's physician extraordinary. Charles was still under the domination of Buckingham, but his character was so different from his father's that other changes began immediately after his accession. By nature he was austere and orderly, and love of ceremonial had been implanted in his heart by the months he had spent wooing the Infanta at the Spanish Court.

On his accession the broad Scots jokes and the drunken romps which had amused his father abruptly ceased. Babbling quarrels in ante-room and corridor were stilled. From the Gentlemen of the Bedchamber to the waiters at the sideboard, each man precisely knew where to be and when, at which table to take meat, when to attend prayers, when the King would rise, when sleep, when ride, when give audience and who, with staff of office in hand or napkin on arm, should walk before him or stand behind his chair. The formality of the Court on all official occasions was rigorous and extreme. The King, alone of all European princes, was served on bended knee, and when the French ambassador complained because neither chair nor stool was set for his wife—as was done for the English ambassador's wife in France—he was told that on official occasions no lady of the English Court except the Queen herself, not even the Princess Royal, was allowed to sit in the royal presence. King Charles lived, with no vulgar ostentation, but with elegance and ceremony.[1]

After the assassination of Buckingham at Portsmouth in August 1628, the King transferred his devotion to his wife, Queen Henrietta Maria, whom he had treated until then with marked coolness. From henceforth his love for the Queen was 'the strongest personal emotion in his life',[2] and her influence served to mitigate the formality of court life, which would otherwise have been intolerably severe. She became pregnant for the first time soon after Buckingham's disappearance from the scene, children and a happy family life gradually replacing the abnormal domination of the favourite.

Charles was 24 at his accession. He had been a sickly child, and remained small in stature, but he had outgrown his early troubles. He

---

[1] C. V. Wedgwood, *The King's Peace*, London, 1955, p. 55.   [2] Ibid., p. 73.

PLATE XVII

KING CHARLES I
Aged about 28, *c.* 1628, by Honthorst

was always shy and withdrawn from contacts with the ordinary life of his people, an impediment in his speech no doubt contributing to this isolation—though it was also, perhaps, a clue to understanding the nervous psychology which gave rise to it. Physically, however, he was tough, and he became an expert and intrepid horseman. His aesthetic faculties were highly developed, love for music, pictures, and all other forms of art and elegance being a leading characteristic. We hear nothing of his suffering from any of the chronic disorders which had plagued his father, and as far as we know Charles remained healthy to the end of his life. He therefore had little need to call on his physician for personal advice, but he had learnt Harvey's worth during James's last illness, and it is plain that friendship between the two men grew steadily throughout his reign. Cordial relations with his doctor were able to overcome the King's usual reticence; he could take a genuine interest in Harvey's scientific work, and Harvey in return derived much pleasure, as we shall see, in helping to increase his master's collections of drawings and paintings.

Under Harvey's influence King Charles took an active interest in medical matters, an illustration of this being the story of the young Irish Viscount, Hugh Montgomery. This incident took place some years later, probably about 1640, but it may suitably be introduced here. Montgomery, born about 1623, was the third Viscount, and later first Earl of Mount Alexander. As a child he had suffered a severe injury to his chest, and some years later the unusual condition which had resulted came to the King's knowledge. Harvey was then commissioned to find out about it. The story is best told in Harvey's own words as they appear in the English version (1653) of *De generatione animalium* (1651). He was discussing the question of the sensitivity of the viscera and of the blood itself, and related this history to show that even the heart does not have any sense of touch or pain.

A Noble young Gentleman, Son and Heire to the honorable the Vice-Count of Mountgomery in Ireland, when he was a childe, had a strange mishapp by an unexpected fall, causing a Fracture in the Ribs on the left side: the Bruise was brought to a Suppuration, whereby a great quantity of putrified matter was voided out, and this putrefaction gushed out for a long while together out of the wide wound. I deliver it from his own mouth, and the testimony of other creditable persons, who were eye-witnesses. This person of Honour, about the eighteenth, or nineteenth year of his Age, having been a Traveller in Italy and France, arrived at last at London: having all this time a very wide gap open in his Breast, so that you might see and touch his Lungs (as it was believed). Which, when it came to the late King Charles his ear, being related as a miracle, He presently sent me to the Young Gentleman, to inform Him, how the matter stood. Well, what happened? When I came neer him, and saw him a sprightly youth, with a good complexion, and habit of body, I supposed, some body or other had framed an untruth. But having saluted him, as the manner is, and declared unto him the Cause of my Visit, by the Kings Command, he discovered all to me, and opened the void part of his left side, taking off that small plate, which he wore to defend it against any blow or outward injury. Where I presently beheld a vast hole in his breast, into which I could easily put my three Fore-fingers and my Thumb: and at the first first entrance I perceived a certain fleshy part sticking out, which was driven in and out by a reciprocal motion, whereupon I gently handled it in my hand. Being now amazed at the novelty of the thing, I search it again and again, and having diligently enough enquired into all, it was evident, that that old and vast Ulcer (for want of the help of a skilled Physitian) was miraculously healed, and skinned over with a membrane on the Inside, and guarded with flesh all about the brimmes or margent of it. But that fleshy substance (which at the first sight I conceived to be proud flesh, and every body else took to be a lobe of the Lungs) by its pulse, and the differences or rythme thereof, or the time which it kept, (and laying one hand upon his wrest, and the other upon his heart) and also by comparing and considering his Respirations, I concluded it to be no part of the Lungs, but the Cone or Substance of the Heart; which an excrescent fungous Substance (as is usual in foul Ulcers) had fenced outwardly like a Sconce. The Young Gentleman's Man did by dayly warm injections deliver that fleshy accretion from the filth & pollutions which grew about it, and so clapt on the Plate; which was no sooner done, but his Master was well, and ready for any journey or excercise, living a pleasant and secure life.

Therefore, instead of an Account of the Business, I brought the Young Gentleman himself to our late King, that he might see, and handle this strange and singular Accident with his own Senses; namely, the Heart and its Ventricles in their pulsation, in a young and sprightly Gentleman, without offense to him: Whereupon the King himself consented with me, That the Heart is deprived of the Sense of Feeling. For the Party perceived not that we touched him at all, but meerly by seeing us, or by the sensation of the outward skin. We likewise took notice of the motion of his Heart; namely, that in the Diastole it was drawn in and retracted, and in the Systole came forth, and was thrust out; and that the Systole was made in the heart, when the Diastole was sensible in the wrest; and also that the proper motion of the heart is the Systole; and lastly, that the heart then beats upon the breast, and is a little prominent, when it is lifted upwards and contracted into it self.[1]

Montgomery was not seriously inconvenienced by having this permanent opening in his thorax, and lived a very active life, fighting first for the King's authority in Ireland and afterwards against Cromwell. He was ultimately forced to surrender to the Parliamentarians and was banished to Holland. At the Restoration he was appointed master of ordnance in Ireland, but died suddenly in 1663 at the age of about 40.

18

HARVEY AND SIR FRANCIS BACON

BY the year 1626, when Sir Francis Bacon died, Harvey had almost reached the zenith of his career, both as physician and as scientist. He must by then have completed most of the experimental work forming the basis of his treatise on the movement of the heart and the circulation of the blood. Being physician not only to the Court but also to many of the noble families and distinguished men of his time his position was fully established. Bacon had never been physically robust and we know from one of Harvey's remarks to Aubrey—'I have cured him'—that he had attended Bacon in one or more of his illnesses, for that is all that the term 'cured' signified at the time. A possible date for Harvey's attendance was during Bacon's attack of 'the stone', reported by Chamberlain on 6 March 1619, the patient having then been 'in greate pain for two or three days'.[2] It is also possible that Harvey was called in during the illlness reported by John Chamberlain in a letter dated 24 May 1617:

His infirmitie is given out to be the goute, and the greatest harme or sense he hath of it is in his heele and sometimes he takes pleasure to flout and play with his disease which he sayes hath chaunged the old covetous course and is become ambitious, for never begger had the gowte but he. But in truth the generall opinion is that he hath so tender a constitution both of body and minde that he will hardly be able to undergo the burthen of so much busines as his place requires.[3]

---

[1] *Anatomical Exercitations*, London, 1653, pp. 285–7.
[2] *Letters of John Chamberlain*, 1939, i. 220.
[3] Ibid., pp. 341–2.

Bacon had his own ideas about the treatment of gout, described in his *Sylva Sylvarum*, and had tried it on himself. This he gives as an example of treatment by a series of remedies applied in a certain order, none being of any use by itself. For gout he used first a poultice, then a bath or fomentation, and lastly a plaster. These remedies, he claimed, had seldom failed, having driven away the gout in twenty-four hours.[1] If Bacon called in the doctor and then told him what treatment to apply, patient and doctor were not likely to remain on very cordial terms. Aubrey, in his account of Bacon, wrote: 'He had a delicate, lively hazel eie. Dr. Harvey told me it was like the eie of a viper', and we can perhaps infer from this that Harvey did not like him. Harvey had certainly read Bacon's works, and in Exercise xxv of *De generatione animalium* he wrote: 'and hereupon (to use the expression of our most learned *Verulamius*) we shall proceed to our *second vintage*, collecting certain *Theorems* out of our former History'.[2] This reference suggests that he had read his Bacon with some care, and he may have resented some of the views he found there. We should value greatly Bacon's thoughts, not only on Harvey as a doctor, but also on his scientific work and attitude, but nowhere in his writings did he mention Harvey by name. We know, however, that Bacon was very critical of doctors and their methods of procedure. 'Medicine is a science', he wrote in *The Advancement of Learning*,[3] 'which hath been more professed than laboured, and yet more laboured than advanced, the labour having been, in my judgment, rather in circle than in progression. For I find much Iteration, but small Addition.' He went on to complain that 'the ancient and serious diligence of Hippocrates' had been neglected, and sought to emphasize the importance of 'Medicinall History'. He criticized the way in which anatomy was studied, saying there was much attention to structure and uniformity of parts, but not enough to diversities, to 'the seats or nestling of the tumours' nor to 'the footsteps and impressions of diseases'—in other words there was neglect of what would now be called pathology. Much might have been learnt from the careful recording of many men's observations in making anatomies of defunct patients, 'whereas now upon opening of bodies, they are passed over slightly and in silence'. This was, of course, written long before the publication of Harvey's *De motu cordis*, the general tenor of which would have answered much of this criticism.

Bacon complained also that doctors, even when they judged the disease to be incurable, made a kind of scruple and religion to go on treating the

---

[1] *Sylva Sylvarum, or, A Natural History*, 1627, p. 19.
[2] *Anatomical Exercitations*, 1653, p. 135.   [3] London, 1633, p. 172.

patient when they ought to be thinking of the best way to assuage the pains and agonies of death. He also thought that they neglected the use of the proper medicines in prescribing, always adding and changing and so 'frustrating the fruit of tradition'. Here he believed 'Empiriques and Old Women' were often happier in their cures because they abided more religiously by their known remedies. Doctors needed more exact knowledge in prescribing and showed no settled providence or project in their ministrations.

Bacon had several illnesses for which he sought medical help. In his essay 'Of Regiment of Health' he had written: 'Physicians are some of them so pleasing and conformable to the Humour of the Patient, as they press not the Cure of the Disease. And some others are so Regular, in proceeding according to Art, for the Disease, as they respect not sufficiently the condition of the Patient.' He advised that a patient should summon a doctor 'of a middle Temper, or if it may not bee found in one Man, combine two of either sort, and forget not to call as well the best acquainted with your Body, as the best reputed of for his Faculty'. Bacon was not, however, always successful in this choice himself. After one of his serious illnesses a doctor visited him several times. 'The first time', Bacon said, 'he told him his pulse was broken-paced; the next time it tripped; the third time it jarred a little.' He had nothing, he complained, but good words for his money.[1]

Bacon approved of vivisection of animals (though its inhumanity had been condemned by Celsus) because of the knowledge that could not be gained in any other way.

Although he valued traditional knowledge in prescribing, it is clear that we may regard Bacon as enlightened in his view of the potentialities of medical science, but that he was thoroughly dissatisfied with the attitude of the doctors. Nevertheless he was anxious to know what some of them thought of his ideas about science. To this end, as he recorded in a notebook, he proposed to introduce himself to Dr. Leonard Poe 'as for my health', but really, as we might say, 'to pick his brains'. His choice of Poe seems somewhat surprising, as he was one of those inferior people who practised in London without a licence from the College. He had a mandate from King James to be created M.D. of Cambridge, though there is no record of his having actually been admitted. He was, indeed, rather an empiric than a proper doctor, and perhaps that interested Bacon, as may be inferred from what has already been said on that matter. In any event Poe had influential patients among the nobility,

---

[1] *Works*, ed. Spedding, 1859, vii. 184.

including the Earls of Suffolk, Northampton, and Salisbury, and they tried to obtain his recognition by the College. In 1596 the College reluctantly gave him a licence to treat venereal, cutaneous, and calculous diseases, gout, and simple tertian ague, but for anything else he was bound to call in a member of the College. It was not until 1606 that these restrictions were removed, and ultimately in 1609, as physician to the Royal Household, he was admitted as a Fellow.[1] So here again we see Bacon distrusting the opinions of orthodoxy.

Bacon also thought of trying to interest two of the King's physicians in his schemes for research, naming Sir William Paddy and Dr. John Hammond. Paddy was certainly a distinguished doctor. He was knighted by James I, held many offices in the College, and was greatly esteemed by his colleagues, particularly by Sir Theodore de Mayerne. He did not, however, leave any writings by which we may judge the qualities of his mind. Hammond was a Fellow of the College, was physician to King James, and was one of those who attended Prince Henry in his illness,[2] but again we have no documentary evidence of his proficiency as a doctor. It seems likely that Bacon was looking particularly to the influential position of these two doctors for their help.

Harvey's somewhat contemptuous remarks about Bacon are well known through John Aubrey's report of his epigram: 'He writes philosophy like a Lord Chancellor.' Aubrey stated further that Harvey 'esteemed Bacon much for his wit and style, but would not allow him to be a great philosopher', and spoke of him in derision. There is no reason for disbelieving Aubrey's statements, and it is of interest to examine the possible grounds for the antipathy between these two great men, whose interests would seem at first sight to have much in common. Although Bacon made no reference in his writings to Harvey's work, he did criticize two of his greatest contemporaries, Galileo and Gilbert. 'These men', he said, 'spend their labour in working out some one experiment', and he regarded their work with suspicion 'because the experiment stops with these few discoveries, and many other things equally worthy of investigation are not discovered by the same means.' 'Gilbert', he said, 'has become a magnet, that is, he has ascribed too many things to that force.' Bacon meditating in his armchair allowed his mind to take a wide sweep. He liked to think that every discovery was only a link in a chain, the gradual unfolding of which should be a consciously controlled process. He was, as J. G. Crowther has said, interested primarily in 'the science

---

[1] Munk's *Roll*, 1861, i. 139–40.
[2] Ibid., p. 138.

of science'.[1] He wrote, indeed, as a responsible and experienced statesman, his vision scanning an horizon far beyond that of the specialist engrossed in a particular technical problem. His book *The Great Instauration*
was concerned with the establishment of scientific method so that mankind might be restored to its condition before the Fall. Man was to
re-establish his conquest of the Universe, and it was perhaps with this
grand object in view that Bacon sought power through politics, so that
he might organize science for the benefit of mankind, not neglecting the
moral difficulties arising from the responsibilities involved in the application of scientific discoveries.

Bacon's mind, in fact, exhibited a quality of universality such as we
cannot detect in the down-to-earth scientist working at his bench. He
believed that he was

born for the service of mankind and that he was specially qualified by his
nature for the study of Truth. If a man (he wrote) could succeed, not in
striking out some particular invention, however useful, but in kindling
a light in nature and bringing into sight all that is most hidden and
secret in the world—that man would be the benefactor indeed of the
human race—the propagator of man's empire over the universe, the
champion of liberty, the conqueror and subduer of necessities.

Harvey's mind did not work like this. He was more like Galileo and
Gilbert, engrossed in his particular problem, unaware of the possible
repercussions of what he was discovering. Indeed, we note that Harvey,
in spite of his advanced views on the circulation of the blood, was still
Aristotelian in his practice of medicine, and we can begin to see what he
meant by deriding Bacon for writing philosophy like a Lord Chancellor.
Harvey was in some ways the lesser man, his mind being narrower in
its scope. Yet his work has had an influence on scientific method wide
and universal enough to have satisfied Bacon, though the realization of
this was for posterity to witness. It could hardly have been foreseen
either by Bacon or by Harvey.

[1] J. G. Crowther, *Francis Bacon, The First Statesman of Science*, London, 1960, p. 10.

19

PROJECTED WORKS—*DE MOTU LOCALI ANIMALIUM* (1627)

I⊤ is well known from Aubrey's account of Harvey that he lost a large part of the notes he had made on his experimental work when his apartments in the Palace of Whitehall were raided by the parliamentary troops in 1642, his particular grief being expressed over the loss of his notes on insects. Harvey's own account of the incident is found in his book *De generatione animalium*, 1651:[1]

And while I am in this discourse, let the ingenious bear with me, (if being mindful of my great wrongs) I let slip a sigh or two, grounded upon this my misfortune: namely, that while I did attend upon our late Sovereign in these late distractions, and more than Civil Wars; (and that not by the Parliaments bare permission, but command) some rapacious hand or other not onely spoiled me of all my Goods; but also (which I most lament) have bereft me of my Notes, which cost me many years industry. By which means, many observations (especially those concerning the *Generation of Insects*) are lost and imbezelled, to the prejudice (I may boldly say it) of the Commonwealth of Learning.

Various references in Harvey's writings indicate that he had in mind to write a number of books or pamphlets on diverse subjects. One of the most interesting would have been his views on the effect his doctrine of the circulation would have on the practice of medicine. Other subjects were the lungs and respiration, quantitative measurements of the circulating blood, observations on the spleen, a work on movement and the structure of muscles, a tract on sex in animals, observations on the treatment of large tumours, a tract on nutrition, and a work on morbid anatomy.[2]

[1] *Anatomical Exercitations*, 1653, p. 418.
[2] The lost works were listed in Charles Goodall's *Historical Account of the College's Proceedings against Empirick's*, London, 1684, Ss. 1–2, as follows:

   I. A Practice of Physic conformable to his Thesis of the Circulation of the Blood.
   II. *Tractatus de pulmonum usu et moti; de eventilatione omni, aërisque necessitate et usu; de variis et differentibus organis hujus causa in animalibus factis.*
   III. *Tractatus de quantitate sanguinis in unoquoque aut singulis pulsationibus protrusa, et quando plus et quando minus, et qua de causa; itidem de circuitis causis, utilitatibus, et sanguinis arcanis.*
   IV. *Observationes de usu lienis.*

Of these works one title, *Observationes de motivis organis animalium*, did after all escape destruction, and it has recently been identified by Dr. Gweneth Whitteridge with the notes for a treatise entitled *De motu locali animalium*, preserved among the Sloane manuscripts in the British Museum.[1] This work had been noticed, but was supposed to be part of the notes for the Lumleian Lectures, though it bears the date 1627. Harvey had himself referred to it in chapter xvii of *De motu cordis*:

This truth about local movement; and the immediate organ of movement which is the contractile element in all movement of all animals in which a spirit of movement is primarily present; and the way the word νεῦρον is derived from νεύω, I nod, I contract; . . . all this would, I should imagine, become clear were I at some time or other allowed to give a demonstration from my observations about the organs of movement of animals and about the functional anatomy of their muscles.[2]

Though now correctly identified, the work is disappointing in that Harvey never carried out his intention of developing his notes to form a treatise on the movement of animals. It remained in the form of abbreviated jottings like those for the Lumleian Lectures already described, but has now been rendered intelligible by Dr. Whitteridge's transcription and translation into acceptable English.[3] Harvey had worked over his notes at intervals after 1627, but never made a final revision, though this is perhaps less regrettable in that the work contains little that can be called original. For the main part, the first seven chapters, consists of 'a rehearsal, with a certain amount of comment, of Aristotle's teaching concerning movement, particularly of animals. The last part is concerned with the structure and action of muscle and its parts. The eighth chapter,

---

V. *Exercitationes de respirationis causis, organis, et usu.*
VI. *Observationes de motivis organis animalium et de musculorum fabrica.*
VII. *Tractatus de animalium amore, libidine et coitu.*
VIII. *Observationes medicinales de herniæ carnosæ curatione, aliisque curationibus præter vulgi sententiam et methodum fœliciter peractis.*
IX. *De nutritionis modo.*
X. *Historia multorum animalium, præsertim insectorum, ab inconspicuis præ exiguitate principiis et seminibus (quasi atomis in aëre volitantibus) a ventis huc illuc sparsis ac disseminatis, ortorum.*
XI. *Anatomia medica ad medicinæ usum maxime accommodata, ubi ex multis dissectionibus corporum ægrotorum gravissimis et miris affectionibus confectorum; quomodo et qualiter partes interiores in situ, magnitudine, constitutione, figura, substantia, et reliquis accidentibus sensibilibus a naturali forma et apparentia permutentur, et quam variis modis et miris afficiantur, enarrare susciperet.*

[1] B.M. Sloane MS. 486, ff. 69–118.
[2] K. J. Franklin, *Movement of the Heart and Blood in Animals*, Oxford, 1957, p. 105.
[3] *De motu locali animalium*, 1627, edited, translated, and introduced by Gweneth Whitteridge, D.Phil., F.S.A., Cambridge, 1959. Henceforward cited as G. W.

"Of the things that are to be known about muscle", links the two parts together, and gives an incomplete summary of the second half of the work'.[1] Besides Aristotle, Galen is the authority chiefly quoted by Harvey, and he is also indebted to his old teacher, Fabricius, though the references to his works on the muscles show that they were often in disagreement.

Since Harvey was so largely using ancient authority, his arguments tend to be deductive from first principles, but he also used induction from observed facts, as when showing, contrary to accepted opinion, that tendon or sinew is not an essential constituent of muscle, the smaller muscles in particular consisting entirely of contractile tissue.[2]

Twice Harvey quoted experimental evidence. By the first experiment he anticipated by forty years Robert Hooke's demonstration to the Royal Society for a different purpose of artificial respiration applied to a dog in 1667:[3]

... a cock's head off, the arteries being ligatured and artificial ventilation being given, movements are seen to persist but they are as the movements of men in delirium and useless and convulsive and irregular as those of drunkards. Embryos and animals at first walk delicately and practise the discipline of local movement just as a man who is learning to play upon the lute is always guarding mistakes; their gait is vacillating, ambling paces.[4]

The second mention of an experiment repeated the description of movements in a decapitated chicken, and added:

NB however WH a frog with its heart excised exhibits movement, but if the brain be injured remains motionless. Is this from the spirits which remain within it as life stays in an eel?

WH muscles are as it were like separate living creatures which when they are in action pulsate so to speak, just as Aristotle describes the heart as like a separate living creature; the brain is like the *mester del choro*, the choir-master.[5]

As a whole, Harvey's treatise is an enlightened and interesting account of the nervous impulse, muscle, and movement as it was known in the seventeenth century, but it has been called unexciting because, compared with the two works on the circulation and generation, it lacks the spice of originality. Yet it has other qualities to recommend it. Harvey always had a command of apt illustrations derived from experience; a good example of this follows his thoughts on tonic action of muscle:

---

[1] G. W., p. 3.   [2] Ibid., p. 81.   [3] *Philosophical Transactions*, 1667, ii. 539.
[4] G. W., pp. 103–5.   [5] Ibid., p. 111.

Because all things are moved either by pushing or pulling, all animals progress either by traction, as insects, or by propulsion, or partly by traction and partly by propulsion, or by tonic movement as birds, the water-snake and the spider; W-I divinely sent.

While I was pondering these things I saw a spider as if divinely sent borne through the air by an invisible thread spun from its own body, yet it held on to the filament with its feet in tonic movement as Mr. Parson's buzzard on a fowl.[1]

The reference to 'Mr. Parson's buzzard' suggests that Harvey, on one of his many visits to Newmarket with the King, had been an interested spectator of falconry on the Heath, where this sport was specially favoured. Lord Brain has noted that in his following remarks on balanced actions Harvey came 'as near as unaided observation could get' to the idea of the inhibition of antagonistic muscles.[2]

Harvey's notes include a number of clinical observations, though his cryptic style sometimes prevents full appreciation of his intention. There is, for instance, an interesting attempt to classify different kinds of movement by a list of examples; these include 'a duck; a crane; crow; Jew of Malta; ambling Turk; trotting servile; dancing; tripping on the toe, cork shoes; stamping the feet', and a few others that are unintelligible.[3] It is suggested that 'Jew of Malta' refers to the gait of an actor performing the part in Marlowe's play; that 'trotting servile' means a servant running beside his master's horse, or, alternatively, the gait of Parkinsonism; that 'tripping on the toe, cork shoes' means walking on high corkheeled shoes, and suggests spastic paraplegia.

In chapter 19 Harvey made a list of thirteen different kinds of distortion of movements, derived, according to Dr. Whitteridge, from Erastus's disputation *De convulsione*. Among these is: '3. Convulsion: in epileptics, hysterics and children; in strabismus of the eyes; risus sardonicus, uncle William Halke dying.'[4] William Halke (or Hawke) was one of the family of Harvey's mother, probably living in Canterbury or the neighbourhood, and the reference suggests that he may have been called down to the country to see his relative in a critical condition, for the *risus sardonicus*, a peculiar sardonic grin produced by involuntary contraction of the facial muscles, is characteristic of tetanus.

Another kind of distortion is: '6. Twinges, palpitation, convulsion from twitches accompanied by slight pain and pricking, or by none. Δ W-I particularly Mr. Rant's eye.'[5] Elsewhere Harvey referred again to

---

[1] Ibid., p. 29.   [2] *Harveian Oration*, 1959, p. 10.   [3] G.W., p. 51.
[4] Ibid., p. 125.   [5] Ibid., p. 125.

'Mr. Rant's eyelid' making convulsive movements, and to movement 'in Rant's eyelids and in the *panniculus carnosus* [the subcutaneous muscle of horses and other animals] after excoriation there is contraction to-wards the centre'. Lord Brain interprets this as meaning that Rant had blepharospasm or facial myoclonia.[1] An unexplained reference occurs in relation to co-ordination of the muscles: 'Δ making a picture or circle, in so far as it is art, or squaring a circle. Mr. Blagrate's dog.'[2] It would be a clever dog indeed that could square a circle.

Another reference shows that Harvey was familiar in a number of patients with the painful effect of rupturing even a few fibres in a calf muscle, for he asked: 'If one fibre is ruptured do pains and maladies ensue as is the case when a nerve is punctured? or does limping follow? Mr. Mapes [probably Harvey's surgical colleague at St. Bartholomew's], Sir Roger Palmer [master of the household to Charles I], Sir Don Germin [Michael Jermin, or Germin, D.D., chaplain to Charles I] my Lord Totnes's barber Will.'[3]

Even though 'unexciting', Harvey's projected monograph, had it been properly developed, would have been an important landmark in the history of the physiology of muscle and nerve.

20

KNOWLEDGE OF THE CIRCULATION OF THE BLOOD BEFORE HARVEY

IN 1666 Dr. John Smith, a graduate of Brasenose College, Oxford, admitted as a Fellow of the College of Physicians in 1672, published a book entitled Γηροκομία Βασιλικὴ *King Solomon's Portraiture of Old Age*, in which he attempted a laborious paraphrase of the first six verses of Ecclesiastes xii. When he came to the sixth verse: 'Or ever the silver cord be loosed, or the golden bowl be broken, or the pitcher be broken at the Cistern', he was carried away by enthusiasm for Harvey's bio-logical discoveries and was determined to fit them into his interpretation of the mystical words of King Solomon. Verses 5 to 7 of Ecclesiastes i were ready to his hand:

The Sun ariseth, and the Sun goeth down and hasteth to the place

---

[1] Loc. cit., p. 16.   [2] G. W., p. 147.   [3] Ibid., p. 85.

where he arose; The Wind goeth toward the South, and turneth about unto the North, it whirleth about continually, and the Wind returneth according to its Circuits; All the Rivers run into the Sea, yet the Sea is not full; unto the place from whence the Rivers come, thither they return again.

Clearly, he thought, this description of 'the Circulations of the greater World' was intended to express those of the lesser:

The Blood wherein is the Life of Man passeth about the Body continually, and returns according to its circuits; the streams thereof run into the Fountain, which is never full, unto the place from whence they come, thither they return again; which is by the Instruments before mentioned thus performed. The *Vena Cava* containing much blood in its cavity, near the *basis* of the Heart, on the right side, doth gently pass it into the right Ventricle of the Heart, which is dilated in its *Diastole*, for its reception, and immediately thereupon contracting it self in its *Systole* (the three pointed Portals hindering the passage back again into the *Cava*) it must necessarily thrust the blood through the open passage of the *Vena Arteriosa* (where the sigmoidal Portals hindering its return) it must pass through the Strainer of the Lungs, and so be received into the branches of the *Arteria Venosa* (and thereby brought into the left Ventricle of the Heart, where again it is with violence pulsed forth into the *Aorta* (the portals here as before always hindering its regress) by the branches of which Artery it is carried to all parts of the Body to enliven them, which work being done, what remains is received into the Capillaries of the Veins in the several parts, whence it passeth of its own accord naturally towards its Center, from the lesser into the greater branches of the Veins, and consequently at last into the great Trunk of the *Cava*, from whence it is recommitted into the right Ventricle of the Heart, to be chased the Foyl.[1] This is the true Doctrine of the excellency and motion of the blood, and of the use of the Heart, and the parts appertaining thereunto; all which were perfectly known to *Solomon*, as will abundantly appear anon, in the explication of the symptoms we are now about. Yet it pleased the Lord that this knowledge should with the possessor of it, sink into dust and darkness; where it lay buried for the space of 2500 years at the least, till it was retrieved thence from by the wisdom and industry of that incomparable, and forever to be renowned Dr. *William Harvey*, the greatest honour of our Nation, and of all Societies of which he was a Member, who stands and ever will do, with the highest note of Honour in the Calendars both of Physicians and Philosophers, and it were but justice to put him with the same eminence

---

[1] Foyl = the track of a hunted animal; so 'to chase the Foyl' is to run over the same track a second time, thus baffling the hounds (*N.E.D.*).

into that of the Church, since he hath Contributed more to the understanding of this, and many other places of Scripture, than all that ever
undertook that Charge . . . By the Pitcher therefore we must understand
the true and proper conceptacle of the Blood, namely the *Veins*, which
throughout the whole body serve only as a vessel, to contain that noble
Liquor, and carry it back again to the Fountain. . . . Now the *Fountain*
can be no other than the right Ventricle of the Heart, for this is yet more
strictly the Fountain of life, and forge of the vital spirits . . . but this
natural Course doth not continue for ever, for this Pitcher is but an
earthen Vessel, and doth not so often go to the Fountain, but at last it
comes broken home. This breaking of the Pitcher here (which is the
Symptom of Old Age just upon the point of death) is the failing of the
Veins.[1]

Harvey did not live to read this tribute to his achievements and probably was not acquainted with the author, who did not become a Candidate at the College until two years after his death; but he would have
appreciated Dr. Smith's fundamentally accurate translation of the facts
of the circulation into allegorical terms.

Smith was not the only one to claim that the doctrine of the circulation
was known to antiquity, the knowledge having been credited to ancient
Chinese and Hindu civilizations; if this were true it would be odd that
Plato and Aristotle did not have a more accurate conception of the heart
and its function than is found in their writings.[2] Plato, influenced by
Empedocles of Agrigentum and writing in the fourth century B.C.,
described the heart in the *Timæus* as protected by the lungs and as being
the origin of the blood vessels (φλέβες); though he did not distinguish
between arteries and veins, he named the main arterial channel the
'aorta' (ἀορτή), by which, he said, the blood was forcibly distributed to
all the limbs—τὸ αἷμα κατὰ πάντα τὰ μέλη σφοδρῶς περιφέεσθαι. At an
earlier date, however, the term ἀορτή had denoted the lower branches of
the trachea, that is, the bronchi, this presumably being connected with
the belief that the arterial system contained only air. Plato's sentence,
quoted above, does not suggest that he subscribed to this delusion,
though his pupil Aristotle did so and carried it on. In his early study of
medicine Harvey had been profoundly influenced, through his teachers
at Padua, by Aristotle, and was always reluctant to find him at fault, yet
in his Lumleian Lecture on the heart he was moved to make the emphatic

---

[1] *The Pourtract of Old Age*, second edition, 1666, pp. 232–8.

[2] This section on pre-Harveian ideas of the vascular system owes much to H. P. Bayon's
'William Harvey, Physician and Biologist: His Precursors, Opponents and successors',
Annals of Science, iii–iv. 1938–9.

protest already mentioned (p. 96) about the three ventricles of the heart.

The distinction between veins and arteries was first made by Praxagoras of Cos (*c.* 320 B.C.), though he thought the function of arteries was to carry air. Erasistratus of Alexandria, a little later, shared this belief, explaining the issue of blood from a severed artery as due to blood passing through free anastomoses from the veins to fill the vacancy caused by the arterial lesion.

The views of Hippocrates of Cos at the turn of the fourth century B.C. are difficult to interpret, since his reputed writings are probably the work of several writers. Passages can be found expressing different attitudes, and any claim that Hippocrates believed in a circulatory system should be taken with caution.[1] A passage from a Hippocratic writing has been translated as follows:

The vessels communicate with one another, and the blood flows from one into another. I do not know where the commencement is to be found, for in a circle you can find neither commencement nor end, but from the heart the arteries take their origin, and through these vessels the blood is distributed to all the body, to which it gives warmth and life; these are the sources of human nature and are like rivers that purl through the body and supply the human body with life; the heart and the vessels are perpetually moving, and we may compare the movement of the blood with courses of rivers returning to their sources, after a passage through numerous channels.

This was mentioned by William Wotton in his *Reflections upon Ancient and Modern Learning,* 1694,[2] but he concluded that although Hippocrates 'did suppose the Blood to be carried round the body by *a constant accustomed Motion* . . . he did not know what this *constant accustomed Motion* was, and believed it as an Hypothesis only'. This seems to be a fair assessment of the position.

So matters remained until the time of Galen in the second century A.D. Galen, the Graeco-Roman physician, was Harvey's true 'father in science', because he believed in the value of experiment in the elucidation of problems in physiology. His conception of the movements of the blood, contained in scattered passages of his writings, has been summarized by Bayon as follows:

The heart attracted the blood by the diastole or dilatation like a magnet

[1] This claim was made by J. A. vander Linden (1609–64) in his *Hippocrates, De circulatione sanguinis, exercitationes xxvii,* Leyden, 1659–63.

[2] Second edition, 1697, p. 226. The passage is a mosaic of irrelevant extracts.

attracts iron; venous and arterial blood were contained in separate and distinct vessels and were in constant oscillatory motion; the venous blood was alimentary and flowed to the limbs to nourish them and the arterial blood was spiritual and the source of vitality. Air was inspired through the trachea, went to the arteries through the lungs, and thus moderated the heat produced by the heart; then the air was breathed out after having performed its function of cooling the blood. Heart and lung formed one system. The lung, however, was frothy and light; and the heart was not really muscular, since it neither possessed nerves like other muscles nor could be moved at will, but consisted of ventricles, separated by a septum, in which certain pores (*foramina*) occurred, affording a direct communication between right and left ventricles, across which the venous blood passed for the purpose of being purified. Three varieties of vessels were distinguished—veins arising from the liver, arteries from the heart, and nerves from the brain. (It has been seen that Aristotle taught that the nerves arose from the heart.) The venous blood was produced in the liver and then perfected by mixing with three spirits, the natural arising from the liver, the vital from the heart, and the animal from the brain. The venous blood nourished the various organs by an irrigatory flow, but was continually oscillating, or flowing and ebbing, by the action of its own vitality. The pulse was caused by a special property, *vis pulsifica*, which, originating in the heart, crept along the artery walls.

Galen's futile experiment on arterial pulsation is referred to in considering Harvey's work (see p. 179). It has been suggested with some degree of probability that Galen saw the openings, particularly well developed in the heart of the ungulates, of the vessels supplying the substance of the septum, and interpreted these as pores through which the cavities of the two ventricles communicated.

After Galen's time his teaching acquired an almost divine authority, so that things stood still for fourteen hundred years. This was partly attributable to the difficulty of disseminating and establishing new doctrines before the invention of printing. Certain theoretical advances had been made in the thirteenth century by an Arabian physician, Ibn an-Nafîs, working in Cairo. Although he carried out neither dissections nor experiments on animals, he somehow came to support the view that there were no apertures in the ventricular septum and that there was a pulmonary circulation. His writings are said to have been translated into Latin and published in Venice in 1547 (a fact which Bayon was unable to verify), and yet they remained for the most part unknown. It is just possible that they came to the notice of the Spanish physician and theologian Miguel Servetus, who first attempted to break through the religious prejudices and scholasticism of the Middle Ages. The contribution made by Servetus, born in Aragon in 1511, has attracted much attention in recent times, because it seems that he certainly had some idea of a pulmonary circulation, his views being contained in a book printed in 1533. Unfortunately his ideas were embedded in a theological treatise, *Christianismi restitutio*, intended to effect a reformation of the Christian religion. This inevitably attracted the attention of the Catholic Inquisition; at Calvin's instigation Servetus was prosecuted and ultimately burned at the stake. The 500 copies of his book were almost totally destroyed. Only three copies are now known, and it is most improbable that the views of Servetus can have had any influence on sixteenth-century knowledge of the circulation, or that his work ever came to the notice of Harvey or other medical writers in the seventeenth century. It is just possible that Rabelais may have been acquainted with Servetus, whose views could have been reflected in references found in *Pantagruel* (1533), but again this, even if true, could hardly have affected general medical opinion.

The same may be said of the work done by Leonardo da Vinci in the latter part of the fifteenth century, since he made investigations for his own satisfaction only. He had, moreover, used as his guide for dissection the popular anatomical handbook of Mondinus first written in 1315, when Galen's teaching was the accepted standard. Leonardo's notebooks show, however, that he made remarkably accurate drawings of the human heart, with its valves and blood-vessels, and that he satisfied himself by experiment that reflux of blood into the left ventricle was completely prevented by the aortic valves. Yet it cannot be shown from his writings that he ever arrived at a clear conception of a pulmonary, or of a general, circulation of the blood, and his contributions to a more accurate description of the anatomy of the heart remained locked up in the privacy of his notebooks.

By 1521 some stirrings of doubt as to the truth of Galen's dogmas had begun to appear. In a work published in that year Berengario da Carpi said that the pores in the interventricular septum were only to be seen with the greatest difficulty, though he did not take the bolder step of denying their existence. Towards the middle of the sixteenth century Andreas Vesalius, working at Padua with his draughtsman, Calcar, initiated a momentous advance in knowledge of anatomy by the publication of *De fabrica humani corporis* (Of the Structure of the Human Body) in 1543. This forms the basis of modern anatomical standards, being founded on careful dissection and observation of the whole human cadaver; yet again Vesalius could not, or did not dare to, shake himself free from Galenic doctrines, though he certainly doubted whether much blood could find a passage through the interventricular septum. Physiology did not keep pace with anatomical advance, and Vesalius missed the opportunity of forestalling the discoveries made by Harvey in the next century. The defect was partially compensated, however, as already mentioned in describing Harvey's Lumleian Lectures (see p. 106), by Realdus Columbus of Cremona, who was assistant to Vesalius and deputized for him during his frequent absences from Padua. Columbus published in 1559 his book *De re anatomica*, which is a critical commentary on the work of Vesalius rather than an imitation. He is said to have been something of a braggart, but at least he formed a definite idea of a pulmonary circulation with aeration of the blood, having demonstrated the presence of bright red blood in the pulmonary vein. There is no evidence that Columbus derived his knowledge from Servetus, and he must be credited with having made the discovery for himself and with having described it better than Servetus had done, basing his conclusions on dissection and experiment.

Next in the time-sequence came Andreas Cæsalpinus of Pisa and Rome, also already mentioned. He is believed to have been a pupil of Columbus, who occupied the professorial chair at Pisa in the years 1545–9. Cæsalpinus was at once physician, naturalist, and philosopher, and was the author of many books. Exaggerated claims have sometimes been made for him as anticipator of Harvey's discoveries. Bayon's careful examination of the evidence shows that, although he had some knowledge of the pulmonary circulation, derived in all probability from Columbus, he had no idea of a general circulation, still believing that the blood was distributed to the body by the vena cava and its branches. He also stated that part of the blood was transmitted through the interventricular septum from one ventricle to the other. When he used the word *circulatio*, he understood it 'to mean a to-and-fro movement like that occurring in chemical distillation, thus combining Aristotelian and Galenical doctrines'. Full examination of the beliefs held by Cæsalpinus was needed, because his claim to be 'discoverer of the circulation of the blood' before Harvey has been maintained with some heat, especially by his compatriots. It is quite clear, however, that this claim cannot be sustained.

Harvey himself referred many times to Columbus and actually quoted his words in discussing the systole and diastole of the heart.[1] He also admitted the claim by Columbus to have invented the theory of a pul-

[1] *Prelectiones*, p. 265.

monary circulation, but nowhere did he mention the name of Cæsalpinus though willing, as he always was, to admit any just claim made for his predecessors.[1]

In 1591 the philosopher Giordano Bruno (1550–1600), following Cæsalpinus, had referred in print[2] to the circular movement of the blood, having already written in a manuscript of 1590 (not published until 1864) the sentence: *sanguis enim qui in corpore animalis in circulum movetur*; but this was a philosophical concept related to the idea of the circle as a symbol of the Creator of the Universe, the perfect being, rather than a statement of a physiological fact. Bruno could scarcely have played any part in influencing Harvey's mind, as has been suggested.[3]

Harvey was probably not aware that any claim of priority was likely to be made on behalf of the learned Servite friar Pietro Paolo Sarpi (1552–1623), yet this has been from time to time advanced. Usually known as 'Father Paul', Sarpi was a profound theologian and student of science, and is acknowledged to have been the greatest Italian of his time. His close friend and biographer, the Friar Fulgenzio Micanzio, stated that Sarpi carried out many dissections of animals and discovered, among other things, the valves in veins. Micanzio asserted roundly that anything new concerning the anatomy of the eye or valves in veins, published by Fabricius in 1603, was communicated to him by Sarpi.[4] There is no doubt that Sarpi's knowledge of scientific subjects was wide, and that he was friendly with Fabricius, who was responsible for treating him surgically in 1607. As official theologian to the Republic of Venice, Sarpi became embroiled in quarrels with the Papacy, and in that year he was attacked by assassins, it was believed at the instigation of the Pope. He was severely wounded, and Fabricius, summoned from Padua to attend him, removed a stiletto which was embedded in his maxilla.[5]

The claim for Sarpi's prior knowledge of the circulation seems to have been originated by Jan de Wale (Walaeus) in his first letter to Bartholin, dated 1640 but first printed in full in 1660 with Harvey's *De motu cordis*.[6]

---

[1] The name of Cæsalpinus has sometimes been supposed to occur at the bottom of p. 75 verso of the *Prelectiones*, but this has been recognized by Dr. Poynter as a reference to Julius Cæsar Arantius (see W. Pagel, *Journal of the History of Medicine* (1957), xii. 150, 152 n.).

[2] *De monade, numero et figura*, Frankfort, 1591.

[3] Felix Marti-Ibáñez, *International Record of Medicine* (1957), clxx. 310. See also D. W. Singer, *Giordano Bruno, His Life and Thought*, New York, 1950, pp. 196–7.

[4] *The life of Father Paul, of the Order of the Servie. Translated out of Italian by a person of Quality*, London, 1651, pp. 29–31.   [5] Ibid., pp. 114–26.

[6] In Harvey, *Exercitationes anatomicae*, London, 1660, p. 228. The two letters to Bartholin were first printed in the Padua edition of 1643, but in a shorter form, and the passages concerning Sarpi were not included.

This source was quoted by Sir George Ent in his enlarged 'Address to Harvey' printed in the second edition of his *Apologia pro circuitione sanguinis*, or defence of Harvey.[1] Ent added that a copy of Harvey's book was taken by Sir Henry Wotton when he returned to Venice as Ambassador from the Court of King James, and given to Sarpi. The notes then made by Sarpi for his own use were found after his death by his heirs, who supposed that they represented his own work on the circulation. Ent had forgotten that Sarpi died in 1623, five years before the publication of *De motu cordis*, so that this book cannot have been the source. It is conceivable, however, that Harvey might have given Wotton some notes of his lectures before 1623, which could have been passed on to Sarpi by the Revd. William Bedell, chaplain to the Ambassador and a close friend of Sarpi. Wotton, in a letter reporting to King Charles, said of Bedell that 'this is the man whom Padre Paulo took (I may say) into his soul; with whom he did communicate the inwardest thoughts of his heart'.[2] The suggestion was made in 1879 by Dr. T. Wharton Jones, who claimed Bedell as his ancestral kinsman.[3] The story assumes that Wotton and Harvey were acquainted, which may well be true, but there is no documentary evidence connecting them.

Bayon was probably correct in believing that Sarpi's first-hand knowledge of the valves in veins and his undoubted association with Fabricius was the beginning of the story,[4] this being later magnified into the unjustifiable statement that he had anticipated Harvey in formulating the doctrine of the circulation. Sarpi's biographer makes no such claim, and it seems to be very unlikely that it has any foundation in fact.

In the foregoing pages the ideas about the movement of the blood current before Harvey's time have been sketched in outline, and it is plain that to his contemporaries in England in 1615 Galen was still the authority whose teachings were generally accepted. Any serious departure from him was a dangerous heresy, and their thoughts would not have run even in terms of a pulmonary circulation, news of which had not yet penetrated to most teachers of anatomy.

Nevertheless, later gossip in College halls at Oxford would sometimes

---

[1] Ent, *Apologia pro circuitione sanguinis*, London, 1685, on p. B3 verso.

[2] See E. S. Shuckburgh, *Two Biographies of William Bedell, Bishop of Kilmore*, Cambridge, 1902, p. 5.

[3] T. Wharton Jones, 'Lectures on the Circulation of the Blood', *Lancet* (1879), 25 Oct., 22 Nov., pp. 601, 751. Wotton did take a book to Venice in June 1610 entitled *De modo agendi Jesuitarum*, which he gave to Sarpi (*Letters of Father Paul*, London, 1693, p. 172). Possibly some confusion arose between *De motu* and *De modo*.

[4] See also P. Flourens, *Histoire de la découverte de la circulation du sang*, Paris, 1857, pp. 125 ff.

try to filch credit for his discoveries from Harvey and to assign it elsewhere with only the slenderest of justification. Thus John Aubrey recorded without comment one conversation of this kind, which concerned
a mathematician and philosopher, Walter Warner (or Warren). According to Aubrey:

Mr. Warner did tell Dr. Pell [1611–85, mathematician], that when
Dr. Harvey came out with his Circulation of the Blood, he did wonder
whence Dr. Harvey had it: but comeing one day to the earle of Leicester,
he found Dr. Harvey in the hall, talking very familiarly with Mr.
Prothero, to whom Mr. Warner had discoursed concerning this exercita-
tion of his *De Circulatione Sanguinis*, and made no question but Dr. Harvey
had his *hint* from Prothero. Memorandum:—Dr. Pell sayes that Mr.
Warner rationated demonstratively by beates of the pulses that there
must be a circulation of the blood.[1]

Anthony Wood embellished this story by adding that Warner 'also
did make it appear (so used to say Dr. G. Morley, sometime B. of Win-
ton, and Dr. John Pell) in a MS. of his composition, that the Blood in
a body did circulate, which he communicating to the immortal Harvey,
he took his first hint thence concerning that matter, which he afterwards
published as the first inventor'.[2]

When Harvey's evidence for his doctrine comes to be examined in the
next chapter it will be seen that he could afford to ignore rumours of
this kind, which were bound to die of inanition if left unnoticed.

21

EXERCITATIO ANATOMICA DE MOTU CORDIS (1628)

IF ever a book of outstanding importance to mankind crept quietly into
the world, it surely was Harvey's *Exercitatio anatomica de motu cordis et
sanguinis in animalibus*, published at Frankfort in 1628, when its author
was 50 years of age. The exact date of composition cannot be determined,
since Harvey had already 'for nine years and more' been promulgating
his views about the circulation of the blood in his anatomical lectures
and demonstrations at the College of Physicians. If, however, the book

---

[1] Aubrey, *Brief Lives*, ed. A. Clark, 1898, ii. 291.
[2] Wood, *Athenæ Oxonienses*, second edition, London, 1721, i. 461.

was finished by 1627, some thought would still be needed before it was put into print. Harvey was never eager to publish his work to the world, but this particular book he knew was soundly argued, complete in itself and of very great importance as a leap forward in man's knowledge of his own body, that is, in human physiology. He would naturally discuss its publication with his friends, and one of these was Robert Fludd the Rosicrucian, whose character has already been described.

Fludd had written a number of books and from 1617 onwards had always given them for publication to Johann Theodore de Bry of Frankfort. When de Bry died in 1626 the business passed to a young Englishman, William Fitzer, who then took over de Bry's stock and publishing interests. Fitzer was born about the year 1600 at Broadway, five miles from Worcester, the family having been established in the district for a long time. He was educated at the King's School, Worcester, and in 1616 was apprenticed for seven years to a London bookseller, Thomas Man; he was granted the freedom of the Stationers' Company in 1624, and soon afterwards moved to Frankfort. In 1625 he married de Bry's daughter, and so, as a member of the family, naturally succeeded to the publishing business at his father-in-law's death a year later.[1]

Fludd, by the esoteric nature of his books, had laid himself open to the charge of practising forbidden arts. His belief in the efficacy of the 'weapon salve' already described added to these suspicions, and a pamphleteer writing in 1631 said of him that he had 'beene written against for a Magician, and I suppose this to be one cause why he hath printed his bookes beyond the Seas'.[2] But Fludd had better reasons than this. It seems likely that he advised Harvey also to employ Fitzer, partly, perhaps, because of the larger public to be reached by a book published abroad, but also because Fludd himself had found he could get better terms there than at home. Of his own books he said: 'I sent them beyond the seas because our home-born Printers demanded of me five hundred pounds to print the first volume and to find the cuts in copper; but beyond the seas, it was printed at no cost of mine, and that as I could wish. And I had 16 copies sent me over, with 40 pounds in gold as my unexpected gratuity for it.' These arguments would weigh with Harvey, and he decided to send his manuscript to Frankfort for Fitzer to deal with as he thought best. This decision was undoubtedly right if Harvey

---

[1] These facts are derived from the researches of Dr. E. Weil, published in 'William Fitzer, the Publisher of Harvey's *De motu cordis*, 1628', *The Library* (1943), xxiv. 142–64.

[2] William Foster, in his *Hoplocrismaspongus: or, A Sponge to wipe away the Weapon-Salve*, London, 1631, 4°, p. 37.

PLATE XVIII

EXERCITATIO
ANATOMICA DE
MOTV CORDIS ET SAN-
GVINIS IN ANIMALI-
BVS,
GVILIELMI HARVEI ANGLI,
Medici Regii, & Professoris Anatomiæ in Col-
legio Medicorum Londinensi.

FRANCOFVRTI,
Sumptibus GVILIELMI FITZERI.
ANNO M. DC. XXVIII.

TITLE-PAGE OF *DE MOTU CORDIS*, 1628

wished to achieve a wider dissemination of his views than could be expected from publication in London, but in other ways it was unfortunate. If Fitzer received a manuscript draft of the book written by Harvey himself, difficulty must have arisen over deciphering his illegible hand. Distance and the state of war on the Continent would prevent easy communication between author and publisher, and it is clear from the number of misprints in the first edition that Harvey can have seen no proofs. When he did first see the finished book he must have been appalled at the number of mistakes it contained; a leaf of 126 *errata* was inserted in part of the edition (even so, only half the number found to be necessary by the editor of the *Opera omnia* of 1766), but most surviving copies of the book do not contain it. Another misfortune was Fitzer's frugal mind. It would admittedly have been difficult for him to appreciate the importance of this apparently insignificant book, and he therefore economized on the production. He had it printed in a small mean type on paper of such poor quality that in most copies it has turned dark and crumbled. Only fifty-five copies are known to have survived to the present day, scattered through the libraries of the Old and New Worlds, and many of these will disintegrate in the course of time unless great care is taken for their preservation. Fortunately Fitzer did have a few copies printed on thick paper of good quality, such as those now in the Hunterian Collection in the University of Glasgow, and at Magdalene College, Cambridge, but of these very few are known.

The two engraved plates with which Harvey illustrated his remarks on valves in veins were not original. The tract by Fabricius entitled *De venarum ostiolis*, published in 1603 and again in 1624, contained the first adequate illustration of the valves. The artist who engraved Harvey's plates clearly did so with the print from Fabricius before him, and he followed it very closely. A man's forearm is represented arranged as for blood-letting. The hand grasps a barber's pole, and the upper arm is bound with a tourniquet so as to distend the veins below. Harvey did not make any acknowledgement of his debt, but Fabricius's work was probably so well known to his contemporaries that none was needed.

Harvey's book, in the mean form Fitzer chose to give it, consists of only thirty-four leaves (sixty-eight pages of type) after the title-page and address to King Charles. Harvey was not so prolix as were many contemporary writers and his brevity contributed to give his book an unimportant appearance, though Fitzer did try to overcome this by providing a handsome title-page with his large and showy device occupying at least half of it. The publication of the book was announced in the

Ostermesskatalog for 1628 and it was issued in the autumn of that year at the price of 6 schilling 2 pfennig.[1]

It is characteristic of Harvey's aloof modesty that very few copies can be shown to have been given to his friends. He must have presented one, probably in a special binding, to the King, but this has not survived. Another, now at Harvard University, has a note on the title-page that it was given by the author to its first owner, Marco Aurelio Severino, an Italian physician and an almost exact contemporary of Harvey whom he might have met as a student at Padua. If he gave away any others they have yet to be identified.

Harvey himself revealed in his preliminary address to Dr. Argent, President of the College, and his colleagues that he had 'yielded to the repeated desire of all and the pressing request of some, and in this small book have published it for all to see'.

A study of Harvey's *Prelectiones* in an earlier chapter led to the conclusion that when he first delivered his Lumleian lectures he was not revealing the whole of what he believed to be true regarding the movements of the blood. It seemed to be possible that up to 1627 or 1628 he was deliberately not revealing the whole of what he knew in order not to incur the odium of serious unorthodoxy. We have Aubrey's statement, attributed to Harvey himself, that after his book was published 'he fell mightily in his Practize and that 'twas believed by the vulgar that he was crack-brained; and all the Physitians were against his Opinion and envyed him'. According to his own statement in the first chapter of *De motu cordis*, Harvey did in the end propound his views both in private and publicly in his lectures. Some of his hearers were interested and wanted to know more, others with biased minds and imperfect understanding tried to make a public laughing-stock of him. Yet Aubrey was certainly exaggerating the position, for Harvey wrote in his Dedication to the President and Fellows of the College that 'I can name many reliable witnesses of almost all those observations which I use either to assemble the truth or refute errors; you so instanced have seen my dissections and have been wont to be conspicuous in attendance upon, and in full agreement with, my ocular demonstrations of those things, for the reasonable acceptance of which I here again most strongly press'. As already pointed out (p. 108), there is little evidence in the lecture notes that he gave many ocular demonstrations before his public audiences. Perhaps, therefore, these were done in private for the benefit of his particular friends.

[1] Maurice Sondheim, 'Die de Bry, Matthaus Merian und Wilhelm Fitzer', *Philobiblon* (1933), i. 17.

The Dedication of *De motu cordis* also contains Harvey's profession of faith in philosophic love of truth and wisdom from whomsoever it might come. In addition he deprecated making attacks on the veracity of his predecessors and teachers or provoking his contemporaries. He found it impossible, however, entirely to avoid making these attacks, and more than once he is found naming his old teacher, Fabricius, as the propagator of erroneous doctrines, though there was no acerbity in his words.

His Introduction is concerned with stating the manifest errors, or even absurdities, that he sought to overthrow in his book. First, the belief that arteries contain air had to be disproved, this being initially improbable from a consideration of the respiratory habits of cetaceans, and altogether impossible in the fœtus. Further, Galen's experiment by arterial section had shown the arterial system to be filled with blood and nothing else. Active diastole of the arteries was also a wrong notion, Harvey himself having publicly shown 'that arteries increase in volume because they fill up like bags or leather bottles, and are not filled up because they increase in volume like bellows'. In this respect Galen was wrong. Another serious error was to regard the blood supply to the lungs as fulfilling 'the single, purely private, function' of nourishing them. The structure of the great vessel leading to the lungs showed that it was a true artery, and 'Good God! How do the mitral valves hinder the return of air and not of blood?'

Another fundamental error was to suppose that the interventricular septum allowed blood to ooze through it from one ventricle to the other. 'But, damme, there are no pores and it is not possible to show such.' All these beliefs appear, Harvey said, 'incongruous, or obscure, or impossible' when considered with care, and it would therefore be useful to look with new eyes at the movements of the arteries and heart both in man and in all other animals with hearts, aided by experiments on animals. He instanced Galen's experiment of incising the trachea of a living dog, filling the lungs forcibly with air by a bellows, and then demonstrating that no trace of air could be found in the heart or great vessels.

In the first short chapter Harvey gave further strong reasons for writing his book and confessed that at one time he 'all but thought, with Fracastoro, that the heart's movement had been understood by God alone'. He noted that Fabricius had refrained from writing of the heart, though he had dealt with almost every other part of the animal body. Finally he himself wished to show that he had not lived an idle life and quoted from Terence the words of the old man in the comedy—

Nunquam quisquam ita bene subducta ratione ad vitam fuit,
Quin res, ætas, usus aliquid apportet novi,
Aliquid admoneat, ut illa quæ te scire credas, nescias,
Et quæ tibi putaris prima in experiundo repudies.[1]

(No life so perfect ever but that circumstance,
Increase of years, experience, can changes bring;
Your so-thought knowledge be but ignorance; those things
That you believed the finest fail to pass the test.)

The second and third chapters proved by observation and practical arguments that the blood was expelled from the heart during systole and that it refilled passively during diastole. At the same time the pulse represented the passive filling of the arteries during the heart's systole. This he had shown conclusively in his *Prelectiones*, so that the book said nothing that was new. Valuable evidence was derived from watching the relatively slow movements in cold-blooded animals, and from a patient with a subclavian aneurysm.

In the fourth chapter Harvey turned to the heart's movements in greater detail, showing that the two auricles are synchronized, as also the two ventricles. Again, dissection of cold-blooded animals showed this more clearly in slow motion, and observation of the slowly dying heart of mammals did the same. Even when the ventricle had apparently stopped beating, the auricles continued, and a finger on the ventricles could feel the pulsations. If at the same time the apex of the motionless ventricles was cut off with scissors, blood would spurt out with the auricular contractions. Harvey also showed that the heart muscle could recover from fatigue when he moistened the dying and motionless heart of a dove with saliva on his finger; the heart would then start beating again owing, he thought, to the warmth thus applied. Additional evidence of the auricular movements was derived from a human fœtus, from the chick embryo, from dissection of snails during hibernation, and from shrimps and insects. This was developed further in chapter v, the movements of auricles and ventricles being seen to be so rapid that the two contractions appear as one. This Harvey compared with the mechanism of a fire-arm, in which the pulling of the trigger, the striking of a spark from the flint, and the ignition of the powder all appear to take place at the same moment. The action of swallowing was also shown to be similar.

The sixth chapter is concerned particularly with the ways by which the blood is conveyed from the vena cava to the arteries, or from the

[1] Terence, *Adelphi*, Act 5, Scene 4, line 1.

right into the left ventricle. He argued that the majority of animals have no lungs and only one ventricle, and that in these the blood was transmitted by an obvious route from the vein to the artery through the single chamber of the heart. Further, the same state of affairs is present in the fœtus of a warm-blooded animal by the communications between the two sides of the heart through the *ductus arteriosus* (not so named by Harvey) and the *foramen ovale*. The lungs are not being used, so that the heart is virtually a single-chambered organ, though both communications close up and cease to exist after birth. He then touched on the subject of respiration, erroneously supposing cooling of the blood to be one of the functions of the lungs, as he had done in his lectures (see p. 104); but preferred to leave the full development of this to a special treatise, which, as we have seen, was never written. He ended by maintaining that 'in the more perfect and warmer animals, and full-grown ones at that (as in man), the blood definitely permeates from the right ventricle of the heart through the artery-like vein into the lungs, thence through the vein-like artery into the left ventricle of the heart. I maintain, firstly, that this can happen; secondly that it has so happened.'

In the seventh chapter Harvey argued more closely, with supporting passages from Galen, that the blood finds its way from the right ventricle through the parenchyma of the lungs into the pulmonary vein and left ventricle. He could not, in 1628, and never did, see the capillary vessels giving passage to the blood, but he called them *pulmonum cæcæ porositates et vasorum eorum oscilla*, 'the invisible porosities of the lungs and the minute cavities of their vessels'. He had seen the capillaries in his imagination, but lack of refined optical apparatus prevented him from demonstrating them. In this chapter he established the existence of the pulmonary circulation, as he had already done in the *Prelectiones*, referring this time to Columbus as well as to Galen. He added a reference to Caspar Hofmann's commentary on Galen's *De usu partium*, lib. 6, in a footnote.

Although Harvey credited Galen with having provided conclusive evidence for a pulmonary circulation by his description of the valves of the heart and the passsage of blood through the lungs, yet nowhere did Galen give a clear, unequivocal statement of it. Harvey was content, however, with his own arguments, using Galen, as far as he went, to support them. He was not, after all, specially concerned to prove the existence of the lesser circulation. His main purpose was to demonstrate a general systemic circulation, of which the pulmonary circuit was only a relatively small part.[1]

[1] See Donald Fleming, 'Harvey and the pulmonary circulation', *Isis* (1955). xlvi, 319–27.

The climax of the book was reached in the eighth chapter, and here he expressed forcibly his fear of the consequences if he spoke freely of what he knew. 'I not only fear that I may suffer from the ill-will of a few, but dread lest all men turn against me.' This seems to strengthen the suggestion that he had hitherto refrained from saying publicly all that was in his mind. But, he admitted, 'the die has now been cast, and my hope lies in the love of truth and the clear-sightedness of the trained mind'. Accordingly he had set about trying to discover by experiment how much blood passed from the veins into the arteries. He had been struck by the symmetry and size of the ventricles of the heart and of the great vessels entering and leaving them, and argued that if the circulation of the blood was admitted in the pulmonary system it might equally well circulate in the larger system of the rest of the body. He thought he had as much right to call this movement of the blood 'circular' as Aristotle had to say that the air and rain emulate the circular movement of the heavenly bodies.

It may very well happen thus in the body with the movement of the blood. All parts may be nourished, warmed and activated by the hotter, perfect, vaporous, spirituous and, so to speak, nutritious blood. On the other hand, in parts the blood may be cooled, thickened, and be figuratively worn out, From such parts it returns to its starting-point, namely the heart, as if to its source or to the centre of the body's economy, to be restored to its erstwhile state of perfection. Therein, by the natural, powerful, fiery heat, a sort of store of life, it is reliquified and becomes impregnated with spirits and (if I may so style it) sweetness. From the heart it is redistributed. And all these happenings are dependent upon the pulsatile movement of the heart.

In these words Harvey clinched his argument and committed himself finally to a full statement of the circulation of the blood.

In describing the Lumleian lecture notes reference was made to the passage on f. 80ᵛ of the manuscript shown by Dr. Whitteridge to have been written later than the body of the work. It was probably now, in 1627, when he had burned his boats by writing *De motu cordis*, that he added the famous passage for delivery in public:

WH it is certain from the structure of the heart that the blood is perpetually carried across through the lungs into the aorta as by two clacks of a water bellows to raise water. It is certain from the experiment of the ligature that there is a passage of the blood from the arteries to the veins. And for this reason it is certain that the perpetual movement of the blood in a circle is caused by the heart beat. Why? Is it for the sake of nutrition, or is it rather for the preservation of the blood and of the limbs by means of the infused heat? And the blood by turns heating the limbs and when it is made cold is warmed by the heart.

The book does not use the simile of the water bellows, but the 'experiment of the ligature' was fully described, as will presently be seen.

It still remained for Harvey to develop the doctrine in his book by adding arguments which he regarded as irrefutable, and he began his ninth chapter by stating three propositions in confirmation of his main theme. First, that the blood is continuously transmitted by the heart beat from the venous system into the arteries, so that the whole mass of blood passes through in a short time. Second, that the blood is driven in an uninterrupted stream into each limb and every part of the body in far greater volume than is needed merely for their nourishment. Third, that the veins are continuously returning the blood from every part of the body to the region of the heart.

Harvey then, by actual measurement of the capacity of the chambers of the heart, calculated how much blood can be discharged by the heart into the arteries in a given time. He made this calculation for the dog and sheep as well as for man. He added that the whole mass of blood must pass, not only to the members of the body, but also through the pulmonary circulation. A simple mathematical sum could then determine that if an ounce of blood is extruded at each contraction, then 83 lb. 4 oz. had been transferred into the arteries in half an hour. The exact amount would obviously vary according to different circumstances —temperament, age, activity, and so forth. All butchers, Harvey pointed out, would recognize the truth of this, since they habitually drained off the whole blood of an ox in less than a quarter of an hour. Harvey's measurements were not accurate, but they were adequate for his argument.[1] He ended the chapter by saying that his suppositions allowed him 'to surmise why no one has yet made a correct statement about the site, mechanism and causation of the anastomosis of the veins and arteries. I am now busy with that research.' The limitations imposed by the times in which he lived prevented him from solving this final problem, but this did not invalidate the truth of his main proposition.

In the tenth chapter Harvey sought to drive home his argument by further illustrations from the physiology of milk production by a cow or a woman suckling a baby, and by experiments on the slower circulations of blood in fishes and reptiles.

[1] For a discussion of this see F. G. Kilgour, 'Harvey's use of the quantitative method', *Yale Journal of Biology and Medicine* (1954), xxvi. 410–21.

The eleventh to the thirteenth chapters are of particular interest in that they show how Harvey had come to appreciate the true purpose of valves in veins, knowledge which he did not seem to possess when writing his *Prelectiones* in 1616. He described the effect of a tight ligature on a limb, which abolished the blood flow and the pulse altogether beyond the site of application, and of a medium ligature which compressed the vein, but still allowed blood to traverse the arteries as proved by the presence of a pulse. With the medium ligature the blood could be seen to accumulate in the swollen veins, followed by their emptying towards the heart as soon as the ligature was released. He illustrated this by the simple example of what happened when 'I once fell from my carriage and struck my forehead on the spot where an arterial branch passes forward from the temples. At once, in the space of about twenty pulsations from receipt of the blow, I developed a swelling the size of an egg without either heat or much pain; because, I presume, of the nearness of the artery, blood was being forced into the bruised part in greater abundance and at greater speed.' The same thing was seen in the ordinary operation of phlebotomy, where blood flowed more freely from an opening in a vein below the ligature than if it were above. This is followed by an accurate account of the venous valves and their purpose. They were first described by 'the celebrated Girolamo Fabrizzi d'Aquapendente, a most skilful anatomist and venerable old man, or else (as the learned Riolan would have it) Jacques Dubois', but their discoverer 'did not understand their real function, and others went no further'. Harvey then explained that 'the sole purpose for which the valves were created was so that the blood should not move from the large veins into the smaller ones (thus rupturing the latter or making them varicose), or from the centre of the body to its extremities, but rather from those extremities to the centre. Hence the delicate valves readily open to allow the latter movement of the blood, but completely suppress the opposite one.'

Observations follow, which had no place in the *Prelectiones*, describing Harvey's dissection of the veins in the limbs and his attempt to pass a probe downwards. The valves invariably provided a complete obstacle, though the probe passed easily in the other direction towards the heart. Now came the celebrated demonstration of the valves in the veins of the forearm, using figures copied from drawings in the book published by Fabricius in 1603. These were the only illustrations in the first edition of *De motu cordis* and they were repeated in almost every subsequent edition of the book except, oddly enough, the first English version of 1653.

In the fourteenth chapter Harvey gave a brief restatement, or summary, of his new doctrine, concluding: 'I am obliged to conclude that in animals the blood is driven round in a circuit with an unceasing, circular sort of movement, that this is an activity or function of the heart which it carries out by virtue of its pulsation, and that in sum it constitutes the sole reason for that heart's pulsatile movement.'

There could be little to add to so clear and conclusive a demonstration of the truth of Harvey's doctrine. Argument from known facts supported by experiments on living animals had shown once and for all a fundamental physiological truth which had escaped every previous anatomist. Clear reasoning and perfect scientific method with quantitive measurements had set a pattern initiating advances in the biological sciences and destined to influence all scientific investigation for the rest of time.

But Harvey had not quite finished his book with the irrefutable statement about the circulation of the blood. He found further illustrations of his theme in the effects of cold on the extremities and their recovery of proper warmth and colour if the heart's activity was unaffected. There were also a number of consequences that seemed to follow, such as the spread of contagion from a poisoned wound or the bite of a mad dog. He further emphasized this point when he told Aubrey in 1655 'that the biteing of a man enraged is poysonous. He instanced one that was bitt in the hand in a quarrell and it swoll up to his shoulder, and killed him in a short time.'[1] Harvey might at this point also have pointed out another practical conclusion which followed, namely the possibility of limiting by means of a ligature the circulation of a poison introduced through the skin, as by a snake bite. Though he did not do so in his book, he must have talked about it, for at a meeting of the Royal Society on 18 July 1678 John Pearson, Bishop of Chester, recalled 'that Dr. Harvey was of opinion that a man might be saved, though shot with a poisoned dart, if a very strong ligature were made above the wound immediately, and the mortified part below the ligature were cut off presently. But it was thought by others, that this means would not be effectual, if at least the poison were so violent as was reported, unless a ligature were made before the person was wounded by the dart.'[2]

Harvey's inevitable ignorance of the later developments of medical science make these concluding chapters of less value, though he displayed wide knowledge of comparative anatomy. Yet, when he came to think

[1] Aubrey, *The Natural History of Wiltshire*, ed. J. Britton, London, 1847, p. 43.
[2] Birch's *History of the Royal Society*, 1757, iii. 425.

of all the consequences that would flow from the illuminating truth in every part of medicine—physiology, pathology, semeiotics, therapeutics —he foresaw that the rest of his life would not suffice for writing down all that he would like to say about it. He also examined closely the details of the structure of the heart and disclosed many new points in its mechanical efficiency. Richard Lower, who came next to Harvey both in time and merit as a writer on the heart, admitted in his *Tractatus de corde*, 1669, that Harvey,

in so far as it concerned his magnificent discovery of the circulation, described the structure of the heart and the movement of the blood in a way that left practically nothing to be added or desired by his successors. But, just as in the *Ptolemaic hypothesis* of the heavens smaller epicycles are allotted to the planets when the enormous revolutions of the worlds have been dealt with, and these epicycles are indispensable for the explanation of observed facts, so in the system of the human body, as also in that of other animals, there are points not mentioned in Harvey's circulation which need consideration. These points are, I grant you, of minor importance, but they do definitely help in the rational study of a number of symptoms.[1]

On the last page of his book Harvey emphasized again the true nature of the great vessels on the right side of the heart, the artery-like vein being in fact an artery, the pulmonary artery, and the vein-like artery being a vein, the pulmonary vein. In his final sentence he stated his belief that 'it is very difficult for anyone to explain in any other way than I have done the reason why all these things have been arranged and carried into effect in the manner that I have described'. Perhaps the German compositor, who no doubt understood the Latin phrases he was printing, thought the claim went too far, for he cynically composed a small 'printer's ornament' below the last line of text in the form (?¿?). Yet Harvey could justifiably write FINIS below this sober conclusion to his scientific masterpiece. He knew that any attempt to overthrow his arguments would fail.

It has often been asked whether the men of any particular generation take just those steps which the intellectual climate of their time demands. Sir Isaac Newton seemed to do exactly what history required him to do at the appropriate time. On the other hand, the reception accorded to Harvey's demonstration of the circulation of the blood proved him to have a creative genius which could leap ahead of his contemporaries on

[1] *Early Science in Oxford*, by R. T. Gunther, vol. ix. *De corde*, by Richard Lower, translated by K. J. Franklin, Oxford, 1932, p. xxxix.

a genuinely new and fruitful path. The intellectual level did not compete with that of Newton's field, but the desire to increase man's understanding of his own body was a consuming flame in Harvey's mind.

22

COLLEGE AFFAIRS, 1628–1633 * JOURNEY WITH THE DUKE OF LENNOX, 1630

ON 29 March 1628, as will be related (p. 218), Harvey and his colleagues elected Dr. Chamberlen to a Fellowship, but at the same time admonished him for his extravagance in dress. Most of the other meetings in 1628 were occupied largely by the usual accusations of malpractice and illicit practice. It seems as if any patients whose symptoms did not improve or got worse could bring actions against their doctors, sometimes in the most violent terms, for it was not only the quacks who were brought before the College.

On 30 September the time had come for Dr. Argent to resign the Presidency. In his farewell speech he claimed to have acted with the greatest care during the past year on behalf of the College, but complained that no one else had shown equal zeal and good will. This aroused much uneasiness, and when the new officials had been elected, including Harvey again as Treasurer, the younger Fellows held a discussion about the retiring President's complaint and resolved to reform their ways by more frequent attendance at the College and by any other means open to them. The Elects were much gratified by this demonstration, and Dr. Atkins, speaking for Harvey and the others, 'openly declared that he had never before in any aspect of the College encountered so much hope or good will regarding the College affairs as on that day'.

Harvey was present at Comitia on 13 October 1628 when the Privy Council sent a document to the College asking in the name of the King for a report on the tobacco made from plants grown in England and Ireland. It was feared it might be injurious both to those who smoked it and to the prosperity of the Virginian plantations. King Charles probably had in mind his father's well-known *Counterblast to Tobacco*, first published in 1604 and reprinted with his *Works* in 1616. James had a very fair notion of the harm addiction to tobacco could do to the human body and his condemnation was whole-hearted. Harvey had a hand in drafting an answer from the Physicians, their opinion being that home-grown tobacco was indeed unwholesome, 'falling short of the perfection of other tobaccos that are brought from other more southern partes where it hath his natural maturity, vigor and efficiency'. They added no rider in general condemnation of the habit.

During 1629 Harvey was attending with some regularity at the College meetings. On 25 June the library was under discussion, a matter which was always near his heart. On this occasion a proposal was made for a new plan of library management, Harvey and four others being appointed as a committee to think about it. The matter had been brought to a head by a bequest of 680 books from the estate of Dr. Matthias Holsbosch, recently deceased. Holsbosch, originally of German nationality, was not a Fellow of the College, but had practised both surgery and medicine for fifty years in England and was greatly respected for his knowledge and integrity. Nothing was done immediately, but the library came under discussion, as will be seen, on many later occasions.

On 4 September Dr. James Primrose presented himself for examination as Licentiate, but was put off until the next month. Primrose, who was to become one of Harvey's leading critics, had graduated at Bordeaux, took his M.D. at Montpellier and studied with Riolan at Paris. He was M.D. by incorporation at Oxford in 1628. He was admitted as Licentiate on 10 December, the letter of his licence being signed by Harvey himself. On 24 August he had also signed a licence for his own brother-in-law, Galen Browne, already mentioned (p. 48).

On 30 September Dr. Argent was again elected President. Harvey was reappointed Treasurer and Censor, a position of signal honour which he was soon to relinquish. It is recorded in the Annals that on 3 December he invited the seven Elects to a splendid feast at his house and there asked their permission to resign the offices on account of an unavoidable duty abroad committed to him by the King. Dr. Fox was then appointed Treasurer in his place. Harvey was at this time still only Physician Extraordinary to King Charles, as he had been to King James, but a year later, on 22 December 1630, it was announced in the College that he had been made Royal Physician in Ordinary, and on that account had become supernumerary in the College. He did not hold any college office, other than Elect, after this, though he remained an honoured participator in their counsels. The exact date of his appointment to the King is not known, but it must have been in the quarter ending on Lady Day 1630. Payment of his emoluments was delayed and uncertain, for according to the Calendar of Domestic State Papers the first instalment was not paid until five years later: '3 July 1635. To William Harvey, one of his Majesty's physicians in ordinary, his annuity for a year ending at Our Lady Day 1631 £300'. Other entries record that he received a further £25 on 17 July 1635, and £150 on 5 February 1635/6.[1]

At Comitia on 22 December 1629 Harvey and Fox laid a complaint that they had not been paid the fees due to them (as Censors) when two doctors had been admitted as Candidates. These fees, recurring through the year, probably added up to a substantial sum, and Harvey need not be regarded as grasping because of his insistence on being paid. On this same day he contributed £20 to the fund for redemption of the college buildings, an instance of his customary generosity. On this day the President announced that a new keeper of the library should be elected, Harvey being the holder of the library Statutes in the meantime, but nothing further was done.

By 9 January 1629/30 the recent Licentiate, James Primrose, was already giving trouble. He had somehow gained the King's ear and persuaded him to advocate his giving a public medical lecture in London. The demand was discussed at an extraordinary meeting of Comitia, and the Physicians evidently found themselves greatly embarrassed, resisting the proposal, while offering that one of their number should read a lecture if the King insisted; Primrose, they said, was not qualified to do so. The matter seems to have been dropped and Primrose ceased pushing himself forward in London. He afterwards settled and practised in Hull, whence he pursued his attacks on Harvey and the doctrine of the circulation of the blood.

On three days in the previous December the Extraordinary Anatomy Lectures had been given by Dr. Helkiah Crooke. At the January meeting it was decided that these lectures should be discontinued and the money so saved added to the redemption fund. At the meeting on 26 February it was quietly announced, without further comment, that Dr. William Harvey had delivered the Ordinary Anatomy Lectures in the College buildings. We would give a good deal at the present time to know just what he said on this occasion. Had he added to his notes the page comparing the action of the heart to the clacks of a water-bellows, or was he developing his thesis without emphasis on its novelty?

In March 1629/30 great concern was being felt in London because of a renewed outbreak of plague. On the 15th it was announced at Comitia

---

[1] *Calendar of Domestic State Papers*, 1635, ccxciii. 24; ccxciv. 5; cccxiii. 34.

that the King had commanded the College 'to write down some directions as well for the prevention of the plague as for its cure'. It will be remembered that the same words had been used on a previous occasion, in April 1625, and now Harvey replied that directions had then been set down, but had been ignored by the City officials. He said also that the College did not wish to accept the appointment of special practitioners paid for treatment of plague. That had been done before and had failed, the stipendiaries having been dismissed after a short trial. In addition a book had already been published with the authority of the College. Dr. Atkins, the bearer of the message from the King, insisted, however, that some attempt must be made to give him satisfaction, and the matter was accordingly referred to Harvey and the other Censors to write down what they believed should be done. This party met three days later in order to make an attempt to draw up health regulations, but little was achieved. In the end several Fellows handed in written statements giving what they thought worthy of consideration, and the Registrar, Dr. Clement, no doubt to everyone's relief, undertook to collect opinions and draw up a new form of directions. On the 22nd the President pressed for these to be delivered, but was told that they could not be dealt with quickly or hastily completed. At length, on 9 April, a small book compiled by the Registrar was read and approved by the Censors; it was taken to the King by Dr. Atkins next day. Yet Charles was still not satisfied. On 20 April he asked that a doctor experienced in plague should go to Greenwich to inspect some bodies lying there. The President was told that a surgeon had already gone and would report. Harvey then proposed a motion, 'as it were from the King', asking if some of the Fellows under favourable conditions were willing to accept responsibility for treatment of the plague. Everyone present except Dr. Clement and Dr. Clarke excused themselves, whereupon Harvey proposed a second motion offering these Fellows an annual stipend of £400 while the epidemic raged and, when it was over, a stipend of £200. If one of them chanced to die during the epidemic, the widow should have an annuity of £100 for life. Clement and Helkiah Crooke accepted these conditions, Clarke having apparently dropped out when the others again excused themselves. On 23 April, with Harvey present, the Candidates and Licentiates were told of the arrangements and signified their approval. At the same time all, including the Fellows, were reproved for not wearing their gowns in the streets. Perhaps, in the circumstances, they were reluctant to advertise that they were medical men lest they should be constantly asked to enter plague-stricken houses.

The regulations for control of the plague seem, as usual, to have failed, and it became so bad that no meetings were held at the College from 3 July to 30 September. Harvey attended at the College on 8 October and 22 December 1630 and on 24 March 1630/1, when the matter of the plague precautions came up yet again. The latest demands made by the King's Councillors were reported and their expectations of receiving an answer in a few days. It was thought that the doctors to whom the matter had been entrusted would report fully what they had done, but little was forthcoming. Dr. Betone contributed a few facts; Dr. Harvey and some others put forward suggestions of what circumstances were harmful and could provide opportunities for the spread of plague, but it was judged that there was not enough material for a discussion. Again the task was delegated and again a meeting was held to consider possible 'annoyances'. Finally, a list of these was drawn up for presentation to the King's Council. These included overcrowding both by the number of houses and of the people in them; uncleansed sewers and streets; slaughterhouses improperly drained; burials of infected corpses in City churchyards, and overcrowding of graves inside the churches; marketing of mouldy corn; the sale of diseased meat by the butchers and of tainted fish, mussels, and oysters by the fishmongers. Harvey certainly had a hand in compiling this horrifying list of current abuses most of which were related to infestation by rats and so, though they did not know it, to the propagation of bubonic plague. For the rest their Lordships were referred to the book delivered to them in the previous year, the College not wishing to add anything to what was then recommended.

The immediate reason for Harvey's resignation of the Treasurership in 1629 was the King's command that he should accompany young James Stewart, fourth Duke of Lennox in the Scottish peerage, on his travels abroad. Lennox was related to the royal family, his grandfather, the first Duke, having been a first cousin of King James. He had been educated at Cambridge and now, being nearly 18, was ripe for wider experiences abroad. He is described as 'a good young man, loyal, sweet-natured and simple-hearted, but not clever'.[1] He became a devoted supporter of King Charles and played an honourable part in the events that followed. He held many appointments at Court and contributed very large sums of money to the King's funds during the Civil War. He was created Duke of Richmond in 1641. In September 1629 Secretary Dorchester procured a licence for him to travel for three years, taking with him Dr. Topham, Dean of Lincoln, John St. Alman, and eight other servants with £200

[1] C. V. Wedgwood, *The King's Peace*, 1955, p. 148.

in money.[1] Harvey is not mentioned in the licence, but in January 1629/30 he was asking for leave of absence from the Governors of St. Bartholomew's in order to take up this duty:

Curia tent. Sabti xxj° die Januarii 1629/30

In presence of Sir Robt Ducy Knight & Barron^t Presedent
[and others]

DR. HARVEY

This day Doctor Harvey Phisicion to this hospitall declared to this court that he is comaunded by the Kings most excellent ma^{ty} to attend the illustrious Prince the nowe Duke of Lenox in his travells beyond the seaes, and therefore desireth that this court would allowe of [Edmund] Smith Doctor in Phisick for his deputy in p'formance of the office of physicion for the poore of this hospitall duringe his absence. It is thought fitt that the Gov'nors of this hospitall have further knowledge & satisfaccion of the sufficiency of the said Mr. Smith Then they to make theire choice either of him or some other whome they shall thinck meete for the execucion of the same place duringe the absence of the said Dr. Harvey.

We have only indirect evidence derived from the Domestic State Papers of when these travels started and what course they took. There seems to have been some delay in getting off, for Sir Henry Mervyn, writing to Nicholas, Clerk of the Council, on 28 July 1630, reported 'having put over my Lord Duke [of Lennox] for the coast of France'. Having reached France, however, the party lingered in the coastal towns, for Mervyn wrote on 10 August that he had landed the Duke at Dieppe. On 23 September Edward Dacres wrote to Dorchester that the Duke had been at Aubigny (a small town in the Pas de Calais of which his younger brother was Seigneur), but was now fixed in Paris for the winter. On 22 November Dacres wrote that 'in the spring the Duke intends the tour de France, and in the end of the summer to go into Italy, unless the continuance of the war or the plague hinders him'. On 5 April 1631 he was still in Paris, but thought of going out of town for a few days. On 12 August Dacres wrote to Dorchester saying:

Blois proved a place not long to be endured by my Lord because of the plague, which grew hot there, as Tours likewise, where we made a little stay, so that we came down to Saumur, there to pass the dog days from whence we are now parting they being at end. My Lord hath continually been in good health and intends now to follow your Lordships directions

---

[1] *Calendar of Domestic State Papers, 1629–31*, cxlix. 108.

for Spain whither we are now bending our course (via Bordeaux) where we shall be before this latter end of September.[1]

In February 1631/2 Lennox was made a Grandee of Spain of the first class, as we know from a letter written by Sir Thomas Edwards to Sir Harry Vane, a privy councillor, and it was probably soon after this that the party returned to England.

Through all these months after December 1629 Harvey must have been expecting a call to start on his travels with Lennox, but the summons never came, as can be inferred from the dates on which he is known to have been in London. It is, in fact, impossible to know exactly how much Harvey shared in the Duke's uncertain movements. He could have been away between 25 June and 30 September 1630, or between 12 December 1630 and 17 February 1631/2. It seems improbable that he went to Spain at all, or, if he did, he certainly did not stay with the Duke until he was made Grandee in February. On the whole it appears likely that he wrote his undated letter[2] to Lord Dorchester in the late summer of 1630 expressing anxiety lest his place at Court might have been given to someone else during his enforced absence. He had heard a report, false as it turned out, that a 'Dr. Mezler', probably Dr. Adam Moesler, a German who was admitted an extra Licentiate of the College in 1627, had been appointed to his place. He was also distressed at his inability to use his time in biological investigation owing to the ravaged state of the country in which he found himself.

Right Hon[ble]

it is more than time than to give your honour thanks for your favour & benefits to me, reseyved [received], when I am to come with a new suite; but it (being but the consummating & perfecting what by your favour I have reseyved already) giveth me the confidence to write at this time, intreating your Honour to be my mediator to his majesty that, my patent being stopped at my Lord Treasurer's (a business I am informed your Honour is already acquainted with) that he would be pleased in his gracious favour unto me, to let it be as already it is for my life, according as the rest of my fellows have, & as by your Honour's extraordinary favours to me you have made me your obliged servant, for you would be pleased to protect me. It is written to me besides that one Dr. Mezler hath gotten to be appointed to wayte in my place for the household (before I went I intreated & appointed Dr. Chambers & Dr. Bethune, &

---

[1] *Calendar of Domestic State Papers, 1630–1*, clxxi. 50; clxxii. 42; clxxiii. 56; clxxv. 83; clxxxviii. 16; cxcviii. 29; ccxi. 45.

[2] Bodleian Library, Clarendon Papers, 2076. Spelling here modernized.

one Doctor Smith of London, one of them at all occasions to perform that duty for me; & I acquainted the officers of the household therewith; it is not usual: for Sergeant Primrose was away above a year (& he is surgeon of the household) & yet none put in his place to wait whilest he was in Germany with my Lord Marquess, Sir Theod. Mayerne, in Switzerland in K. James his time, was away very long & none put in his place. I beseech your Honour that no prejudice arise thereof to me, according (as I humbly thank your Honour) the K. Majesty made to me his declaration, no such thing should be done, by your Honour's mediation. The miseries of the Countries we have passed & the hopes of our good success & all such news Your Honour hath from better hands, I can only complain that by the way we could scarce see a dog, crow, kite, Raven or any bird, or anything to anatomize, only some few miserable people, the relics of the war & the plague, where famine had made anatomies before I came. It is scarce credible in so rich, populous & plentiful countries as these were that so much misery, desolation & poverty & famine should in so short a time be as we have seen. I interpret it well that will be a great motive for all here to have & procure an assurance of a settled peace. It is time to leave fighting when there is nothing to eat, nothing to be kept & gotten & the same parties rob one the other if they get but once out of sight.

Your Honour's
Humble servant
Will Harvey

It is inferred from these indications that, if the Duke had intended to visit Venice and other parts of Italy, he was deterred by the state of war and the virulence of the plague in the northern provinces. It is said that over a million died of the disease in the districts Lennox would have crossed to reach Venice, and that 33,000 died in Verona alone.

As already shown, Harvey must have been in London in 1631 from March onwards. He was at the College on 25 June and 30 September, and at the house of the Treasurer, Dr. Fox, on 25 October when the annual accounts were rendered. On 2 November he was appointed to a Committee to consider a wealthy donor's offer to establish an Extraordinary Anatomy Lecture at the College, and to another concerned with making the library accessible. On 12 December he was a member of yet another Committee to deal with a petition sent by the College to the King and passed on by him to the Privy Council about 'obtaining a suitable garden and of all things relating to its construction and culture', that is, for the cultivation of simples and medicinal plants. According to the Annals 'much was said by many on this matter'. The Committee had been asked to meet at the house of the senior member, Dr. Atkins, but found that he was ill. They therefore postponed any discussion, awaiting his recovery. Perhaps it was Atkins who was the prime mover in this project, for it was not mentioned again. Dr. Atkins attended only a few more times at the College and died at the age of 77 in 1635.

Harvey was next present at Comitia on 17 February 1631/2, when a question was raised about the number of foreigners practising in London with or without a licence. Dr. Winston 'thought they ought to be suppressed by every means'. Twenty-one names were given, including those of Sir Theodore de Mayerne, Paul de Laune, brother of the celebrated Gideon, and the Hameys, father and son, none of whom could have merited suppression; some of them were, moreover, under royal protection. Probably it all arose over the trouble caused by Dr. Boet, a Dutchman, who was being examined on the same day. 'He was advised by the President to adopt the correct means of obtaining a licence, for impudence and insolence would avail him nothing with the College.' The general question of foreigners was dropped. On 26 March Harvey was present when various proposals were made about the library, though he does not seem to have had any direct responsibility for its maintenance. The following proposals 'seemed suitable until more proper provision could be made for it':

1. The names of the books were to be fixed to the book cases so that it was evident what books were included in each case.
2. The Library was to be open to Fellows, Candidates and Licentiates on the days of the Comitia both Majora and Minora.
3. No one was to borrow a book from the Library unless a pledge for twice the value of the book was given, the pledge to be given to the Censors on the day of the Minora Comitia.
4. The President was to hold the key of the Library in his possession.
5. The keys of the book cases were to be kept carefully by the senior Censor.

At the end of May 1632 the case of the poisoning of the man Lane first came up at the College, as already related on another page (p. 79), and also the examination of Dr. Goddard and Dr. Boet in June and July (see pp. 36, 41). The quarrels with the Apothecaries in the latter part of the year have also been described (pp. 80–81). On 9 November Harvey, with the President, Clement, and Fox examined 'Jarvyyes Dixson of the Countye of Yorke' at the President's house; 'after admonition given to him that he should followe his studye, be carefull of his practize, and in difficult cases should call some learned phisition to Counsell, hee had his letters testimoniall graunted to him'. This was signed by the four examiners. Harvey was present at the College again on 22 December and on 15 April 1633. In May he left London for Scotland with the King.

23

THE FIRST VISIT TO SCOTLAND, 1633

HARVEY'S constant attendance on the King and his court was making inroads into the time that he could devote to his duties at St. Bartholomew's, and his colleagues began to complain of the difficulties arising from this new situation. In January 1632/3 matters came to a head, and arrangements were made to find a remedy without prejudice to Harvey's position, as is recorded in the hospital Journal:

Curia tent. Sabti xix° die January Anno Dni 1632/3

DOCTOR HARVY

It hath bine thought convenient uppon complaint of some of the chirurgions of this hospitall that wheras Doctor Harvy phisicion for the poore of the said hospitall by reson of his attendance on the King's Matie cannot soe constantly be present wth the poore as heretofore he hath bine, but sometymes doth appoint his deputy for the same, That therefore Doctor Andrewes physicion in rev'cion of the same place to this hospitall in the absence of Do^r Harvey doe supply the same place wherby the said poore may be more respected and Do^r Andrewes the better acquainted to p'forme the same office when it shall fall, & in the mene tyme to be recompenced by this yerly as shalbe thought fitt. This order not to p'iudice Dr. Harvy in his yerly ffee or in any other respect then aforesaid.

In May of the same year Harvey was required to accompany the King to Scotland and he tried unsuccessfully to plant his own nominee, Dr. Edmund Smith, to act in his absence. Smith, an old friend, was educated at Caius College, where he matriculated in 1613. He took his Cambridge M.D. in 1627 and became a Fellow of the College of Physicians in 1632. He had a distinguished career and was fully worthy of Harvey's support; but Dr. Andrews had powerful influence in the City of London to recommend him, and so won the day. The contest was recorded in the hospital Journal on 13 May:

xiii° die May Anno Dni 1633

This day came into this Compting howse Doctor Smith phisicion by the appointm^t of Doctor Harvey, phisicion to this hosp^ll whoe is to attend the King's Matie into Scotland, & tendred his s'vice to Mr. Threr and other the Gov'nors for the poore in the behalfe and absence of Doctor Harvey. Aunswer was made by Mr. Threr that Doctor Andrewes phisicion in rev'cion to this howse was by the Court ordered to attend the occasions of this howse in the absence of Doctor Harvey & to have allowance from this howse accordingly. Nevertheles if Doctor Smith pleased to accompany Doctor Andrewes in the buisines, this howse would be very well content, unto wch Doctor Smith replied that if Doctor Andrewes were appointed & did p'forme accordingly; There is noe need of twoe.

The Treasurer, Martin Bond, was careful not to offend the King's physician by a blank refusal to accept his candidate, but clearly the matter had been settled at the meeting held on 13 January and the decision could not be reversed. Harvey was now free to absent himself for an indefinite time from the Hospital and he left for Scotland shortly afterwards.

King Charles had not been in Scotland since he left the country with his father in 1603. Thirty years later, in May 1633, as King of Great Britain, he decided to revisit his native land for his coronation in Edinburgh. His journey there was a Royal Progress of great magnificence with lavish entertainments on the way. Among the large party attending him were two physicians, Dr. Harvey and Dr. Betone, or Bethune (a Scot), three surgeons and a barber.[1] The two physicians were jointly allowed eight servants and the same number of horses. The cavalcade followed the Great North Road, passing by Huntingdon, Stamford, Grantham, Newark, Doncaster, York, Durham, Newcastle, Alnwick, and Berwick, the 337 miles being covered in eighteen stages each of about nineteen miles. One of the grander entertainments was held by the Earl of Newcastle at Welbeck Abbey, between Newark and Doncaster, and, when it was found that the King's retinue was too numerous to be accommodated there, the Earl of Arundel offered hospitality to the Earl of Portland and some others of the party at Worksop Manor. Among those invited was Dr. Harvey. Lord Portland, formerly Sir Richard Weston and now Lord High Treasurer, was taken ill at his

[1] Sir Henry Wade, 'Harvey in Scotland', *Edinburgh Medical Journal* (1938), i. 761–81.

host's house, and Arundel wrote to the Royal Comptroller, Sir Henry Vane, who was with the main party, to excuse both his guest and himself from continuing the journey with the King. His letter, dated 23 May began: 'I thought good to advertise you that my lord treasurer hath this night had no rest, but bin in a continuall fitte of the stone, not without some aguish Distempere, which Dr. Hervye conceives to be only an evidence of the fitte of the stone; and soe doe I, out of what I have often felte in the like kinde.'[1] He hoped they would be able to travel a day or two later, and in fact they did so, as he wrote on 2 June from Durham to Sir Francis Windebank, Secretary of State. There is no further mention of Harvey on the journey, but there can be no doubt that he was in close attendance on the King throughout the expedition. He would certainly have been a witness of the splendid occasion when the King was crowned in the Abbey Church at Holyrood. Another ceremony in which he must have felt some interest took place on 24 June in the Chapel Royal; tuberculosis was probably then, as later, particularly common in Scotland and the King there 'touched' about a hundred people for 'the King's evil' or scrofula, hanging round each person's neck a specially minted gold coin suspended on a white silk riband. On the previous day there was a banquet and the Freedom of the City was conferred on several of the King's suite, including Harvey with the other medical members. The three surgeons and the barber were also admitted to the Freedom of the Barber-Surgeons' Guild, but there was then no College of Physicians to honour Harvey, as it had not yet been founded. After fifteen days in Edinburgh the King made a tour northwards, visiting Linlithgow, Stirling, Dunfermline, where he was born, and Falkland. On 10 July the party on its way back to Edinburgh crossed by sea from Burntisland and the vessel immediately following the King's boat capsized, thirty-three out of thirty-five passengers, mostly the King's servants, being lost, together with much household stuff and silver.

While the King was in Edinburgh the Bishop of Moray preached a sermon in St. Giles Kirk and gave great offence to the Scottish people by wearing vestments regarded as Popish; and they resented still more the order that ministers were in future to wear surplices instead of the plain Geneva gowns to which they had been accustomed since the Reformation. These were the preliminary events leading to riots in 1637 against Laud's Liturgy and ultimately to the 'taking of the Covenant', which played so important a part in the disturbances of the Civil War. It may be assumed that Harvey took no great interest in these eccle-

[1] *Calendar of Domestic State Papers*, Charles I, 1633, cxxxix. 37.

siastical events. His thoughts were centred on giving medical advice when required to do so, and on making any observations on biology and natural history for which chance provided opportunities. One such chance was given him when his presence in Edinburgh enabled him to visit the Bass Rock, a few miles off the coast, with its vast concourse of birds. He was interested in the nature of egg-shells, which he was convinced were laid down while the egg was in the oviduct, or 'uterus' as he called it. He described what he saw in a well-known passage in his later book, *De generatione animalium*, 1651, which is concerned largely with eggs and the development of the chick. It is of interest to read this passage in full as an example of Harvey's capacity for observation.

In the Eastern barren Islands of Scotland, there is such a mighty affluence of all-most all sorts of Sea-fowle, that if I should relate all that I have heard, though from persons of great integrity, I fear I should be suspected more Fabulous then those several Authors, who discourse of the Scotish or Soland-Geese, which they story to be born from the fruit of certain Trees falling into the Sea (which fruit or Geese themselves never saw).[1] However I shall venture to relate what my owne Eyes have seen.

There is a little Island, the Scots call it Basse, (by this, Reader, guess at the rest of them) it is not far from the shore, seated in the Main Sea; standing upon a rugged and dangerous Clift, (you may call it rather one great continued Stone, or Rock, then an Island) it is not above a mile about. The superficies of this Island (in the moneths of May and June) is almost covered quite over with Nests, Egges, and Young-Ones, that for their infinit abundance, you can scarce set your foot in a spare place, and such a mighty flock hovereth over the Island, that (like thick clouds) they darken and obscure the day: and such a cry and noise they make, that you can hardly hear those that stand next you. If you look down into the Sea beneath you (as from a steep Tower, or Precipice) you shall see it all spread over with several sort of fowle, swimming to and fro, in pursuit of their Prey, just at the rate as some ditches and lakes in the Spring time, are paved with Frogs; and open Hills, and steep mountains, are stuck and embossed with flocks of sheep and Goats. If you saile round the Island, and look up into the several Clifts and Cavernes of it, you shall finde them all peopled and inhabited with several colonies of Birds and Fowle, of distinct Kinde and magnitude: more indeed, then in a clear night when the Moon is absent, there are Starres to be discerned in the Firmament: and if you observe the several Regiments of those that sally out, and those that flock homewards at the same time,

[1] This refers to the supposed origin of the solan-goose from barnacles, or the barnacle-tree, as related in Gerard's *Herbal*, 1636, pp. 1587-9.

you would take them for an infinite swarm of Bees. It is not to be imagined what a vast yearly revenue the Lord of the Island maketh of the Plumes and the Remainders of the Nests (which are useful for firing) together with the Egges which he seetheth and then trafficketh away: that which he himself told me, was indeed incredible. But this one thing which reflects nearer upon our discourse, seemeth to me remarkable in chief, and doth give a clear testimony of the excessive multitude: which is, that this Island as you approach it, shineth with a white glasing, and the clifts resemble mountaines of the purest Chalke, though the native complexion of the Stone be obscure and black. That which thus discoloureth the Island, is a white crust, which is friable, and of the very same Consistence, Complexion, and Nature with the Egge-shell; so that all parts of the Island are plaistered over with this hard tegument, and crumbling or friable crust or shale. The bottome of the Island which the Tyde washeth every day, retaining its natural colour, clearly sheweth that that fucus, or sophisticated whiteness, proceeds from the liquid Excrements of the Birds (which they discharge when they disburden their Bellies) and by which, as it were with an Egge-shell, white, hard and friable, the Walls are crusted and disguised: And after the same manner, doe Aristotle and Pliny consent, that the Egge-shell is formed. None of these birds are Citizens of the place, but Forreigners all, and resort thither for convenient Laying, and there they continue some weeks as in their Inne; till they and their Young-ones be all in condition to fly away together. But that white Ruff-cast is so solid, firme and thick, that you would think it were the genuine and natural substance of the soile. . . .

Amongst the so many several kindes of Birds (which make their conflux to the aforesaid Island for Procreation sake) and so many several structures of their nests, wherein they hatch their young, there was one Bird shewed me above all the rest, which layeth one onely egge, fixing it upon the steep point of a sharp stone, (having neither nest, nor any other materials to support it) and that so secure, and firmly, that the mother-bird can leave it there, and return again to it at pleasure, without any prejudice to the egge at all. But if this egge be once removed from its station, no art nor cunning in the world can fasten it again, but it instantly falleth into the sea, as from a precipice, without redemption. The reason is, because the place where it is mounted, is incrustated all over with the white cement; and the egge being newly layed, wreaketh with a stiff and viscous humidity, which presently congealing, it is agglutinated to the subjacent stone, as it were with a kinde of soulder.[1]

The solan-geese observed by Harvey were gannets, but the bird laying a single egg on the bare rock was a guillemot. It seems that someone else

[1] *Anatomical Exercitations, Concerning the Generation of Living Creatures*, London, 1653, pp. 53–56.

told him the story about the egg being cemented to the stone. If he had examined it on the spot, would he have noticed that the real reason why the egg does not roll off is its pyriform shape?

Soon after the King's party had left Theobalds for Scotland alarm was caused in the royal nursery at St. James's by the sudden illness of the Prince of Wales, then almost three years old. On 22 May 1633 Dr. Chambers, one of the household physicians, though not a Fellow of the College, wrote to the King reporting that the Prince had been seized with an acute fever accompanied by loose stools. Harvey not being available, Chambers called in Sir Theodore de Mayerne and Dr. Lister, adding next day Drs. Atkins, Robbin, Cademan, and 'others your Majesty's physicians' to the clinical team. The patient was given a cooling drink 'to temper the great acrimony of the humour which he did void; the like whereof I did never see come from a child of his age'. The stools soon became flecked with 'sparks of blood' and the child suffered severe colic. Then 'we did resolve first upon some clysters of milk to refresh his intestines and suage his pain, and thereafter (the sparks of blood no more appearing) we appointed the same more detersive with the broth of a chicken'.[1] Gradually the boy improved and in eight days began to recover his appetite, so that by the time Harvey and the patient's father heard about the illness all anxiety was past. When the King arrived back at Greenwich on 25 July, 'the prince welcomed him home with the prettiest innocent mirth imaginable'.[2]

24

AFFAIRS AT ST. BARTHOLOMEW'S HOSPITAL AND THE COLLEGE OF PHYSICIANS, 1633–1634

THOUGH Harvey was therefore back in London before the end of July little more was heard of him until October, when he raised a matter of importance at a meeting of the Governors of St. Bartholomew's Hospital:

---

[1] *Historical Manuscripts Commission. Twelfth Report, pt. ii.* Manuscripts of Earl Cowper, ii, 1888, p. 11.

[2] Ibid., p. 26.

Sabti quinto die Octobr. Anno Dni 1633

In presence of Sr Robt Ducie Knight & Baron^t Presedent
[and others]

Dr. Harvey

Uppon mocion of Do^r Harvey Phisicion to this howse, It is thought fit that Tuesday senight in the afternoone be the tyme that the Gov'nors shall heare himselfe and the chirurgions uppon some p'ticulers conc'ninge the good of the poore of this howse & reformcion of some orders conceaved to be in this howse, And the chirurgions & the apothecary to be warned to meete accordingly. And Mr. Aldr'an Mowlson Sr Maurice Abbott Mr. Aldr'an Perry & others the Gov'nors here present are intreated to meete at the compting howse to heere & determine the same.

This was the preliminary to passing the set of rules designed to control the activities of the surgical members of the staff that was printed on a previous page, and so to assert the ascendancy of the physician over his surgical colleagues. The official preamble to the rules was as follows:

Curia tent. xv° die Octobris Anno Dni 1633

In presence of Sr Robt Ducie Kn^t and Barron^t Presedent
[and others]

DR. HARVEY

This day Do^r Harvey Phisicion to this hospitall p'sented to this court c'taine articles for the good & benefit of the poore of this howse, wch the Gov'nors have taken into theire consideracions & doe allowe & order them to be putt in practize And all defaults in the not p'formance of any of the said articles to be corrected & amended by the Gov'nors as they in theire discresions shall thinck fitt & convenient.

Forasmuch as the poore of this howse are increased to a greater number then form'ly have bine, to the greate charge of this hospitall & to the greater labour & more necessary attendance of a phisicion; And beinge much more alsoe then is conceaved one phisicion may conveniently p'forme.

And forasmuch as Do^r Harvey the nowe physicion to this hosp^ll is alsoe chosen to be phisicion to his Matie & therby tydd to daily s'vice & attendance on his Matie.

It hath bine thought fitt & soe ordered that there shalbe for this p'nte occasion two phisicions for this hospitall, And that Dr. Andrewes Phisicion in rev'cion be nowe admitted to be alsoe an imediat phisicion to this hospitall And to have the sallary or yerely ffee of xxxiii^ld vi^s viii^d. for his paines henceforth duringe the plesure of this court.

And this court for the longe s'rvice of the said Dr. Harvey to this hosp^ll & in consideracion that he is phisicion to his Matie doe give &

allowe him leave & lib'ty to dispose of himselfe & tyme, and to visit the poore noe oftener then he in his discretion shall thinck fitt.

And it is ordered that Mr. Threr shall alsoe pay unto the said Do^r Andrrewes the some of xx^l for his paines in visitinge and p'scribinge for the poore of this howse for this yeare last past by the direcion and att the request of the Gov'nors of this howse.

Also at the suite of the apothecary (for the consideracions above-said) It is thought fitt & soe graunted that x^d be yerly added to his sallary from Mich'as last past for & towards the mainten'ce of a Jurnyman to be daily p'sent in the apothecaryes shopp in this hospitall to helpe him in the dispatch of his busines, duringe the pleasure of this court.

Likewise at the mocion of Dr. Harvey It is graunted that Mr. Threr shall pay unto Do^r Smith whoe was the deputy of Do^r Harvey and by him appointed in his absence to visite the poore of this hospitall the some of x^ld in gratuity from this court, and he is thereuppon intreated in respect the hospitall hath nowe two phisicions that he doe not henceforth troble himselfe any more to visite or p'scribe to the poore of this hospitall.

Then follow the new rules printed at page 69. It appears from the last paragraph that Dr. Smith did in fact sometimes work at the Hospital during Harvey's absence although he had said in the previous May that he would not do so, since the attendance of two physicians was not necessary.

In May 1633 Dr. Richard Andrews had been appointed successor in reversion to Harvey at St. Bartholomew's, but he did not live for this to take effect. He died on 25 July 1634, and it became necessary to make another appointment. This was decided at a meeting of the Governors on 7 August 1634:

Cur. tent. septimo die Augusti Anno Dni 1634

In p'sence of Sr Nicholas Rainton Knight P'sedent [and others]
CLARKE

This day, — Clarke Doc^r in Phisick is chosen to be assistant to Do^r Harvey Phisicion to this hospital in the roome and place of Do^r Andrewes late deceased And it is ordered that he have the salary of xxxiij^ld vj^s viii^d yerly paid to him for his paines duringe the plesure of this Court. And the charge of the phisicion hath bine redd unto him, wch he hath p'mised in all ptes faithfully to observe & pforme And this hospitall doe order that after Do^r Harvey his death or dep'ture, there be but one phisicion forthwards.

Dr. John Clarke had been educated at Christ's College, Cambridge, and was elected a Fellow of the College of Physicians in 1622. He became

President for the years 1645–9. Although his appointment in 1634 was nominally as assistant to Harvey, he must have done most of Harvey's work during his frequent absences on other duties. According to the hospital ledgers Harvey received his last payment of £33. 6s. 8d. in February 1643, and it is presumed that he retired at that time. Dr. Clarke then acted as full physician to the Hospital till his death ten years later.

During 1633 Harvey took little part in the proceedings of the College of Physicians. He had attended on 9 November and 22 December 1632, but his name does not appear again in the Annals until 20 September 1633, when he and Dr. Atkins, a very senior Fellow and Physician in Ordinary to the King, wrote a letter tendering their resignations as Elects. The other Elects after due consideration decided that there were no adequate reasons for this and the resignations were not accepted. It is clear, however, that Harvey's duties at court made him feel justifiably that he was not able to give proper attention to College affairs. He did not appear again at Comitia until 25 October, when he was requested by the President to attend with four other Fellows at the Star Chamber 'to answeare to a Complaynte made by the Courte of Aldermen to the Lords of the Counsell concerninge the quill of water latelye taken by the Colledge which had bine fraudulently cutt of by the plummer some nine moneths before our taking it agayne, and for which the Colledge had bine sutors to the Lord Maior and Courte of Aldermen, but wear putt of with good words'. A 'quill of water' is to be understood to mean simply a small water-pipe. Harvey's deputation met the Aldermen, and the result was a proposal that if the College could prove their right to the water, they should have it; otherwise they should have 'such a quill as should runne 24 gallons in 24 houres, and the Colledge should att their owne charge make a Cisterne to receave so much water'. When this proposal was considered at Comitia it was 'utterly disliked', and a committee of nine with Harvey at their head was deputed to think further over the matter. The final outcome of this squabble was not recorded in the Annals.

Harvey attended again on 23 December, when the President gave notice that the library was to be open on all College days, and on 23 March 1633/4, when Comitia decided that 'ther must bee dilligent enquyrye made for the proof of the alehouses selling purging ale'. We are left in doubt as to whether this was to protect the drinking public or the physicians' monopoly in the administration of purging drugs; probably it was the latter.

On 25 June 1634 the President was complaining of the continued disrespect shown by the Apothecaries and particularly by a 'Mr. Smith dwelling in the old balye'. He had ignored a subpœna to attend at the College, but, having been advised by Dr. Harvey to come to the President, he had announced that he feared nobody under the degree of Privy Councillor. He was accordingly 'excommuned' by Comitia, presumably with Harvey's acquiescence, since he was present.

We are given a glimpse of Harvey's medical practice during February 1633/4 in the form of a licence for a patient to eat meat during Lent. After the Reformation the observance of Lent had resolved itself into abstinence from animal food other than fish. This was also observed on ordinary Fridays, and Queen Elizabeth had added Wednesdays, not, as she said, because she was superstitious, but in order to benefit the fishing industry.[1] An additional Act was passed in the fifth year of her reign allowing meat to be eaten during Lent on production of a doctor's certificate that this was necessary.[2] Commonly the illness was fictitious, the 'patient' obtaining a licence from the churchwardens on payment of a sum of money to be added to the Poor Box of the parish. A Lord of Parliament and his wife paid 26*s*. 8*d*., a Knight and his wife 13*s*. 4*d*., and a lesser person 6*s*. 8*d*. If the sickness continued for more than eight days, the licence was to be registered in the churchwardens' book, 4*d*. being charged for this. Harvey sometimes took the Act seriously, and the following entry is found on the paper fly-leaf of a volume of the Baptismal Registers of St. Anne, Blackfriars:[3] 'A licence to eate flesh was granted to Sʳ Tho Edolph Knight by reason of his weaknesse certified by William Harvey Dʳ of Physick wʰ continued above eight daies from 24 Febr 1633.' Sir Thomas Edolph was the son of Simon Edolph, to whom Elizabeth had granted St. Radegund's Abbey, Ringswould, near Dover. Sir Thomas seems also to have had a London residence in the parish of St. Anne's, Blackfriars. Two of his servants were buried there in February and April 1634.

Soon after this incident Harvey became involved in the vexed question of witchcraft and its supposed practitioners.

[1] See C. Pendril, *Old Parish Life in London*, Oxford, 1937, p. 52.

[2] 5 Eliz. I. cap. 5. An Act touching certayne Politique Constitutions made for the maintenance of the Navye, section xii, 'Proviso for Persons having Licences to eat Flesh on Payment of certain sums to the Poors' Box of the Parish'.

[3] Guildhall Library, MS. 4508/1, noticed by Mr. Brian Burch, one of the Library staff, who communicated it to me in 1964, with notes on Sir Thomas Edolph.

25

HARVEY AND THE WITCHES, 1634

HARVEY lived through a period when witchcraft was arousing interest, fear, mass hysteria, and controversy. Responsibility for this must be laid to some extent on Harvey's master, King James, though Harvey did not, as far as we know, become directly concerned in the examination of witches until the succeeding reign. Stories of witchcraft and witch-hunting had been rife in Scotland in the sixteenth century and Reginald Scott, an Oxford graduate, had published his book *A Discovery of Witch-craft* in 1584 in an attempt to illuminate the dark places of superstition with the light of reason and so to cast doubt on the reality of witchcraft. Shakespeare used this book as a source for the witches in *Macbeth* in an endeavour to provide a dramatic setting which would satisfy popular beliefs, without implying that he himself believed in witchcraft. King James, however, was indignant at Scott's disbelief and wrote his *Daemon-ologie in form of a Dialogue*, published in Edinburgh in 1597; there were two further editions in 1603, and it was reprinted in his collected *Workes*, London, 1616. The King was honestly convinced of the reality of magicians and witches and so of the evil consequences that might be suffered by his subjects from their spells. He therefore enjoined 'vigilance and great severity' when persons accused of witchcraft had been tried and found guilty. He was quite aware of the danger of condemning innocent persons for a crime so difficult to prove, but, nevertheless, argued that because English law allowed the evidence of children and women to be taken against persons accused of treason, then still more must such witnesses be credited in trials of witches.[1] The admission of this kind of evidence was one of the most serious features of the horrible cruelties committed on the bodies of supposed witches almost throughout the seventeenth century in all parts of the country. Belief in witchcraft even survived export across the Atlantic, and arose in an acute form in the epidemic of witch-hunting investigated at Salem in New England in 1694.

It was in 1633 that the events took place in Pendle Forest near Burnley in Lancashire that led to Harvey's being called as a witness in the following year. This remote area in the north-west had been for some years

[1] James I, *Workes*, 1616, p. 135.

agitated by a series of crimes attributed to witches, gossip leading to fanciful accusations conceived in the fertile brains of imaginative children or even taught them by their elders. The particular story that ultimately concerned Harvey began on 10 February 1633. A boy of 11 named Edmund Robinson made an elaborate deposition before two Justices of the Peace, Richard Shutleworth and John Starkey, at Padiham, alleging that on All Saints Day last (1 November 1632) he was gathering wild plums in Wheatley Lane, when he saw two greyhounds, one brown the other black, running in his direction over the next field. Each dog, he noticed, had a collar which 'did shine like gold', but though each had a string attached there was no one with them. At the same moment he saw a hare, and, thinking to set the dogs off after it, cried 'Loo, loo, loo', but they would not run. This angered him, and tying them by their strings to a bush, he beat them with a stick. Thereupon the black dog stood up in the person of the wife of one Dickenson, and the brown dog as a small boy he did not know. In his fright Robinson made to run away, but was stopped by the woman, who, producing a silver coin from her pocket, offered to give it to him if he would hold his tongue. This he refused, saying, 'Nay, thou art a witch'. She then pulled from her pocket a sort of bridle that jingled, put it on the head of the boy that had been a dog, who then turned into a white horse. Seizing young Robinson, the woman mounted him on the horse in front of her and rode with him to a house called Hoarstones, a locality well known as a gathering place for witches.[1] Many other people then came riding up on horses of various colours to the number of about threescore, and meat was roasted. A young woman tried to make him eat some of this and to drink something out of a glass, but he refused after the first taste of it. He then saw various people go into a neighbouring barn, where six of them kneeled and pulled on ropes fastened to the roof. This brought down smoking flesh, lumps of butter, and milk, which they caught in basins. Then six more people repeated the process, making such fearful faces that he stole out in terror and ran home, where he told his father that he had also seen the woman pricking pictures with thorns. When it was noticed that the boy had escaped, a party of people, several of whom he named, started in pursuit and had nearly caught up with him at a place called Boggard-hole, when two horsemen came up and rescued him. On the same evening Robinson's father sent him to tie up two cows in their stalls, and on the way, in a field called the Ellers, he met another boy who picked a quarrel and made him fight until his ears were made

---

[1] Hoarstones is still marked on the map close to the road from Padiham to Barrowford.

very bloody. Looking down he saw that the aggressor had a cloven foot, which aroused fresh fears. He ran on to find the cows and saw the light of a lantern; thinking it was carried by friends he ran towards it only to find a woman on a bridge, whom he recognized, and turned back to meet again the boy with the cloven foot, who gave him a blow on the back and made him cry. The boy's father in confirmation of the story said he had gone to look for him and found him in a state of terror and crying pitifully, so that he did not recover for nearly a quarter of an hour. In his deposition[1] to the magistrates the boy gave the names of seventeen persons whom he knew as present at Hoarstones and said he could recognize others.

On the principles laid down by King James this fantastic story had to be believed, and the boy was taken round by his father to various churches in the district and identified many more people among the congregations, money being paid for his services. It so happened that at the church of Kildwick,[2] where he was taken, the curate was David Webster, who in 1677 published an important book, *The Displaying of Supposed Witchcraft*, exposing the frauds perpetrated in witch-hunts. Webster related that he asked the boy if he had truly seen and heard the strange things that he described, but two ill-favoured men who were in charge of him forbade the boy to answer, saying that he had already been examined by two Justices. As a result of this nearly thirty people were imprisoned, and a variety of other accusations were hurled at them by their enraged neighbours. A trial took place at Lancaster after the prisoners had been searched for any suspicious marks on their bodies, and seventeen were found guilty on this evidence. Great importance was attached to the discovery of marks on witches' bodies, since it was believed that the devil put his marks on those allied to him, and these places then became callous and insensitive. The law therefore required that the accused should be scrutinized by a jury of the same sex together with one doctor or several. The head was to be shaved and every part of the body handled. Any callous spot that was found was to be pricked with pins, and, if it was insensitive, that was evidence of guilt. Search was also to be made for anything resembling a teat capable of suckling the witch's familiar or imp, which might take the form of a rat, mouse, frog, toad, bird, fly, or spider; sometimes the imps were in the form of larger animals such as a cat or dog. King James in his *Daemonologie* believed firmly in two 'good helps that may be used for their triall: the

---

[1] Printed in full by David Webster in *The Displaying of Supposed Witchcraft*, London, 1677, pp. 347–9.   [2] A village near Skipton in Yorkshire.

one is, the finding of the marke and the trying the insensibleness thereof: the other is their fleeting on the water',[1] since those in whom the devil resided were lighter than normal people and so floated when thrown into a pond.

Fortunately for the seventeen Lancashire prisoners found guilty, it was requested that seven of them should be seen by John Bridgeman, Bishop of Chester, in whose diocese they lived. The Bishop went to the gaol, but by then three of them had died and a fourth, Jennet Hargreaves, was very ill. Of the remaining three, two denied all knowledge of witchcraft, but the third, Margaret Johnson, declared herself to have been a witch for six years. She had stated on 9 March 1633 before the same Justices who had examined Edmund Robinson, that in a fit of anger and discontent a devil had appeared to her in the form of a man 'apparrelled in a suite of blacke, tied about with silk pointes, whoe offered her, if shee would give him her soule, hee would supply all her wantes, and at her appointment would helpe her to kill and revenge her either of men or beeste, or what she desired'. To this she agreed and the devil bade her call him Memillion, and when she called he would be ready to do her will. She denied being at the meeting at Hoarstones (or Hare-stones) on the particular day described by Robinson, but admitted being there on the next Sunday, when various evil plans were concerted. She further declared 'that such witches as have sharpe boanes are generally for the devil to prick them with which have no papps nor duggs, but raiseth blood from the place pricked with the boane, which witches are more greater and grand witches then they which have papps or duggs'. After further boastings she said that since 'this trouble befell her, her Spiritt hath left her, and shee never saw him since'.

After his examination the Bishop reported the affair to the Secretary of State, Sir John Coke, and so it came to the ears of King Charles. The King was a less credulous man than his father, and he ordered the Lord Privy Seal, Henry Montagu, Earl of Manchester, to write to the Court doctors as follows:

To Alexander Baker Esq., and Sergiant Clowes his Majesty's Chirurgions.

These shalbe to will and reqire you forth with to make choise of such Midwives as you shall thinke fitt to inspect and search the Boddies of those women that were lately brought by the Sheriff of the Countie of Lancaster indited for witchcraft and to report unto you whether they

---

[1] Loc. cit., pp. 135–6.

finde about them any such markes as are pretended; wherein the said midwives are to receave instructions from Mr. Dr. Harvey his Majesty's Physician and yourselves;

Dated at Whytehall the 29th of June 1634.

H. Manchester[1]

The four prisoners, including Jennet Hargreaves, who had now recovered, had been brought to London and were held at the Ship Tavern in Greenwich. They were now examined by the prescribed jury at Surgeon's Hall in Monkwell Street, and the following report was returned:

Surgeons Hall in Mugwell Streete London 2[d] July A[o] D[ni] 1634 We in humble obeyance to your Lordshipps have this day caled unto us the Chirurgeons and Midwyves whose names are hereunder written who have by the directions of Mr. Doctor Harvey (in our presence and his) made diligent searche and Inspection on those women which weare lately brought upp from Lancaster and ffynd as followeth vidz.

On the bodyes of Jennett Hargreaves, Ffrances Dicconson, and Mary Spencer nothinge unnaturalle neyther in their secrets or any other partes of theire bodyes, nor anythinge lyke a teate or marke nor any Signe that any suche thinge haith ever beene.

On the bodye of Margaret Johnson wee fynd two thinges maye be called teats the one betweene her secretts and the ffundament on the edge thereof the other on the middle of her left buttocke. The first in shape lyke to the teate of a Bitche, but in our judgements nothinge but the skin of the ffundament drawen out as yt wilbe after the pyles or applicacion of leeches. The seacond is lyke the nipple or teate of a woman's breast but of the same colour with the rest of the skin without any hollowness or yssue for any bloode or juyce to come from thence.

Midwives

Margryt Franses	Anna Ashwell
Aurelia Molins	Ffrancis Palmer
Amis Willuby	Katheren Manuche
Rebecke Layne	Clifton
Sibell Ffellipps	Joane Sensions

Surgeons

Alexander Read

W. Clowes	Rich[d] Wateson
Alex. Baker	Ja. Molins
Ric. Mapes	Henry Blackley[2]

This statement, bearing every mark of Harvey's precise and logical

[1] Public Record Office, *Domestic State Papers*, 1634, cclxx.   [2] Ibid., cclxxi.

mind, was not signed by himself, Alexander Read having taken his place. As a result four of the seven witches were pardoned by the King, who had himself seen them. Subsequently the boy Robinson, having been brought to London with his father, was re-examined alone and confessed to being an impostor. His father, he said, and some others had taught him what he was to say with a view to making some money out of the story; in fact at the time of the supposed meeting at Hoarstones he was some distance away gathering plums in another man's orchard. David Webster said Robinson was still alive in 1677 and was known as Ned of Roughs;[1] probably he was living in the village of Roughlee in Pendle Forest.

Corroboration of the importance attached at the time to the presence of insensitive spots in the skin both of supposed witches and of their victims is to be found in Harvey's writings. It is evident that Harvey quite early in his career had become aware of the kind of hysterical symptoms in young women which led to their making false accusations of witchcraft against persons believed to have bewitched them. About the year 1605 a girl named Anne Gunter was reported to have suffered by witchcraft and was brought to London to be examined on behalf of King James. Harvey had been admitted as a Candidate at the College of Physicians in October 1604, and it was in March 1604/5 that the Bishop of London requested the College to investigate the girl in order to ascertain whether she were indeed possessed of the devil. The College appointed Drs. Wilkinson, Dunne, and Argent to do this; the doctor in charge of the patient was Dr. Edward Jorden (or Jordan), who became a Fellow of the College in 1597. Jorden reported that in his opinion she was a cheat. The King then undertook the investigation himself and got her to confess that she had pretended to be bewitched in order to revenge herself on another woman with whom she had quarrelled. 'After which Confession she was very quiet, and the King giving her a Portion, she was afterwards married, being by this subtle artifice perfectly cured of her mimical witchery.'[2] All of the men concerned in the inquiry were friends or acquaintances of Harvey, who a few years later showed his knowledge of the case by a cryptic passage in his lecture notes:[3]

> . . .//Nan gunter &c puto callum
> fecisse//the mad woman pins in her arme
> Mary pin her cross-cloth . . .

[1] Webster, loc. cit., pp. 277–8.
[2] Jorden removed soon after 1611 to Bath. The quotation is from his book, *Discourse of Natural Bathes and Mineral Waters*, ed. Guidott, London, 1669.
[3] Harvey's *Prelectiones anatomiae universalis*, London, 1886, f. 11, verso.

The Latin words have been interpreted as meaning, 'I consider that Nan Gunter made a callous', that is, an area of skin insensitive to pain, such as those to which King James attached so much importance. Harvey's reference to the girl's fraud is followed in his notes by mention of two other similar cases. One of these, a girl called Mary, a patient in St. Thomas's Hospital, was described many years later to Robert Boyle,

by that excellent and experienc'd Lithotomist, Mr. Hollyer, who told me that among the many Patients sent to be cured in a great Hospital (of which he is one of the Chirurgions) there was a Maid of about eighteen Years of age, who, without the loss of motion, had so lost the sense of feeling in the external parts of her Body, that when he had, for tryal sake, pinn'd her Handkerchief to her bare Neck, she went up and down with it so pinn'd without having any sense of what he had done to her. He added, That this maid having remained a great while in the Hospital without being cured, Dr. Harvey, out of Curiosity, visited her sometimes; and suspecting her strange Distemper to be chiefly Uterine, and curable onely by *Hymeneal* Exercises, he advised her Parents (who sent her not thither out of poverty) to take her home, and provide her a Husband, by whom, in effect, she was according to his Prognostick, and to many Mens wonder, cured of that strange Disease.[1]

We can thus see that Harvey already had experience of practical psychiatry when he applied his mind to the problem of the Lancashire witches, and so brought to a conclusion one of the most celebrated episodes in the history of witchcraft, the fraud being exposed by his objective evidence.

Another incident, this time little known, is related in what purports to be a seventeenth-century manuscript printed in the *Gentleman's Magazine* for 1832.[2] Here, a letter to the Editor, dated Malmesbury 5 May, and signed B. C. T., is sent with a copy of 'a manuscript containing some particulars upon the subject of Demonology', particularly in Wiltshire. The copy begins with an account of the ancient Corporation of Malmesbury and some particulars of its history. Then follows a letter headed *Ash Wednesday 1685/6* addressed to 'Most Honoured and Reverend Sir'. It appears in the first part of the letter that the writer is one of the Justices for the County of Wiltshire and the recipient a clergyman at

---

[1] Boyle, *Some Considerations touching the Usefulness of Experimental Philosophy*, Oxford, 1663, pp. 72–73. The cases of Nan Gunter and Mary were first fully discussed by Richard Hunter and Ida Macalpine in their papers, 'A Note on William Harvey's "Nan Gunter"', *Journal of the History of Medicine* (1957), xii. 512–15, and in *St. Bartholomew's Hospital Journal* (1956), lx. 200–6.

[2] Vol. cii, N.S. xxi, pt. i for 1832, pp. 405–10, 489–92.

Cambridge. He describes the trial of thirteen persons accused of witch-craft, and draws attention to the pains he took to prevent injustice being done and to discover whether there was 'any practice in the case, or any madness, deep melancholy or hatred of life in *Tilling*' (one of the persons on trial). Then follows an anecdote about Dr. Harvey and a witch's 'familiar', and with this the letter ends, unsigned. A long account is then given of a number of individuals who had suffered because of witches, with details of the events supposed to have taken place. The names of persons include John Barlowe's wife, executed about fifty-five years since; Alice Elgar, widow, dwelling in Westport about 1643; Orchard, widow, thought to be a confederate of Elgar, who came to the house of Hugh Bartholomew and was eventually executed. The copy concludes with an account, dated 16 January 1685/6, of the trial of Ann Tilling, with Peacock, Mitchell, and others; these were not convicted, but those named were to be kept under constraint and the Justices ad-vised that two or more of the ablest divines should be summoned to confer with them.

The authenticity of the manuscript, said to have been copied, has never been confirmed and it seems possible that it was a fabrication, although the anecdote about Harvey, interpolated in an otherwise circumstantial account of trials of witches in Wiltshire,[1] would seem to be pointless if it were invented. The story, if genuine, has certainly been embellished in the telling, but Harvey's attitude to the presumed 'familiar' and his trial of its supernatural pretensions by direct experiment with his dissecting knife is quite in line with his character. He is known to have been some-times with King Charles I at Newmarket, and we have clear evidence that he was there in February 1636, Mayerne having addressed his letter to Newmarket when advising Harvey about the treatment of the Elector Palatine.

The anecdote is as follows:

I acknowledge with wonder sufficient I have heard severall persons, very learned otherwise, affirme there were not, neyther could be, any witches; amongst others, Doctor Harvey was induced by a very weake experiment to be of that mind; I was very familiarly acquainted with him, and was often abroad with him, and had severall discourses with him of things in his faculty, but principally about natural philosophy, I

---

[1] Aubrey in his *Natural History of Wiltshire* (p. 121) stated that in the 1670's 'there was a cabal of witches detected at Malmesbury. They were examined by Sir James Long of Draycot-Cerne and by him committed to Salisbury gaol. I think there were seven or eight old women hanged.' The account of the trial is regarded as genuine; see Wallace Notestein, *A History of Witchcraft in England from 1558 to 1718*, Washington & London, 1911, pp. 160, 269.

agreeing with him for much the more part. I once asked him what his opinion was concerning Whitchcraft; whether there was any such thing? Hee told mee he believed there was not. I asked him what induced him to be of that opinion? He told me that when he was at Newmercat with the King, he heard there was a woman who dwelt at a lone House on the borders of the Heath, who was reputed a Witch; that he went alone to her, and found her alone at home, alighted, and went into the House to her. Hee said shee was very distrustful at first; but when hee told her he was a vizard, and came purposely to converse with her in their common trade, then shee easily believed him; for, say'd hee to mee, you know I have a very magicall face, and looking upon mee, and gathering up his face, I indeed thought hee had; so hee proceeded. I asked where her familiar was? and desired to see him. Shee immediately fetched a little milk, and put it in a flat dish, and went to a chest and chucked with her mouth, as toades doe when they call one another; and immediately a toad came from under the chest, and drunk some of the milke. I sayd it was enough, and caused her to take awaye the dish before the toad had done, and asked the Woman whether she had any ale to sell, for they beinge Brother and Sister must drink together. She sayd there was ale to be sold about halfe a mile thence; hee desired her to goe to fetch some, whilst he stayed, and gave her a shilling; away she went for the ale. Hee tooke milke, when she was a goode waye on her way, went to the chest, chucked as shee did, the toad came out. His tongues [tongs] were ready in his hand, he catched up the toad in them; his dissecting knife was ready alsoe, he opened the toades belly, out came the milk. Hee examined the toades entrayles, heart, and lungs, and it no ways differed from other toades, of which hee had disected many, ergo it was a playne naturall toad. The Old Woman was melancholy and poore; found the toad some evening abroad eating spiders, for hungry toades will eat spiders and other reptiles or insects; carried it home, made it tame by feeding it, and so it became a spirit, and that spirit a familiar. From hence he concludes there are no witches very logistically; his argument in effect is this:—A Woman had a tame toade, which she believed to bee a spirit and her familiar; the toad upon disection proved an arrant naturall toad, and had really eaten milk, and not in appearance onely, therefore there are no witches. The Good Doctor upon the Woman's returne, who found him busy in observing what the toad would doe in the Pickle hee had put him in, was in danger to have a more magical face than hee had before, and habit too; the Woman let or rather threw down the Pitcher of Ale, flew like a Tigris at his face; twas well hee had nothing but bare bones and tough tanned skin, neyther hair nor bearde, and twas well his eyes were out of reach, well guarded with prominent bones, otherways it had gone ill with him, but for his short very short old black coat, that scaped not so well, that pay'd for killing the poor Woman's Divell. The Doctor intreeted fayrly, offered money, would have persuaded twas not a Divell, but a meer toad. That way not prevayling, hee turned his tale, sayd hee was the King's Phisitian, sent by the King to discover whether indeed shee was a witch; if a witch, to have her apprehended; if not, to undeceave her, if hee could. The Name of the King, and the word apprehending, brought her into a better temper; and after having been called 1000 old cheating rogues, and as many times freely given to the Divell, the Doctor got away; tolde the Kinge, whose leave he had to go upon the expedition, the whole story, which was pleasant entertaynment for that good King at his dinner. I did know the Doctor's temper well, and that it did not much concern me what opinion he was of in that poynt. I onely say'd, I think I have heard their Spirits have recourse to toades or other animalls (which the witches keep and feed) at set times, or wherefore Spirits are called upon extraordinary occasions, but doe not exert them constantly, for then the poor divells would have a very bad time of it. I am certayne this, for an argument against Spirits or witchcraft, is the best and most experimentall I ever heard, and as logically managed as I ever expect to have any.— Pardon this long trouble, I beseech you, S^r, and bee pleased to beleeve there is no one honours you more than, Reverent S^r,

[no name]

So ends the episode of Dr. Harvey and the toad, but it is recorded in Hutchinson's *History of Witchcraft*, 1712, that in 1645 a witch was hanged at Cambridge for keeping a frog—further evidence, perhaps, of an East Anglian preference for having imps in the form of amphibians.

In spite of the endeavours of a scientist such as Harvey and of enlightened writers like Reginald Scott and David Webster, belief in witchcraft continued to be widespread. This is partly attributable to the religious beliefs of avowed Christians, who, in postulating a personal God, had perforce to believe in a personal Devil, or Principle of Evil; belief in Saints could lead logically to a belief in Witches. On this basis so enlightened a person as Sir Thomas Browne testified to the existence of witches, when some unlucky women were tried and condemned at Bury St. Edmunds in 1664 by Sir Matthew Hale, and still later Richard Baxter, the celebrated preacher, compiled a book entitled *The Certainty of the Worlds of Spirits, Apparitions and Witchcrafts*, which he published in 1691.

In contrast to this, it may be noted that neither of Harvey's friends John Selden and Thomas Hobbes believed that witches had any real powers, but held that acknowledged practitioners of the art deserved punishment because of their malign intentions. Selden delivered his opinion as follows:

The Law against Witches does not prove there be any; but it punishes the Malice of those People that use such means to take away Mens Lives. If one should profess that by turning his Hat thrice and crying Buz, he could take away a Man's Life (though in truth he could do no such thing) yet this were a just Law made by the State, that whosoever should turn his Hat thrice and cry Buz with an intention to take away a Man's Life shall be put to death.[1]

26

THE COLLEGE OF PHYSICIANS AND THE MIDWIVES* DR. PETER CHAMBERLEN

THE part played by Harvey at this time in the quarrels with the Society of Apothecaries has already been described, the dispute having had its origins at a much earlier date (see pp. 77–84). It would seem from the Annals that he tried to keep out of these disputes as far as possible by non-attendance, though on 28 August 1634 he was named *in absentia* as one of a Committee 'to consider and take care of our bussines'. Harvey's colleagues, as we have seen, invariably turned to him as the man of sense and influence who would help them to overcome their troubles. Probably, however, he was not a very active member of this particular body. He would, nevertheless, have been interested in a matter that arose in Comitia on 8 September of this year, when a petition from the Midwives of the City of London was received and answered. His name had been associated with those of ten midwives when he investigated the 'Lancashire witches', and it is generally accepted that he was an expert in this branch of medical practice. He has, indeed, been called 'the father of English midwifery' on the ground that he wrote what amounted to being the first English textbook on midwifery and gynaecology in the final section of his book, *De generatione animalium*, published in 1651. It is true that this section does not seem properly to belong to the rest of the book, being less a scientific treatise than a clinical study based on extensive personal experience.

[1] John Selden, *Table-Talk*, second edition, London, 1696, p. 186. Thomas Hobbes, *Leviathan*, London, 1651, chapter 2, expressed the same opinion.

Something more will be said about this part of Harvey's work in considering the book of 1651 and elsewhere. In the present connexion it is enough to note Harvey's opinion of the midwives. Young practitioners were supposed to be trained for seven years under older women, and some of the more intelligent ones no doubt learned a great deal. When their apprenticeship was over they were not subjected to any real test, since they were licensed to practice by the Bishops, a relic of the days when doctors too looked to the Archbishop of Canterbury for their licences. In Harvey's time the midwives of the City of London regarded themselves as an important and responsible body of women, who did, no doubt, possess a certain rough and ready competence born of experience. The appallingly high mortality among both infants and mothers which accompanied their work seems to have been accepted as natural and inevitable. Harvey, however, was not of this opinion and did not admire their methods. He wrote in *De generatione animalium* concerning parturition:

And therefore the younger, more giddy, and officious Midwives are to be rebuked; which, when they hear the woman in travaile cry out for paine and call for help, lest they should seem unskilful at their trade, and less busie then comes to their share, by daubing over their hands with oyles, and distending the parts of the Uterus, do mightily bestirre themselves, and provoke the expulsive faculty by medicinal potions: so that being impatient of a competent expectation by their desire to hasten and promote the Birth, they do rather retard and pervert it, and make it an unnatural and difficult delivery; and leaving the Membranes, or some part of the After-burden still adhering to the Womb, they do both expose the poor woman to the injuries of the Aire; and vainly perswading them to their three-legged stoole, weary them out and bring them in danger of their lives. It is much happier with poor women, and those that dare not own their great bellies, where the Midwives help is never required; for the longer they retain and retard the Birth, the easier and more successfull proves the delivery.[1]

Harvey believed in patience and gentleness, and thought, rightly, that a natural process should be left chiefly to Nature. His friend Dr. Willughby of Derby entirely agreed with him:

I know none but Dr. Harvey's directions and method, the which I wish all midwives to observe and follow, and oft to read over and over again, and, in so doing, they will better observe, understand and remember the sayings and doings of that most worthy, good and learned Dr.,

[1] *Anatomical Exercitations*, 1653, p. 488.

whose memory ought to be had for ever in great esteem with midwives and childbearing women.[1]

Male doctors were then still put at a disadvantage by the popular prejudice against the presence of a male person in the bedchamber during childbirth. If he wished to direct the delivery he must do his manipulations under the bedclothes without seeing what he was doing. Dr. Willughby had a way of getting round this. When his daughter, who was a trained midwife, was in difficulties with a breech presentation he crept into the room on hands and knees, so that he was not seen to be assisting, and succeeded in effecting the delivery.[2]

The midwives' petition to the College concerned the overbearing behaviour of Dr. Peter Chamberlen, who claimed the right to make the midwives attend monthly at his house with a view, they rightly suspected, to subjecting them to licensing by his own authority. Chamberlen was not *persona grata* at the College. He had graduated at Padua in 1619 and had become a Fellow of the College on 29 March 1628,[3] though not without misgivings among his colleagues, including Harvey. Although he was elected by a good majority of votes, he must have been a somewhat flamboyant person, for he was 'gravely warned by the President regarding the need to alter his style of clothing from that more like the dress worn by the very gay young men at court, and that he would not be admitted until he first accustomed himself to the decent habits of the College and the Fellows, and wore quiet garments'. He proved indeed to be an insubordinate person, and in 1659 was dismissed from his Fellowship for repeated contumacious acts. He was a prolific writer on many subjects, and among his books was *Dr. Chamberlain's Midwives' Practice*, London, 1665. In theory his attempt to regulate the practice of midwifery and so raise its status might have been thought worthy of support, but his trying in 1634 to constitute himself head of a Company of Midwives was evidently regarded as being chiefly for his own advantage. The Fellows of the College seemed to believe the midwives' charge that he was a rapacious and dishonest practitioner, and they supported the petition. His claims were considered at great length, and the ecclesiastical court, to which the matter was referred, refused to give him any countenance. Harvey appears not to have been able to find time to take any part in this affair. Several of the iron delivery forceps used by

[1] Percival Willughby, *Observations in Midwifery. As also The Countrey Midwife's Opusculum*, edited by H. Blenkinsop, Warwick, 1863, pp. 119–20.

[2] Ibid., pp. 135–6.

[3] Munk's *Roll*, 1861, i, p. 181 n.

PLATE XIX

THOMAS HOWARD, EARL OF ARUNDEL
From an oil painting by Rubens

PLATE XX

THOMAS PARR IN 1635

at the reputed age of 152. By an unknown painter

Chamberlen may be seen today at the Royal College of Obstetricians and Gynaecologists.

27

THE EARL OF ARUNDEL AND OLD PARR, 1635

THOMAS HOWARD, Earl of Arundel and Surrey, is famous as courtier, diplomatist, statesman, and connoisseur of pictures and objects of virtu during the reigns of James I and Charles I. He was the constant companion of Henry Prince of Wales during his short life, aiding and abetting him in his acquisition of pictures and books. With his noble lineage, great possessions, and intellectual distinction, Arundel was inevitably a leading personality in the society of the time, and he left his mark on the history of aesthetics in England. It has been reasonably conjectured[1] that the person responsible for moulding the tastes and interests of both Arundel and the Prince was the painter and architect Inigo Jones. He knew more than any other Englishman of the day about Italian art and architecture; he was intimately concerned in devising masques for the Prince on court occasions, for advising about the purchase of works of art, and for designing rooms to hold his pictures and his books. After Prince Henry's death, Charles, the new Prince of Wales, inherited his collections, and was soon eagerly collecting pictures on his own account, certainly with Arundel as one of his advisers. Arundel was made Earl Marshal of England by King James in 1621, and his name is thereafter associated with most events of importance in England until his death at Padua, aged 61, in 1646. His special passion in pictures was for the works of Hans Holbein the younger, who was also of interest to King Charles, but they shared more particularly a taste for Italian pictures in general, and an admiration for the work of Rubens and Van Dyke.

Harvey's position at the Court of King James from 1618 onwards must have brought him into contact and acquaintanceship with Arundel, whom he would undoubtedly have come to know well during the King's last illness. Both men were in assiduous attendance at the bedside and many grave conversations must have taken place as the King's symptoms worsened. There is evidence besides that Harvey had been in medical attendance on Arundel's family at least as early as 1616. In or about

[1] Mary Hervey, *The Life of Thomas Howard Earl of Arundel*, Cambridge, 1921, p. 63.

this year Anne Arundel, widow of Philip, the first Earl of Arundel and Surrey, wrote a sad letter to her son, the second Earl, telling him of the death of his small boy, Charles. Harvey had been called in at the last, and, after giving some details of the child's illness, the Countess wrote from Sutton in Surrey:

It pleased our blessed Savyour to take him to himselfe something before 4 o'clocke this after none, having suffered very sharp pains before his ende. Mr. Doctor Harvy is of the sam opinion that my Gilford neighbour Mr. Raner was today when he did purseve what he did avoyde [void], which is that some continued impostum caused his ende. I trust Mr. Doctore will so early be sturring as Mr. Ardern shalbe able to lett yr Lo. bee satisfyed of the inward true occasion, and I beseech you for godsake to conforte your selfe and my good sweet daughter with the true good of the sweete soule of your littel sonne.[1]

In 1635, ten years after the King's death, we have clear evidence of the friendship between Harvey and Arundel, for Aubrey remarked that Harvey was at this time 'a great favourite of the Lord High Marshall of England, Thomas Howard'.

Arundel is described as having been a person of peculiar distinction, of massive proportions in head and frame with high-bred aquiline features, brilliant dark eyes, and courteous manners.[2] This is well brought out by the portraits attibuted to Rubens now in the National and the National Portrait Galleries. Arundel was of hasty temper and autocratic will, but was warm and steadfast in his friendships. It is obvious that he greatly liked Dr. Harvey, a very positive character, also dark-eyed and courteous, but small in stature and tirelessly active and alert. It is from Harvey's closeness to Arundel that we infer he had a genuine interest in pictures and works of art, a taste which was to obtain some gratification during the Continental adventures to be described later.

In 1635 Arundel had occasion to visit some of his properties in Shropshire, and his attention was directed to an aged resident in the hamlet of Winnington, near Alberbury, thirteen miles from Shrewsbury. This ancient, by name Thomas Parr, was reputed to have been born in 1483 and so to have lived through the reigns of ten sovereigns from Edward IV to Charles I. The story of his life was written in doggerel verse by John Taylor, the self-styled 'Water-poet', this work, *The Old, Old, Very Old Man*, being published in 1635 soon after Parr's death, which the autopsy

[1] *Historical Manuscripts Commission, Twelfth Report*, i, 1888 (Earl Cowper, Melbourne Hall), p. 93.
[2] Hervey, op. cit., p. 234.

suggests was premature, if this term can be used of a man who died at
the supposed age of 152. Arundel was amused and interested by this
human phenomenon and decided to bring him up to London as an
exhibit for the King. He had a special litter constructed for his safe conveyance and, when he arrived in London, lodged him in his own house.
Parr's real age remains unknown, but John Taylor made the most of
what the old man related of his life. According to his account Parr was
first married at the age of 80, when he was 105 did penance for adultery
by standing in a white sheet in Alberbury Church, and married for the
second time at 112. It was forty years later that he came to London with
his wife and was on view for some weeks at the Queen's Head tavern in
the Strand. Parr boasted to the King that he had done penance as a cen-
tenarian, and when questioned about his religious beliefs wisely replied
that it was safest to be of the religion of the reigning King or Queen,
'for he knew that he came raw into the world and accounted it no point
of wisdom to be broiled out of it'.

John Taylor described Parr as follows:

> He will speak heartily, laugh and be merry,
> Drink ale, and now and then a Cup of Sherry;
> Loves Company, and understanding talk,
> And on both sides held up, will sometimes walk;
> And though old Age his Face with Wrinkles fill,
> He hath been handsome, and is comely still;
> Well fac'd, and though his Beard not oft corrected,
> Yet neat it grows, not like a Beard neglected;
> From Head to Heel, his Body hath all over
> A thickset, quickset, natural hairy Cover.

Parr's portrait by an unknown artist, perhaps commissioned by Arundel, shows that this description was justified by the facts—though it may
be that the growth of hair was fostered by its owner to support the
illusion of fabulous old age. Unfortunately his patron had brought about
too abrupt a change in the circumstances of Parr's life. Previously a frugal
husbandman, who had flailed corn at the age of 130, he was unaccus-
tomed to the more plentiful life of a celebrity in London, and he suc-
cumbed, it was thought, to the rich food and frequent toastings by his
new friends in the Strand. He was taken ill and quickly died in Arundel's
house on 14 November 1635, and Harvey, who had probably attended
him at the Earl's request, was commanded by the King to perform an
autopsy. The examination, performed on 16 November, did not reveal

any great ageing of the tissues of the body, but Harvey thought that the condition of the lungs showed that the old man had died of 'suffocation', and, indeed, his description of them suggests that there was pulmonary oedema, due perhaps to a rapidly failing heart, with a terminal pneumonia. Harvey gives a clinical history, followed by an account of his examination expressed in the terse language of the post-mortem room. It was the work of an experienced morbid anatomist and no relevant detail was omitted. Parr's remains were given the honour of burial in Westminster Abbey.

Harvey's report was as follows:[1]

On the sixteenth day of November in the year of Our Lord one thousand six hundred and thirty-five, that day being also the anniversary of the birth of her most Gracious Majesty Henrietta Maria, Queen of Great Britain, France and Ireland.

Thomas Parr, an Englishman and a native of Winnington, a village in Shropshire, was a poor farmer of extremely advanced age. My Lord Arundel, who happened to be in those parts and whose interest had been aroused by reports of this man's incredible age, had broken his journey to see him, and then carried him off from his rural surroundings to London. Both on the journey and in his own home, my Lord looked after him with every attention, and exhibited him to the King as a remarkable phenomenon. But when he had completed 152 years and nine months of life, and had outlived nine sovereigns and enjoyed ten years of the present joyful reign, he finally failed, and died on the fourteenth day of November in the year of our Saviour 1635.

The dissection of his dead body, carried out in accordance with the commands of his Gracious Majesty, was attended by some of the foremost physicians of the time. I made the following notes.

The appearance of the body was well nourished, the chest was hairy, and the hair on the forearm was still black, although the shins were hairless and smooth.

The genital organs were in good condition, the penis was neither retracted nor thin, nor was the scrotum, as is usual in old persons, distended by any watery hernia, while the testicles were large and sound—so good in fact as not to give the lie to the story commonly told of him that, after reaching his hundredth year, he was actually convicted of fornication and punished. Moreover his wife, a widow, whom he had

---

[1] The manuscript of Harvey's Latin report was given by his nephew, Michael Harvey, to Dr. John Betts, who printed it in his book *De ortu et natura sanguinis*, London, 1669, pp. 319–25. An abstract was printed in the *Philosophical Transactions of the Royal Society*, 1668, iii. 886–8. The translation given here is by Arnold Muirhead and was first printed in *St. Bartholomew's Hospital Reports*, lxxii, 1939.

married in his hundred and twentieth year, in reply to questions, could not deny that he had had intercourse with her exactly as other husbands do, and had kept up the practice to within twelve years of his death.

The chest was broad and full; his lungs were not spongy but, particularly on the right side, were attached to the ribs by fibrous bands. The lungs also were considerably distended with blood as is usual in pulmonary consumption (peripneumonia), so much so that before the blood was drawn off, a quantity seemed to become black. To this cause, too, I attributed the facial pallor, and, a little before death, a difficulty in breathing and orthopnœa. As a result, the armpits and chest remained warm long after death. To sum up, there were clearly visible in his dead body this and other signs customarily found in those dying from suffocation. I concluded that he was suffocated, and that death was due to inability to breathe, and a similar report was given to his Gracious Majesty by all the physicians present. Later, when the blood had been drained off and wiped away from the lungs, they were seen to have a quite white and almost milky parenchyma.

The heart was large, thick and fibrous with a considerable mass of fat around its wall and partition. The blood in the heart was blackish, liquid and scarcely grumous. Only in the right ventricle were some clots seen.

When the sternum was dissected the cartilages were not more osseous than in other men, but rather were flexible and soft.

The intestines were in excellent condition, fleshy and vigorous: the stomach was the same. The small intestine appeared muscular, but had some ring-shaped constrictions due to the fact that frequently he ate any kind of food both by day and night without any rules of diet or regular hours for meals. He was quite happy with half-rancid cheese and all kinds of milk dishes, hard brown bread, small beer, but more usually sour milk. By living frugally and roughly, and without cares, in humble circumstances, he in this way prolonged his life. He had taken a meal about the midnight shortly before his death.

The kidneys were hidden in fat and were quite large. Only on the front surface there were visible watery abscesses or small serous gatherings, one of which however was the size of a hen's egg, and contained light yellowish water in a separate cyst, and its round cavity penetrated into the kidney. To this cause some attributed the suppression of urine from which he suffered a little before his death; others, with greater probability, seem to have conjectured that the suppression of urine was due to all the serosity being drawn up into the lungs.

There was no stone in the bladder nor in the kidneys, nor was there any sign of one elsewhere.

The mesentery was very fat, and the colon and bands of fatter omentum were connected to the liver round about the fundus of the gall-bladder; the colon was attached on one side to the peritoneum, on the other to the hinder parts.

The intestines were good, although whiter on the outside as though they had been lightly boiled; inside (as was also the blood) they were stained the colour of black gore.

The spleen was remarkably small, and scarcely equal in size to a kidney. To sum up, all the internal organs seemed so sound that had he changed nothing of the routine of his former way of living, in all probability he would have delayed his death a little longer.

It was consistent to attribute the cause of death to a sudden adoption of a mode of living unnatural to him. Especially did he suffer harm from the change of air, for all his life he had enjoyed absolutely clean, rarefied, coolish and circulating air, and therefore his diaphragm and lungs could be inflated and deflated and refreshed more freely. But life in London in particular lacks this advantage—the more so because it is full of the filth of men, animals, canals and other forms of dirt, in addition to which there is the not inconsiderable grime from the smoke of sulphurous coal constantly used as fuel for fires. The air in London therefore is always heavy, and in autumn particularly so, especially to a man coming from the sunny and healthy district of Shropshire, and it could not but be particularly harmful to one who was now an enfeebled old man.

Moreover he had always hitherto existed on one kind of diet and that the simplest; therefore after he had gradually taken to a generous rich and varied diet, and stronger drink, he ruined the functions of almost all his natural parts. Finally, as the result of an increasingly sluggish stomach, less frequent expulsion of excreta, a slowing-up of the process of digestion, congestion of the liver, a less vigorous circulation of blood and numbness of his spirits, suppression of the activity of his heart which is the fount of life, constriction of the lungs which allowed no free passage of air, and the growing bulk of his body that prevented easy breathing and perspiration, it is not surprising that his soul was far from happy in such a prison and left it.

His brain was sound, and quite firm and solid to the touch. Therefore until just before his death, although he had been blind for twenty years, he could hear very well and understand what he heard, answer questions readily, and react normally to situations. He was even able to walk when lightly supported between two men. His power of memory however had failed considerably so that he had no clear remembrance of his own actions as a young man, of the public events, famous kings and leaders, wars and civil disturbances in his early youth, of customs, men, prices of goods offered for sale or the other occurrences usually remembered by men. He remembered only his actions of most recent years. However, even in his one-hundred and thirtieth year in order to be able to earn a livelihood it was his custom to be vigorously engaged in some work on the land, and he even threshed wheat.

Harvey's reference in his report to the impurity of London air anticipated John Evelyn's plan for improving it, developed in his *Fumifugium, or the Inconveniency of the Aer and Smoak of London Dissipated*, 1661. Evelyn was a schoolboy when Parr was in London, but he must have heard talk about the famous old man, and found him of use as an example; he wrote in *Fumifugium* that Parr 'was not so much concern'd with the change of Diet (as some have affirmed) as with that of the Aer, which plainly wither'd him, and spoyl'd his Digestion in a short time after his arrival in London'.

We do not know if another remarkable instance of longevity came to Harvey's notice. This was one Henry Jenkins, 'who is said to have lived from 1501 to 1670, 169 years. He remembered carrying arrows as a boy to the Battle of Flodden in 1513'.[1]

Harvey was in London during the remainder of this year, 1635, as is shown by his occasional attendances at the College Comitia, but nothing of note occurred in which he was personally concerned.

28

PRINCE CHARLES LOUIS, 1636

EARLY in the following year, 1635/6, Harvey addressed a petition to the King on behalf of his 'kinsman, Richard Francklyn'. The relationship between Harvey and Franklin has not been traced, and Franklin's name does not occur anywhere else in connexion with Harvey. The document,[2] with Harvey's petition and the King's reply, runs as follows:

To the King's most Excellent Matie—The humble petition of Doctor Harvy one of yor Maties physitions in ordinary for yo: household.

Humbly sheweth that whereas Richard Francklyn yor pet^s kinsman havinge a philizer's office in the Court of Common pleas of the Countie of Wiltes, Hants and the towne of South^ton duringe his life the value of 120 pounds.

[1] Sir A. S. MacNalty, 'William Harvey. His Influence on Public Health', Presidential Address to the Royal Society of Health, 1957, p. 9.

[2] *Calender of Domestic State Papers*, 1635–6, London, 1866, p. 339. The actual document has recently been found in the Bodleian Library, Oxford, Bankes Papers 41/20.

yor pet^r humbly praieth yor most Excellent Matie to grant the Revercion of the said office to Richard Francklyn his sonne for his life havinge beene in the said office & fitt for the execucion thereof

And yor pet^r shall ever pray for yor Matie

At the Court at Whitehall: 20 Mar 1635 His Maty is pleased to grant the Pet^r his desire and Mr. Attorney Gnll is to prepare a Bill for his Mats Signature accordingly for wch this shalbe his warr^t.

Fran. Windebank

Endorsed in the margin:

20 March 1635

Warrant for Mr. Fanklin's office of philizer to Mr. Franklin his sonn

Mr. Sec Windebank

A 'philizer' (also spelt filizer, filacer, or filazer) was formerly 'an officer of the superior courts at Westminster, who filed writs, &c., and issued processes thereon'. The office was abolished by an Act of 1837.[1] Sir Francis Windebank, Secretary of State to Charles I, will be frequently mentioned in the next episode in Harvey's life, in which he is seen travelling widely in Europe during the nine months immediately following the presentation of this petition.

In January 1635/6 Harvey was at Newmarket with the King and was having trouble in controlling Charles's nephew, Prince Charles Louis, eldest surviving son of the Queen of Bohemia, and prospective Elector Palatine. The youth, now aged 21, had been ill, but was impatient of the sensible advice given him by the King's physician, who thereupon wrote to his senior colleague, Sir Theodore de Mayerne, for help. Mayerne's reply[2] contains much grave counsel on the irresponsibility of princelings and how to deal with them, and illustrates incidentally the difficulties inherent in making consultations by post with insufficient clinical details.

To Master Doctor Harvey the King's Physician, Newmarket
For the Lord Prince Elector Palatine

Your Excellency

His Serene Highness would have done better if he had followed reason rather than desire and youthful advice, and had stayed in town till the King's return, and had applied himself seriously and patiently to revivifying his strength which was much exhausted by his previous illness.

---

[1] *New English Dictonary.*

[2] The Latin text is printed in de Mayerne's *Opera*, London, 1700, pp. 361–2. It is here translated for the first time by W. R. LeFanu. The original manuscript copy is in the British Museum, Sloane MS. 1998, pp. 19^v–20^v.

He ought to have deferred the more violent exercises of riding to the hunt and playing at ball till a later and more suitable time, particularly when rough and very changeable winter weather with raging north winds not merely advised but imperiously commanded.

But truly such is the race of all Princes, to adventure what they will, even at the cost of health, so that their physicians ought deservedly to be thought unfortunate since they must play the part of Cassandra on the Court stage, and whatever they advise or propose by way of precaution on the ground of a dangerous outcome, either they are not heard or, if not laughed at, at least ignored. In the end this spurned advice reverts upon their Lordships themselves.

Your letter says that His Highness was worn out by his labours and fell into a fever, whose type it was very difficult to explain with certainty in such a short space of time. To be sure a body may be quite abundant in humours, and rather sharp ones I should think, yet turning to the better part I flatter myself so much that I may persuade myself the fever arose from the cold he took, perhaps from his condition being suddenly restrained while playing ball and not resolved by rubbing, which the Prince avoided, as was right, and that in its boiling-up the fever was inclined by its inward nature to be a putrid one, once the matter has been acquired it acts and suffers by turns. I should write variously about the idea of the disease, if I knew more of the peccant humours' motions and circuits, which at least the physician who is present has opportunity to observe thoroughly. I can scarce imagine in recovery any malignancy recurring after the raging of the measles, though a violent agitation of the humours could be cause enough to produce a new ferment by which smallpox very often breaks out, after measles; now let that be enough for my hypothetical discussion with you.

The present fever is not of one tone, but you thought it remarkable not only for remission but for intermission; there is headache, perhaps from roughness of the brain and disposition to catarrh, which has here wearied the Prince beyond measure. You did well to administer clysters, well to prescribe a diet light in both kinds, and to give cardiacs with caution. Now, as you write, since the fever continues you have a mind to let blood from the basilic vein. All continuing fevers are most successfully shortened by blood-letting, particularly when the body is young, accustomed to drinking strongish wine and troubled with fullness on the vessels, though languid powers may not support this noble protection. The strength of the pulse seems to me naturally somewhat weaker than normal in His Most Serene Highness, wherefore if disease of the blood should demand evacuation (and it will demand it if the inflammation continues with burning urine, which would indicate that inflammation had arisen in the greater vessels), be careful as to the quantity of the evacuation. Nay be very careful, if there is no great urgency in deciding on a remedy whose application, however skilfully done, will scarce escape calumny.

You know how evilly petechial fevers may develop, and their slight beginnings acquire deadly increase in a few days. You know that around their first augmenting there is very frequently a dribbling eruption of blood with a very unhappy prospect, let me not suggest any evil, but in a princely person, particularly, abundant caution will never do harm; as I am absent I suggest this to you but vaguely and close my letter with this advice to a prudent friend.

In more serious cases Hippocrates bids physicians be advised by physicians; in Princes all things are serious, and Galen himself feared to prescribe wine and pepper (things harmless, nay healthful) for the Emperor's son who was suffering from wasting of the stomach. So if the affection continues, take care not to be alone, and while you study to show your skill in the art by contending single-handed and to make your own immediate decisions, take care that the mischance of an uncertain or prolonged (I would not say dangerous) outcome fall not on you by the judgement of the crowd who too readily dislike our art. While I strive daily to exercise my professional experience outside the Court without criticism or advice, though I never refuse it, yet I always attack royal illnesses with a group of physicians fighting at my side.

Greet the Prince's Most Serene Highness in my name and in our colleague Mr. Lister's. I hope that here likewise we might be able to fight the enemy which we hope to drive away quickly. May all succeed happily for you in your arduous duty. Farewell for my sake, who am Your very loving

Mayerne

You will remember that the Prince was very lightly purged, and should be better purged when the fever has abated, not to feed the ferment of a new calamity. A gentleman from the Prince's household, M. de Beringhem, after exercise at ball fell into the measles (he had admittedly been purged too often before), was gravely ill, and is still oppressed by a very importunate diarrhoea.

London, 3 February 1636.

29

CONTINENTAL JOURNEY WITH THE
EARL OF ARUNDEL, 1636

IN 1635 the Catholic Emperor Ferdinand of Germany had concluded a treaty of peace with the Elector of Saxony. One result of this treaty, if ratified by the Electors, would be that the Duke of Bavaria, also a Catholic and recently married to the Emperor's daughter, would be confirmed in the possession of the Upper Palatinate and in the title of Elector, thus depriving Prince Charles Louis of his rights. It was impossible for King Charles to go to war on behalf of his nephew, and he decided that the best he could do would be to send an impressive embassy to see the Emperor at Ratisbon (Regensburg), where a Diet was about to be held. The embassy was to be led by the Earl of Arundel, who realized that his mission was probably hopeless, but was prepared to do his best for the sake of the King and his sister, the Queen of Bohemia, to both of whom he was devoted. A very large retinue was necessary if any impression was to be made and was also advisable for reasons of safety, the country to be traversed being still much disturbed by the presence of Spanish troops engaged in the seemingly endless fighting of the Thirty Years War, now in its eighteenth year.

Arundel chose to take as his personal attendants a secretary, Edward Walker, whom he had first met when they both accompanied the King to Scotland in 1633; a lawyer and officer in the College of Arms, Sir John Borough; an official recorder, William Crowne; and a doctor, William Harvey, leaving no doubt as to where his preference lay by his choice of a medical adviser from among the many available at Court. The King's care for his physician's interests is shown by an order signed by Secretary Windebank on 5 April 1636: 'A letter to the Earle of Arundell & Surrey, Earle Marshall of England and his Majesty's Ambassador extraordinary to the Emperor of Germany, Signifying his Majesty's pleasure that Dr. Harvy his Majesty's physitian in Ordinary attending his person who is now to attend his lordship in the said Ambassage be not prejudiced in any sort by reason of his absence.' At the same time 'A safe Conduct in Latine for the said Dr. Harvy' was to be provided.[1]

[1] Public Record Office, Signet Docquet Book, 5 April 1636.

As we have seen, Harvey had been looking after the health of the young Elector Palatine and had found him a headstrong youth, unwilling to take advice. Harvey's interest in politics seems always to have been small, but this personal touch may have given him some sympathy for the purpose of the mission. Yet the chief pleasures he anticipated in the expedition were certainly the possibility of meeting distinguished foreign members of his profession and of finding new kinds of animals for dissection and study. He was also going to enjoy seeing the pictures and other works of art in the principal cities to be visited. The whole journey was described by Crowne and printed in his *True Relation*[1] published in 1637. The party left London on 7 April 1636 and went by barge from Greenwich to Gravesend; then by coach to Canterbury and Margate, where they embarked on the King's ship *Happy Entrance*. They landed at Helvoets Sluis in Holland on the 10th, and travelled by boat and waggon to Brill, Delft, and The Hague, where they were met by the Queen of Bohemia. Here Arundel had the difficult task of trying to convince the Queen that everything possible was to be done, short of war, to obtain recognition of her son's rights.

At Arnhem the party found themselves in the middle of hostilities, and the Spaniards refused them a passage at Schenck's Sconce (Schenkenschanz), but next day the Dutch commander, having made a successful assault during the night, allowed them through. Again and again they were to be delayed by the dangerous conditions of their journey, and their feelings were constantly harrowed by the pitiful state of the few remaining inhabitants of the ravaged towns and villages. Arundel frequently gave money and provisions in an attempt to alleviate their misery.

They sailed up the Rhine to Wesel, but there slept in the boats to avoid another danger—a virulent epidemic of the plague, which was killing the inhabitants at the rate of thirty a day. Passing through Duisberg and Dusseldorf, they reached Cologne; this they found to be free from plague and so stayed there for a week. Here we get the first of several glimpses of Harvey provided by Arundel's letters to his friends at home. On 6 May he wrote to Secretary Windebank telling him that his son Francis, one of the junior members of the party, had been ill, but was well again after staying a night at Leiden under Harvey's care. He ended the letter: 'I have been this evening at the Jesuits' fair new

[1] William Crowne, *A True Relation of all the Remarkable Places and Passages Observed in the Travels of Thomas Lord Howard Earle of Arundel and Surrey . . . Anno Domini 1636*, London, 1637.

Plan of Harvey's journey with Lord Arundel in 1636 to Regensburg, Vienna, and Prague, with his independent journey to Venice, Rome, and Naples.

Church and College in this town, where they used me with all civility.
. . . I found in the College little Dr. Hervey, who means to convert
them.'[1] Arundel evidently enjoyed his doctor's occasional flashes of
sardonic humour. It should not be assumed, however, that Harvey hoped
to 'convert' the Jesuits to the protestant religion. It might have been the
doctrine of the circulation of the blood to which they were to be converted. Crowne relates that at Cologne the party viewed the Dome
where the 'Three Kings of Collein' were interred, and the Church of
St. Ursula, 'in which lyeth the bones of 1100 Virgins with St. Ursula'.

On 28 April they left Cologne in a barge pulled up the Rhine against
the current by nine horses, and so reached Coblenz. There a battle was
in progress, but both sides obligingly suspended the fighting to allow
them to pass in safety, and on 2 May they reached Mayence (Mainz).
Travelling up the river Maine they reached Frankfort, where they stayed
four days. Here the Church of St. Bartholomew was one of the places
visited, and the associations of the name may have aroused Harvey's
interest. During the next week the journey traversed country still disturbed by active war, and it was necessary to have armed guards patrolling
their stopping-places at night. They usually had to sleep, as Crowne says,
'on the plancher', that is, on the floor of their lodgings. Harvey at the
age of 58 cannot have enjoyed these discomforts, though he was not
accustomed to spending his money on luxuries and no doubt accepted
philosophically any unavoidable hardships.

On 11 May the embassy reached Nuremberg, where they stayed eleven
days, giving Harvey time to make the acquaintance of a distinguished
anatomist and Professor of Medicine at the University of Altdorf, near
the city. This was Caspar Hofmann, who had been an implacable
opponent of Harvey's doctrine of the circulation of the blood. It is
uncertain how many times the two scientists met, but the last occasion
was on 18 May, when Harvey gave a public demonstration[2] in an attempt
to convince Hofmann of the truth. Hofmann had promised to let Harvey
know his thoughts after he had seen the demonstration, and accordingly
on the next day wrote Harvey the following letter, from which it appears
that his views were still unchanged.

Your unbelievable kindness, my Harvey, makes me not only like you
but love you. Hence you have more readily obtained from me my

---

[1] Public Record Office, *Clarendon State Papers*, i. 519. Quoted by Hervey, op. cit., p. 361.
[2] Presumably in the anatomical theatre at Altdorf. Dr. Maurice Hofmann told Dr. Edward
Browne that this was the first theatre built in Germany and was rather larger than the one in
Vienna, holding a little over 200 auditors (Sir T. Browne's *Works*, ed. Keynes, 1964, iii. 203).

PLATE XXI

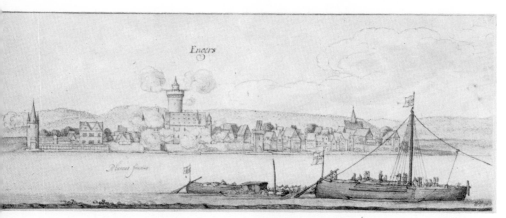

(i) ARUNDEL'S BARGES TOWED BY HORSES UP THE RHINE PASSING
ENGERS

(ii) ARUNDEL'S PARTY ROWED IN THEIR HOUSEBOATS DOWN THE
DANUBE

(iii) THE EXECUTIONS AT LINZ (p. 240)

Drawings by Hollar

fulfilment today of what I promised you yesterday, namely my opinion of your circulation. I hope, moreover, that you will accept it in the spirit in which I give it to you, with no malice to vex you, and without any conceitedness to make it appear that I know more than you. But simply and frankly. For this reason I guarantee you that if, after the clouds have been dispelled, you will show me the truth which is more beautiful than the evening and the morning stars, I will with Stesichorus publicly recant and retire from the field. And in order that I may not appear to seek circumlocutions, I think your sense is, *the blood carried to the arteries from the heart, etc.*

I will first deal with you here rhetorically. I. You appear to accuse Nature of folly in that she went astray in a work of almost prime importance, namely, the making and distribution of food. Once that is admitted, what degree of confusion will not follow in other works which depend on the blood?

II. You appear to disapprove in fact of that which you praise in word, namely the universally accepted view of Nature, that she is not lacking in the essentials but does not, however, abound in unnecessary things, etc.

To discharge my pledge, I wish you to receive these messages from my own hand. Fare you well, my Harvey, and walk well with your most illustrious Count, my most gracious Lord, whose hands I humbly kiss.

Written at Altdorf, the 19 May 1636.

Harvey succeeded in swallowing his annoyance, and immediately composed a long and good-tempered reply:

Your frank opinion of me, my learned Hofmann, and of the movement and circulation of the blood, was very pleasant to me, and I rejoice at having seen and spoken with a man so learned, whose affection I so gladly accept as to return it. First you thought fit to indict me rhetorically, and tacitly to censure me because I seemed to you to charge and convict Nature of folly and of error, and to characterize her as a very stupid and idle worker to the extent that she would let the blood recrudesce, and with a view to its concoction let it return again and again to the heart, and with a view to its recrudescence equally often to the body in general, and this with the object that Nature, in order to have something to do, may uselessly destroy the formed and perfected blood, But indeed, as I am quite unaware where or when I said and thought such things, and as I have always been full of admiration for Nature's skill, wisdom, and industry, I was not a little upset to have been given such a reputation by a man so very fair-minded as yourself. In my published booklet I simply assert that there is a continuous and uninterrupted movement of blood from the heart through the arteries to the body as a whole, and likewise back from that body as a whole through the veins to the heart, with such flow and ebb and in such quantity and amount that it must somehow move in a circle. But with respect to the coction and the causes of this movement of circulation, especially with respect to its final cause, you will find it clearly stated (if you will kindly re-read chapters 8 and 9) that I have made no mention, indeed, that I have deliberately quite forgone any discussion of these matters.

Nay more, you proceed to find fault with me as being too little of an analytical anatomist in that I try to investigate the final cause without establishing the facts; I shall be grateful, my frank and very well-wishing friend, if you will read the summary of the whole of my assertions in chapter 14. You will be able to discover that I give merely the facts and add no physiological speculation or extra causes, nor the reason why Nature produces this movement of the blood through the pulsation of the heart. I do not deny that in chapter 8 I insert incidentally for the sake of illustrating what might well happen that the parts are nourished from the heart through the inflow of heat in the blood, and that contrariwise the blood is impaired or undergoes something in the parts so that to recover again its perfect state it seeks once more the heart and source of its warmth. But I do not claim to have shown whether or not this is so or to have said very much about it. Similarly in the last chapters I concluded from the consequences and from my anatomical observations that a circulation probably occurs, though I nowhere give causes for such (save for the movement of the heart and for its pulsatile power).

By way of demonstration, since you crave ocular evidence, the circulation of the blood has been clearly described everywhere, and I now declare to you that I have also seen it clearly with my own eyes, and that I have very often demonstrated it by repeated vivisections to very clear-sighted folk among very many most learned men, that the blood moves from the veins to the ventricles of the heart, and thence through the arteries by means of the heart-beat to the body as a whole, and finally from the parts of that whole the blood seeks out the heart by means of the veins, and that in such amount and with so vigorous a flow that there appears to be no place left for doubt about a circulation.

But bear me no ill-will, I pray, that I, as an anatomist (and a thinking animal) make use of reasons derived from sensation and taken from the selected admissions of anatomists as a whole, not for the sake of a rhetorical exercise but to confirm, probably, for those who have never visually examined anatomy or who shun such sights, a statement of fact deriving from an autopsy. Can it displease you that Primrose is making calculations on the same lines as I myself, since anatomists as a whole acknowledge that systole and diastole, or constriction and dilatation, do occur in the heart and in dilatation the blood received from the vena cava fills the dilated heart and in its constriction they cannot deny that blood is transfused into the arteries (as they have been taught by the texture of the organ and the cunning device of the valves and many other things about the heart). If any transmission of blood occurs in any amount in individual pulsations, let them suppose whatever quantity they wish (I am not referring to how much I saw), immediately convinced on this basis by the computed pulsations, they must agree that the blood goes around. If, however, you wish to see and feel for yourself how much the single constrictions of the heart account for, and see with your own eyes facts which make your belief more certain, what happened to me will be as surely, clearly and evidently apparent (with the techniques properly carried out) as you know you saw yesterday at Altdorf, and I am as certain that the blood is diffused through the arteries into the body as I am certain that our Thames falls into the sea, and within the smaller veins to the larger ones and to the base of the heart from the body as a whole, with such free passage and confluence as your Pegnitz flows into your Regnitz or your Main and Moselle into the catchment of the Rhine.

Up to this point the opinion of a very good man has spoken against me personally rather than against the circulation. For granted that I am not much of an anatomist, and a very bad analyst, and it appears to an upright and learned man that I have slandered Nature, it does not therefore follow that the circulation of the blood is non-existent. You are wrong, my very dear friend, if you judge me so vainly obstinate on behalf of that or any other opinion that I am quite unable to bear contradictory words (especially from my Hofmann, to the sight of whom I had so looked forward that I could not in any way miss the chance of seeing him whose friendly discourse used so to delight me, and whose letters, written in his own hand, now bring me so great joy). Indeed, there have not been wanting in England such people as have striven in their public anatomy lectures to deny me the discovery of the blood circulation and (quoting your writings) have taught that I was indebted to your training and instruction for my doctrine so that I had to compare our letters and dates in order to defend and clear myself. Finally, I accept gratefully and favourably your [conclusion] that the blood in its vessels is not like water in its aqueducts or our Thames rolling its streams in their channel straight to the ocean, but, (as the great Scaliger more correctly interprets the fluctuation in Aristotle which, you say, holds me captive) as there is always some flow of water in a pond or in the sea, and as the river-bank takes up moisture in no small amount by absorption, so the parts requiring nourishment are ever thirsty. But I shall be happy, my dear and learned friend, if you now take your hammering. Does water flow in ponds? (You will forgive me, but I do not understand.) Or does it flow as in the sea? A suspect alternative, but supposing it does flow as in the sea? There is a flow and ebb at set times and equally the blood must penetrate and return in its vessels and Nature would wish [something] distinct and definite rather than indefinite and confused in her vessels. Moreover, why do the lands of Egypt not get such moisture from the Nile as it flows past, just as if it were inundating? I do not grasp it. Equally how the nourishment drawn off in the effluent blood adheres and is changed into cambium escapes me. The remainder of the doubts advanced in your letters against a circulation are there because you boggle at porosities and blind meanderings of the flesh. The method of passing and possible routes for which you ask are frankly hindrances to the contrary movements of expulsion and retention and you seek the final cause and you say the solution of doubts [is] a sign of a perfectly constituted truth. The heart draws from the liver, why is this latter's attractive and retaining power no obstacle to you? And by what ways and vents, by anastomosis, or directly through the parenchyma of the liver can the blood reach the cava from the mesenteric veins? You have never seen it but you have no doubt that it is so. Does the liver raise nutriment from the narrow and capillary branching of the portal vein and at one and the same time is blood distributed quite unimpeded to the intestines? You cannot stop me by affirming a contrariety of movements or a confusion. But I fear lest, if I were to reply to single points, this page would expand into a volume and I should overmuch abuse your patience. And listen, either you did not pay attention to my booklet in reading it or you forgot so to do. But do you not grasp the book? Or unless my memory is at fault your objections raised here have their answers treated of in the book and do not refute me. For the man is not to be rejected who admits the circulation through autopsy or probable proof, even if he does not know the routes or facilities, for such inquiry comes later, and contradiction from such things is too argumentative. But since you seek solutions so that I could free you from your doubts, and not to prevent your allowing the cause itself, I promise them, but more correctly according to analytical science when you know the facts correctly and acknowledge them.

Now I fear lest you truly judge me too little of an analyst, assigning causes or solving doubtful points for him who will not admit the existence of the facts; for it is a sophistical way and like speculating about the nonexistent; my fingers are already painfully tired from holding the pen and other matters call me away. I have wanted to say these things in order to remove misunderstanding and to free myself from the disrepute of censure on such a scale, and I beg you, most learned and fair-minded friend, if you wish to see with your eyes anything that I affirm about the circulation, just to let me know the facts and I guarantee, as is more becoming in an anatomist, to be present whenever you wish and I am given the opportunity. If, however, you are unwilling for this, or it does not please you to investigate by your own efforts in dissection, at least, I adjure you, refrain from despising the industry of others or turning it into a fault, and do not refuse to trust an honest man, who is not un-skilled or mentally deranged, in respect of something which he has tested so often over so many years.

Now farewell and take care to act as I do, for I am accepting your letter in the frank and friendly spirit in which you say that you wrote it. Do you also treat me similarly as I reply to you with equal good-will. Nuremberg, 20 May 1636.

Your
William Harvey, Physician to the King
and Professor of Anatomy at the College
of Physicians of London. Englishman.[1]

This dignified and reasonable appeal to his ageing critic had no effect, and another correspondent of Harvey, Paul Marquard Slegel, of Ham-burg, said of Hofmann:

Though my ever greatly valued teacher Hofmann taught me and others the first beginnings of the circulation from the structure and use of the heart and lungs, whence it became easy to understand the new movement of the blood, yet he himself could never be brought to admit the circular course of the blood.

Even Harvey could not prevail so far, either in person, when he visited Hofmann during his German journey, or by letters which he several times sent to him; nor did I succeed in obtaining his consent in many discussions with him in 1638, when I was welcomed in his house, where I stayed for four months.[2]

Tradition relates that Harvey, having made his demonstration at Alt-dorf, and meeting with no response from Hofmann, threw down his scalpel and walked out of the theatre, but there is no discoverable evidence of the truth of this story.

[1] Until recently Harvey's letter was known only in an abbreviated form as printed in the *Opera omnia*, ed. Akenside, 1766; the original source had not been detected. In 1959 E. V. Ferrario of Milan discovered a manuscript of Harvey's letter in its full form among the collections of Albrecht von Haller in the Bibliotheca Brescia at Milan, and soon afterwards Akenside's source was identified as *G. Richteri J.C., ejusque familiarum, Epistolæ selectiores*, Nuremberg, 1662. This was found to contain also Hofmann's letter, previously unknown, but also abbreviated. The two letters were then included in an article in the *Journal of the History of Medicine* (1960), xv. 17, with a discussion by Dr. F. N. L. Poynter and translations by Professor K. J. Franklin. The English versions are given here by the kind permission of Professor Franklin. The opinion has been expressed that the manuscript at Milan is Harvey's holograph, but the facsimile published with the article does not bear this out.

[2] *Pauli Marquati Slegelii De sanguinis motu commentatio*, Hamburg, 1650, *Præfatio*, leaf A3 verso. Translation by W. R. LeFanu. Harvey's other letters to Hofmann mentioned by Slegel are not known.

A remarkable passage in Harvey's letter states that lecturers on anatomy in England had asserted that the discovery of the circulation had been taken from Hofmann himself, and that Harvey 'had had to compare our letters and dates in order to defend and clear myself'. It has been shown by Dr. Poynter and by earlier commentators that in 1622 Hofmann did indeed have the opportunity of anticipating Harvey when his pupil, Helvicus Dieterich, suggested to him that the movement of the blood must be in a circle. Dieterich described the incident as having taken place at a public disputation in which he was defending a thesis on the function of the brain. Dr. Poynter's translation of the passage is as follows:

Moreover, I there dissected several animals, both living and dead, and in more than one vivisection of a dog I carried out, as physicians still living will testify, almost the identical experiment by which, not long afterwards, the learned Harvey taught the whole medical world the movement and circulation of the blood. Then, like Terence's young Phædria, I was overwhelmed with delight and immediately announced the new discovery which had been revealed to me to my teacher, Master Hofmann, really persuading myself that surely the motion of the blood could hardly be otherwise than circular. From him, however, I had for answer only his customary 'Pah!' together with this wisecrack, 'You don't want to become a circulator, do you?'[1]

At Nuremberg news came to Arundel that the Emperor was still at Linz and in no hurry to go to Ratisbon, where the Electors had not yet assembled. Arundel accordingly used his spare time searching for pictures, though without any success, as he reported in a letter of 17 May to his agent, the Revd. William Petty, who was at Venice:

I am come in Portte, as it were, and found a most miserable Countrye, and nothinge by the way to be bought of any momente, heere in this towne being not one scratch of Alb. Du[r]ers paintinge in oyle to be sold, though it were his Countrye nor of Holbein, nor any other greate Master. They say within these three or four yeeres greate store of good thinges have bin carryed out at easy rates; and not longe since a Lifehever [Liefhebber, or 'lover of art'] dyinge, an Italian hath bought and carryed away many of A D drawings... I have one Hollarse with me, whoe drawes and eches Printes in stronge water quickely and with a pretty spiritte.[2]

---

[1] From Dieterich's *Vindiciæ adversus Otthonem Tachenium*, Hamburg, 1655, p. 194. Dr. Poynter notes that Phædria is the naïve young man in Terence's play *The Eunuch*, and that 'circulator' signifies an itinerant quack.

[2] British Museum, Add. MSS 15970, f. 26, quoted by Hervey, loc. cit., p. 365, and by F. C. Springell, *Connoisseur and Diplomat, The Earl of Arundel's Embassy to Germany in 1636*, London, 1963, p. 240.

PLATE XXII

ARUNDEL'S PARTY EMBARKING ON THEIR HOUSE-BOATS AT STRAUBINGEN ON THE DANUBE

Drawing by Hollar

Wenceslaus Hollar, a Bohemian artist, born at Prague in 1607, had been encountered by Arundel at Cologne. Being attracted by his delightful drawings and etchings, the Ambassador attached him to his party and brought him back to England, where he lived most of the time practising his art until his death in 1677. Hollar thus became acquainted with Harvey, and he afterwards spoke to Aubrey of the doctor's rash behaviour on the journey. Aubrey duly reported his words in his account of Harvey: 'Mr. W. Hollar told me that, in his voyage, he would be making of excursions into the woods, making observations of strange trees and plants, earths, etc., naturalls, and sometimes like to be lost, so that my Lord Ambassador would be really angry with him, for there was not only danger of thieves, but also of wild beasts.' Hollar made many vivid drawings and etchings of the scenes witnessed by the party on this journey, some including members of the party and the boats on which they travelled, so providing a true impression of how Harvey and his friends fared on this adventure. A number of these drawings are now in the collections preserved at Chatsworth, and four of them are reproduced here by the courtesy of the Duke of Devonshire.

Arundel and his party left Nuremberg on 22 May for Ratisbon, passing through a place called Hemmaw, which Crowne said had been pillaged twenty-eight times in two years and twice on one day. They reached Ratisbon three days later, but, finding the Emperor had still not arrived there, went on, after a week, down the Danube to see him at Linz. They disembarked for one night at a town called Vilshoven, and

the next morning as his Excellency was taking Boate, he spied a poore Boy standing among other poore people begging for reliefe, who looked very strangely and could neither speake nor heare, but a little at his mouth and nose, having neither eares nor passage to heare with, and his face very thin & drawne aside, yet when one hallowed hee heard and answered againe with a noise; there was with him his sister, a pretty girle, who when one spake to him, made him understand by signes, these two his Excellency tooke along with him in his Boate to a City called Passaw seated on the right side of the Danuby, where we landed and lay, and there commanded to have new clothes made for them & gave them monie and sent them home to their friends.

Harvey can be pictured examining the unfortunate deaf mute and explaining to Arundel the defects from which he suffered, so that finally compassion for the boy's condition dictated another of the Ambassador's generous acts.

Having arrived at Linz, Arundel was at last given three audiences by the Emperor, but negotiations, as expected, did not help Prince Charles Louis's prospects, though Harvey seems to have felt optimistic. Sir Thomas Roe, an experienced negotiator, told the Queen of Bohemia that he had heard 'that Dr. Harvey assured his private friends of great hopes of justice and equity from the Emperor', but he believed the doctor judged by symptoms, like a physician, and that the Ambassador was so wise or so warned as not to show discontent, nor what he hoped and feared.[1]

It was evident that the Ambassador anticipated a prolonged stay in Germany, and, writing from Linz on 17 June to Petty in Venice, he commended to him Sir John Borough's son, who, with Francis Windebank, wished to break away and visit Italy.

Crowne described without comment a horrible scene that took place at Linz on 6 June, but does not indicate which of the party, if any, cared to witness it. Hollar recorded the spectacle in a drawing now preserved in the collections at Chatsworth. The early seventeenth-century mind was not squeamish about public executions; they were all in the day's work, and every such spectacle had a certain medical interest. Harvey may have seen it, though he made no comment on it in letters written soon afterwards. Seven men, Crowne relates, were beheaded.

The first that was executed was said to be one that inchanted himselfe, that no bullet could hurt him, and the only seducer of the others: after he was upon the scaffold and his face covered, two men held him fast to the blocke, then came the Executioner with a red hot pair of pincers, and violently clapt hold of both his brests, that done nailed his right hand fast to the blocke, and chopt it off, then presently whipt out his sword from his side, and cut off his head, one of the hangmen presently took it up, and cryed at the ears of the head *Jesus Jesus;* then the Jesuite which came along with him admonishing of him, desired everie one to joyne in prayers with him for him.

We do not have to depend entirely on Crowne's narrative and Arundel's letters for knowledge of what happened at Linz, for in June Harvey himself wrote two letters to his friend Basil Feilding, then King Charles's Ambassador Extraordinary to the Republic of Venice. Feilding was the eldest son of the first Earl of Denbigh and nephew of the Duke of Buckingham. Harvey would certainly have come to know him, after the death of King James, through being court physician, Feilding having been created Viscount at the age of about 19 on the occasion of King

---

[1] *Domestic State Papers,* 1636, cccxxix. i, 1 Aug. 1636.

Charles's coronation in February 1626. After spending a few years abroad in various capacities, he had returned to England and had married the Earl of Portland's daughter. He was appointed Ambassador at Venice in 1634, and there spent the next five years, giving much attention to collecting works of art for the King. Harvey seems to have been on very friendly terms with his Lordship, if the conventionally subservient manner of address to a nobleman be discounted. Feilding returned to England from Venice in 1639, but by that time he was out of favour at Court, and Harvey's friendship with him is not likely to have been resumed. Indeed, after 1642 he joined the parliamentary forces. He succeeded to the Denbigh title in 1643 after his father had died in action for the King, and later performed important military services for Parliament. The orthography of Harvey's letters to Feilding is very erratic and it has here been modernized for ease in reading.[1]

Linz

Not to let slip any occasion of presenting my service and thanks to your Excellency for your letters, at this time I am bold to write and to congratulate your Excellency of the honourable fame and esteem of your despatches and abilities, whereof I hear in that Honourable employment you are in, with the expectation of your future increase and perfection therein as will be to our master and the Kingdom of great and benificial use and to yourself honour. My lord here hath not yet had answer; (we hope) it will be good and satisfactory though we are not out of fear of delays; our greatest certainty groweth from the necessity they have here of making peace on any condition, where there is no more means of making war or scarce of subsistence, and this warfare in Germany without pay is rather a licence to prey and of oppression, and threateneth in the end anarchy and confusion, than a just and laudable war to establish peace and justice. I have been twice or thrice ahunting with the Emperor, who certainly in his own disposition is a pious good man, desirous of all love, quietness, peace and justice. How the concurrents and interest of the times will permit him I know not. Yesterday, my Lord was feasted by the nobility at the house of the Court of Melan, the chief major-domo of his Majesty; we drank hard and had many expressions and many good wishes; what will succeed is of no less expectation and consequence than our desires are to know it. We hear from England the plague increaseth not much, yet is so feared as the

[1] Harvey wrote eleven letters in all to Feilding. These were first printed by the Historical Manuscripts Commission, *Denbigh MSS*, pt. v, 1911, pp. 28–41, and were bought from the Earl of Denbigh in 1912 by Sir Thomas Barlow for the Royal College of Physicians. They were then transcribed at Cambridge and privately printed for Sir Thomas Barlow; this text has been used here.

term is for that cause put off. James Querk earnestly desires to have his service remembered to your Excellency and hath done well, though he lost his *fede*.[1] My sweet Lord, with all the commendations I can, I desire to remain

Your Excellency's
humble at command
Will. Harvey

Linz June 16/26
Il Illust^{mo} et ecc^{mo} Signor
il Signor Ambass. extraordin^s
di sua M^{ta} della grand
Brittagnia
Venetia.

The dinner at the major-domo's was also mentioned by Crowne, who there heard a story which would certainly have pleased Harvey; it was just the type of 'yarn' that he exchanged with Aubrey in later years. 'In Moravia not far from this place was a Baron whose name was Rabell having a wife, which couple had beene married fortie yeeres together, and had many children, and when he was eightie two yeeres old and his wife seventie five, she conceived and brought him forth two children at a birth, a sonne and a daughter, which children lived a yeere and died.'

Lintz

Right hon^{ble}

My sweet Lord: so much the more I now condemn my self (having at this hour received such sweet and loving lines from you) in that I did not send those letters I intended by the bearer hereof, his sudden and unexpected departure was the cause that from Nuremberg I did not by writing present my humble service which I beseech you to accept in excuse, and not lay me so foul a fault as neglect of one so extremely well deserving, and to me ever so kind and friendly. I thank your Honour that you vouchsafe to advertise me of one, whom I heard before would write against me, but till now never heard he did, or even yet saw that Book; we are here lately arrived through that ruined desolate country of Germany into Austria and at Lintz have had only twice audience; our business, to expect the delivery of the Palatinate, is not unknown to your Excellency. My Lord will omit no diligence or labour to effect it. This day some of us accompanied his Majesty the Emperor ahunting, which was the killing of two deer encompassed by a toil in a little wood, and so put forth for the Emperor and Empress to shoot with Carbines, which they perform with great dexterity. The post stayeth for this letter upon

---

[1] This term is derived from *fœdus de sanitate*, that is, 'health certificate'.

thorns and therefore I must defer any further until the next occasion. If ever I have done and may be able to do service to you, there is nothing will be more comfort and joy unto me, where all good endeavours bring forth much good fruit and all service is so plentifully acknowledged.

I should be glad of any occasion to see Venice once more, so much the rather to have the happiness of your conversation until which time I will live in hope to see your Excellency and in certainty ever to remain

Your Excellent lordship's
Humbly at command
Will. Harvey

Your letter received by James Querk
Lintz June 9/19

It is of interest to notice in the letter just quoted Harvey's reference to 'one whom I heard before would write against me, but till now never heard he did, or even yet saw that Book'. The writer to whom Harvey refers was Emilio Parigiano, known as Parisanus, who published in 1635 the first reprint of the greater part of *De motu cordis* with detailed 'refutations' of Harvey's book paragraph by paragraph. He was an elderly Venetian physician, born in 1567, who had studied under Fabricius at Padua. His book was published in Venice, so that it had naturally come to the notice of Denbigh, who was living there. Harvey's ignorance of the book was shared by his admirers for the next three centuries; it was not again noticed until the first full bibliography of Harvey's works was published in 1928.[1] His reception of Denbigh's announcement of this criticism was characteristically indifferent. He showed no sign of wishing eagerly to defend his doctrine. Whether he troubled to see Parigiano when he reached Venice we do not know. One remark about the heart-sounds in his opponent's book may, if Denbigh showed it to him, have struck Harvey as so stupid that no defence was worth while—'Our poor deaf ears, nor any physician in Venice, can hear them; thrice fortunate those in London who can.'

Harvey remained for the time being with Arundel, accompanying him to Vienna and Prague, where they saw the sights and, according to Crowne, enjoyed the pictures. While at Vienna, Harvey visited Baden, a short way to the south, and wrote again from there to Denbigh.

My sweet Lord,

So great is my desire to do your Excellency all service as I cannot let slip any occasion, whereby I may give any testimony thereof. This gentleman,[2] who is now coming for Venice, although I love, yet I a little envy

---

[1] Geoffrey Keynes, *A Bibliography of the Writings of Dr. William Harvey*, Cambridge, 1928, second edition, 1953, p. 8.   [2] Probably Sir John Borough's son.

that he should enjoy the happiness of that place and your Excellency's sweet conversation, and that I cannot; my Lord Ambassador here now at Vienna, did receive at Linz such an answer to his demands as caused him to send an express to England before whose return I think we shall not see the Emperor again. Yesterday we visited at Vienna the Queen of Hungary and the Archduke, and two very fine little babies her children; tomorrow my Lord intendeth to return by Prague in Bohemia to Ratisbon, where is expected the diet will be; we find here great expressions and many wishes for the success of my Lord, his embassage. How the effects will prove, we hope well, but cannot certainly assure ourselves; I think the miserable condition of Germany doth more than require it. I am this night here by chance with this Gentleman to see these baths, where such is my bad pen and ink and the shortness of my time, as I am humbly to entreat your Excellency his pardon for this hasty and rude scribling, and so your Excellence his

Assuredly devoted
servant
Will. Harvey

Baden July 9 1636[1]
  Al Illustriss° et Excellentiss°
  Sig^r p sa Maes
  del Re della grand Brittan. in Venetia.

Harvey did not mention in his letter having made any visits to medical acquaintances in Vienna. It is likely, however, that he would at least see the Emperor's personal physician, Dr. Johann Wilhelm Managetta.[2]

Harvey must have returned to Vienna shortly after writing to Denbigh for on 1 July (11 July, English style) the party set out for Prague, arriving there on 6 July. Their stay lasted for seven days, spent seeing the sights of the three towns—Neustadt, Aldstadt, and Schloss-Stadt. Harvey would have been specially interested in the pictures and curiosities to be seen in the castle of the King of Bohemia in the Schloss-Stadt, and he may also have accompanied Crowne to see the ceremony of circumcision performed by a Rabbi in the Jewish quarter of the Aldstadt. On 7 July the party was entertained at the Jesuit College, where they witnessed a Masque given by the students in Arundel's honour.

Another incident of some interest at Prague was Harvey's meeting with Marcus Marci of Kronland, known as the Hippocrates of Prague, or the Bohemian Galileo. Although only in his forty-first year, Marci had been a professor in the faculty of medicine for nearly ten years, and had

---

[1] This date is English style. According to Crowne's reckoning it was ten days earlier.
[2] B. Juhn, 'Harvey in Wien', *Wiener Medizinische Wochenschrift* (1951), cvii. 58.

worked fruitfully at the 'application of optics to the elucidation of organic life against the ideological background of Aristotelianism'.[1] Marci would naturally have been eager to meet the famous discoverer of the circulation, and has himself provided the evidence for their encounter having taken place. In 1635 he had published a book[2] on generation anticipating a number of theories brought forward by Harvey in *De generatione animalium* in 1651. In a later work Marci complained that Harvey in this book had neglected to notice his contribution and stated that he could not have been ignorant of it, 'for I gave the book into his hands, here at Prague, talking to him familiarly'.[3] Marci's name was known in England and he was quoted as an exponent of empiricism against scholasticism, which makes it all the more remarkable that Harvey should have ignored Marci's work in his own writings. Marci had not, however, published anything concerning Harvey's doctrine of the circulation. The first Bohemian contribution in this connexion was a dissertation by Jacobus Forberger, defended in a disputation before Marci as dean of the faculty, in April 1642.[4] Marci's interest in the physiology of the circulation was shown by his invention of an apparatus in the shape of a pendulum for accurate measurement of the pulse.[5]

When Arundel's party returned to Ratisbon on 17 July it was found that the Emperor was still absent elsewhere, and Arundel decided to make an excursion to Augsburg. In a letter of 20 July to Windebank from Ratisbon he reported that 'Honest little Hervey is going a little start into Italy and I give him some employment to Mr. Pettye about pictures for his Majesty. I hope ere long he will be back. Your good son hath a great mind to be going with him; and truly, I think, he could not go in better company for safety, if he were to go.'[6] He refused at first, however, to allow Francis Windebank to go without his father's permission, and soon Harvey set off alone except for a boy and such servants as the Ambassador allowed him. The boy, Henry van de Burgh, was to be

[1] See Walter Pagel and Pyarali Rattansi, *Medical History* (1964), viii. 78.

[2] *Idearum operatricium idea*, Prague, 1635. 'This speculative embryology, based on optical conceptions, is typical of the seventeenth century baroque period.' See Professor V. Kruta, 'Harvey in Bohemia', *Physiologia Bohemoslovenica* (1957), vi. 433.

[3] *Philosophia vetus restituta*, Prague, 1662; second edition, 1676, p. 352. This reference was first published by Pagel, op. cit., p. 79. It was also known to Professor Kruta (personal communication).

[4] V. Kruta, op. cit., p. 435. Kruta has here indentified the places mentioned by Crowne with their correct Bohemian designations.

[5] According to Josef Sajner, M.D., of Brno, in a letter dated 6. xii. 1957 now in the library of the Royal College of Physicians.

[6] Hervey, op. cit., p. 377.

well known in later years as the portrait painter, Henry van der Borcht. Francis Windebank followed Harvey some weeks later.

On 19 August Arundel wrote to Petty from Ratisbon:

I write still unto you, though I am uncertain where my letters will find you, but I hope at Florence or Rome, and that little honest Dr. Hervey will be with you ere these. For Henry, the young youth I sent unto you with the Doctor, I hope you shall find him a very good boy, free from vice, and most obedient unto you. I pray you show him all of art that you can. I hope in time he will have a good guess of originals from copies.[1]

On 3 September Arundel wrote again to Petty, seemingly in some anxiety about Harvey's safety:

Doctor Hervye parted from hence tomorrow shall be five weeks, and since we never heard from him: but of him once that he was in *contumacia*;[2] he means to come to you. I pray you go on with buying some of Ludovisio's best pictures for the King.

And again the next day:

I wrote yesterday unto you by the ordinary, and cannot omit now to write again by the occasion of my good friend Mr. Francis Windebank's departure, unto whom I pray, do all the curtesy you may. . . . Doctor Hervy parted from hence five weeks since, and from him we never received soe much as one word since he went, where he was or howe he did, which seemes strange. He longs much to be with you, and, as I wrote unto you, he will be gladde to see those pictures of Ludovisio's, and helpe with creditte to buy them for our Kinge, which I thinke his Majestie would like very well. I have sent with the Doctor Hervy a youth called Henry van de Burg, son of a painter in Frankfoerte, to attend you and retorne hither with you. He is a very honest youth and loves all matters of arte deerly. I pray have care of him, and let him see all things of art you may.[3]

'Ludovisio' mentioned in these letters was Don Niccolo Ludovisi, a famous collector of pictures, living in Rome.

Arundel's anxiety for Harvey's safety must have been increased by learning of the barbarous murder of two of his trumpeters in a wood near Nuremberg, but his fears were partly set at rest by 8 September, when he wrote to Petty: 'I hope poor Dr. Hervey is with you by this.

[1] Hervey, op. cit., p. 383.
[2] Ibid., p. 384. The word *contumacia*, referring to Harvey's bad treatment at Treviso, was not read by Hervey, but was supplied by Springell, p. 248.
[3] Hervey, op. cit., pp. 384–5, and Springell, p. 251.

I received a letter from him yesterday, that he hath bin miserably vexed in the lazaretto at Treviso. I hope he will recover his time lost with satisfyinge his curiosity, which you will assist him in at Florence and Rome. I pray thinke of the safest ways to come hither, both for the Plague and other dangers.'[1] The references to Harvey's misfortunes are fully explained by his own series of furiously indignant letters written to Lord Denbigh at Venice about the treatment he was receiving not far away at Treviso, where he was held prisoner in quarantine for more than a fortnight. The *fede*, to which he frequently refers in these letters, was the *fede di sanita*, a pass which had to be signed by officials at various points to certify that he was free from infection by the plague. Why he was held so long in quarantine and so abominably treated is unexplained.

My sweet Lord,
  I came this morning to the gates of Treviso with great joy and hope this night to have had the happiness to have been with you at Venice, but I have received here a very unjust affront, being stayed and commanded by this podesta to have gone into the Lazaretto, without any cause or suspicion alledged. I tooke my first *fede* under the seal of Ratisbon, a place free and now destined, as your Excellency knoweth, for the meeting of the Emperor and all the rest of the princes, which, if it had not been so, they would not have come hither, it being infected or suspected. Since, in every place as I came, I caused my *fede* to be underwritten, so that there is no ground for them to lay any suspicion upon me. And at this sentence on me by the podesta (that I should go to the Lazarett) I absolutely refused and said and offered to shew, that I had the pass and recommendation of his Majesty the King of Great Britain and of the Emperor's Majesty and of my Lord Ambassador his excellency, and that I had to go to princes and men of quality and that my business required expedition, and desired they would not hinder me, but as my passes further me, and that I might not bring that suspicion and infamy on me, besides my own security to go to such a place as Lazaretto where they use to put infected persons, and that I had shewed them sufficient *fede*: notwithstanding all this, here I am to lie for ought I see in the open base fields, & god knows how long. The podesta refuseth to see or read my passes: and I cannot come at him to speak and use my reasons. I am afraid this lying in the field will do me hurt in my health. I beseech your Excellency to lament hereof. It is unjust to proceed with any man thus, without cause, and otherwise than Venetians are used in England, or so merit to be used here, and otherwise than is fitting for the respects there should be used to the passes forenamed. I pray pardon this scribbling

[1] Hervey, op. cit., p. 385, and Springell, p. 249.

on the grass in the field and procure with all expedition my freedom from this barbarous usage.

> Your distressed friend
> and humble servant of your excellency
> Will Harvey

Treviso Aug. 3/13 1636
Al Ilustriss° Excellentiss° sign^r
il sig^r Embassador *p* il
sereniss° Re della grand Brittagnia in Venetia.

Harvey's indignation at his treatment can be well understood, and the high-handed action of the *podestà* in committing him to the *lazaretto* has not been explained. At the same time it must be remembered that the position of Venice in regard to infection by the plague was exceptional. Since the tenth century Venice had enjoyed almost a monopoly in conducting trade from the Far East to the western world. It was the natural gateway for trade from India, China, and Persia, and the caravans bringing the goods by land for shipment by sea passed through areas where plague was endemic. The subsequent trade routes from Venice to northwest Europe were by land through central Germany, so that, if no precautions were taken, plague could be disseminated through Venice to a very wide area. Already in 1403 the Venetian authorities had established a system of quarantine with *lazarettos* two miles from the city for the treatment and isolation of patients coming by sea. From 1485 quarantine for a minimum of forty days was enforced. The *lazarettos* had buildings with quarters arranged to accommodate healthy travellers in small groups, these being shut off by high walls from the sheds where goods were unpacked and thoroughly exposed to air and sunlight, since it was believed that these would dissipate the infective principles. These Venetian regulations and arrangements were, up to a point, effective in limiting infections by plague and they remained in force almost unchanged for the next 400 years.[1]

Harvey's unhappy experience suggests that the arrangements at Treviso were not so good as those at the port of Venice, and that the *podestà* was too stupid or too illiterate to be able to understand the position of the distinguished stranger he was subjecting to so much indignity. Perhaps Harvey was in the end fortunate not to have endured the whole forty days of quarantine usually enforced. Denbigh's influence was partly effective in changing the attitude of Harvey's jailors, as his next letter shows.

[1] See W. J. Simpson, *A Treatise on Plague*, Cambridge, 1905.

Saturday

My sweet Lord,

I perceive by their behaviour to me how much your Excellency is pleased there to stir and labour for me, for yesterday, after I had sent my letters to your Excellency, they sent some in a Coach to me, as from the podesta, that I should go to the other place, where I was before (if I would) or that I should have here a bed, or that he would do for me what he could, to which I answered, that since it had pleased him with so much rigour and cruelty to inflict upon me the greatest misery he could, and had brought so much infamy upon me as to put me into this lazaretto without any just cause, without any respect of the recommendations I had from my Lord Ambassador his Excellency or from the Emperor Majesty or from his Majesty my master, not so much as to read them or give notice of them in his first despatch to Venice, nor to make any difference of a servant of his Majesty the King of Great Britain, but by force and threatening of muskets to compell me into the very nasty room where the vitturin and his two servants and saddles lay, and not at my request granting me a bed or any commodity, scarce straw, his offers now were unseasonable and like physic when a man was dead, and that I had now hardened myself and accommodated as I did content myself and resolved, since it had pleased God by his hands to humble me so low, I would undergo it as a penance and that I had written to your Excellency and hoped by your intercession within some few days to have release, and therefore determined to receive and acknowledge all my comfort from you, and to trouble the podesta with no other request but that he would with all expedition free me and shew a respect to my master and my business, and debating the business and urging them for a reason of all this and that it was unjust to detain any man and not shew him the cause, or to receive a man into their territories and then imprison him, they should have denied me entrance at the first and then I had gone some other way, or they should have put those towns they suspect into their Band and then I had shunned them, or make known at his entrance, to every man, what he was to do. Otherwise this was a surprize and catch-men, and they, knowing not well what to answer, sometimes alledged that Villach was suspected, sometimes I had not gotten my *fede* subscribed at Conian [Conegliano] or Sacile, sometimes that the vitturin had brought a boy with him, his son, to get a master, whose name was not in the vitturin's *fede*, so sometimes I was stayed for him, sometimes (they said) he and his horses stayed for me.

Touching their suspicion I answered, Villach took as great care and examined my *fede* as strictly as they could and had given me *fede* of their safety, which they ought in civility to trust, and that the Duke of Alkalay, viceroy of Naples, with 100 persons choosed to stay there, and that upon bare suspicions of their own without any just ground, ought not to be, though cause enough, to use me in all Respects as if I had the plague for certainty on me, and that if I had had it would they not have granted me in charity a house, bed and succour from my money, though all had been burned after, and I have paid for it. It was against all manhood and Charity. And for not having my *fede* subscribed in their own towns as we passed, they knew well I could come no other way from Pontevi [Pontebbe], and that they were all without suspicion, and that I was told, and it was and is in every man's mouth, there was no need, and that it was upon accident, for our vitturin, who should have directed us being strangers, got his own *fede* subscribed at Conian, and for the horses we rode on, and did not tell us until it was too late, thinking his was sufficient. But for all these cavils, I said the word of an honest man or his oath in this case ought to suffice. I write the larger to your Excellency of those passages, because I know not what they may make of my conference in their letters, that you may know the truth, and indeed, my Lord, I am a little jealous of them, and to take any beds now of their sending, for since their manners and cruelty hath been so shame-full to me, and they so little reason for what they have done, it would be like the rest of their proceedings if they sent me an infected bed to make their conjectures and suspicions prove true; therefore I choose to lay still to be redeemed by your Excellency out of this innocent straw. Yesterday, likewise, the patron that owned the house where I first took my straw bed (a little poor garden house full of lumber, dirt and gnats, without window or door, open to the highway at midnight) was to offer me that again, because I had chosen that to shun the infamy of this lazarett and the suspicion I had that some infected person had lately been here, and from which they forced me with terror of muskets, I write this to shew your Exc. that all they do here upon your stirring, is but formal to salve their own errors. I tell them, I desire nothing of them, or expect or will accept, but only beseech the podesta that I may be at liberty with all expedition, and that at last he will have respect to princes' recommendations and to my business: and now, as I am writing, I humbly thank your Exc. your servant is arrived and hath been with me and is gone to the podesta according to your order. He will tell you of a trick to burn my pass and the injury they have offered me therein.

When your lordship shall mark how tedious I am in writing, I pray give it this interpretation, I have no other thing to do and infinite greedy to be gone, and that I scribble thus, in haste and the want of good pens and ink, &c. If your Excellency go to the College you may justly lament the little respect this podesta hath given the recommendations I have from my lord Ambassador and his Majesty, or the business I am sent in, who would not so much as receive it and read it being offered, nor send information thereof to Venice, nor make difference thereupon between me and the vitturin's servants, would give me no relief or assistance, not so much as a barn or stall free to my self, but force that infamy, danger, suspicion and base usage of their lazarett upon me, not to suffer me to write to your Excellency until 5 or 6 hours past, that in the meantime he might procure an order from Venice to contenance his act and injure me upon unequal relation; and your Excellency may justly resent that the despatches to you and business of yours should be thus used, and not upon your letters released, and that you may have that respect therein which is due and that I may have reparation and testimony for the burning my pass and for the clearing me of the suspicion and infamy of having been in this lazarett, and my unjust stay, and that I may have again my *fede* to make appear to the world wheresoever I go, that I am clear, or else that I may have a full *fede* from this state: if they make difficulty of my coming to Venice, I pray that I may have sufficient *fede* from hence and I will go by Padua to Florence and see your Excellency as I return. I pray pardon me for propounding this to your Excellency, who know better herein what is to be done, which I doubt not but you will perform, that I may be free and we rejoice together hereafter; and in good sober truth I fear lest this ill usage and base place and the unquiet of my mind may not bring some sickness on me this extreme hot weather. Therefore I beseech, etc.

Your Excellency's
humble servant
Will Harvey

this Saturday morning
 Aug 6/16

My sweet Lord,

 This place is so incommodious to me, and affordeth me so little comfort as I beseech your Excellency to pardon me if I take the boldness herein to make my complaints unto you: the great longing I have to be gone and free maketh me think these 4 days past (since I had the comfort to see your servant here) to appear so many years, wherein I hoped either they would have relented of their cruelty or your Excellency effected something for my relief. I had thought with joy to have presented my service to you, and now am sorry instead thereof to put your Excellency to the trouble I know you take for me. The ill diet I have here and the worse usage hath produced this ill effect that now these two nights I have had a sciatica in my right thigh and leg that much discourageth me, and maketh me lame. I would fain S. Francesco would come unto me; I will pay for his coach and expense, to direct and advise me, and to deliver him the business I have to him from my Lord Ambassador and the letters I have else to Venice; and if he bring my freedom with him, I shall have the more joy, if not, he may get me here some garden house with fire, bed and other necessaries, lest I fail worse. If his being there effect better for me, then that some man be hired there to come and go between, by whom I may hear often what is or can be done, and may certify me of the receipt of my letters, at the least, that I may hear what I may hope or look for. They tell me here, if there be any truth in them, that they have sent to the Duke for my liberty and that they desire I would write this to your Excellency, that by your joint help it may be procured. I pray that Sign. Franceso would come.

Thus in haste, I pray pardon and relief.

> Your Excellency's
> Humble servant,
> Will Harvey

this present Tuesday afternoon.
Al Illustriss° et Excellentiss°
sign^n Embassiador p il sereniss°
Re della grand Britannia
in Venetia.

My sweet Lord,

Although I know your care and diligence for my liberty, and make no doubt but your Excellency doth what is possible and omitteth no occasion, yet the longing I have to be out of this thraldom and the daily hope from you maketh me so often look out as having not heard from you since your man was with me (on Saturday last). I desire much to know how the case standeth, what is the cause, what I may expect. There is nothing can bear any colour of just objection but that my *fede* was not underwritten at Conian and Sacile, which towns they know well enough are clear and by the computation of my journey from Pontevi it is not possible I could take any other way, but that I passed those towns, where it was told me that it was not necessary for my *fede* to be underwritten, since I had the seal of St. Mark at Pontevi, and yet the vitturin had his *fede* underwritten at Conian for him and the horses we rode on, and ours had been underwritten too, but that he, which was to guide us, told us, when it was too late, and said his underwritten was sufficient. And whereas it was said we had one in our company more than we had *fede* for, that was not so, for that party had a *fede* for himself at Pontevi, though after not underwritten. I fear lest there may be some other matter in it than I imagine, and they meant to stay me had I the best *fede* could be (as I think I have), and that they seek but cavils to colour their intent, otherwise the word of an honest man or his oath would easily give satisfaction for such slight doubts they have since and before letten pass others upon as little testimony. I hoped much on your Excellency's complaint to the College, but now, because I hear not, I doubt much lest they neglect you too. I have now been here 10 days and my *fede* giveth me testimony of health for 40 days almost before that, so that I cannot guess other than some malice in this, considering with what cruelty and severity they have proceeded with me. My sciatica, which I got here by injurious lodging, I thank God mendeth well. I beseech you my sweet Lord, let me hear from you at least, that I may know these letters come to your hands which I write, and what I may hope for, and what reason there can be of the great neglect they have used to the recommendation and the pass I brought from my Lord Ambassador, the King his Majesty and the Emperor. I would be glad, since my stay is so long, to have a trusty messenger to send all my letters I have to Venice, and to that end I have sent to Signor Francesco, to whom the greatest part are, that he would come hither; my Lord Ambassador in my last letter from Augsburg commendeth him unto your Excellency and saith there is nothing yet fallen out worthy of your knowledge, otherwise he would have written to your Excellency ere this. Even as this morning I had finished these lines, came one from this podesta to view us how we were in health and saith within these 2 days we shall have liberty, but what trust may be given to their words I cannot tell. I fear it is but a shuffle to detain me here yet a week longer, which is the extremity they do to the worst *fede* and meanest man. Likewise it is told me Signor Francesco should write so much to a friend of his here, who is restrained to his house, who sent, I think, him to me to excuse him. I wonder Signor Francesco, I having written so earnestly to him, he did not write a word to me. I know not the passages of your Excellency being in the College, but sure I am they have used a neglect and contempt of his Majesty's recommendation in his pass and of the Emperor, worthy to be hotly complained of, and to me have done barbarous injustice and incivility. There is a post cometh every day from Venice. I beseech your Excellency to be a comfort to me that I may have but one word.

Of your Excellency's
humble servant
and faithful friend,
Will Harvey

Treviso
this present Friday
I humbly desire to know when the soonest post goeth for Ratisbon, that I may provide letters.

My sweet Lord,
   Because I see here nothing but injury, deceit and juggling every day these 11 days, that tomorrow and at night and tomorrow and shortly I

shall be released, and do not hear from Venice any certainty by any hand, and I lie here in a miserable case, I pray pardon me if to your Excellency I seem in this often sending importune; except by your Excellency his means (in whom is my only hope to get release from these barbarous oppressions) they delight here so to exercise their tyranny, as I am like [to] lie for every day they promise a week. I fear none of my letters come to your Excellency's hand, or to Signor Francesco. I make no doubt but your Excellency hath done for me what is fitting and have procured my release long before this time, but that your letters and your help is kept from me. Therefore I pray earnestly that I may have but one word in answer that I may know my letters come to you and what is done, which was my chiefest request to the gentleman your Excellency pleased to send to me seven days ago. The post cometh every day, and even to him that night this podesta said he expected from Venice, and so will do, by his good will, I fear this month.

To your Excellency's
humble servant
Will Harvey

August 23

My sweet Lord,
   I wrote to your Excellency yesterday what a heavy message these of the Sanita here delivered to me from the Senate at Venice, which was that I must stay here yet until further order, and, asking how long, they said 7 or 10 or 20 days, so I perceive they do but abuse your Excellency to bear you in hand that every day I shall have my liberty and therein they betray me and make me lose my time, with whom, if they had dealt plainly and roundly, I might have gone back at the first to Villach and from thence to Gorizia, and there gotten shipping and been by this time at Rome or Florence, and seen your Excellency and despatched my business at Venice coming back. Now, if I stay a week or 10 days more here, I shall lose so much time as the intent of my journey will be broken and I must return without going farther. Good my Lord, I beseech you put them speedily and roundly to it, either that I presently go, having now been 18 days, or that I may return, which is a thing is usual here, and a little while ago they did it, sending their officer with them until they were out of their territory, and in justice they cannot deny your Excellency one of these and indeed neither, if either they did respect anything your intercession or would do justice. I perceive I am fallen into the hands of most base and evil people and now they begin to accuse one another, and when I ask them the cause of my stay, they forge lies, as that I was at Saltzburg and that Villach hath the plague, and I know not what. And in this place they have talked so much that tomorrow and tomorrow I

should be free and when they heard your Excellency stirred in it, expected no less than present delivery, that now they begin to disesteem what your Excellency's favour can do for me. My Lord, I pray therefore urge further the disesteem and neglect of his Majesty's pass and your intercession, that they stay me for coming from Villach and yet it is neither a town in their Band. And they let all others pass from thence but me, two having passed by *fede* from thence since I lay here.

I beseech your Excellency to pardon me and not think this often writing importune, for having so often written and receiving no answer from you, which in all my letters I did so earnestly require, and it did so much concern me to know the particulars as fearing my letters come not to your hands, I send this messenger of purpose to bring me or write me, whether your Excellency have any hope, or have or intend anything, and what answer they give, and whether you have, or intend to, complain of the unjust and barbarous dealing with me at the first, so much to neglect the K. his Majesty's pass and recommendation as not to read it, not thereupon to have made some difference between the usage of me and the vitturin and his servants, but chiefly in staying me and putting me into their lazarett, having brought sufficient *fede* and such as they let others pass withall, but if of these they will not be sensible of, to give present reparation, then to demand my *fede* back again out of the Sanita and a testimony of my being here in Lazarett, and my pass burned, and that I may go back (which I now, if I cannot go presently forward, would be glad to do with Signor Francesco). Either to go forward or backward presently they cannot in any justice deny. And I never longed for anything in all my life so much as any way and on any condition, to be gone from this place and barbarous people, and fearing lest I should be sick and then they would cry me into the plague and keep me and cheat and tyrannise over me, god knoweth how long. Signor Francesco was with me on Sunday last, and told me (I humbly thank you) with what desire and earnestness your Excellency dealt for me, and that you hoped every day, but other particulars I could not learn by him, nor since. I send by this bearer the letters I had to deliver at Venice, both to your Excellency and others. And a packet for my Lord Herbert, which was carried to Ratisbon by James Querk, and my Lord being not in those countries, is returned back. Your Excellency please to pardon this trouble which my unfortunate change hath enforced me to put you to.

Your Excellency's
humble servant
Will Harvey

Treviso [Aug.] 16/26 1636
  for his Excellency
  my Lord Ambassador

At length, late in August, Harvey was allowed to proceed on his journey to Venice, and so, by Padua, Ferrara, and Bologna, to Florence. We have no information as to how long he was in Venice or what he did there except for one passing statement in *De generatione animalium* that 'when I was at Venice, Aromatarius, a famous Physitian, shewed mee a small leaf formed between the two shales [shells] of a Pease cod, though with us in the like case there is onely a small knob of the future pulse to be seen. So much doth the indulgent temper and clemency of the Heavens, Soil and Aire, conduce to the fecundity and happy increase of things.'[1]

Harvey would have plenty of matter to discuss with Giuseppe degli Aromatari (1588–1660), who had stated in 1625 that he intended writing a book on the generation of animals.[2] He had propounded the hypothesis that the chick is delineated in the egg before it is fostered by the hen—the theory of 'preformation', supported by many embryologists, including Highmore, Power, Swammerdam, and Malpighi, and not fully discredited until the middle of the eighteenth century.[3] As will be seen when Harvey's views on generation come to be discussed, he was not of this school, and would have found himself arguing against Aromatari's hypothesis.

When Harvey reached Florence he paid his respects to the Grand Duke; he was splendidly entertained by his Highness and was greatly gratified. On 7 September he sat down to write a letter of thanks to his friend at Venice, Lord Denbigh.

Florence Sept 7/17

My sweet Lord,
    With many thanks I humbly present your Excellency for all the favour I have received at my being at Venice. Since I came safe to Florence I have seen this fair city and enjoyed much contentment therein, with health and mirth. The Grand Duke his Highness received my letters and me with great courtesy, favour and respect, talked often long and familiarly with me, presented me with fruit, fowl, wine &c., gave order for one of his coaches to attend me wheresoever and whensoever I went abroad, shewed me himself many of his rarities, would have given order for a galley to have carried me from Leghorn to Naples, and when I thanked his Highness for his affection and love to his Majesty and his affairs, said there was nothing in his court or power that was not at the K. of

---

[1] *Anatomical Exercitations*, 1653, p. 57.
[2] *Epistola de generatione plantarum ex seminibus*, Venice, 1625.
[3] See H. P. Bayon, *Annals of Science* (1938), iii. 74.

England his service, seemed to love and honour him very much, much inquistive of him, his health and welfare, customs and virtues. I told him, as your Excellency commanded me of your devotion and promptness and order you had to do him all service, which he accepted very kindly, and commended him unto you, and certainly if you came hither would do you all possible honour (it may be his marriage is shortly to be consummated), it will be a fit occasion to have order to congratulate. I perceive myself to have much acceptance, access and familiarity, whereby it may be (at least I desire) to perform his Majesty's service or for your Excellency, or any your affairs. Here is a great court, the Duke of Loraine and his Duchess, to whom the Grand Duke giveth the hand, the Duke of Guise his lady and his son's prince, Janviel, the Duke of Joyeus and two little ones, Knights of Malta, and a daughter marriageable, besides the Duke's sister, his two brothers and the Cardinal and one of his uncles.

Your Excellency's
humble servant
Will Harvey

At the same time, Arundel in Ratisbon was still worrying about the purchase of pictures for the King. On 16 September he wrote to Petty: 'I have received yours [of the] 30 August from Florence, and am gladde you are hasteninge to Rome, where I hope ere this you have dispatched our businesse, and that little Doc^r Hervey is with you, whoe will assiste for the buinge the Kinges of Ludovisioes.'[1]

It appears that Harvey met Petty at some point on his way to Rome, for Arundel's son, Lord Maltravers, who was also in Italy, wrote to Petty in Florence on 21 October: 'Wee were all heare extreamly troubled to heare out of Germany that Doctor Hervy went by Sienna, and left you there sicke, but I hope in God there was no danger, but that you are recovred againe beefore this.'[2]

When Arundel next wrote, on 18/28 October, to his agent, Petty was in Rome: 'I hope I shall see the little perpetual mov[ement] called Dr. Harvye heere yet before my go[ing].'[3] Harvey had arrived in Rome at least a fortnight before this, having dined on 5 October in the refectory of the English Jesuit College in the company of a young doctor, George Ent, as we know from the records kept there giving the names of all the English visitors who enjoyed their hospitality.[4] It seems to have been a meeting place for travellers, and Harvey's companions all shared the

[1] Hervey, op. cit., p. 389, and Springell, p. 253.   [2] Springell, p. 259.
[3] Hervey, op. cit., p. 389, and Springell, p. 257.
[4] Henry Foley, S.J., *The Pilgrim Book of the English College of the Society of Jesus*, vi, 1880, p. 614.

entertainment provided by the College. Francis Windebank had been there on 6 and 7 September; young Borough was there on 9 and 12 October, and William Petty, just arrived in Rome, on 14 October.

George Ent, who first enters the story of Harvey's life at this point, had probably met Harvey in Rome by chance rather than by design. Ent was another man of Kent, much younger than Harvey, having been born at Sandwich on 6 November 1604. He was educated at a school in Rotterdam and at Sidney Sussex College, Cambridge, and then spent five years studying medicine at Padua. He had taken his degree of M.D., Padua, on 28 April 1636 and presumably was still pursuing his medical studies on the Continent when he met Harvey in Rome. The two men became close friends, and, as will be seen later, Ent gave Harvey affection, admiration, and loyal support in his later years. In Rome Harvey was treated with great kindness by Cardinal Francesco Barberini, who styled himself 'Protector of the English Nation'. Harvey was at first full of hope and anticipation about the pictures he was going to buy, though in the end he was to be sadly disappointed.

Little has been known hitherto of how Harvey occupied his time between the beginning of September, when he arrived in Rome, and early November, when he set out to rejoin Arundel's party. An unexpected source has recently provided information which helps to fill this gap in our knowledge. For several years Harvey had been concerned with other Fellows of the College of Physicians in an effort to prevent the London apothecaries from selling various poisonous substances without authorization by physicians. As already related (see p. 79), the matter had arisen in an urgent form when a patient died by taking corrosive sublimate. Harvey had been one of the signatories in 1632 of a document[1] requesting the King to forbid the sale of these substances. This had led to prolonged legal proceedings between the Apothecaries and the College, and Star Chamber hearings were taking place in the years 1635 to 1639; various depositions were made by many witnesses, and a document, used probably in the autumn of 1637, has been found to contain evidence by Harvey; this could not have been written before January 1636/7, soon after his return from the Continent. In his deposition at the Star Chamber Harvey said:

That in all places where he hath travelled As at Cullen, Frankford, Norremberg, Vyenna, Prage, Venice, Sienna, Florence, Rome, Naples, The Apothecar[ies] are in reference & dependency upon the Physicions,

---

[1] Goodall, *The Royal College of Physicians Founded*, London, 1684, pp. 435-7.

for the most part tyed by oathes to certaine orders (as in France is expressed by Renodeus[1] in his dispensatory) their numbers lymitted, their medicines taxed, & tyed to make only such medicines for common sale as are appointed by the dispensatoryes of every severall place, And their Medicines searched & corrected by the phisicions in all places.[2]

From this we learn that, as might have been expected, Harvey was inquiring into the conditions of medical practice in all the main cities visited in 1636, and further that, in addition to the visits already known, he travelled as far south as Naples. He is likely to have made this journey during September or October, and it is reasonable to conjecture that he was accompanied by his new friend, Dr. George Ent.

Harvey set out early in November on his journey from Rome back to Ratisbon to rejoin Arundel, who wrote to Petty on 4 November:

I am sory to have heard nothinge from you these two weekes, but I hope you are well, and made some good dispatch at Rome, of which I hope to understand shortly from you; and I hope Dr. Hervey (whom I expecte daily heere) will bring me some good tidings. I know not yet howe soone I shall depart hence, for though I have my revocation, yet these Princes desire my stay awhile to see if they can accomodate thinges better to our Kinges satisfaction then hiterto it hath bin.[3]

Writing again on 11 November, Arundel told Petty: 'Dr. Hervey wee heare hath bin tenne dayes on his way hither from [Rom]e as wee dayly expect him and de[sire if] he come well to have longe dis[course of his tr]availes and adventures.'[4]

Harvey arrived at Ratisbon shortly afterwards and immediately wrote his thanks to Denbigh:

Right Hon: and Excell.
My sweet Lord,
I have, within the time prefixed at my departure from Venice, now safely attained my Lord Ambassador at Ratisbon, where I find him ready within two days to depart for England having his letters of revocation, and yet visited and visiting as if all were on better terms than yet it seemeth to me to be; but more certain particulars your Excellency I presume shall understand by himself. I only write thus much to be an

[1] i.e. Jean de Renou, *Dispensatorium Galeno-chymicum*, Paris, 1608; an English translation was published in 1657.
[2] Society of Apothecaries, MS. 8286, f. 14a, first read and printed by Dr. E. Ashworth Underwood in his revised edition of Wall and Cameron's *History of the Society of Apothecaries*, London, 1963, p. 304.
[3] Springell, p. 259.   [4] Ibid., p. 261.

introduction to present my humble and hearty thanks to your Excellency for my kind entertainment and the rest of your many favours to me, which as I can never forget, so will I never omit any occasion wherein I may (by performing to your Excellency any service) testify my gratuity or get any opportunity to wish and pray for your Excellency all happy success and prosperity.

Your Excellency
his Humble servant
Will Harvey

Ratisbon November 5/15
for his Excellency my lord Ambassador

The journey homewards was begun on 8 November, and the party reached Nuremberg from Ratisbon in three days. At Nuremberg the City Fathers treated Arundel with great courtesy, coming to him with a gift of forty flagons of wine and a quantity of fish, 'which was brought in by thirty men all in red coats, guarded in the arms, with white and red caps'. They insisted that his Lordship should visit the Stadthaus, where there were many pictures. Among them were 'two pictures of Albert Durer and his Father, done by him, which they presented to his Excellence'. At last Arundel and Harvey were recompensed for the dearth of good paintings they had hitherto experienced, and this was not all, for next morning before their departure the Bishop of Wesburg visited Arundel and gave him 'the picture of our *Ladie* done by Albertus Durerus, being one of his best peeces'. Arundel described this in a letter from Frankfort, saying that 'though it were painted at first upon an uneven board and is varnished, yet it is more worth than all the toyes I have gotten in Germanye and for such I esteeme it, having ever carried it in my owne coach since I had it'.[1]

The party then passed through wooded and hilly country and were in some danger from the Croats, 6,000 of whom were ravaging the district. On the twentieth day from Ratisbon they reached Frankfort, where Harvey could have visited his publisher, William Fitzer, if, indeed, he had not already done so on the outward journey in May. On 26 November they reached Mainz, and Arundel, anxious to see if conditions had improved since his first visit, 'found it as miserable as before, with divers poore people lying on Dunghils almost starved, being scarce able to crawle for to receive his Excellencies almes, and presently returning to our Boate to dinner, wee afterwards releeved many poore hungry soules with the fragments'. Going on their way they cast anchor for the night

[1] Hervey, op. cit., p. 394, and Springell, p. 264.

by an island a mile from Coblenz, which they could not pass without leave from the Governor. They were again in some danger from the guards, and muskets were discharged, fortunately without injury to anyone.

The next morning, his Excellence sent againe to the Governour for passage, who like a base fellow made us stay that night also, and the next day untill three of the clock in the afternoone, and would not let us passe, for all that his Excellence had sent him the Emperors Passe and Letter, wherein hee was commanded, not onely to give passage, but to assist him in anything he required; yet for all this, hee kept us still, and would not give way that our Trumpeter might goe to the French in the Castle; but they perceiving how unworthily hee did deale with his Excellence, discharged 4 or 5 Cannons at his house, and shot quite through it.

At length, after experiencing further dangers and indignities the party reached Cologne on 1 December, and there they spent three days. On 4 December they set out again in larger boats down the Rhine and so reached Holland, where they encountered fresh dangers from masses of ice on the river. On 12 December they arrived at Utrecht, and at Leyden next day they visited the Anatomy School before going on to The Hague. Here they stayed for eight days, making many visits of courtesy to the Prince of Orange, the Queen of Bohemia, and other notabilities. They embarked on the ship *Garland* on Christmas Eve, reaching Deal on 27 December.

Arundel had written to Petty from shipboard at Mainz on 7 December giving Harvey's account of the complete failure of his efforts to buy pictures for the Royal Collection.

Dr. Hervey told me heere yesternight, that he is confidente one thousande poundes sterlinge would buy all Bartholomeo della Nave[s] collection. I doubte his memory is quicker heere upon the water then it was on the lande, and his fancye outrunnes his desire of buyinge, especially good thinges, havinge made only such an unknowne collection as you mencion at Rome, whither he went with such a desire to buy some excellent thinges, and had creditte at will. But nowe he layes all upon wante of seeinge the collection of Lodovisio, and that he could find nothinge good to be sold. . . . I pray doe you helpe me with thinges of Leonardo, Raphaell, Corregio, and such like.[1]

A few days after Harvey's return to London George Conn, the Papal agent in England, was writing to Cardinal Barberini:

Last Thursday the Earl of Arundel arrived at Court, and was received

[1] Hervey, op. cit., p. 395, from British Museum, Add. MS. 15970, f. 62, and Springell, p. 265.

with much favour by their Majesties. . . . With the Earl there returned that Doctor, who at Rome received so many favours from your Eminence, for whose kindness he declares himself eternally obliged. Their Majesties came to London on Tuesday, and stayed one night *incognito*, without admitting anyone. The King went privately to the house of the Earl of Arundel to see the pictures he has brought from Germany.[1]

Harvey also met Salveti, the Tuscan envoy in London, who wrote to Ciolo, Secretary of State in Florence, on 13 February 1636/7: 'Dr. Harvey, the King's physician, who went with the Great Marshal to Ratisbon and thence journeyed to Florence, is full of praises of his most Serene Master and publishes everywhere the great courtesies received from his Serene Highness [the Duke of Florence].'[2] Though we know nothing further of Harvey's activities in Florence it is clear that he had been treated with much kindness and respect. We may be sure that he saw the best pictures and visited the important hospitals.

So ended the most adventurous episode of Harvey's life, coloured for him by the friendship of one of the most attractive and intellectual men of the period. They shared a deep interest in pictures, which Arundel had the means to gratify as a collector; there is no evidence that Harvey ever attempted to acquire fine pictures for himself, but he could enjoy their pursuit on behalf of others. Arundel's health broke down in the autumn of 1639; in 1641, cruelly disappointed in his hope of being awarded the Dukedom of Norfolk in recognition of his devoted services to the King, he was given 'permission' to travel abroad. He left England in August, virtually an exile, in company with the Queen Mother. He never returned, dying at Padua on 24 September 1646 in his sixty-second year.

Arundel did not live to hear of the judicial murder of the King he had loved and served so well, or of the ruthless dispersal of the Royal collection of pictures by Cromwell's agents. On 26 June 1649, soon after the King's death, an Act was passed by Parliament that 'the personal estates of the late king, queen and prince shall be inventoried, appraised and sold, except such parcels of them as shall be found necessary to be reserved for the uses of the State'. An amendment to this was added, in deference to Puritan opinion, that all pictures containing representations of 'the Second Person of the Trinity or the Virgin Mary shall forthwith be burnt'. Fortunately the reserved 'parcels' did contain Mantegna's

---

[1] Hervey, op. cit., p. 399.

[2] Anna Maria Crino, 'Inediti su alcuni contatti Tosco-Britannici nel seicento', *English Miscellany*, xii, Rome, 1961, p. 185.

'Triumph of Julius Caesar' and Raphael's cartoons, and not all the superstitious subjects were burnt; but the bulk of the collection, one of the
finest ever made in the history of art collecting, was sold at auction.
Harvey may have been a melancholy spectator when so many of the
masterpieces he knew so well were bought at bargain prices by the
agents of the Crowned Heads of Europe and of the chief connoisseurs.
The sale produced £18,000, doubtless only a fraction of the true value
of the whole, though allowance must be made for the fact that the Act
permitted such goods as 'by reason of their Rarity or Antiquity' might
yield higher prices abroad, to be exported by a merchant adventurer,
who should receive for his trouble fivepence in the pound of the price
realized. This clause may have covered some of the most valuable articles
that were sold.

30

COLLEGE AFFAIRS, 1635–1637 *
THE EXAMINATION OF JAMES LEVERETT

HARVEY's last appearances at the College of Physicians before his
departure for Germany had been on 16 February and 5 March 1635/6.
At the February meeting the College had received a letter of remonstrance signed by a number of 'Merchants and Shopkeepers of London
touching the abuse in garbelling of Sena'. Garbelling of spices and drugs
was the process of sifting and cleansing the material to remove impurities,
for which the garbeller was paid a fee. A package of a drug such as senna
could not, however, be garbelled without being opened, whereupon
exposure to the air deprived the substance of some of its virtue. The
letter explained that the Venetian merchants, finding that the senna was
spoiled by opening, had taught the Alexandrians, who produced it, to
cleanse it in the first place. Regarbelling was therefore unnecessary,
though prejudicial, if done, to the interests of the physicians, their
patients, and the merchants who supplied the drug. The name of none of
Dr. Harvey's brothers appears among the twenty signatories of this
letter, though their trade, as Levant merchants, is likely to have been
affected. Harvey and his colleagues considered the remonstrance and
were willing to give an opinion if a Court of Law wished for it, but were
unwilling to say anything more at the moment.

On 5 March Harvey had witnessed the arraignment of two 'empiriques' for giving physic to children who had died under their hands, but no sentences were recorded.

During Harvey's absence from London there occurred a severe epidemic of the plague, and the College was asked to consider remedies for its prevention and cure. Soon afterwards the epidemic became so serious that in June it was decided to hold no further meetings for six months, most of the Fellows having left the city. Meetings were resumed in January 1636/7, but Harvey did not attend until February, when, on the 13th and 17th, ordinary business was transacted. On 3 April Dr. Fludd raised a serious matter when he reported 'that in Gunpowder Alley at the signe of the Megpy [Magpie] antimoniall cups are to be sold, with that inscription upon the signe. He asked the price and they asked 50*s*.' The President said that 'Sir Nathaniel Kitch died of a vomit made by the antimoniall the last summer', and Dr. Wright said that 'the Lady Ayme Blunt died of this same medicine in Charterhouse yard'. Another case of the same kind was reported by Dr. Harvey. A compound called tartar emetic, containing a bitartrate of antimony and potash, had long been used by physicians to procure a vomit, but it is also a powerful poison if given in excess, and so was dangerous in the hands of unskilled practitioners. Nevertheless the Annals of the College do not record any action taken to suppress this grave abuse in Gunpowder Alley.

At another meeting on 29 April Harvey was one of thirteen Fellows who reviewed the question of fining 'those who refused in their time and year to read the Anatomy Lectures according to the form of the Statutes when asked by the President'. The President now proposed that the fine should be increased from £4 to £20. Only three voted against the infliction of this very heavy penalty, and we may be sure that Harvey, with his known views on the importance of anatomical knowledge, was one among the majority of ten. The matter was raised again on 12 May, when only two out of sixteen were in opposition; it was finally approved and included in the Statutes on 26 June.

Harvey did not attend another meeting at the College between May and November in this year, and we have no knowledge of his movements; so long an absence suggests that he may have been away from London on other business. At length, on 3 November 1637, he was present at the first hearing of an important and interesting case of malpractice referred to the College by the Privy Council. This concerned a gardener, James Leverett, aged about 60, who was accused of pretending to effect the cure of all kinds of disease solely by the touch of his fingers. He was introduced to the Comitia by a Councillor of Gray's Inn named Harvey, though he was no relation of his namesake. The tribunal was asked to begin proceedings by examining men, women, and children who had been cured by 'touching', but this they declined, saying that they wished first to go forwards, not to look back. As will be seen, they proposed to make Leverett give a demonstration of the powers he claimed to have by touching actual patients, allowing time enough for the effect, if any, to be apparent. Leverett said at once that he was not in custody, but had come of his own free will, evidently thinking that this would give an impression of honest purpose. Further, he had not claimed special virtue as the seventh son of a seventh son, though in fact he said he was the seventh of the eight sons in his family.

Giving evidence, he said

that about some three yeares since and a half, hee did his first cure uponn his owne wife, who had bene full of paine 3 quarters of a yeare from her wrist to her elboe. In all which time, although hee did live with her, yet hee never touched her arme, till at last upon her entreaty shee desired him to take off the Splints and Rowlers and looke on it, which hee did, it being bound up by a surgeon. Hee felt it, and sought for kernells, but found none; his wife found present ease and therefore desired him to hold her by the wrist, which he refused; but she earnestly desiring it, saying shee felt ease, hee did it, and the next daie was perfectly cured of her paine and was weeding in his garden.

Some 6 moneths after, a Maid dwelling in Thames Street was his second Patient, who desired to bee touched by him for a paine in her elboe, which hee did and shee was cured. The third was a woman in Turnbull street, who came to him and craved his helpe for a paine in her arme, but he answered shee was foolish woman, but shee said God had given him the guift of healing; so by her importunity shee prevailed that hee touched her, and shee was very well; their names he knoweth not. In the touching of these hee did not use any words, nor till he had cured about a dozenn. And hee hath used these wordes: God give a blessing. I touch, God heals. He saieth that uponn the touching of some 30 or 40 in a day hee findes himself weakened by the vertue which goes out of him, more then whenn hee was a gardiner by digging up 8 rods of ground, so that hee is brought to that weakenes by touching that hee is forced to goe to his bedd to recover his strength, which in his daily labour hee was not wont to do.

He saieth hee is not alwaises disposed to touch, especially if his handes be cold. He saieth hee hath cured 300 at the least. Hee takes money for his cures, but not by contract; if hee should not take money hee might sterve, having forsaken his trade by the calling of God. Hee denies vertue to bee either in his gloves or lynnenn, or any thing that toucheth his naked bodie, although it was then objected against him.

He saieth that whilst hee dwelt at Ratcliff hee was assaulted in the high waye one evening by some Surgeons or Phisitions, and his thumbe was wrunge and strayned, but by his owne touching hee cured it, and that hee stood in feare of his life from some Phisitions and Surgeons, but of whom hee knowest not.

Hee cures the Kinges-Evill, dropseys, feavers, agues, all diseases and sores in any part of the bodie; but he promiseth not any cure to any as hee is a Synner, but God cures and hee doth his dutie.

Hee saieth that hee toucheth none above twice or thrice, and that the first time they find ease and good effect of his touching.

Leverett was then told to attend again on 8 November, when he would be given patients to touch. 'Hee seemed to be verie joyfull at it, and insisted that they might bee of the Kinges evill, for that hee had cured those that the King had touched, and also some of them under the surgeons handes which could not be cured by them.' He was thus directly challenging the belief that the touch of a King had any greater efficacy than his own. He attended on the appointed day, but Harvey was not present. Leverett seemed now to begin to anticipate criticism if his touch were ineffective, saying that he was grown weak with touching and must touch four or five times before cures followed. Nevertheless he was today 'in good disposition to touch'. He was accordingly faced with a man aged 23, named Richard George, who for two years had complained of a tumour in his right knee.

This George was presented to him to be touched; when he saw his knee hee seemed to be discontented, hee asked if it was not out of joynt; he was answered that it was not; hee lamented that the Colledge did not according to promise present to him those that were troubled with the Evill, yet in fine he touched this George. Hee began with the wordes I doe not promise any cure, God cures, God give a blessing, I doe but my dutie; then bowing downe and laying both his handes a little above the kneee, stroaking it downwards, Hee said to the Patient, You must pray to God to give a blessing to my hands that they maye take effect. And soe hee touched and said very softly, God blesse, I touch, God heals. These words he repeated thrice, thrice, and thrice, still stroaking downwardes, and then spake to the Patient with some iterated vehemency to praie to God to give a blessing to his handes. In putting on the Lynnenn to his knee, the Patient touched his own knee with his fingers, whereat he grew into Choller, and saied that he had spoiled all, for neither hee nor any bodie else must touch it, nor any oyles nor oyntments nor plaisters must come uponn it, and soe hee touched it twice as before and repeated the wordes six tymes againe; then he wiped his hand about the Clothe on both sides and so pinned the Lynnenn about his knee himself and commaunded him not to touch it agine till himself should see it. And likewise that the Patient should pray to God for a blessing uponn his hand, that his hand might take effect. And further commaunded the Patient to drinck noe small beere, but strong, nor wash his handes or face in cold water, but warmed.

A second patient, Elizabeth Appleton, with swellings in her neck and under her ears, was touched with the same words as before.

On 10 November Leverett touched these two patients for the second time, with three others—a woman with a running sore in her breast and two with 'ulcerated and tumified fingers'. The same kind of ceremony was observed. On 14 November the same patients came again; George was unwilling to be touched again, for his leg and foot had now become swollen, but he was persuaded to submit once more. On 17 November Leverett was expected to attend again, but did not come. He appeared, however, on 21 November before Harvey and ten others, and excused his non-appearance four days before, because he did not feel disposed to touch. On 25 November he brought with him three children whom he had touched, one with a sore under his arm and two with trouble in their eyes; all these he claimed to have cured. The second was a girl aged 11, who said that

shee had the Kinges Evill in her eyes 7 yeares with scales in her face which hung by Geometry. Shee learned that word from her Father. Her head likewise brake forth, and was well and ill of itself. Leverett layd his handes only on her eyes and bid her serve God. Leverett touched her 3 tymes in 9 daies and three daies intermission betweene every time. Shee fell to a looseness before hee touched her. Shee had bene with the King 2 yeares before and carries the Angell still, but was not well by the Kinges touching, but within 9 daies after Leverett touched her shee was well.

The third child declared he was not yet well of the King's evil in his left eye, and the College was of the same opinion. These various demonstrations seem to have been unconvincing enough to brand Leverett as an impostor, but the main stroke against him followed on 28 November. Serjeant Clowes now brought to the College a number of people who signed certificates testifying to Leverett's impostures, together with a general indictment accusing him under seven different heads, including slighting the King's sacred gift of healing. Finally, it was proved by reference to the Parish Register of St. Clement's Eastcheap that the accused was merely the fourth of the six sons of his father.

After this painstaking investigation was completed, the College drew up a long report for the Privy Council, concluding with the following summary:

Wee therefore the Presidant and Fellowes of the said Colledge of phisicions in contemplacion of the premisses since it hath pleased your Lordships by your aforesaid order to commaund us to deliver our opinion therein doe conceave the said Leverett to be an Impostor and a deceavor of over Credulous people, who are heartened in theire Credulitye by an erroneous opinion of some prodigious vertue inherent in a 7th sonne which yet this Leverett is not. Also wee conceave his pretended cures with the manner of them to be full of superstition and sorcery and not to savour of any skill of phisick and surgery or the operacion of naturall causes. All which notwithstanding wee in all humility submitt to your Honors grave wisedomes and consideracions etc.

Harvey was not one of the seven signatories of the report, since he held no special office in the College, but he had taken an active interest in the proceedings and no doubt was reminded of his part in the investigation of the Lancashire witches only four years earlier—another affair 'full of superstition and sorcery'. The action taken by the Privy Council in asking for the inquiry was doubtless partly in order to assert the King's prerogative as the only person so divinely inspired that his touch could be credited with the power of healing. The King certainly knew about the inquiry, if, indeed, he did not himself stimulate the Privy Council to act, and he would surely have discussed it with his personal physician and friend. It is impossible to refrain from wondering what were Harvey's inmost thoughts on the subject. Did he really believe in the efficacy of the royal touch? Or did his objective mind reject this too as a superstition, and did he even deliberately encourage his master to ask for the inquiry as an oblique way of suggesting a rational disbelief in this manifest absurdity? Whatever he may have thought, the belief died hard. Having been started in the time of Edward the Confessor, it had become too valuable an adjunct to the conception of the divine right of Kings to be readily abandoned, and the practice of touching survived through the next two reigns, reaching a climax under Charles II, who is reported to have touched 260 people at Breda before taking ship for England and touched more than 92,000 of his own subjects between 1660 and 1682.[1]

[1] See the Register at the end of John Browne's *Charisma Basilicon*, appended to his *Adenochoiradelogia: or, An Anatomick-Chirurgical Treatise of Glandules & Strumaes, or Kings=Evil= Swellings*, London, 1684.

It was revived for a short time by Queen Anne, Samuel Johnson being among her patients in 1712. It may be noted that the Royal touch was commonly credited only with the power of curing 'scrofula', that is, tuberculous glands in the neck, whereas an impostor such as Leverett extended his claim to the cure of many other conditions. Glandular tuberculosis was the more reasonable limitation, since it so often reaches a natural term with spontaneous healing of the superficial ulcers.

31

CORRESPONDENCE WITH VESLING AND BEVERWIJK, 1637–1638 * THE PETRIFIED SKULL

A T the beginning of December Harvey signed a certificate[1] on behalf of a patient, Sir Thomas Thynne:

Having had experience of the disposition and weakness of the body of Sir Thomas Thynne Knight (who hath beene and still is our patient) Wee testifie that wee are of opinion that it will be dangerous for the health of his body to travell this winter into the Contrie and place of his usuall abode untill hee hath better recovered his health & strength.

Dec. the 2nd 1637

Will Harvey
Daniel Oxenbridge

The patient was presumably a member of the Thynne family of Longleat in Wiltshire, the great house built by Sir John Thynne in the years 1567–79, though the relationship is not clear. The colleague who signed the certificate with Harvey was an M.D. of Oxford and Fellow of the College of Physicians, also practising in London.

Later in the same month, on 22 December, Harvey was present at the College Comitia when Dr. Thomas Bathurst was elected a Fellow, although he had only been elected a Candidate on the same day. The President was anxious that this should not be taken as a precedent, and had only agreed to the irregular procedure because the Fellows were unanimously in favour of it. Bathurst was evidently a man of unusual distinction, and his eminence was later recognized when he became personal physician to Oliver Cromwell, as well as to the Royalist Sir Richard Fanshawe and his family. He even persuaded Cromwell to release Sir Richard from imprisonment at Whitehall on medical grounds. Bathurst

[1] Public Record Office, *Domestic State Papers*, ccclxxiii, no. 8.

was named Elect on 9 July 1657 to fill Harvey's place at the College after his death.

There is thus plenty of evidence to show that Harvey was actively pursuing his avocations in London in the latter part of 1637. There are, however, letters from two friends on the continent of Europe suggesting that he may have paid a visit to Germany in that year, perhaps during the six months' period for which we have no other information about his movements. These letters passed between Harvey and friends in Germany and Holland. The first, written late in 1637, was from Johan Vesling, who was nominally Professor of Anatomy at Padua from 1632 to 1648, but he belonged at Minden in North Germany and the evidence of Harvey's letter to his second correspondent suggests that he met Vesling in Germany. The implications of these letters as to Harvey's movements in 1637 have not previously been noticed. The printed version of Vesling's letter carries no address; if Thomas Bartholin had his papers in 1664, when he was editing them, they would probably have been destroyed by fire with his library in 1670, and so cannot now be consulted for verification of the date.

The letter, dated 20 December 1637, suggests that Harvey's visit to him had been very hurried, since it begins: 'I have borne your departure heavily and impatiently, as it was sudden and wholly unexpected by me, and with the violence of a storm, as it were, cast out from me all hope of sweet conversation.' He then explains that he has decided to overcome his bad luck by writing, since the seed sown by letters can come to fruition by their frequent interchange. He has read what Primrose and Parisanus have written against the circulation, and thinks little of it.

He accepts as true what Harvey has written about the origin, form, and action of the heart and the function of the lungs, and has confirmed it by autopsy. The return of the blood through the veins to the heart does not seem absurd, 'although I may confess that, after examining oviparous embryos, I do not understand the manner of it. The umbilical arteries go to the albumen, the veins to the luteum. In the arteries the blood is bright red, in the veins dark purple. The arteries move with an obvious systole, but expel nothing into the clear white liquid. The veins as usual lie quiet.' He asks Harvey to dispel the mists which surround him.

In a second undated letter[1] Vesling returned to the same difficulties about the foetal circulation, but in a letter, also undated, to Fortunio

---

[1] The two letters are printed in *De quæsitis per epistolas a claris viris responsa*, Bologna, 1640–50, pt. vii, and in *Observationes anatomicæ & epistolæ medicæ ex schedis posthumis selectæ & editæ a Th. Bartholino*, Copenhagen, 8°, 1664, pp. 96–100. Translation by W. R. LeFanu.

Liceto, a Professor of Philosophy at Padua, he confessed that his doubts had been resolved by Harvey's letters; these are unfortunately not known to have survived.

Harvey's second correspondent was Johann Beverwijk, a Dutch physician (1594–1647) and a relative of Vesalius. Although a doctor, he was also Mayor of Dordrecht, Lord President, and a naval administrator. The Beverwijk correspondence was printed in 1641,[1] and it may be noted that the earlier letter contains one of the first acknowledgements of Harvey's work on the circulation of the blood. It is as follows:

Johan van Beverwijk to William Harvey, great physician-in-chief of the King of Great Britain: Greeting.

Your Excellency—No one who knows how much I support the incomparable gifts of your genius will wonder how vehemently I regret that you were in these parts without my knowing it. I first recognised your gifts in the new discovery (which can never be praised enough) of the circulation of the blood. Just as we rejoice that you have with incredible sagacity made this plain for this and later ages, so (if the dead could feel) would Hippocrates, Aristotle, Galen, and the like spirits grieve exceedingly that you were born too late.

As everyone here wonderingly admires this doctrine, so I too embrace it with both arms in the little book which I send 'On the calculus of the kidneys and bladder.'[2] I urgently request that your Excellency may deign to bring this [book] to the ballot[3] of your perspicacious judgement and let me share [your judgement].

Wishing you health and long life to the glory of the age and the increase of our Art. In haste.

Dordrecht, 21 December 1637

Harvey replied at length, referring to the journey which he 'lately took to Germany'. His letter was written on 20 April 1638, and the term 'lately' would relate rather to the latter half of 1637 than to November 1636, when he was returning through Germany from his expedition with Lord Arundel. The reason for this otherwise unknown journey it is now impossible to guess.

William Harvey to Johan van Beverwijk, councillor and physician of Dordrecht; Greeting.

Distinguished Sir. That I was not able, in the journey which I lately

[1] In his book, *Exercitatio in Hippocratis Aphorismum de calculo ad N. V. Claudium Salmasium*, Leiden, 12°, 1641, pp. 190–9. Translation by W. R. LeFanu.

[2] *De calculo renum et vesicæ. Cum epistolis et consulationibus magnorum virorum*, Leyden, 1638, pp. 20–24.

[3] A pun on *calculus* (pebble) meaning 'stone' in the medical sense, and also a 'ballot-ball'.

took to Germany, to see you, the ornament of your country and of the art of Medicine, in like manner as your agreeable letter (which I received, with your book, a week since) indicated that you were affected by no mean sorrow; so you can know that I grieve alike, since you know my feeling for men of wisdom, sagacious searchers of nature like yourself. That the discovery of the circulation of the blood does not displease so learned a head, by the same token it has begun at last to please me more, and will give encouragement to my meditations on more and greater things, since I have learned that my efforts please the erudite.

Pleasing to me, learned and elegant, and truly original, your *De calculo renum et vesicæ*, in which you have laid a firm and solid foundation for your name and fame; go on and build further day by day, and erect a splendid monument of your genius. I will, not unwillingly, add my stone, nor I think will others refuse theirs, particularly those Medical men who are the most notable of the present age.

How little Stephen Roderic de Castro, physician to the Grand Duke of Tuscany, and your own Sennert differ from your view, he will best judge who has read the latter's *Institutiones* and the former's book *De microcosmi meteoris*. This gem, which you have dug from his mine, ought to please Paracelsus and his followers; but you have given it into the hands of the public polished with more authority of the ancients, and brightened and decorated with the best observations and arguments. I do not think it would displease even Hippocrates or Galen, if they could now be called back across the threshold. You treat their views with such reverence that (if the knowledge and opinions of the ancient princes of medicine are not to be refuted so much as candidly explained) you judge them acceptable in a better sense. If finally any assertor of scientific liberty prefers growing wise from things themselves and the bosom of nature to learning from books, knowing rather than believing, you have what would much please such an one.

By your skill you have correctly observed the similar process of Nature in the generation of stones of the macrocosm and calculi of the microcosm. But to answer with something to exercise your wits, see what all these hold to the contrary and how best we can satisfy them:

Hippocrates calls for a certain glutinous substance, which he noticed in his case of Theophorbus' boy (*Epidemics V*), for the generation of calculus, beyond the supply of earthy matter and dissolved salt, which you assign.

Galen—something more closely impacted from the coarser juices in the hollow of the kidney (*Epidemics VI*, comment 1, text 6).

Each passage is in your book.

Roderic de Castro—a sulphurous mucilage out of Paracelsus, a somewhat viscid and glutinous chain of sands, which you yourself, with me and others, have often seen in calculous patients. You call it the aliment of the bladder, but [it is] the material cause of calculus itself. For it has been observed, when exposed by itself to the air for a night, and sometimes more quickly, to coalesce into a sandy, friable, nay stony matter; I too have made the experiment; and I knew a noble lady, afflicted with calculus, who used to make little balls with her own hands out of this kind of mucilaginous matter, which was a sediment in her urine; she taught and showed that when these were kept by themselves in a small box [*scatula*] they formed calculi spontaneously.

Chemists and the observation of nature will perhaps call the insensibility of the kidneys, which you elegantly establish, superfluous. For in springs, rivers, and almost all water, in which there is petrifying liquid, sulphureous matter seems to concrete as it were spontaneously or by the cold of the environment. You yourself admit that this matter can adhere to our teeth and all the other parts of our body. Others assert as very true that France has seen a stony fœtus in the womb. Stones of the same material are noticed in the joints of the gouty. Indeed it is known that an abundant crop of very small calculi has burst through the skin of an arthritic. Besides the insensibility, most people are satisfied that there seems to be an innate quality of stony matter in these coagulables. I, to speak freely, have brought under my observation, with the same intention as yourself, the method of the concretion of stones in the Megalocosm, have experimented, have observed many and rare things. Also that I might understand more clearly the causes of the thickening, drying and concretion discussed in Aristotle *Meteora IV*, I have done much and seen much, and have found it possible to make stones out of many a man's urine or at least sandy concrement, like salt out of lye; but since I did not clearly satisfy myself, must enquire further of others.

When time allows, you shall hear further from me at leisure hereafter. Meanwhile farewell, honoured Sir, and live happily for the light and splendour of your country. If you have further thoughts, let me share them, as you have so generously begun.

London, 20 April 1638.

Beverwijk's second letter, dated 16 September 1638, enlarges on the subject of 'glutinous humours' and the generation of urinary calculi and need not be transcribed here, but about the time when this letter was written another remarkable example of the effect of a 'petrifying liquid' had come to Harvey's notice. In 1627 a Captain William Stevens of Rotherhithe, an authority on maritime affairs and one of the eleven elder brethren of the London Trinity House, had brought from Crete a skull discovered about 30 feet below the surface of the ground when a well was being dug out near Candia, a town on the northern coast of the island. Captain Stevens gave this skull to the Master and Fellows of Sidney Sussex College, Cambridge, where it may still be seen preserved in a carved oak cabinet. The skull is that of a child about 12 years old[1] and is thickly encrusted with a brown calcareous deposit, giving it the appearance of having undergone petrifaction of the soft parts during its prolonged immersion in the waters of the well. Harvey had heard about this curiosity and spoken of it to the King, who expressed a wish to see it. Harvey accordingly wrote to Dr. Samuel Ward, Master of Sidney Sussex and Lady Margaret Professor of Divinity, asking him to send the skull to London for the King's gratification. This Dr. Ward, a devoted royalist, was delighted to do, writing at the same time to Harvey the following letter:

Sir—I receyved y^r Lett^r by wch I understand his Ma^{tys} pleasure that I should send up the petrifyed scull, wch wee have in our colledg library, wch accordingly I have done, wth thee case wherein we keep it. And I send in this Lett^r both the key of thee case and a note wch we have recorded of the Donour & whence he had it. And so wth my affectionate prayers & best devotions for the long life of his sacred Ma^{ty} & my service to y^r selfe, I rest

At y^r command
Samuel Ward

Sidney Coll Junii x [1638?][2]
Die solstitiale

Addressed: To his much honoured friend Doctor Harvey one of his Majestys Physitians att his house in the Blackfriars be this delivered. Deliver wth this a foure square box

Soon afterwards Harvey returned the skull in its cabinet to Cambridge, writing on the back of Dr. Ward's letter the following undated and unsigned reply:

Mr Doctor Ward, I have shewed to his M^{tie} this skull incrustated wth stone wch I received from you, & his M^{tie} wondered att it & looked content to see so rare a thinge. I doe now wth thanks returne to you & you^r Colledg the same wth the key [of][3] the case & the memoriall you sent

[1] This is the opinion of Professor Dixon Boyd of Cambridge, who examined the skull at my request.
[2] The year is conjectural. Sir George Paget, who first printed the letters in a small brochure in 1850, read the date as 'June 10, Sunday', thereby fixing the year as 1638. In fact Dr. Ward wrote the date as above, leaving the year uncertain; 1638 seems to be a probable date, so the incident is inserted here.
[3] The letters enclosed in brackets are missing owing to damage to the paper.

PLATE XXIII

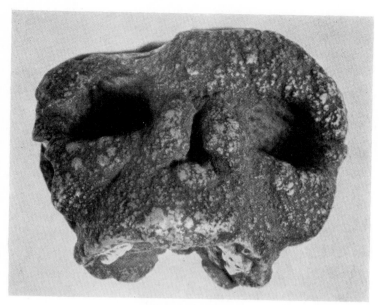

(i) from the front

(ii) from beneath, showing the teeth

THE PETRIFIED SKULL

me inclosed hearin, thinking it a kinde of sac[rile]dg not to have returned it to that place wh[er]e it may, for the [in]struction of men heare after, be conserved.

The documents are preserved in the College archives. The skull, a rounded object, heavy with its stony incrustation, lies comfortably when held in two cupped hands; as it is turned over to show the hard palate and the teeth it is natural to feel some satisfaction at the thought that it must have lain exactly so in the hands of both Harvey and the King about 1638. Harvey's letter is of further historical interest in that the characteristic handwriting served to identify the authorship of the *Prelectiones* when the manuscript of Harvey's lecture notes was rediscovered in the British Museum in 1876.

32

THOMAS HOLLIER AND THE ROYAL SOCIETY PAPER, *c.* 1640

IN the account on an earlier page (p. 211) of examples of hysteria in young women that came to Harvey's notice mention was made of a lithotomist named Hollyer. He was Thomas Hollier (sometimes called Holliar or even Hollyard), surgeon to St. Thomas's Hospital. He was a much younger man than Harvey and had been appointed surgeon for 'scald heads' at St. Thomas's in 1638. Five years later he became lithotomist to the Hospital in succession to Edward Molins and acquired some celebrity as a successful practitioner of 'cutting for the stone'. Samuel Pepys, whom he cut in May 1658, was one of his most grateful patients and his name is found on very many occasions in the Diary. In 1663, six years after Harvey's death, he was also appointed to the staff of St. Bartholomew's Hospital. He told Boyle of Harvey's visits to St. Thomas's to see the hysterical girl Mary, and must certainly have been well acquainted with him. Further evidence of this is a little-known manuscript by Harvey, which was brought to the notice of the Fellows of the Royal Society through Hollier on 4 May 1687. At a meeting on that day Dr. Gale presented a paper 'said by him to have been copied by Mr. Holliar the chirurgeon from the original of Dr. Harvey, containing several anatomical remarks made by him of the phaenomena proving the circulation of the blood, and others hinting the use of the viscera'. It was ordered that the paper 'be filed and preserved' and it is to be seen today in the archives of the Royal Society (*Register*, vol. vii, p. 5). It is difficult to understand for what purpose it was composed, since it consists of thirty-four brief numbered paragraphs on subjects so various as the circulation of the blood (nos. 1–7), the structure of the kidney, the functions of the liver and spleen, and other miscellaneous observations in anatomy and physiology, including the cause of sleep. Many of them correspond to statements found in Harvey's lecture notes or elsewhere, and there is no reason to doubt their authenticity.[1]

One of the most interesting of the paragraphs relates to the diaphragm. No. 19 lists the various actions of this muscle, and no. 20 continues: 'The diaphragma is exceeding sensible, and of so different a sense from the rest, that I am almost induced to think it the organ of the sixth sense.' Harvey wrote of the five principal senses in *De generatione animalium*,[2] but speculation on the existence of a sixth sense is not found elsewhere. The final observation states that: 'No creatures in proportion have so great a spleen and brain as a man.' These observations could have been written when Hollier was working at St. Thomas's about 1640, but it seems impossible to assign them to a more definite date.

At the meeting of the Royal Society when Dr. Gale presented Harvey's paper Thomas Henshaw 'observed that he had an account concerning swallows from our watermen, viz. that they have found them in the river Thames and that towards the end of the year they assemble in great numbers on the little islands of the river, and then submerge themselves in the water'.[3] At the next meeting on 11 May, when the minutes of the previous meeting were read: 'Mr. Henshaw remarked that Dr. Harvey had considered the state of swallows in the winter, and had dissected some of them which had been found under water, and could not observe that there was either warmth or motion in them.'[4] Henshaw (1618–1700) was a man with scientific interests and, at the beginning of the Civil War, was attached for a time to the King's retinue, so that he is very likely to have known Harvey. He may, therefore, have had this information about supposedly hibernating swallows from Harvey himself, whose reported action in immediately subjecting the claim to the test of dissection is

---

[1] They were printed in Birch's *History of the Royal Society*, 1757, iv. 535–7, and are reprinted in Appendix III, pp. 445–7.

[2] *Anatomical Exercitations*, 1653, p. 350.   [3] Birch's *History*, iv. 534.

[4] Ibid., p. 537.

entirely in character. That Henshaw's statement was true is perhaps the more probable since Harvey does not appear to have given any support to this popular delusion shared nearly a hundred years later by Dr. Samuel Johnson and taken seriously by Gilbert White of Selborne. Harvey did not mention elsewhere having done any dissection of swallows. John Ray, the greatest naturalist of the seventeenth century, writing within twenty years of Harvey's death, did not believe that swallows hibernated, thinking it more probable that they flew away to hotter countries.[1] Ray is certain to have made Henshaw's acquaintance at meetings of the Royal Society.

33

COLLEGE AFFAIRS, 1638–1641 ✳ THE SECOND JOURNEY TO SCOTLAND

AFTER the failure of Arundel's mission to Ratisbon in 1636 the rightful Elector Palatine, young Charles Louis, had been advised to look after his own interests himself. In consequence he rashly made an unsuccessful attempt in 1638 to assert his claim by an act of war. With Dutch help he had mustered a small army with which he attempted to join the Swedes. He was promptly intercepted by the Emperor's forces and his army was routed at Vlotho on the Weser. The most serious result of Charles Louis's disastrous private war was the capture of his brother Rupert. Charles himself had run away; Rupert, with greater courage, had attempted to recover a lost standard, but had only succeeded in losing his own liberty. News reached King Charles in the autumn that his nephew was unhurt, though imprisoned in a remote Austrian fortress, and there he remained until the autumn of 1641.[2]

These events concerned Harvey only in so far as they affected the fortunes of his master, the King. We have, in fact, little direct knowledge of Harvey's movements during the years 1638 and 1639. He was seldom able to attend the meetings at the College, and he was not there on 27 April 1638, when the President proposed at a full gathering 'that the Colledge would apply themselves to dissection of bodies with their own

---

[1] See Ray's *Ornithology of Francis Willughby*, London, 1678, p. 212. He made extensive use of Harvey's *De generatione animalium* in the introductory chapters of this work, first printed in Latin in 1676.

[2] C. V. Wedgwood, *The King's Peace 1637–1641*, London, 1955, p. 246.

hands, that the Company may be enabled to perform the bysinesse of the Anatomy Lecture without assistance of any man which is not of the body of the Colledge'. Harvey would have enthusiastically supported this, and his influence, though he was not there in person, must have contributed to the unanimity of the assent given to the proposal. He was present on 1 October 1638, when Dr. Simeon Fox reluctantly allowed himself to be re-elected President for another year after making 'a brilliant speech in which he complained at length about the treachery of certain Fellows towards the College', this complaint probably relating to the difficulties the College was experiencing in dealing with the encroachments of the Apothecaries. He was present also on 11 October.

Harvey next attended on 9 February 1638/9, when Hugh Haslam was examined and approved as a practitioner of medicine, his certificate being signed by the President with Doctors Argent, Harvey, and Baskerville. He was not there when his particular friend, George Ent, attended for examination on 1 March, 5 April, and 8 April 1639/40. On 5 April Ent had exhibited the diploma given to him at Padua in 1636, couched no doubt in the same glowing terms as were inscribed in Harvey's document.

Not only was the College missing Harvey's attendance; his Hospital also can show little evidence that he was able to see his patients as often as he would have liked. We have only an oblique reference found in a ledger with the date 23 March 1639 concerning 'the Scurvy-grasse drinke', which was to be made according to the directions agreed upon by the physicians, Harvey and Clarke. The chief ingredients of the drink were beer and the fresh juices of scurvy-grass and watercress, together with infusions of several other herbs, laced with pepper, nutmeg, and sassefras. Scurvy-grass (*Cochlearia officinalis*) was a specific remedy for scurvy, and the prevalence of this deficiency disease is shown by the fact that many barrels-full of the drink were prepared at one time. The plant was common, growing freely on the banks of the Thames and along the coast; two bushels of it cost 4*s*. The full prescription with the cost of the several ingredients is given with Harvey's other prescriptions in Appendix II.

With the evidence of these irregular attendances at Hospital and College we can assume that Harvey's duties as personal physician to the King compelled him to take part in the various expeditions undertaken in attempts to subdue the rebellious covenanters in the north. On 29 March 1639 the King left London to join his army at York, but by the time he reached the city his sympathizers in Scotland had already been defeated. He nevertheless decided to strengthen the defences of

Berwick and remained for some weeks in the north of England. In May he was at Newcastle and on 1 June Harvey's friend Lord Arundel, in all the panoply of the Earl Marshal of England, crossed the Tweed to proclaim Charles's sovereignty, while the King himself remained in camp south of the river. But peace negotiations followed instead of fighting, and on 19 June the so-called 'Pacification of Berwick' was signed—with mental reservations on both sides. So Harvey's second journey to Scotland took him no further than the border, whence he returned with the King to London.

Up to this point in his career Harvey had had the title of 'Physician Extraordinary' to the King, this office having carried on from the reign of King James into that of Charles at his accession in 1625, but it was not so important or valuable as that of 'Physician in Ordinary'. Harvey had been given this title in 1631, when he was granted an annuity of £50, though he still remained in a junior position. Dr. Bethune, the senior holder of the office, died in July 1639. A dispatch from Berwick dated 10 July contained a postscript: 'P.S. Dr. Beten [Bethune] is buried this day and Dr. Harvey is in his place, and Dr. Johnson has Harvey's place.'[1] So at length Harvey could be appointed to this coveted position with full emoluments. The warrant for the appointment, which carried with it a lodging in Whitehall and some other perquisites, is to be found in the Letter Book of the Lord Steward's office:

CHARLES R.

Whereas we have been graciously pleased to admit Doctor Harvey into the place of Physician in Ordinary to our Royal Person, our will and pleasure is that you give order for the settling a diet of three dishes of meat a meal, with all incidents thereunto belonging, upon him the said Doctor Harvey, and the same to begin from the seventeenth day of July last past and to continue during the time that the said Doctor Harvey shall hold and enjoy the said place of Physician in Ordinary to our Royal Person, for which this shall be your warrant.

Given at our Court of Whitehall the sixth of December 1639.

To our trusty and well beloved Councillors Sir Henry Vane and Sir Thomas Jermyn, Knights, Treasurer and Comptroller of our Household or to either of them.

The dietary extras were no doubt welcome and the lodging in Whitehall would be a convenience, though the removal of Harvey's possessions to the insecurity of the rambling buildings in Whitehall was to prove a great misfortune to Harvey himself and to all posterity, who have lost

[1] *Calendar of Domestic State Papers, 1639*, London, 1873, ccccxxv. 384.

thereby so large a proportion of the results of his scientific work. The immediate rewards, however, were gratifying. At the College of Physicians was an account of the sums of money due to Harvey from the Royal Exchequer, docketed: 'Money due out of the Exchequer for my pension 21 April 1642 and also since for my pension of £400 p.ann.'[1]

One duty of the royal physician was the control of the medicines dispensed for the use of the members of the royal household. Two documents signed by Harvey in this connexion have survived. One dated 4 January 1639/40 is as follows:[2]

Quarto die Januarii anno Regis: Charoli Angliæ, Scotiæ, Frantiæ et Hiberniæ decimo quarto

Adriaen Metcalfe deputy Apoth[ecary] for his Ma'ties most honourable household desireth allowance for Phisicall stuff delivered & spent upon his highness poore household servants from the feast of St. Michal the Arch Angell until the feast of the Birth of our blessed Saviour last past the some of fifteen pounds to be paid out of the recept of his highness Exchequer accordinge to a warrant dormant in that behalfe.

Will Harvey

A similar document[3] authorizing payment of the same sum for the third quarter of 1636 and signed by Harvey is dated 2 October 1636. It cannot actually have been signed by Harvey on that date, since he did not return from Germany until 27 December of that year; the payment was, however, a quarterly routine, so that the precise date of signing was not of consequence.

Meanwhile the 'Pacification of Berwick' had proved illusory. Another army had been assembled in Scotland during July 1640 and it crossed the Tweed into England in August. Advancing to the Tyne, it occupied Newcastle, Durham, and other towns, while the King fell back to York, not having advanced very far north of the city. On 7 September he signed writs summoning the peers to a Great Council to meet at York on 24 September, and as a result fresh negotiations were opened with the Scots. Meetings were held with their representatives at Ripon and an armistice was signed there at the end of October, the terms implying that King Charles had suffered defeat at their hands. Peace seemed to have been once more established at a price, and the Long Parliament

---

[1] Mentioned only in Munk's *Notæ Harveianæ*, *St. B. H. Reports* (1887), xxiii. 6. Not now known.

[2] Max Thorek Collection of Autographs, Parke–Bernet Galleries, New York, 15 November 1963, lot 263.

[3] Offered for sale at auction by J. A. Stargardt of Marburg, cat. 534, lot 337.

met in London on 3 November with William Lenthall as the Speaker. It is probable that Harvey was in attendance on the King throughout these troubled months. While they were at York he received a warrant by Royal Sign Manual addressed to the Comptroller of the Household and dated 25 September 1640 giving him £200 'for his diet'.[1] The award was presumably in compensation for his not having received during this time the three dishes of meat due to him as King's Physician in Ordinary.

By November Harvey was back in London and beginning to attend again to his own affairs. On 24 November he was present at the College Comitia and 'asked for authority to sue the heirs and successors of the most illustrious Baron Lumley in the name of the College for the recovery of the fee granted by the same Lord for the surgery and anatomy lecture. Permission was granted.' It is probable that he obtained no satisfaction, and the matter was not mentioned again in the College Annals until 31 May 1647, when 'a letter was read from Dr. Harvey, wherein he desired the College to grant him a letter of Attorney to one Thompson to sue for the Anatomical stipend. It was presently generally granted, and shortly after sent to him under our common seale.' Again Harvey failed to obtain the fees due to him, and, according to Dr. Charles Goodall, historian of the College, the unfortunate Lumleian lecturer spent at least £500 in a series of lawsuits which were not actually settled until after his death, the costs being met by Dr. Scarburgh, his successor in the chair.

Harvey's personal relations with the King after his appointment as Physician in Ordinary are illustrated by a record of courtesies which passed between them in the form of gifts for the New Year, 1 January 1640/1. Harvey was one of forty-two members of the household receiving gifts from the King. His share was a handsome one—24 oz. of silver plate. In return he gave the King 'a box of marmalade'.[2] Marmalade was then a somewhat general term covering preserves made of several different fruits, but various references suggest that quince was most favoured in the seventeenth century.

Harvey was not present again at College Comitia until 19 March 1640/1, when 'John Staley of the parish of St. Martin-in-the-Fields charged Mark Belwood Doctor of Medicine because he had given many vomits, purgations, pills and often let the blood of a certain melancholic

---

[1] Sir D'Arcy Power, *William Harvey*, 1897, p. 121.

[2] *Historical Manuscripts Commission, Seventh Report*, 1879, Appendix, 594b: House of Lords, 1640. Manuscript book containing a list of New Year's gifts.

woman then a widow, now the wife of the plaintiff, whom he left in a worse state than he found, namely afflicted with convulsions. Belwood was summoned on April 1.' So, while political convulsions rent the body politic, the bodies of the King's subjects were still receiving the grave attention of the College of Physicians for their trivial complaints.

At Harvey's next attendance on 19 April 1641 a remarkable incident took place. On the previous 4 February a Dr. Roger Drake, a Cambridge graduate, had been examined for the third time and been approved as a Candidate. On 19 April he 'presented a pamphlet on the circulation of the blood against Dr. Primrose, which he wanted to be printed with the approval of the College'. This was in line with a resolution propounded by the President for the second time on 12 June 1635 in full Comitia, including Harvey, 'that no Fellowe, Candidate or Licentiate shall sett his hand to anye booke which concerneth anye parte of phisicke or surgerye, unles the said booke bee first approved by the President and Censors, nor writte anye Epistle or verses to any booke not so licensed, and that the President shall not allowe any such booke without the consent of the foure Censors.' Nevertheless Dr. Fox, the President in 1641, expressed in Harvey's presence the opinion that Drake's book should neither be approved nor condemned, but should be left to the author. It appears, therefore, that twelve years after publication of *De motu cordis* the senior Fellows of the College, including Prujean, Smith, Alston, Hamey, and Bathurst, looked coldly upon an attempt to defend Harvey's work against the stupidity and obscurantism of James Primrose, whose attack on Harvey had been published together with 'refutations' by Parisanus in 1639. Drake had previously obtained a medical degree at Leyden and had read his thesis in defence of Harvey before the President, Jan de Wale, also a supporter of Harvey, in 1639. The thesis was printed at Leyden in 1640 and this was no doubt the 'pamphlet' presented at Comitia in 1641. It is to Drake's credit that he did not allow this rebuff at the College to discourage him, his book being reprinted in London in the same year under the title *Vindiciæ contra animadversiones D.D. Primrosii.* He had at least the support of Dr. George Ent, who published at the same time his *Apologia pro circulatione* in answer to Parisanus, the Venetian opponent already mentioned in connexion with Harvey's visit to Venice in 1636 (p. 243).

A few years later, on 4 December 1646, Drake politely resigned his position as Candidate at the College and asked to be released from his undertaking to obtain University incorporation with a view to becoming a Fellow. The Parliamentarian Dr. Clarke was then President, and Drake may have disliked his personality as heartily as Harvey did, but he was also giving up medicine in order to become a Presbyterian minister.

Early in May 1641 both Harvey and Drake were visited by a young Dutch medical man, Philip de Glarges (sometimes written Glargis or even Clargis) who had recently graduated at The Hague, his thesis being on palpitation of the heart, though his interests also included history and theology.[1] For five years he had been collecting autographs in a small *Album Amicorum*, attractively bound in calf with gold tooling on the covers.[2] He was provided with good introductions. In Holland he had secured among his thirty-five autographs those of Constantine Huygens, diplomatist and poet; Adolph van Vorst, botanist; Jan de Wale, anatomist; Marc-Zuerius Boxhorn, historian; and Daniel Heinsius, philologer, poet, and historiographer. In England, besides Harvey and Drake, he had visited Harvey's critic Dr. James Primrose, and William Twiss, a nonconformist divine. Harvey was kind to the young man, and wrote his contribution on leaf 38 of his album with a motto recommended to him by his own experience:

> *Dii laboribus omnia vendunt*
> *Nobilissim° Juveni Medico Phillipi d Clargi*
> *amicitiae ergo*
> *Libenter Scripsi*
> *Gul Harveus Anglus*
> *Med. Reg. et Anatomie*
> *professor*
> *May: 8: A.D. 1641*   *Londin.*

> The Gods sell everything for toil
> To the most noble young physician Philip de Glargis
> in friendship therefore
> I have written willingly
> Will Harvey Englishman
> Royal Physician and Professor of Anatomy
> May 8 A.D. 1641   London

Harvey was present again at Comitia on 6 May 1641, but did not put in another appearance for more than a year, presumably having been occupied by constant attendance on the King. Strafford had been executed on 12 May and the King's political manœuvres became ever more complex and less successful. He was also anxious to improve his position in

[1] Sir D'Arcy Power, *William Harvey*, London, 1897, p. 123.
[2] British Museum, Add. MS. 23105.

Scotland and decided to make a short visit to Edinburgh. So it came about that Harvey's third journey to Scotland took place in August of that year.

34

THE THIRD JOURNEY TO SCOTLAND, 1641 * VISIT TO NOTTINGHAM * THE BATTLE OF EDGEHILL * HARVEY AT OXFORD, 1642

THE King left London with a retinue of about a hundred people on 10 August. He made the journey in five days and in Edinburgh was entertained at a sumptuous banquet costing the city £12,000. Harvey was now in such constant attendance on the King that he no longer applied to the College of Physicians or to the Governors of St. Bartholomew's for leave of absence. It was assumed that his duties with the King were paramount. The Royal party stayed for some weeks in Edinburgh and its neighbourhood, and Harvey took the opportunity to visit Aberdeen in company with the King's apothecary, Adrian Metcalfe. It is conjectured that the reason for his visit was to consult on the King's behalf with the leading men in the two Aberdeen colleges about their possible union to form a Caroline University. The city had supported the Royalist cause, and the King, anxious to confer some benefit in recognition of this loyalty, gave his assent to the union and signed an Act at Holyrood on 8 November. The union was confirmed by Cromwell in 1654, but was dissolved in 1661, when all Charles's acts in Scotland from 1637 were repealed by a single Act of Parliament. If Harvey was representing the King in important affairs of this kind, it was proper that the City of Aberdeen should do him some honour in return, and accordingly on 30 August Harvey, together with Metcalfe and Alexander Middleton, sub-principal of King's College, were admitted as honorary burgesses. The entry in the Burgess Roll has been translated as follows:

On 30 August 1641 in presence of the baillies and the dean of the guild. On the same day the honourable gentlemen, the learned William Hervye, Physician to the King, Adrian Mitcalff, Apothecary to the King, and Mr. Alexander Midletun, subprincipal of King's College, Aberdeen, were received and admitted as free burgesses and brethren of guild of the Burgh of Aberdeen by grace of the Magistrates and Council of the same, each of them having paid five shillings in a white purse, as is the custom, and having taken the customary oath.[1]

It appears that the new burgesses were entertained by the city at the customary banquet, for, although no documentary evidence of its cost has been found, it is known that there was a protest. The Revd. Mr. Andrew Cant, a leading Covenanter, returned shortly afterwards from preaching before the King in Edinburgh and 'cried out against the Magistrates of Aberdeen for making strangers burgesses and spending the common good upon wine and other things, superfluously'. But his protest was too late; Harvey had already left the city and further small expenditure had been incurred by escorting him on his way: 'Item, to Alex Rollandis wyiff, for ane quart of wyne and one breid, quhilk was careit to the Bow Brig at command of the Magistrates at the gude nicht taking with some strangeris of Edinburgh £o. 18s. od.'

We have no further knowledge of any of Harvey's activities during the next six weeks in Scotland, but presumably he stayed with the King and left Edinburgh in his company on 8 November. They arrived back in London on 25 November.

In Scotland Harvey had watched the King trying to win over his former adversaries to his side by giving them new titles and powers of government, and as the Royal party made a triumphant entry into London on 25 November, it seemed for the moment that the King's position in England was secure. He had made concessions to Parliament, but, while he was on his way back from Edinburgh, the House of Commons, led by John Pym, had passed the Grand Remonstrance condemning 'in detail and at length the King's policy in Church and State, at home and abroad, throughout his reign'.[2] Although Pym's majority for the passing of the Remonstrance was small, he was too clever and too unscrupulous not to be able to follow up his advantage. He so shaped events as to provoke the crisis which came to a head on 3 January 1641/2. The Attorney-General in the House of Lords accused Pym, Hampden, and three others of High Treason, but the King subsequently failed in his attempt to arrest these men, known to history as the Five Members. Soon afterwards the King had been ousted from his own Capital and the Parliamentary junta had taken command.

It seems to be unlikely that, when, on the night of 10 January, the

[1] W. C. Souter, 'Dr. William Harvey in Aberdeen', *Aberdeen University Review* (1931).
[2] C. V. Wedgwood, *The King's War*, 1958, p. 22.

King and his family fled from London to Hampton Court, Harvey was in attendance, but he is likely to have joined them soon afterwards. The Queen left for France on 23 February to see what help she could summon, parting in tears from the King at Dover. The King then travelled northwards, passing through Royston, Newmarket, and Cambridge, where it was still possible for the Prince of Wales to be entertained by a play, *The Guardian*, hastily composed by Abraham Cowley, who had remained in residence at Trinity College. There is reason to believe that Harvey was now at the King's side. Civil war had become inevitable, and for a time the King held court at York, while the organizing of a royalist army was begun, until he went through the formality of raising his standard at Nottingham on 22 August.

It was probably about this time that Harvey was deprived of his papers to his and our great loss. Aubrey related that 'I remember I have heard him say he wrote a booke *De insectis*, which he had been many yeares about, and had made curious researches and anatomicall observations on them. This booke was lost when his lodgings at Whitehall were plundered in the time of the rebellion. He could never for love nor money retrive them or heare what became of them and sayed *"twas the greatest crucifying to him that ever he had in all his life"*.'

Harvey is assumed to have been with the King at Nottingham, because in September he is known to have ridden over to Derby to visit his medical friend Percival Willughby,[1] who had been in practice there for many years. Harvey was, no doubt, glad of an opportunity to absent himself from the disturbing atmosphere of a King's court in wartime and to have a quiet medical discussion. 'There came to my house at Derby', Willughby recorded, 'my honoured good friend Dr. Harvey 1642. We were talking of severall infirmities, incident to the womb. After that I had related the aforegoing story *de cauda mulieris*,[2] and how

---

[1] Willughby (1596–1685) was son of Sir Percival Willughby and uncle of Sir Francis Willughby of Wollaton Hall. He practised for many years in Derbyshire and became an extra Licentiate of the College of Physicians in February 1640/1, but is not known to have taken any medical degree.

[2] This story was a description of a condition now recognized as being an example of a large papilloma of the cervix uteri. 'There is an infirmity (though it seldom happeneth, or is seen by physicians, or chirurgions) called Cauda mulierum, and it causeth great flouding, of which I will make some mention, because I have seen it.

'There was a maid, a miller's daughter in Darbyshire. Shee oft, at severall times lost much blood, issueing violently, before it stopt.

'Shee came to mee Anno 1638 for help. Shee shewed mee a long, round lump of flesh, like a dog's pizzle in shape, and thicknes, which shee could put forth of her body, when shee stooped downward.

'It lay on one side vagina uteri, and had a hollow sheath to cover it. When shee stood

shee flouded, and was cured, hee added to my knowledge an infirmity, which hee had seene in women, and hee gave it the name of a honey-comb, which also, hee said, would cause flouding in women.' Harvey's observation is regarded as being a reference to cancer of the uterus, the nature of which was not known. Willughby himself saw an example of it twenty years later.

The King's wanderings in the next weeks took him westwards to Shropshire and the Welsh marches, while assembling troops for the expected clash of armies, and by the middle of October he was starting on his march towards London. Prince Rupert had been victorious in one of the first skirmishes of the war near Worcester, but had not attempted to hold the city, since it was indefensible. The Parliamentary troops, under the command of the Earl of Essex, were therefore able to vent their spite by occupying the city, desecrating the Cathedral and plundering the inhabitants. From there they moved to Warwick in order to intercept the Royalists, and on 22 October Essex was at Kineton (or Keynton), a short way south of Warwick, with most of his artillery a day's march behind him. Rupert had the foresight to occupy during the night the steep escarpment of Edgehill with his cavalry, and so the scene was being set for the first major engagement of the war, with Harvey as a witness. Edgehill overlooked Kineton and the main road from Warwick to Banbury, with the Avon valley away to the west.

Rather surprisingly, the King had kept with him up to this point two of the Royal children, the Prince of Wales aged 12 and the Duke of York aged 9. On the morning of 23 October the boys were in Dr. Harvey's charge. Our primary authority for knowledge of this fact is Aubrey, who had it from Harvey's own mouth:

> When Charles I by reason of the tumults left London, he attended him, and was at the fight of Edge-hill with him; and during the fight, the Prince and Duke of York were committed to his care: he told me that he

upright, it went up into her body, and then it was not to bee felt, and from this cauda the flux of blood issued.

'I used severall wayes for her ease, without any good successe. At last I resolved to take it off with a ligature, for that it had no great root.

'But this maid, grieving at her affliction, went alone into the garden, took hold on it, and, with a violent twitch, pulled it off. She did greatly bleed afterwards. Being taken up from the ground, shee was supposed to bee dead. Being carried into the house, and laid on a bed, shee came againe unto herself. And thus, casually, shee was cured, and was not afterwards any more troubled with bleeding, or any other infirmity of the womb.' Willughby's *Observations in Midwifery*, ed. H. Blenkinsop, Warwick, 1863, pp. 256–7. Quoted by Dr. Aveling in his *Memorials of Harvey*, 1878, from the manuscript of Willughby's writings on obstetrics then in his possession.

withdrew with them under a hedge, and tooke out of his pockett a booke and read; but he had not read very long before a bullet of a great gun grazed on the ground near him, which made him remove his station.

Sometimes doubt has been cast on Aubrey's veracity, in spite of his plain statement that Harvey told him this, but it was not hearsay, and examination of original authorities shows that he was certainly correct.

The King's forces consisted of 8,000 foot, 2,500 horse, and 10 pieces of cannon. The Parliamentarians had 10,000 to 11,000 foot, with rather more horse and cannon than the King, but the disparity was not great. An anonymous witness relates that the Prince and the Duke of York were at the battlefield by 8 o'clock in the morning with the King, and that

it was at least two of the clock in the afternoon before the armies came together in the field where the rebels had kept themselves in order without motion from the morning and had gotten the advantage of the hill, and saluted us with 2 or 3 canon-shot before our ordnance came and were planted. The shot from the canon on either side did not much hurt in the beginning, though where his Majesty and his Children were, many shots fell very near his Royal Person.[1]

This account agrees perfectly with Aubrey's statement, since there is no difficulty in believing that Harvey was with the King in the morning and in charge of the boys. It is not surprising that he should read a book during the tedious hours of waiting from eight in the morning until after two o'clock in the afternoon when at last the battle was joined.

When the fighting started, the King marched immediately behind his foot-soldiers, the boys at his side and with a scarlet cornet, or standard, carried before him to mark his position. Both sides opened fire with their cannon, but still little harm was done, though again several shots fell near the King and the princes. The Prince of Wales, finding himself not far from the front of the fight, delightedly cocked his pistol and cried loudly, 'I fear them not'. His father thought discretion was better and ordered, first the Duke of Richmond, and then the Earl of Dorset to escort the boys to the rear. Both refused lest they should be thought cowardly, and finally Sir William Howard, in command of fifty mounted pensioners, consented to take charge of them; they had started to retreat when they saw a party of enemy horsemen advancing upon them. They therefore drew behind a small barn surrounded by a hedge, and the enemy, thinking they were a more formidable force than they were, also

---

[1] T. Carte, *A Collection of Original Letters*, London, 1739, p. 10.

withdrew, so losing their chance of making prisoners of the princes. Inside the barn a number of wounded men were being dressed, and it seems likely that Harvey, being a non-combatant, had already withdrawn and might have been seen at work there. Howard and his party retreated further up the hill as dusk was falling. Anthony Wood seemed to confirm this when he wrote that Harvey at the battle of Edgehill 'was withdrawn under a hedge with the Prince and the Duke while the battle was in its height.'[1]

There were others who claimed to have had the honour of protecting the Prince of Wales at Edgehill. Dr., later Sir John, Hinton, a Royal physician after the Restoration, sought to obtain Charles's favour by telling him that he had saved his life during battle by receiving the charge of an enemy trooper, who was riding at the boy, and then persuading him to move out of danger.[2] Edward Hyde, the future Lord Clarendon, also let it be known that he had been entrusted with the Prince's safety when he had only the protection of a company of pensioners.[3] These claims may have some truth in them, but they relate to the confused fighting late in the afternoon when Harvey was no longer in any way responsible.

Meanwhile, earlier in the afternoon, Essex was seen by Rupert to have his infantry so disposed that, although their right wing rested on the hamlet of Radway and so had some protection, their left wing was exposed and unsupported. He accordingly gave orders to charge, and his cavalry swept down the slope on to the exposed infantry, who were broken up and fled in disorder towards Kineton, followed both by Rupert's cavalry and by the reserve of horsemen from the other wing, who should have stayed to protect the infantry in the centre with the guns and the King's standard. The Parliamentary troops thus had the opportunity to attack the King's party and almost overwhelmed it. Rupert's troops returned from the chase just in time to save the situation and to rescue the standard, temporarily captured after the standard-bearer, Sir Edmund Verney, had been killed. Sir D'Arcy Power suggests (though it does not seem likely) that perhaps Harvey now saw one of the most picturesque acts of the battle.

The Royal Standard carried by Sir Edmund Verney at the beginning of the fight, had waved over the King's Red Regiment—the Royal Foot Guards. Verney slain and the Guards broken, it passed to the

---

[1] *Athenæ Oxonienses*, ed. 2, 1721, ii, Fasti, 27.
[2] Sir Henry Ellis, *Original Letters*, Third Series, 1846, iv. 299–300.
[3] T. H. Lister, *Life and Administration of Clarendon*, 1838, i. 207.

Parliamentary army, and was committed to the charge of the secretary of the Earl of Essex, the Commander-in-Chief. Captain Smith, a Catholic officer in the King's Life Guards, hearing of the loss, picked up from the field the orange scarf which marked a Parliamentarian and threw it over his shoulders. Accompanied by some of his troop, similarly attired, he slipped through the ranks of the enemy, found the secretary holding the standard, and telling him that so great a prize was not fitly bestowed in the hands of a penman, snatched it from him. Then, protected by the scarf, he made his way once more through the hostile force and laid his trophy at the feet of the King, who knighted him upon the spot.[1]

After the battle was over, both the tired armies camped on the field. Harvey certainly remained in the vicinity and took a hand in attending to the wounded, for he told Aubrey that Sir Gervase Scrope 'was dangerously wounded there, and left for dead amongst the dead men, stript; which happened to be the saving of his Life. It was cold, cleer weather, and a frost that night; which staunched his bleeding, and about midnight, or some houres after his hurt, he awaked, and was faine to drawe a dead body upon him for warmeth-sake.'[2] Anthony Wood further reported that he was 'brought off by his son and recovered by the immortal Dr. Will Harvey'.

Essex claimed a victory, but was forced to retreat in disorder, harassed all the way to Warwick by Rupert's cavalry and suffering much damage. If further confirmation be wanted of the part taken by Harvey at Edgehill, it will be found in a picture given to him by the King and clearly intended as a memento of the occasion. It represents the Prince of Wales in armour attended by another boy, said to be his page, but looking rather like the Duke of York. In the lower left-hand part of the picture, above a Medusa-head symbolizing the discord of war, is a battle scene with a cavalry skirmish, sufficiently indicating the purpose of the gift. The artist was William Dobson, whom the King had summoned to Oxford soon after the battle. The picture descended in the family of Harvey's brother Eliab, and was sold in 1935 to the National Portrait Gallery of Scotland in Edinburgh.

After the battle of Edgehill, the King, instead of pushing on at once to

---

[1] Power, *William Harvey*, London, 1897, pp. 128–9. The incident is recorded in Edmund Ludlow's *Memoirs*, ed. C. H. Firth, Oxford, 1894, i. 43.

[2] Aubrey mistakenly said that it was Sir Adrian Scrope who was wounded. Adrian was the son of Sir Gervase, who raised a regiment of foot for the King's army and in spite of his sixteen wounds sustained at Edgehill lived until 1655. Adrian was not knighted until the coronation of Charles II and died in 1667. Anthony Wood (loc. cit.) also confused Sir Gervase with his son in his account.

PLATE XXIV

CHARLES, PRINCE OF WALES

ed 12, 1642. Painting by Dobson given by King Charles to Harvey as a memento of the Battle of Edgehill

London as Rupert advised, preferred a milder course, believing that it would be better to reoccupy his capital by consent of the people rather than by force. He therefore moved slowly, took possession of Banbury without meeting with resistance and then marched quietly to Oxford. There was even talk of a treaty with Parliament, and a sort of truce was arranged. The King moved his advanced forces to Brentford, where fighting began again without any decisive action taking place, and the Royalists fell back, the King going by way of his palace of Oatlands to Reading. The Venetian Ambassador reported to the Doge on 12 December that: 'Before approaching Oxford he stayed for some days in the town of Redin owing to a heating of the blood by which the prince was overtaken, so violent that he had to take to his bed, and preventing him from continueing his journey. He is now in perfect health and remains at his Majesty's side.'[1] Another correspondent writing on the same day said it was a mild attack of measles, and there is no mention of its having caused Dr. Harvey any anxiety.[2]

Winter was now coming on and everything was in a state of uncertainty. King Charles thought it best to settle for the time being in Oxford, and set up his court there, a decision which certainly suited Harvey's inclinations. He was devoted to the King and his cause, but his devotion was more personal than political, and in Oxford he could find the sort of society he liked—people who could talk intelligently about medical and scientific matters and take an interest in the investigations that he immediately set on foot. Aubrey stated that he first saw him in Oxford, but was 'then too young to be acquainted with so great a doctor'; nevertheless he remembered Harvey's coming several times to his college (Trinity) to see George Bathurst, 'who had a hen to hatch eggs in his chamber, which they dayly opened to discerne the progress and way of generation'.

Harvey was in fact immediately taking advantage of his leisure in Oxford to resume the embryological studies interrupted by the political upheavals. He had lost many of his notes, but could remember enough of what he had done to be able to build again on the foundations he had laid. Some of the observations recorded in *De generatione animalium* must have been made in Bathurst's rooms in Trinity. Bathurst was, however, not a doctor, but a Bachelor of Divinity. He served the King loyally and died in 1644 of a wound in the thigh sustained during the defence of Faringdon.

[1] *Calendar of State Papers, Venetian*, xxvi, 1925, p. 210.
[2] British Museum, Add. MS. 27962 K.

On 7 December 1642, shortly after arriving in Oxford, Harvey took the degree of M.D. He was described in the Register Book[1] as *Cant. incorporatus*—'incorporated from Cambridge'—although no evidence that he was ever given this degree at Cambridge has yet been discovered.

Harvey had been suffering from family anxieties while political affairs, profoundly affecting his own life, were drawing to a crisis. His brother, Matthew, had been ill for some time under the care of William's friend Dr. Baldwin Hamey, and had died on 21 December 1642. Matthew's twin brother, Michael, now aged 49 and father of three children by his second wife, Mary Mellish, was also seriously ill and filling Dr. Hamey, who was again in charge, with grave forebodings. In January 1642/3 Harvey was not available in London for consultation by word of mouth, and Hamey wrote him a letter in Latin describing Michael's condition, which was clearly very serious. This letter[2] provides an interesting clinical report on an illness diagnosed by Hamey as scurvy.

For Dr. Harvey

Your Excellence!

At last, as you have heard, your brother [Matthew] has gone hence, after your prognosis had held him as a stranger for so long. What help I gave him it would not be right to describe, but that the present condition of the other twin [Michael], who also frequently threatens departure, would not bear this useless delay. There is frequent sleeplessness from troublesome cough; pulse ever feeble and frequent; respiration not infrequently very difficult; continuous want of appetite; movements involuntary; urine, as Hippocrates says, thin crude and mostly red, and, I add, with a kind of brightness shining like soap; and lately towards evening some swelling about the ankles.

Meanwhile, as Galen says, among negative signs he is without thirst, and no spots arise obviously on the body; finally you will easily remember the trouble which his teeth and gums already gave in the past. If you now, ask, 'what disease I should call all these symptoms?' I shall say 'scurvy'; so do you, as I have heard from yourself here more than I should wish. I am safe in agreeing with your opinion and with ancient opinion. Do you ask what has been done and is to be done? When I was first called in, he was in fever every night, cold in the evening, sweating in the morning. By day he was similarly ill, and nothing answered as hoped. At once therefore after midday I ordered a clyster to be applied, and prescribed a julap of specifics for liver and spleen. The following day

---

[1] Oxford University Archives, Register Q 16 (1634–47), Congregation Register, f. 191. See also Anthony Wood, *Athenæ Oxonienses*, ed. 2, 1721, ii, Fasti, 6.

[2] Preserved among Hamey's papers in the Royal College of Physicians. Now first translated by W. R. LeFanu.

when he had vomited again, I advised a light vomitory, and when he had taken that after dinner, two hours later he first brought up a great quantity of phlegm, all at one time, and with it threw off the fever, with which thereafter he had clearly finished. And the previous discolourations of the urine became free from all sediment, deposits or reddish clouding. Then I used an ointment for opening the imposthume, altering and attacking the earthy and ashy humour, so that when the obstruction had been loosened it could thereafter be thrown off more easily. The next day I purge[1] gently and with relief, so that fortified by an electuary of antiscorbutics he would not hesitate to go out. But this improvement did not last long; the stomach not doing its duty, and dyspnoea at intervals oppressing him so severely that he was not fit for a step on an easy slope nor for a light stroll. Again therefore I correct the humour (which I consider tartaric and malignant) with preparations, and next day two hours after dinner, since it was helpful before, I exhibit an emetic medicine, which he took like the previous one and brought up no less. This was done and a decoction ordered for some days, of aperients and alteratives, and with them those things which are used for this disease with hidden property, as is believed. And purgation by mixture was started on the third or fourth day to avoid nourishments. Meantime while these things are a-doing, I seek your advice (glory of physicians), either to guide me further, or recall me hastily; either to agree with me, or to indicate your opinion. At night for soothing his cough (and I had almost forgotten this) a lohoch[2] of constringents is used, not without relief to him, as he says. About the use of these and of all else to be done later, I seek your advice, most learned Sir, and recommend myself most dutifully, praying for the health of your family,

Your Honour's most devoted servant

15 Jan: 1642 [1642/3] Bal. Hamey

Hamey's treatment did not succeed in prolonging Michael Harvey's life, and he died on 22 January, a week after Hamey wrote his report. It may be doubted whether Hamey's diagnosis of scurvy was correct, common as the disease was at the time, though it would, perhaps, be unwise to attempt suggesting an alternative. Hamey asked Harvey for further guidance, but probably the patient died before the application of any other treatment was possible.

Hamey had sometimes sent his patients to Harvey for a second opinion, and one reply[3] from him has been preserved; this does not give any clue

[1] The present tense is used here and in the following sentences. W. R. LeFanu.

[2] That is, a *linctus* (O.E.D.).

[3] Found among Hamey's correspondence now in the Royal College of Physicians. The translation is by Robert Willis (1878), verified by W. R. LeFanu.

as to the year in which it was written. It seems to be possible that the patient had suffered from a *melaena*, that is, passing altered blood in the stool from a haemorrhage somewhere in the gastro-intestinal tract.

Most learned, humane and dear Sir,

The woman appears to me, from her own account and her mode of life (with deference to your judgment), to be affected with a cholic passion of a hot and bilious nature. Suppose it was pitchy stuff that was formally discharged, still I do not believe that there is any imposthume in the hypochondriac or epigastric region; I should else have detected either some enlargement or some tension there. I therefore approve of your decision as to blood-letting; for the plethoric body of the patient, accustomed to generous diet, hot, robust and vigorous, requires it. I also commend purging by the Chologogue Pills, with half a scruple of Euphorbia added; this medicine having an excellent effect in soothing colic pains. I also advise the frequent use of the powder of ivory and *calcaneum cervi*. Everything else I leave to your discretion.

Farewell, my very dear Sir,
Yours with all my heart,
Jan. 19   Will Harvey

Having reached Oxford with the King, in December 1642, Harvey remained there until the surrender of the city to the Parliamentary forces on 24 June 1646, so that he was there altogether for three and a half years. It was a period when he could sometimes pursue his avocations in reasonable peace—peace, however, of circumstances rather than of mind, while he watched the slow decay of the King's fortunes and the growing disorganization of life in the University. We know nothing of his medical practice in Oxford, though it must have been a busy one among the changing crowd of the King's supporters and hangers-on. Occasionally he was sent on a distant mission, as when, in October 1643, he went to Milton Abbot during the siege of Plymouth to attend Prince Maurice, who was suffering from fever due to an undiagnosed cause. With him went his old friend Dr. Edmund Smith, and Dr. John King, incorporated M.D. at Oxford in January 1640/1. At Milton they were joined by Dr. Robert Vilvain (1575–1663), a cultivated practitioner working in Exeter. He was at once doctor, theologian, and antiquary, and his friend Dr. Thomas Fuller, the historian, recorded[1] that he possessed an important curio in the shape of a skull, no bigger than a bean, reputed to be that of one of the 365 children brought into the world in Holland at

[1] T. Fuller, *History of the University of Cambridge*, London, 1655, p. 28.

one birth by Margaret, Countess of Henneberg some centuries before. Harvey's interest in abnormal births would have been tickled by this strange object, though if he had ever seen a 'hydatidiform mole', as this curious delivery would now be called, he would have known that it contained nothing that could have been mistaken for a skull.

A report[1] signed jointly by the four doctors was sent to Prince Rupert by Richard Cave, one of Rupert's most trusted officers until he was killed at the battle of Naseby.

May it please your Highness

This last night arrived here att Millton Doctor Harvey and Doctor Smyth and this morning they with the other two Doctors having seene and spoken with his Highness your brother intreated me to write as followeth.

That his sicknesse is in the ordinary raging disease of the Army, a slowe feaver with great dejection of strength, and since Fryday he hath talked idly and slept not, but very unquietly, yet the last night he beganne to sleepe of himselfe, and tooke his rest soe quietly that this present morning when Doctor Harvey came to him he knew him and wellcomed Doctor Smyth respectively, and uppon Doctor Harvey's expression of his Majesty's sorrowe for and great care of him he shewed an humble thankefull sence thereof: Doctor Harvey asking his Highness how he did, he answered that he was very weake, and he seemed to be very glad to heare of and from your Highness as was delivered by Doctor Harvey.

Now the Doctors having conferred, and computed the tyme, have good hopes of his recovery, yet by reason that the disease is very dangerous and fraudulent, they dare not yet give credit to this allteration. And concluding the disease to be venemous they doe resolve to give very little phisick, only a regular dyett and Cordyall Antidotes. The Doctors present theyr most humble service to your Highness and subscribe themselves

Sir your Hyghness most humble servants

Will: Harvey
Robert Vilvain
Edmund Smith
Tho. King

Millton, Octob. 17th. 1643

The doctors stayed several days at Milton, Cave ending his report with the assurance that: 'About two or three days hence at the farthest the doctors intend to send new information.' Their cautious attitude was justified and the Prince made a good recovery from his illness, though it had clearly been bad enough to give real alarm. It may have been an

[1] British Museum, Add. MS. 18980, f. 125.

attack of typhus, which had caused many deaths in Oxford and in the army elsewhere. The seriousness of the 'pestilent fever', of which Prince Maurice is believed to have been a victim, may be realized by reading Thomas Willis's account of it as he saw it in 1643. At this date Willis, aged 22, was a student at Christ Church, and his later writings show that he was already actively engaged in observing and recording disease, and perhaps even treating it, though he was not yet qualified with a medical degree. It was not unusual for medical students at Oxford in the seventeenth century to be allowed to practise their future profession under supervision.[1] Harvey must have been well acquainted at Oxford with this remarkable young clinician, who was certainly not deterred by any risks of contagion from pursuing his medical interests.

In his work on fevers, published in 1659, Willis wrote as follows:

The pestilent Feaver, of late years, hath more rarely spread in these regions, than the Plague itself: of the only one of this kind, which fell under our observation, I will give you a brief description. In the year 1643, when in the coming on of the Spring, the Earl of *Essex* beseiged *Reading*, being held for the King, in both Armies there began a Disease to arise very Epidemical, however, they persisting in that work, till the besieged were forced to a surrender, this Disease grew so grievous that in a short time after, either side left off, and from that time, for many months, fought not with the Enemy, but with the Disease: as if there had not been leisure to turn aside to another kind of Death, this deadly Disease increasing, they being already overthrown by Fate, and as it were falling down before this one Death. *Essexe's* Camp moving to the *Thames*, pitched in the places adjacent, where he shortly lost a great part of his men: But the King returned to *Oxford*, where at first, the Souldiers being disposed in the open Fields, then afterwards among the Towns and Villages, suffered not much less: For his Foot, (which it chiefly invaded) being pact together in close houses, when they had filled all things with filthiness, and unwholsom nastiness, and stinking odors (that the very Air seemed to be infected) they fell sick by Troops, and as it were by Squadrons. At length the Feaver now more than a Camp Feaver invaded the unarmed and peacable Troops, to wit, the entertainers of the Souldiers, and generally all others, yet at first (the Disease being yet but lightly inflicted) tho beset with an heavy and long languishment, however many escaped. About the Summer Solstice this Feaver began also to increase with worse provision of Symptoms, and to lay hold on the Husbandmen, and others inhabiting the Country. Then afterwards, spread through our City and all the Country round, for at

[1] Information from Dr. Alistair Robb-Smith.

least Ten miles about. In the mean time, they who dwelt far from us, in other Counties remained free from hurt, being as it were without the sphere of the contagion. But here this Disease became so Epidemical that a great part of the people was killed by it; and as soon as it had entred an house, it run through the same, that there was scarce one left well to administer to the sick; strangers, or such as were sent for to help the sick, were presently taken with the Disease; that at length, for fear of the Contagion, those who were sick of this Feaver, were avoided by those who were well, almost as much, as if they had been sick of the Plague.[1]

Willis then gives a closely observed clinical description of the epidemic.

Harvey had been ordered by the Parliamentary party earlier in the conflict to stay in attendance on the King,[2] but he had, nevertheless, remained nominally at his post at St. Bartholomew's and was still receiving his emoluments from the Governors. This continued until 1643, when the final entry in the leger reads: 'Itm to Doctor Harvey Phisicion xxxiii¹ viˢ viiiᵈ.' At this point his hospital appointment was officially ended by order of Parliament. The Journal of the House of Commons has the following entry under the date 12 February 1643/4: 'A motion this day made for Dr. Micklethwayte to be recommended to the Wardens and Masters of St. Bartholomew's Hospital, to be physician in the place of Dr. Harvey, who hath withdrawn himself from his charge and is retired to the party in arms against the Parliament.'

Dr. John Micklethwaite had taken his M.D. at Padua in 1638 and became a Fellow of the College of Physicians in November 1643. No action followed this order because Dr. John Clarke was already in charge at the Hospital; he had been there since August 1634 as Harvey's assistant. Dr. Micklethwaite was not appointed physician in reversion until May 1648, becoming full physician in 1653. He was knighted by Charles II after attending him during an illness in 1681.

[1] See *The Remaining Medical Works of Dr. Thomas Willis. Englished by S. P[ordage]*, London, 1681, 'Of fermentations, &c.', pp. 134-5.

[2] *Anatomical Exercitations*, 1653, p. 418.

35

HARVEY AS WARDEN OF MERTON COLLEGE, 1644/5–1646 * ACTIVITIES AND FRIENDS AT OXFORD

A WELL-KNOWN, though relatively unimportant, episode at Oxford was Harvey's temporary connexion with Merton College in the nominal position of Warden. Sir Nathaniel Brent, a lawyer, had been made Warden in 1622, but, when the Civil War began, his sympathies lay with the Parliamentary party and he absented himself from Oxford. He was made Judge Marshal by Parliament and even signed the Covenant. In July 1643 Queen Henrietta Maria had ridden with the King into Oxford and, after being received at Christ Church, was given accommodation in the vacant Warden's Lodging at Merton. She occupied what has ever since been known as 'the Queen's room' and the adjoining drawing-room, most of the other parts of the College being filled by various members of the Court and by officers of the King's army. Anthony Wood gives some indication of the changed circumstances in the College by recording that 'divers marriages, christenings and burials took place in the College Chapel.' Collegiate life must have been largely disrupted, apart from the disturbance caused by the epidemic fever raging in the city in that year and by the fire which followed in the area west of St. Aldate's and the Cornmarket.

By April 1644 the general situation had become so uncertain that the Queen felt unsafe in Oxford, and left for Exeter, where, attended by Sir Theodore de Mayerne and Dr. Lister, she gave birth to the Princess Henrietta. In July she set sail from Falmouth and, after her ship had narrowly escaped being sunk by a parliamentary vessel, landed safely at Brest. She did not return to England until after the Restoration in 1660.

We do not know exactly where Harvey had been living for the eighteen months since he entered Oxford. Probably his time was much broken up by attendance on the King in his campaigns and he did not enjoy much comfort. He was ageing, and evidently the King wished to find some situation for his physician where he could live and work in reasonable security. It seemed that the Warden's Lodging in Merton, vacant since the Queen's departure, might now offer him a position of dignity and convenience. Accordingly, on 24 January 1644/5, the Chancellor, Lord Hertford, wrote a letter[1] on behalf of the King to the Subwarden and Fellows drawing attention to the unsatisfactory state of affairs in the College. The letter stated that the Warden, Sir Nathaniel Brent, had for almost three years been absent and working for the rebels. He had even assumed the office of Judge Marshal and had 'contemptuously refused to repair to our Royall Person'. The College was in consequence suffering from Brent's neglect of his duties and it was now the King's pleasure 'to displace and put out' the absent Warden. The Subwarden and Fellows were therefore instructed to nominate forthwith, according to their custom, three men, one of whom should be chosen to succeed Brent as Warden.

The Subwarden, John Greaves, was an eminent mathematician, who had succeeded John Bainbridge as Savilian Professor of Astronomy in 1643. His younger brother, Edward Greaves, later knighted by Charles II, to whom he was physician in ordinary, had taken his Oxford degree of M.D. in 1641 and was Linacre lecturer in 1643, so that both men were certainly acquainted with Harvey. It is believed that John Greaves initiated the movement to appoint Harvey to the Wardenship, an idea which met with the King's ready approval. This accusation was, indeed, one of the counts against Greaves when the parliamentary visitors in October 1648 secured his ejection from the College and from his professorial chair.[2] He was also accused of having surrendered to the King money and plate belonging to the College, but his brother Thomas testified that when the King demanded these things John Greaves had 'kept himself private' for as long as three weeks in his chambers to avoid having to give his consent. There was no doubt, however, where his sympathies lay. His biographer states that he was the 'intimate friend'[3] not only of Selden, Ussher, Ent, and Scarburgh but also of Harvey, to whom his knowledge of how eggs were hatched by incubation in Cairo[4] would certainly have endeared him.

On 28 January the Fellows of Merton held their meeting in the college hall and next day duly reported their proceedings to the King:

May it please your Most Excellent Majesty

In humble obedience to your Majesties Commands, we, the subwarden and fellowes of Merton College, haveinge convened our present company

---

[1] Merton College Register, pp. 355–6.

[2] Thomas Birch, *Miscellaneous Works of Mr. John Greaves, with a Life of the Author*, London, 2 vols. 8°, 1737, i. xxviii.   [3] Ibid., p. lviii.

[4] *Philosophical Transactions*, xii, 1677, p. 923. 'The manner of Hatching Chickens at Cairo observed by Mr. John Greaves and communicated by Sir George Ent.'

for the Election and Nomination of a warden in this present vacancy of the place, havinge first consulted with the Junior fellowes, and observed althings required by our Statutes, the seaven seniors deliver'd their votes in this manner, the Junior fellow first deliveringe his voice:

Mr. Sayer
Mr. Brent
Mr. Greaves } Nominate Dr. William Harvey, Dr. Hinton, Mr. Sellar.
Mr. Fisher

Mr. French Nominates Dr. Higgs, Dr. Earles, Mr. Hales.
Dr. Turner Nominates Mr. Hales, Mr. Morley, and himselfe.
The Subwarden Nominates Dr. Harvey, Mr. Morley, Mr. Sellar.

Having in all humility and obedience to your Maiesties Commands represented to your sacred Maiesty these our nominations, In testimony thereof we have applied our common seale at: 29 January A.D. 1644 et Regis Carol. vicesimo.[1]

On the same day two Fellows, French and Greaves, presented their nominations to the King, but owing to an objection raised by Dr. Turner, who had nominated himself, the actual election was suspended. Dr. Turner was strenuously opposed to the election of Harvey to the Wardenship and he presented a petition to the King. He might have invoked an injunction issued by the Visitor, Archbishop Peckham, in 1284.[2] The College had been founded twelve years earlier by Walter de Merton, chiefly with a view to the education of young men before becoming parish priests, and admitted graduates only. Not until 1380 were scholarships founded for undergraduates. Nevertheless the study of medicine had not been excluded, and already in 1284 Peckham complained that medical students had been admitted, contrary to the regulations of the College, having crept in under the name of 'students of physics'. But 'physics' did not by common usage mean 'medicine', and whereas 'in the times of the author of these regulations no medical student was wont to reside at your College, we do desire that all students in Medicine be excluded from either giving or receiving instruction in your College'. This regulation is theoretically in force at the present day, but has been 'honoured more in the breach than in the observance', for the College has produced many graduates eminent in medicine, including six Presidents of the College of Physicians, and has had seven medical Wardens, one of them being Harvey. Turner's chief objection

---

[1] *Register*, p. 357.
[2] See Dr. A. M. Cooke's introduction to the catalogue of an exhibition held at the Royal College of Physicians, 8 April 1963.

PLATE XXV

MERTON COLLEGE, OXFORD

From an engraving by Loggan, *c.* 1690. Mob Quad is on the right side beyond the Chapel with the windows of Harvey's workroom in the right-hand corner

however, was on another ground, that Harvey was a 'stranger' and should therefore not be elected. His petition was carefully considered by the Chancellor, who refuted his points one by one; but Turner 'framed several replies', pleading especially 'that only once in three hundred years had a stranger been nominated Warden'. All this caused considerable delay, and it was not until three months later, when the matter had been left 'to His Majesties great Wisdom', that the King signified his very definite decision in the following letter, recorded in the College Register (p. 359):

> To our Trustie, and Welbeloved the Sub-Warden
> and Fellowes of Merton College in
> Oxon.

Charles R

Trustie and Welbeloved we greett you well. Whereas we have chosen and by these our Letters thought fitt to signifie unto you that Wee doe choose our Welbeloved Servant Dr. William Harvey, *one* of our principall physitians to be your Warden of Our house or Colledge in Oxon called Merton College, being one of those wch according to your Statutes you have elected and nominated unto us for the Wardenship thereof: Our Will and Command therefore is that according to your accustomed manner you forthwith receive and admitt the said Dr. William Harvey (alreadie sworne by Our Command before Our right Trustie and Welbeloved Cozen and Councellour the Marquesse of Hertford Chancellour of our Universitie of Oxon as well to our Royall Authoritie as to observe the Statutes and Customes of the said Colledge according to the foundation thereof) to be your Warden of our said House or Colledge in the stead of Sir Nathaniel Brent deservedly removed by us from that place, to have and enjoy the Wardenship of the said house or Colledge, with all the rights, Emoluments and profitts thereunto belonging in as ample and beneficiall manner as the said Sir Nathaniel Brent or any of your Wardens heretofore have had or enjoyed the same, or by the Foundation and Statutes of the said College, he or they had, or ought to have had or enjoyed straitly charging and commanding you and [every] one of you, to give him the said Dr. William Harvey obedience in all respects as to your Warden does of right appertaine and belong.

Given att Our Court att Oxon this seaventh day of Aprill 1645
Subscribed by his Maties Command
Hertforde

On 8 April Harvey signified his acceptance. On the following day at 8 o'clock in the morning, after Dr. Turner had protested by resigning his Fellowship, the King's letter was read and Harvey was duly admitted as

Warden in the presence of Dr. Stuart, Dean of St. Paul's, Dr. Fell, Dean of Christ Church, Dr. Morris, Professor of Hebrew, Dr. Clayton, Professor of Medicine, and Mr. Thomas Rives, King's Advocate.

On 11 April Harvey met the Fellows in the College Hall and made a brief speech recorded in the College books as follows:

Dominus Custos, Convocatis in Altâ Aulâ sociis, hæc verba ad illos fecit. Forsitan decessores Custodiam Collegii ambiisse, ut exinde sese locupletarunt, se vero longe alio animo nimirum ut Collegio lucro et emolumento potius foret: simulque socios, ut concordiam amicitiamque inter se colerent, sedulo solliciteque hortatus est.[1]

Or, in English:

The Fellows having been called together in the Great Hall the Warden addressed to them these words. Perhaps [some] predecessors in office had entered on the Wardenship of the College in order to enrich themselves, but he himself came truly with a far different mind, so that he might bring to the College greater wealth and benefit; at the same time he exhorted the Fellows to cultivate among themselves harmony and friendship.

These sentiments were unexceptionable, but there was in fact little enough in the disturbed conditions that Harvey could do, and he left no visible mark of his influence on college affairs other than his having signed some bursar's accounts in the College books and having held a formal survey of the furnishings of the Warden's Lodging on 11 June 1645. This was recorded as: 'A note or inventory now given by Avis Smith who was left in trust with the lodging goods by Sir Nathaniel Brent.' First were listed some kitchen utensils, but 'Will Noble, Cooke, acknowledged these things to be for the use of the Lady of Northampton'. A list followed of various pieces of furniture, carpets, and bedroom goods, which were acknowledged by Anthony Harsey to be also in the possession of the Countess of Northampton. Some other hangings and chairs were certified by John Browne to be in Lady Cobham's lodgings. The final and longest list of the contents of the Lodging, room by room, included the Warden's linen and much furniture—though some had been disposed of at the Queen's coming by Mr. Greaves and some had been borrowed by the Countess and Mr. Greaves. Finally, 'All these was taken from the mouth of Avis Smith in the presence of Dr. Harvey the Warden and us

Fran. Brode
Charles Scarborough.'

[1] *Register*, p. 360.

To this Avis Smith subscribed his mark, a note being added that he 'hath of the College Goodes One Sylver Salt, Seaven sylver spoones, whereof one broken, another crack'd'. These were afterwards changed by agreement into twelve new silver spoons.[1]

It is to be hoped that Harvey enjoyed some degree of peace in his new surroundings, but events were drawing to a crisis during his Warden-ship. In January 1644/5 the King attempted to arrange a treaty, and to this end sent his Commissioners to Uxbridge for discussions with the representatives appointed by Parliament and the Scots. The party from Oxford was led by the Duke of Richmond, who included his old friend Dr. Harvey in his suite, Dr. Edmund Smith being in attendance on the Earl of Southampton.[2] For three weeks conversations continued, but ultimately broke down in deadlock on every point under discussion. Both sides viewed the prospects with the utmost concern, but no agree-ment was possible and the King's party returned to Oxford.

In Scotland Montrose was still sanguine of success, but in England the Royalists were suffering reverses. For fifteen days from 22 May 1645 General Fairfax laid siege to Oxford, but the action was abortive and for a time the forces were withdrawn. On 14 June the Battle of Naseby was fought and lost, with the final ruin of the King's cause. At Oxford difficulties multiplied. The College books record that in November Merton College, though much impoverished, was required to lay in provisions against another expected siege. In December it was ordered that a special form of prayer should be used in the college chapel on Wednesdays and Fridays 'for these bad times'. On 24 March the College was reduced to giving a bond for £94 instead of cash in order to pur-chase necessary food.

In the early morning of 27 April 1646, the King left Oxford, riding over Magdalen Bridge disguised as a servant with his chaplain, Michael Hudson, and John Ashburnham, a groom of the bedchamber. Harvey's feelings at this moment of disaster may be imagined. It marked the virtual end of his professional career; the master whom he had served so long with so much devotion had gone to an unknown fate, and the future must have seemed dark indeed. He had been treated with some consideration by the Parliamentary party, but now, as an adherent of the defeated Royalists, he could look for little further recognition of his professional eminence. He was, in fact, fined £2,000 as a 'delinquent',

---

[1] *Register*, pp. 360–2.

[2] Journal of the House of Lords, quoted by Sir W. Herringham, *Annals of Medical History*, (1932), N.S. iv, 267.

that is an adherent of the King, as recorded by David Lloyd, in his chronicles.[1]

The City of Oxford surrendered to Fairfax on 24 June under honourable terms, the garrison of 3,000 men marching out eastwards over Shotover Hill. The young Duke of York, who had remained throughout with his father, was sent to join the Prince of Wales at St. James's Palace. The Princes Rupert and Maurice were ordered to leave the country. As for William Harvey, it was plain that further tenure of the Wardenship of Merton was impossible. He may have formally resigned, or he may just have left—there is no indication in the college books. Sir Nathaniel Brent resumed his place as Warden and presently rendered his accounts for the years 1642 to 1646, completely ignoring the fact that Harvey had ever been there. Merton College hall was described in the college books as *situ et ruinis squalida* (foul with dirt and destruction) —sufficient comment on the demoralization that had overwhelmed Oxford as a whole, the colleges bankrupt, students dispersed, and lectures abandoned.

The name Charles Scarborough (or Scarburgh, as more usually spelt), written as witness to the inventory of furnishings made by Harvey at Merton College, is a reminder of one important consequence of Harvey's time at Oxford. This was his friendship with young Scarburgh. It has been stated that Harvey's reputation attracted Scarburgh from Cambridge in order to join him, but it is clear that he really left Cambridge because it had become an uncomfortable place for a young man with Royalist sympathies. He had been educated first at St. Paul's School and then, like his father and grandfather, at Caius College, where he was elected to a scholarship in 1634. He stayed at Cambridge, becoming a Fellow of his college, and began to study medicine in 1640. The organization of medical teaching in the University was still very imperfect and it failed to distract his mind from his main interest, which lay in mathematics. He still resorted to his friend William Oughtred, a mathematician and former Fellow of King's College, for help on knotty points. Soon after the start of the Civil War Cambridge became definitely aligned on the parliamentary side. Scarburgh, because of his political views, was deprived of his Fellowship and his library, and, very understandably, migrated to Oxford, where he immediately attached himself to Harvey at Merton. Probably they were already acquainted, since his uncle was Harvey's old friend Dr. Edmund Smith. In spite of the thirty-eight years

[1] D. Lloyd, *Memoires of the Lives of those that suffered for the Protestant Religion and Allegiance to their Soveraigne*, London, 1668, p. 700.

of difference in their ages Harvey and Scarburgh became close friends, the younger man acting as assistant in Harvey's work in anatomy and embryology. Anthony Wood states that they worked together 'in the little chamber beyond the library' in Merton. The library, with its carved Jacobean presses and panelling, occupies the upper floor of the south and west sides of Mob Quad, the oldest college quadrangle in Oxford. The room used by Harvey can be seen today beyond the north end of the west limb of the library. It is almost square, being roughly 18 feet long by 22½ feet wide, and is lit by a wide embrasure on either side, the eastern one overlooking the quadrangle. The room would have been eminently suitable for use as a dissecting room and laboratory, and Harvey can be imagined working with his assistant in happy seclusion away from the turbulent life of the Court, which filled so much of the rest of the College. Harvey enjoyed young Scarburgh's keen interest and attractive personality, and it may be that their more serious studies were sometimes interrupted by jokes and laughter. The atmosphere of 'the little chamber' is now far from solemn, since it is filled by a collection of drawings by the late Sir Max Beerbohm and is dedicated to his memory.

Harvey did all he could to advance his friend in his profession, and, with help of the Chancellor, procured for him the degree of M.D., conferred on 23 June 1646, by certifying that he was well learned in physic, philosophy, and medicine;[1] but Scarburgh, being young and active, could not avoid taking some part in military affairs, and while he was marching up and down the country with the University Legion Harvey addressed to him the oft-quoted message: 'Prithee leave off thy gunning and stay here. I will bring thee into practice.' Yet, for all his opportunities, Scarburgh never gave up his first love—mathematics; his published works are few, the most notable being an English version of Euclid, produced by one of his sons in 1705 after his father's death. Meanwhile, in 1647, just as Scarburgh had attached himself to Harvey, the brilliant boy Christopher Wren, then aged 15, had attached himself to Scarburgh; he soon became adept at constructing pasteboard models for anatomical demonstrations.

It is believed that Scarburgh had left Oxford by 1648. He appeared for the first time for examination at the College of Physicians on 6 November 1647 and was admitted as a Candidate on 25 January 1647/8; he became a Fellow on 26 September 1650. On 12 October 1649 he was appointed Reader in Anatomy to the Company of Barber-Surgeons, and

[1] See J. J. Keevil, 'Sir Charles Scarburgh', *Annals of Science* (1952), viii. 113.

lectured there for the next seventeen years. Although his knowledge of mathematics had not led him to improve Harvey's optical methods in research, it contributed to the exposition of the muscles of the human body and helped Wren to make his models for use at lectures, as reported by the younger Wren, who added: 'Hence came the first Introduction of *Geometrical* and *Mechanical* Speculations into *Anatomy*.'[1] Wren even 'composed a Treatise of the Motion of Muscles, explaining the whole Anatomy by Models form'd in Pasteboards. These were presented to Sir Charles Scarburgh, but lost at the Fire of London.'[2] Harvey's influence can be seen acting through Scarburgh on Wren in 1665 when he expressed a wish that

we were frequent in Dissections of Animals, of any sort whatever, and that figures be drawn, where Nature appears anomalar, as she is most in Fishes and Insects; especially in the parts that serve for Concoction. And with this we may take in the Experiments about Generation. The Spring should not be lost, for observing the Progress of hatching Eggs; and likewise the springing of Grain and Seeds; which in a ruder Proportion gives some Light to the Generation of Animals. Tame Rabbets may be kept purposely for Dissection, as well because they are frequently pregnant, as because of late, some Observations have been made from them, which seem to thwart those of Dr. Harvey, how truly will be worth our enquiry.[3]

Harvey's work was perhaps also inseminating Wren's speculative faculty when this 'miracle of a youth', as John Evelyn called him, performed experimental splenectomies on dogs and initiated Richard Lower's researches into the possibilities of blood transfusion by suggesting the infusion of fluids into veins. This was reported in 1665 as having been proposed by Wren 'many years since',[4] indicating the mental continuity —Harvey, Scarburgh, Wren.[5]

Harvey's friendship with Scarburgh lasted to the end of his life, and he remembered him in his Will by the bequest 'to my loving friend' of his velvet gown and his surgical instruments. The gown was symbolic of Harvey's determination that his mantle should fall on to Scarburgh's shoulders in a figurative sense. When Harvey resigned the Lumleian Lectureship on 24 July 1656 he handed over the office to Scarburgh as the anatomist most worthy to succeed him. Another symbol of their

---

[1] *Parentalia*, London, 1750, p. 187.
[2] Ibid., p. 238.   [3] Ibid., p. 222.   [4] Ibid., p. 231.
[5] It may be noted as pure coincidence that Scarburgh by his post-mortem report on James II helped to dispel the rumour that the King had been poisoned, just as Harvey had done for James I.

PLATE XXVI

WILLIAM HARVEY

Aged 79. By an unknown painter

PLATE XXVII

SIR CHARLES SCARBURGH

Aged about 42, *c.* 1656. By an unknown painter

friendship is to be seen in portraits of each of them, so similar in pose and attributes that it seems plain that they agreed to have the pictures painted by the same artist at the same time. The portrait of Harvey, now in the Hunterian Collection at Glasgow, represents him in his eightieth year seated in a chair with a large book lying on a table before him, and in the background a view of Rome showing the Church of S. Maria di Loreto and Trajan's Column. The book is open at a page showing Vesalian engravings of a skull and is identifiable as the *Works* of Spigelius, 1645, which contains, besides many Vesalian plates, a reprint of Harvey's *De motu cordis*. The portrait of Scarburgh, now in the Royal College of Physicians, depicts him similarly seated, though facing the other way, so that should the pictures be hung on the same wall the two friends would be looking towards each other. Scarburgh also has an anatomy book before him, again showing a Vesalian illustration and a Roman view behind, this time with St. Peter's and the group of statuary known as The Horse-tamers. Harvey, as we know, had been to Rome, and his library building at the College of Physicians suggests that he was attracted by classical architecture. Scarburgh is not known to have had any particular interest in Rome. The painter of the pictures is unknown, but they were probably done in England, prints of Rome being used for the backgrounds.[1]

Scarburgh's only medical publication, *Syllabus Musculorum*, printed with the second edition of William Molins's *Myotomia, An Anatomy of Muscles*, 1676, is no more than a summary of his demonstrations given at the Surgeons' Hall twice a day over three days. He developed a large practice as a physician, was knighted in 1669, and led the team of doctors who tortured Charles II by their misdirected treatment during his last illness; but his mind displayed no originality and he contributed nothing to the advancement of medicine or science. Harvey's attachment to him seems to have been based on his personal qualities and shared interests rather than on admiration for his intellect.

John Greaves, whose part in introducing Harvey to Merton College has already been described, left other evidence of his friendship with him. Greaves was the author of a number of learned treatises one of them being *Pyramidographia, or a Description of the Pyramids in Egypt*, published in 1646, the year of the surrender of Oxford. In this work Greaves discussed the history of the pyramids and described them as he found them in the years 1638 and 1639. In the course of his description of the largest pyramid he told how he had penetrated to the tomb-chamber of Cheops through a series of passages, remaining for three

[1] See Geoffrey Keynes, *The Portraiture of William Harvey*, London, 1949.

hours inside the foundations of the pyramid. In a footnote to his description he remarked:

That I and my company should have continued so many hours in the Pyramid, and live (whereas we found no inconvenience) was much wondered at by Doctor Harvey, his Majesty's learned physician. For, said he, seeing we never breathe the same air twice, but still new air is required to a new respiration (the *succus alibilis*[1] of it being spent in every expiration) it could not be, but by breathing we should have spent the aliment of that small stock of air within, and have been stifled; unless there were some secret tunnels conveying it to the top of the Pyramid, whereby it might pass out, and make way for fresh air to come in at the entrance below. To which I returned him this answer: That it might be doubted, whether the same numerical air could not be breathed more than once; and whether the *succus* and aliment of it could be spent in one single respiration; seeing those *urinatores*, or divers under water for spunges in the *Mediterranean* sea, and those for pearls in the *Sinus Arabicus* and *Persicus*, continuing above half an hour under water, must needs often breathe in and out the same air. He gave me an ingenious answer, that they did it by the help of spunges filled with oil, which still corrected and fed this air; the which oil being once evaporated, they were able to continue no longer, but must ascend up or die: an experiment most certain and true. Wherefore I gave him this second answer, that the fuliginous air we breathed out in the Pyramid, might pass thorough those galleries we came up, and so thorough the streight neck or entrance leading into the Pyramid; and by the same, fresh air might enter in, and come up to us: which I illustrated with this similitude; as at the streights of *Gibraltar*, the sea is reported by some to enter on *Europe* side, and to pass out on *Africa* side; so in this strait passage, being not much above three feet broad, on the one side air might pass out, and at the other side fresh air might enter in. And this might no more mix with the former air, than the *Rhodanus*, at *Pomponius Mela* and some others report, passing through the *Lacus Lemanus*, or lake of *Geneva*, doth mix and incorporate with the water of the lake. For as for any *tubuli* to let out the fuliginous air at the top of the Pyramid, none could be discovered within or without. He replied, they might be so small, as that they could not easily be discerned, and yet might be sufficient to make way for the air, being a thin and subtil body. To which I answered, that the less they were, the sooner they would be obstructed with those tempests of sand, to which these deserts are frequently exposed: and therefore the narrow entrance into the Pyramid is often so choaked up with drifts of sand (which I may term the rain of the deserts) that there is no entrance into it. Wherefore

[1] i.e. the nourishing draught.

we hire Moors to remove them, and open the passage, before we can enter into the Pyramid: with which he rested satisfied.[1]

In 1644, two years before the publication of this book on the pyramids, Greaves had been working on the compilation of a Persian lexicon and had contemplated going to Leyden to see their oriental manuscripts. Writing to James Ussher, Archbishop of Armagh, about this project on 14 September of that year he added a postscript: 'If I may serve Dr. Harvey I shall be most ready either here, or at Leyden, to do it.'[2] Why he should make this offer in a letter to Ussher is not at present clear. Ussher had left Ireland for political reasons in 1640 and was then for a time in London, but with the permission of Parliament moved to Oxford in 1642. Here he must have known Harvey and have received the letter from Greaves, but we know nothing further of their relations. Ussher left Oxford in March 1644/5, accompanying Prince Charles to Bristol and going on to Wales. After many vicissitudes he died in London on 21 March 1656/7, not long before Harvey, whose junior he was by three years.

Harvey was no doubt acquainted, if not on terms of friendship, with many other persons of greater or less distinction during his time at Oxford. A long list of conjectural names could be compiled from among the kaleidoscopic changes of Oxford society, all of them with royalist sympathies. One such was John Birkenhead, a self-made man, son of a Chester saddler. He had worked as Laud's amanuensis, and the Archbishop procured him a University degree in 1639 and an All Souls Fellowship in the following year. Possessed of a ready wit, he was responsible for the issue of a royalist newspaper, *Mercurius Aulicus*,[3] in Oxford from 1642 to 1645. He was knighted by Charles II in France in 1649. Birkenhead's possible acquaintance with Harvey is to be inferred from a reference found[4] in a comendatory poem among the many prefixed to William Cartwright's *Comedies, Tragi-comedies, and Other Poems*, 1651. In praising Cartwright's verse Birkenhead likened his wit to Harvey's description of the circulation of the blood, showing some knowledge of the new doctrine:

> *For as immortall* HARVEY'S *searching Brain*
> *Found the* Red Spirit's *Circle in each Veyn,*

---

[1] *Pyramidographia*, i. 136–7.

[2] Richard Parr, *The Life of James Us[s]her*, London, f°, 1686, Letter ccxi, pp. 509–10.

[3] This was concerned mainly with political and military events, and has no mention of Harvey. He referred to Harvey in *The Assembly Man. Written in 1647*, London, 1662/3.

[4] By R. A. Hunter and I. Macalpine, *Journal of the History of Medicine* (1962), xvii. 403.

Hath open'd Straights, *and saild our* World *about,*
As if He *made* that Sluice, *not found it out:*
So Wit, *the bloud of* Verse, *in every line*
Drawn by thy hand, doth shoot, and work, and mine,
This Gulfe, *that* Isthmus, *through each* Science *darts,*
And proves its Circulation *through all* Arts.
All-over Wit, *ne'r runs a-ground, but rides*
In ever-flowing never-ebbing Tides.

There is firmer ground for suggesting that Harvey was on terms of friendship with a much greater man, the poet Abraham Cowley. They might have met when Cowley's play was acted before Prince Charles and other members of the King's suite at Cambridge in 1641 (p. 286). Two years later, in 1643/4, Cowley was ejected from Cambridge owing to his royalist sympathies and took up residence in Oxford. His proximity to Harvey and his known interest in scientific matters would surely have led to their meeting. Harvey would certainly have found a receptive listener in the poet, and it is not too fanciful to suggest that Cowley's *A Proposition For the Advancement of Experimental Philosophy*, published in 1661, owed much to Harvey's influence. The insistence on *experiment* is found on the title-page, and the organization of Cowley's admirable 'Philosophical College' gave liberal allowance for experimental investigation. The staff was to include a surgeon at a salary of £30 a year; many animals were to be kept for experimentation. There was to be an 'Anatomy Chamber adorned with Sketches and Anatomical Pictures, and prepared with all conveniences for Dissection'. The buildings were to be graced by 'a Gallery to walk in, adorned with the Pictures or Statues of all the Inventors of any thing useful to Humane Life; as Printing, Guns, America, &c., and of late in Anatomy, the Circulation of the Blood, the Milky veins, and such like discoveries in any Art, with short elogies under the Portraictures'. It was clearly intended that an image of Harvey was to find a place in this scientific Valhalla, and it is plain that Cowley fully understood his position in the history of science as the man who had, in his two great books, established the basic theory leading to realization of a fundamental life process. Cowley's 'Ode Upon Dr. Harvey', here printed on another page (p. 427), was his final tribute to Harvey's mind and character.[1] Another link between the two men was Cowley's friend-

---

[1] Cowley's 'Elegy upon Mr. William Harvey' was written to commemorate another individual of the same name—a young man who had entered Pembroke College, Cambridge, in 1636. He was cousin of Henry Jermyn, later first Earl of St. Albans, whom Cowley served in France, and was not related to Dr. Harvey. He died at Cambridge in May 1642.

ship with Charles Scarburgh, who stood bail in £1,000 for Cowley when he was wrongfully arrested on his return from France to England in 1656. Scarburgh mentioned in his Harveian Oration Harvey's unfulfilled project of endowing a chair of experimental philosophy (presumably at Oxford), equipped with laboratory and physic garden. Conversation with Cowley may have added stimulus to this intention, only prevented by the civil strife from being realized, for Harvey used to say with tears in his eyes, that if he had dedicated his property as he had intended to the promotion of the discovery of truth and to the public good he might just as well have made Anabaptists, fanatics, robbers, and murderers his heirs.

Harvey's scientific work in Oxford was done before the group of men forming the Invisible College had begun, by their work and discussions, to lay the foundations of the Royal Society, but this influence, as Sir D'Arcy Power suggested,[1] is likely to have made itself felt. Harvey's attitude to science was provocative. In *De generatione animalium* he showed a fearless determination to advance knowledge by experiment, induction, and speculation. This must have left its mark on Oxford minds, and it seems right to claim that Harvey's residence there acted as a definite stimulus to the enthusiasm for science and research that afterwards spread so widely from its Oxford nursery. There are a number of names that can be put forward as those of men who were influenced directly or indirectly by Harvey's presence at the University.

One of the first men that Harvey met in Oxford must have been Dr. Thomas Clayton, Regius Professor of Medicine and Master of Pembroke, who was organizing the University Legion, a body of 600 students under arms, ready to fight for the King.[2] Among Clayton's pupils was George Joyliffe, who had entered Worcester College in 1637, but had migrated within two years to Pembroke. He served for a time in the army under Lord Hopton, but afterwards devoted himself to the study of anatomy at Oxford and with Clayton's help 'made some discovery of that fourth sort of Vessels, plainly differing from veins, arteries, and nerves, now called *Lympheducts*',[3] that is, lymphatic vessels, and it would be reasonable to suppose that his work came to Harvey's notice, though the old man seems to have remained unconvinced. Joyliffe afterwards took his M.D. degree at Cambridge, and by 1653 was lecturing on anatomy in London at the College of Physicians, where 'he made a full and open

[1] Power, *William Harvey*, London, 1897, p. 133.
[2] A. Robb-Smith, 'Harvey at Oxford', *Oxford School Medical Gazette* (1957) xii. 71.
[3] Anthony Wood, *Athenæ Oxonienses*, 1721, ii. 170.

disclosure of the said *Vasa Lymphatica*'.[1] Harvey must, therefore, have heard yet more about Joyliffe's discoveries, but when urged by Dr. Johann Daniel Horst of Darmstadt to investigate this new system he replied: 'My now too long tale of years causes me to repress from sheer weariness any desire to explore new subtleties, and after long labours my mind is too fond of peace and quiet for me to let myself become too deeply involved in an arduous discussion of recent discoveries.'[2] Even if Joyliffe had tried to draw Harvey's interest, he evidently failed. He did not have the opportunity to take part in forming the Royal Society, dying in 1658 while still under 40. Yet he had shared enjoyment of the scientific atmosphere of Oxford in Harvey's company and made his contribution.

A more definite link connecting Harvey with the originators of the Royal Society is to be found in the person of Dr. Ralph Bathurst, brother of George Bathurst and, like him, a scholar of Trinity College, Oxford. Born in a village near Market Harborough, Northamptonshire, in 1620, Bathurst entered Trinity in 1637 and was ordained priest in 1644. According to his own statement he was 'constantly in Oxford from the beginning of the wars in 1642 until the towne surrendered, 1646'.[3] He was a Royalist, but when he saw that the King's cause was declining he prudently turned his mind to the study of medicine, thinking he might earn a livelihood thereby. After the parliamentary visitation of Oxford he was not subjected to interference and was, indeed, employed by the State as physician to the navy. He also became very friendly with Dr. Thomas Willis and later joined him in practice. In 1650 Bathurst was associated with Petty, Willis, and others in the resuscitation of Anne Greene, a woman who was hanged in Oxford for infanticide and was supposed to be dead until she arrived in the dissecting rooms.[4] In 1654 he delivered in Oxford three lectures on respiration and others on medical questions such as *An Fœtus materna sanguine nutriatur?* Although Bathurst is not known to have claimed friendship with Harvey, he could hardly have avoided acquaintance with him during the Civil War years in Oxford. Dr. George Ent was Bathurst's friend and, indeed, in his *Apologia pro circuitione sanguinis* called him *amicus singularis*. Bathurst's medical writings contain many references to Harvey's *De generatione animalium*.[5] After the Restoration Bathurst abandoned the practice of

---

[1] Wood, loc. cit.
[2] K. J. Franklin, *The Circulation of the Blood*, Oxford, 1958, p. 93.
[3] T. Warton, *The Life and Literary Remains of Ralph Bathurst*, M.D., London, 1761, p. 204.
[4] Richard Watkins, *Newes from the Dead*, Oxford, 1651.
[5] Warton, loc. cit., pp. 127–238.

medicine, becoming a chaplain to the King and President of Trinity College, but his interest in scientific matters persisted and he became a Fellow of the Royal Society in 1663.

Another scientific character who added his mite to knowledge was a clergyman, Francis Potter.[1] He was an Oxford man, born in 1594, who had entered at Worcester College, but became a commoner at Trinity in 1609, continuing there until 1637, when he succeeded his father as vicar of Kilmanton in Somerset. His special turn was for mechanics, but about the year 1640 he had the idea of curing diseases by blood transfusion. He did not carry out any experiments, however, until 1652, when he wrote to John Aubrey that he had attempted to transfuse blood from one pullet to another, but had been unable to obtain more than a few drops of blood by his primitive technique. His attempt seems to have come to Harvey's notice, for another hand wrote a comment on his letter: '*Hanc designationem Dr. Harveus frivolam et impossibilem omnino esse asseruit sed tamen quære.* Consult Dr. Glisson.'[2] The plan was utterly impossible, Harvey thought, but the commentator was not sure, and Potter's name has survived as a humble precursor of Wren's and Lower's more successful efforts.

Among those who were granted the degree of M.D. at Oxford by the King's wish was Dr. Walter Charleton. He was appointed a physician to the King and certainly knew Harvey. He was a voluminous writer of semi-scientific works and became a Fellow of the Royal Society in 1667.

We have but the scantiest knowledge of the experimental work actually carried out by Harvey at Oxford. The names of Scarburgh and George Bathurst are definitely known as participators with him in embryological work done in Merton and in Trinity, but there are no others. It has been suggested that Robert Grove's *Carmen de sanguinis circuitu, a Gulielmo Harvæo Anglo, primum invento*, London, 1685, was written by an eyewitness of the vivisection of a dog by Harvey while he was at Oxford.[3] This Latin poem, written in heroic hexameters, represents Harvey as describing his discovery of the circulation, promising to write a treatise *De animalium generatione*, and predicting the Civil War, the Restoration, and the founding of the Royal Society. There follows a description of the binding of the dog and its sufferings, with a long account of Harvey's dissection in detail and of his demonstration of the

[1] Anthony Wood, *Athenæ Oxonienses*, 1721, ii. 612.
[2] Aubrey's *Brief Lives*, Oxford, 1898, ii. 166–8.
[3] S. Weir Mitchell, *Some Recently Discovered Letters of William Harvey and Other Miscellanea*, Philadelphia, 1912, p. 41. This contains a prose translation of the *Carmen* by Dr. Astley Paston Cooper Ashurst. See also L. R. C Agnew, *Bull. Med. Hist.* (1960), xxxiv. 318–30.

circulation. At the beginning Harvey is credited with justifying the seeming cruelty of the experiment by his hunger for fame and knowledge, and at the end he is supposed to have reflected on the everlasting fame the dog would have earned as a recompense for his sacrifice. The whole composition is a *tour de force* and interesting as a more or less contemporary tribute to Harvey and his skill as anatomist and operator, but it is certainly not to be regarded as evidence that Harvey ever performed any such demonstration before his friends at Oxford. Grove, born in 1634, was only 8 years old when Harvey went to Oxford, and he received his education at Winchester and Cambridge. Clearly he was interested in anatomy, but his career was centred on the Church, and at the time of his death in 1696 he was Bishop of Chichester. The *Carmen* is pure fiction, expressed with elegant scholarship, but not to be taken seriously as a contribution to the story of Harvey's life. Grove himself makes no such claim in his preface.

36

WITH THE KING AT NEWCASTLE, 1646 *
RUMOURS OF HARVEY'S DEATH

WE know very little of Harvey's movements after the surrender of Oxford. As already mentioned, a clause in John Harvey's Will indicates that Mrs. Harvey was alive in 1645, but we do not know whether she had accompanied her husband to Oxford or whether she had remained with one of his brothers elsewhere, nor do we know the year of her death. Harvey himself was regarded by the party in power as a 'delinquent'. It seems unlikely, therefore, that he would have been allowed to return immediately to London. More probably he stayed for a time in Oxford, where he could occupy himself in carrying on his scientific work with Scarburgh at his side. Scarburgh took his M.D. degree in the summer of 1646 and is believed to have stayed in Oxford until 1648.

Meanwhile the King had made his way northwards, travelling by night, and at Southwell, near Newark had ridden into the quarters of the Scottish Covenanters and surrendered his person to them under the pretext of obtaining their protection. This event took place on 5 May and was announced by the Scots on the following day. They were astonished, but delighted, and forthwith marched off with their prisoner to Newcastle, where he was kept until he was handed over to Parliament in January 1646/7. As far as is known the King remained in good health until his execution in 1649, but he missed his familiar friends, among them his doctors, and he let it be known that he wished for Harvey, and perhaps others, to attend him. Harvey accordingly drew up a petition to the House of Lords asking that he might join the King at Newcastle or elsewhere as a matter of duty. The document, written out by a secretary, was signed by Harvey himself and gives interesting details of how he proposed to travel:

To the right hono^{ble} the Lords Assembled in Parliament att Westminster
> The humble petition of William Harvey doctor of physicke
> & one of his Ma^{tes} principall Phisitions in ordinarie

Whereas you^r Lord^{pps} humble petitioner hath for many years given his diligent & perpetuall attendance one his Ma^{tes} person according as by duty he conceived him selfe bound, wch he being desirous to continew especially understandinge att this present there is none (sworne in ordinarie) wth his Ma^{te}

He humbly prayeth you^r honnors passe for him selfe wth three servants & four horses, or in coach wth other ne[ce]ssaries to goe to Newcastell or else where to repayer to the Kings Ma^{te} and attend & retorne as his service shall requier & he shall pray for your honors health and happiness

Will Harvey

The paper[1] was marked when received: 24 November 1646, and on the same day it was ordered that: 'Doctor Harvey should have a pass to go to Newcastle to the King, or where ever He is, he being Physician to His Majesty.'[2] Presumably Harvey stayed with his Master until his next move in January 1646/7 to Holmby in Northamptonshire. Thereafter the King's companions were chosen for him by his captors. He was not allowed to have any of his own chaplains, or to choose his doctors. Nearly two years later, when the King was imprisoned in Carisbrooke Castle at Newport in the Isle of Wight, a letter was written by his secretary, Sir Edward Walker, on 12 September 1648 to William Lenthall, Speaker of the House of Commons, desiring by the King's command passes for Dr. Harvey and Dr. Wetherborne, his physicians, and Humphrey Painter, his surgeon, to attend him there, and also for passes

---

[1] *Historical Manuscripts Commission, Sixth Report*, 1877, House of Lords, 142a (*L.J.* viii. 577). Stated to be holograph, but this is an error; not previously transcribed.
[2] *Journal of the House of Lords*, viii. 577a.

for three of his servants, to be employed as messengers or door-keepers.[1] Dr. Wetherborne (or Wedderbourne, afterwards Sir John) was a distinguished Scottish physician, though formerly a Professor of Philosophy at St. Andrew's University, but neither he nor Harvey was allowed to go; it was certainly not to be expected that the King would be allowed to have his own door-keepers in his prison. On 9 September the House of Commons replied that 'Reives and Ducke' might go, but no others.[2] These two men, Sir Thomas Rieves and Mr. Duck, were not doctors, but were lawyers, who were included in a party of the King's supporters allowed by Parliament to be present at a pretended discussion of a treaty. Rieves had been at Harvey's induction at Merton College in 1645. Sir Philip Warwick, who was himself at the conference, wrote of it: 'Now when the King had no earthly hope, the Parliament seemed to vouchsafe to admit him to a Treaty.'[3]

It was at Newcastle, therefore, that Harvey had his last sight of King Charles, and it is probable that in 1647 he was allowed to return to London or its neighbourhood. He must have suffered acute distress at the turn taken by political events after he had parted from the King, and have found his chief solace in scientific work and meditation. He was presumably staying with one of his brothers near London when King Charles's tragedy reached its climax on the scaffold in Whitehall on 30 January 1648/9.

During these years of disturbance and uncertainty Harvey's friends and acquaintances on the Continent would have heard little of his doings, and it even came to be believed that he had died. Inquiries about this had been made by Marcus Aurelius Severinus, Professor of Anatomy at Naples, in a letter to his friend John Houghton, physician at Norwich since 1640.

On 7 May 1646 Severinus wrote: 'I was exceedingly glad to receive word that the immortal Harvey is still living, though his whereabouts are uncertain, especially since his death had been rumoured, much to everyone's sorrow, through a friend at Padua. But, as you are my friend, Houghton, you must confirm the certainty of it, if it be true that the Fates have spared him yet awhile.'[4]

---

[1] *Historical Manuscripts Commission, Thirteenth Report*, pt. i, 1891, p. 497, Welbeck Abbey (the Duke of Portland).

[2] *Journal of the House of Lords*, x. 498a.

[3] Sir Philip Warwick, *Memoirs of the Reign of Charles I*, London, 1701, pp. 321–2, The Treaty at the Isle of Wight.

[4] See Josiah C. Trent, 'Five Letters of Marcus Aurelius Severinus to John Houghton', *Bulletin of the History of Medicine* (1944), xvi. 306–23.

Presumably Houghton assured Severinus that Harvey still lived, but the rumour of his death persisted and became so widespread that a Dutch version of *De motu cordis* published at Amsterdam in 1650 contained lines 'On the Death of Harvey' composed by the translator, Nikolaas van Assendelft. These lines as rendered into English seem uninspired, though they express well the admiration for Harvey felt by medical men on the Continent, and it is interesting to note the emphasis placed on his use of experiment to prove his arguments:

> The English light that used to shine so bright
> And unto Medicine a new glory gave,
> Arousing wonder in the eyes of all,
> Has its clear rays withdrawn, alas, too soon.
> Closed is the mouth that ere it had played through
> Its role, replete with golden scholarship,
> Pregnant with wisdom, was to the perplexed
> A lodestar on the yet untrodden paths.
> Closed also are the hands, alas, too soon
> Which often plunged the steel into the hearts
> Of beasts and gathered knowledge from the brutes,
> Searching their entrails, muscles, fibres, till
> At last and of a certainty he saw
> A sun break through the murky darkness, yes
> A sun which drives away the fogs and fumes,
> Illuminates our senses, tells us of
> The pitfalls and diseases which afflict
> Our feeble human race, a sun indeed
> Which guides us through the deepest mysteries,
> Where lack of knowledge often made us fail.
> This knowledge dropped like honey from his tongue
> Whene'er he pleaded for the pure, clear truth,
> Clothing his arguments with reason, and
> Supporting them with many experiments.
> Forgive us now our inexperience,
> If we have not explained it all aright,
> If our interpretation be at fault.
> Making the sun a little star in Dutch.[1]

---

[1] Translated by Mr. John Van de Leuw for Dr. W. W. Francis, Osler Librarian, Montreal, Canada. See *Journal of the History of Medicine* (1957), xii. 254–5.

37

OPPONENTS AND SUPPORTERS ✻ REPLIES
TO RIOLAN ✻ DR. MAY'S MONSTER

THE account given in earlier sections of the development of Harvey's revolutionary ideas on the heart and the circulation of the blood as revealed in his lecture notes and in his final statement in his book *De motu cordis* does not give any indication of how his doctrines were received by the audiences who listened to his discourses. Nothing is heard of any protest being made against him at the time that he was subverting accepted authority, though that was in fact what he was doing. It seems as though those outside the inner circle of Harvey and his intimates at the College either did not fully appreciate what he was saying, or could not believe their ears; some, perhaps, could understand, but chose not to take too seriously the full implication of what they heard. In the dedication of his book to the President, Dr. Argent, Harvey claimed to have convinced many of his colleagues that his views were right, but it seems certain that their percolation through the general medical consciousness was a very slow process.

It is plain also that some of Harvey's immediate associates resolutely refused to accept the new doctrine. An example of this attitude is found in the lectures given by Dr. Thomas Winston (1575–1655), who gave instruction in anatomy at Gresham College from 1613 to 1643 and 1652 to 1655. His lectures were published in 1659, and his editor pointed out that 'you may find his name next Dr. Harvey's' in the Dispensatory of the College of Physicians. Winston also served as Censor ten times between 1622 and 1637, and must have known Harvey very well indeed. Yet he made no reference whatever to Harvey, while following Galen's errors and mentioning Columbus and Riolan. Of the heart itself he said: its 'substance is thick flesh, red, not musculous; it's made of the thicker bloud, not so red as muscles, yet harder. . . . It is not a muscle, because it hath all sorts of fibres: besides, it hath naturall motion, not voluntary as muscles have'—curious reasoning in view of what he must have known from Harvey's demonstrations.

Another outstanding resister was Harvey's contemporary and surgical colleague Alexander Read (1586–1641), lecturer in anatomy at the Barber-Surgeons' Hall and associated with Harvey at the examination of the Lancashire witches in 1634. Read was elected a Fellow of the College of Physicians in 1624 and, again, must have known of all that Harvey had done. Yet in his *Manuall of the Anatomy, or Dissection of the body of Man*, published in 1634, once reprinted in his lifetime and four times afterwards up to 1658, Harvey was completely ignored. Small wonder, then, that knowledge was slow to percolate, when the London teachers, both in their lectures and in their popular textbooks, chose to condemn by omission a doctrine of which they were perfectly well aware.

A refreshing example of the opposite attitude is found in the writings of a younger man, Henry Power (1623–68) of Halifax, whose *Circulatio sanguinis*, written in 1652, enthusiastically supported Harvey. He erroneously ascribed Harvey's 'invention' to the year 1614, but then he wrote:

Amongst all the rabble of his antagonists, wee see not one that attempts to fight him at his own weapon, that is by sensible and anatomical evictions to confute that which he has by sense and autopsy so vigorously confirmed. And therefore wee cannot but look upon such scepticall and Tyrrhenian Authors as Disciples to Anaxagoras, that in defiance to the noblest of his senses would needs maintain the snow was black, and shall only confute them as the walking Philosopher did the Stoick, that peremptorily asserted there was no such thing in the world as motion.

Power himself carried out a number of experiments on animals in confirmation of Harvey's claims and even came nearer than he did to describing the as yet invisible capillaries. Power was a friend and admirer of Sir Thomas Browne, who had said in a letter to the young man in 1646: 'Be sure you make yourself master of Dr. Harvey's piece *De Circul. Sang.*, which discovery I prefer to that of Columbus.' This may be assumed to refer to Christopher, not Realdus, Columbus. Owing to his admiration for his friend, Power allowed his language to be coloured by Browne's example. After describing the manner in which blood passes through the liver, and 'percribrates and trickles into the vessels of the vena cava', he continued:

Therefore there only remains the other part of the disjunction to be embraced, viz. that the transvasation (or elutriation to use Plinyes terme) of the blood is perform'd by percolation or transcribration through the spongious substance and poresityes of the flesh: for no third way is imaginable. And indeed if the circulation were performed any other way, how can wee conceive every particle of the flesh and muscles of the body can be nourished, for this required that the alimentary humour should percribrate and diffuse itself, through every particle and atome of the parts to be nourished as wee see the Blood doth in the Body, there being not the least particle or atome of fiber which is not continually irrigated with this humour, as wee absolutely see the nutricious juice does in plants and vegetables, for there it runns out of the capillary fibers, and diffuseth itselfe into every atome and particle of the leafe or fleshy parts of the plant, as may easyly be observed in the greater celandine, dandelion and all kind of spurges and such like hearbs where the alimentitious humour is of another colour then the plant it selfe.[1]

Unfortunately Power's treatise remained unprinted, though preserved by Sir Hans Sloane in his collections.[2] In contrast to Power, his more eminent contemporary Thomas Sydenham (1624–89) made no reference to Harvey in any of his numerous published works.

Attention has already been drawn to the fact that Harvey's friend and colleague Dr. Robert Fludd made the first printed acceptance of the new doctrine in 1629, though his views were likely to have been influenced by his mystical religion. The first opposing voice was heard soon afterwards, when James Primrose published his book, *Exercitationes et animadversiones in librum G. Harveii de motu cordis et circulatione sanguinis*, in 1630. He was not only congenitally unable to accept new ideas, but had a compulsive urge to combat them in print, as can be seen from his various publications. He said[3] that he 'wrote in fourteen days' his refutation of the work that had occupied Harvey for over twenty years. It is difficult now to read with patience the 'arguments' advanced by Primrose and his like. The book consists, as Robert Willis wrote in his *History of the Discovery of the Circulation of the Blood* in 1878 (p. 213), 'of obstinate denials, sometimes of what may be called perversions of statements involving matters of fact, and in its whole course appeals not once to experiment as a means of investigation'. Primrose returned twice more to the attack when he tried to refute both Roger Drake and du Roy (Regius) in books published in 1640. Parisanus of Venice, already mentioned in connexion with Harvey's presence there in 1636 (p. 243), was another early adversary, and others have been noticed elsewhere. It would be tedious to recount these in detail and their names will be found, together with those of Harvey's supporters, set out in chronological order in Appendix IV. It can be understood that older minds had difficulty in accepting so startling a novelty. Younger men might have been

---

[1] These passages by Power are taken from Sir Humphry Rolleston's paper, 'The Reception of Harvey's Doctrine' in *Essays on the History of Medicine presented to Karl Sudhoff*, edited by Singer and Sigerist, Oxford, 1924, pp. 248–54. The whole Manuscript was translated and published by F. J. Cole, *Journal of the History of Medicine* (1957), xii. 291–324.

[2] British Museum, Sloane MS. 1343.

[3] See C. Daremberg, *Histoire des sciences médicales*, Paris, 1870, ii. 614.

expected to receive it more readily, yet even some of them found it hard and suffered mental distress in making the adjustment. On 13 July 1631 Jacob Schwabe, a Danish undergraduate aged 21, wrote to his respected teacher, Ole Worm, in Copenhagen, after having read *De motu cordis*:

This doctrine so greatly impressed my mind that, for a full week, I was quite heart-sick owing to these profound thoughts. Hardly being able to calm myself by my own efforts I revealed the whole matter to an industrious student of medicine of the name of *Conringius*, who is a friend of mine. Having been shown Harvey's dissertation he explained the circulation of the blood so admirably and plainly, that he himself almost seemed to be of the same heretical opinion. He soon perceived, however, that, being very desirous of a new thing, the mind inclines to be much titillated and allured, and now he said: 'Certainly this explanation in itself is elegant, and, at first glance, highly probable. If Harvey had only been able to prove it by means of autopsies and anatomical demonstration, he would have solved the whole problem.' After that I took myself to the famous men, *Heurnius* and *Falconburgius*. They were willing to accept the opinion of *Conringius* with all their hearts, as the saying is, if they had not to add that in changing old theories and approving of new ones we must rather be timid and hesitating than audacious and temerarious.[1]

It is remarkable that Conringius failed to appreciate that Harvey had given him exactly the kind of proof he demanded, but afterwards he must have seen this, for a decade later he had certainly accepted the new doctrine. Ole Worm was less receptive, arguing against it in 1632 and on several other occasions.

Of more interest than most were the opinions of the great French philosopher and physiologist, René Descartes. He had read *De motu cordis* in 1632 and he gladly accepted Harvey's doctrine of the circulation of the blood, but disagreed with his explanation of the movements of the heart. Descartes was unable to entertain the idea of the heart acting as an involuntary muscle, believing that all muscles were controlled by the will, though he could allow that some movements, such as scratching, could be reflex, that is, initiated without conscious direction. The distinction between voluntary and involuntary movement had not worried Harvey. In his notes for a work on *The Movement of Animals*, written in 1627 (see p. 163), he had observed: 'WI it is fit that some movements

[1] *Wormii Olai et ad eum doctorum virorum epistolæ*, Hafniae, 1751, Tom. i, p. 460. See E. Gotfredsen, 'The Reception of Harvey's Doctrine in Denmark', *Acta Medica Scandinavica*, Copenhagen (1956), Suppl. 266. 75. The translation of Schwabe's letter is reprinted by permission.

should be carried on incessantly and should not be regulated by free will, as the movement of the heart and the intestines, etc.'[1] The heart's movement, which Harvey had demonstrated by experiment to be due to contraction, Descartes maintained was expansion, since he believed that the blood was heated by the heart, or 'perfected' as others called it, this including the change from venous to arterial blood as evidenced by the colour. To him the heart was a kind of furnace, supplying motive power to the circulation by virtue of its 'innate heat', which caused the blood to expand. Descartes was unable to support his views by any convincing experiments, but was satisfied with his mechanistic explanation and so remained an unsatisfactory adherent of the new doctrine.

Harvey perhaps found most of his opponents and their futile arguments as tedious as we sometimes do, and he took no steps to defend himself in print. He was certainly irritated, as is evident from his remarks recorded by George Ent in the introduction to *De generatione animalium* (see p. 331) and he must have been pleased to receive public support in 1641 both from Ent in London and from so distinguished a foreigner as Werner Rolfink of Jena. Sir Kenelm Digby had also supported Harvey and criticized Descartes in chapter xxvi of his *Two Treatises on the Nature of Bodies and the Nature of Man's Soule*, Paris, 1644.

Harvey was on principle averse from indulgence in controversy and had complete confidence in the truth of his doctrine derived by induction from experiments, a brilliant innovation of method in 1628, when Galen's use of experiment had been forgotten. Sir Charles Scarburgh recalled in his Oration of 1662 Harvey's answer to those friends who asked why he did not reply to his critics:

It is not weighty enough for me to trouble the Republic of Letters again on my own behalf. I shall be neither Founder nor Advocate of a new doctrine which can be disputed either way. Perish my thoughts if they are empty and my experiments if they are wrong—if I have observed them less than accurately, I am, anyway, satisfied with my diligence. I am not a disturber of human affairs; but if I am wrong (for I am human) let my writings lie neglected. If I am right, sometime, in the end the human race will not disdain the truth.

In *De generatione animalium* Harvey had written, probably about 1647: 'I perceive that the wonderful Circulation of the blood, first found out by me, is consented to almost by all: that no man hath hitherto made any objection to it greatly worth a confutation.'[2] Yet the breaking point

---

[1] *De motu locali animalium*, edited by Gweneth Whitteridge, Cambridge, 1959, p. 111.
[2] *Anatomical Exercitations*, 1653, p. 283.

came twenty years after the publication of *De motu cordis*, when he received from Jean Riolan *fils* a copy of his *Encheiridion anatomicum et pathologicum*, Paris, 1648. The lives of Riolan and Harvey covered almost exactly the same span, for they were born within two years of one another and died in the same year. Riolan, a Regius Professor in Paris as early as 1613, was physician to Marie de Medici and doyen of the Faculty of Medicine in 1648. He is believed to have met Harvey when he accompanied Marie de Medici on a visit to her daughter, Queen Henrietta Maria, in London in October 1638, and it may be supposed that they then discussed a matter so profoundly interesting to both of them as the circulation of the blood.[1] It is plain enough from the views advanced by Riolan in his book that intellectually he was no match for Harvey, but for personal reasons added to sheer annoyance Harvey at length brought himself to the point of composing a reply, or rather, two replies, for the result was published simultaneously in Cambridge and Rotterdam in 1649 as a small book[2] containing two letters, or 'exercitations', both addressed to Riolan. The year 1649, with its political events, was a time of great distress for Harvey, added to which he was ageing and suffering from chronic and painful illness. Yet he was able to approach his critic with perfect courtesy and patient argument, a pattern, indeed, for all who feel constrained to engage in scientific controversy with an unreasonable opponent.

The early pages of Harvey's first letter are concerned with his views on the importance and purpose of making observations in morbid anatomy. He regarded the examination of one body dead from disease as of more value than the anatomies of ten healthy people who have been hanged. Reference has already been made to this (see p. 97). He then welcomed Riolan as an adherent to his doctrine, but pointed out that he tried to have it both ways, saying: 'You will see how such a circulation takes place without causing upset and mixing of the body's humours and destruction of traditional medicine.' For Riolan had tried to argue that, while a Harveian circulation took place in the large vessels, the blood moved in the opposite direction in their branches. He also maintained that the blood in the portal vein does not circulate as it does in the vena cava. Harvey politely pointed out 'that it was not love of truth (which he [Riolan] could not have missed seeing), which led him to refrain from

---

[1] See R. Willis, *William Harvey*, London, 1878, p. 224; no references are given.
[2] *Exercitatio anatomica de circulatione sanguinis. Ad Joannem Riolanum filium Parisiensem*, Cambridge, 1649. Extracts quoted are from K. J. Franklin, *The Circulation of the Blood*, Oxford, 1958.

speaking freely, but rather excessive caution lest he should offend traditional medicine, or perhaps appear to retract from the physiology he himself put forward in his *Anthropographia*', a book published in 1618. Riolan had taken up an impossible and ridiculous position, but Harvey examined his argument point by point, referring to Riolan as 'the learned gentleman', while he systematically exposed his lack of learning and common sense.

A further absurdity was exposed when Riolan claimed that 'if a circulation of the blood be admitted and if it passes usually through the lungs and not through the median septum of the heart, then the blood circulation must be thought of as twofold'. This gave Harvey the opportunity of pointing out that 'it was possible for the learned gentleman here to add a third, very short circulation' in the coronary system of the heart itself.

Near the end of the letter Harvey discussed the old difficulty of being unable to demonstrate any arterio-venous anastomosis, though finally getting very close to the idea of a capillary system in describing the choroid plexus and the vascular system of the testicle, and noting that 'the terminal threads of the arteries going to the umbilical vein are lost in the coats of that vessel'. No experimental evidence was called upon to strengthen his case until the penultimate paragraph of the letter:

Open an animal's chest and ligate the vena cava near the heart so that nothing can go into that viscus by that route. Forthwith let the neck arteries be opened up without damage to the veins on either side. If as a result you see the arteries, with their free egress, empty, but not the veins, I think it will be obvious that the only route for the blood to be drawn off from veins into arteries is through the ventricles of the heart. For otherwise we should see the veins, like the arteries, emptied of blood in an extremely short space of time (as Galen noted) through the outflow from the arteries.

Having demolished Riolan in every detail, Harvey politely congratulated him on having written 'a learned, polished and concise book of unsurpassed elegance', but this final praise sounds a little hollow after what has gone before.

In the second letter Harvey began by describing his own impression of how his doctrine had been received. It suggests that constant discussion had been going on, the echo of which has failed to reach our ears because so little of it appeared in print:

It is now many years ago, learned Riolan, since with the assistance of the press I published a part of my work. Since that birthday of the circuit of the blood there has of a truth been scarcely a day, or even the smallest interval of time passing, in which I have not heard both good and ill report of the circulation which I discovered. Some tear the as yet tender infant to bits with their wranglings, as undeserving of birth; others by contrast consider that the offspring ought to be nurtured, and cherish it and protect it by their writings. The former oppose it with strong dislike, the latter defend it vociferously. These think that by means of experiments, observations, and my own visual experience I have established the circuit of the blood against the whole strength and force of arguments; the others that it is scarcely as yet sufficiently elucidated, and not yet freed from objections. There are, moreover, those who cry out that I have striven after the empty glory of vivisections, and they disparage and ridicule with childish levity the frogs, snakes, flies, and other lower animals which I have brought on to my stage. Nor do they abstain from scurrilous language.

Harvey then explained his silence by saying that he did not think any of his detractors worthy of an answer. He can be forgiven for adopting this rather lofty tone when the kind of criticism to which he was exposed is examined. In this second letter he appealed more often to experimental evidence than in the first. He recalled Galen's experiment of ligating a large artery above a reed introduced into its lumen in order 'to show that the pulsation of arteries is brought about by a property transmitted from the heart through their coats, and not by the impact of the blood within their cavities; that, in consequence, arteries increase in volume like bellows and not like bags'. Vesalius, he said, also mentioned it, but neither he nor Galen ever tried it in the same way as he had done. Anyway, it was pointless, only serving to show the opposite of what they both supposed. He had found confirmation of his own views in demonstrating a calcified aorta removed from a very noble gentleman, who was both his patient and very close friend, and again in another 'very noble and powerful gentleman'. In these men the aorta was incapable of pulsation for a considerable length and so could not propagate the pulse by any contraction of its coats, yet a pulse could be felt in the vessels below the rigid aorta.

Another experiment recommended was to draw off equal quantities of arterial and venous blood into separate vessels and allow them to clot. It would then be found that the two clots were exactly the same, dispelling the idea that these were two sorts of blood, one of them 'more florid, and in some unknown way bubbling up with abundance of spirits, and blown out like milk or honey boiling up over a fire, and swelling up to occupy more room'.

Harvey next brought up the old question 'of the emptiness of the arteries in dead bodies (which is perchance what misled Erasistratus into thinking that arteries only contained aërial spirits)'. It derived 'from the fact that when the lungs subside on closure of their passages they are no longer respiring. So the blood cannot pass freely through them. The heart, however, continues for a space of time to force blood out. In consequence, the left auricle of the heart, and the left ventricle, are relatively contracted, and equally the arteries appear empty and devoid of content, being unfilled by their due succession of blood.' Thus another long-standing mistake was simply explained. Harvey then discussed what is meant by 'spirits', a term used by Erasistratus, Galen, and Fernel, and explained that blood has a property of strength and vigour like that of brandy, though this did not mean that it became turgid or blown up with vapours because of it. It was always just fluid blood. A long elaboration of this point followed, which need not here be further pursued.

Harvey then came to the common question, *cui bono*? What is the good of it all? For

there are those who set themselves against the circulation because they are unable to solve medical problems with it admitted; or, in curing diseases and using drugs, they are unable to collect thence the causes of appearances; or they fail to see that the causes given them by their teachers are false; or they deem it dishonourable to desert the views they approved; and they consider it impious to throw doubt upon the traditional discipline of so many centuries and the authority of the old. To all these let my reply be that the facts manifest to the senses wait upon no views, the works of Nature upon no antiquity; for there is nothing older or of greater authority than Nature.

His answer seems to be simply that all knowledge is worth seeking for its own sake.

He next recommended 'all students of truth' to make another experiment, taking a length of an animal's intestine and filling it with water between two ligatures to make 'a sort of sausage'. Tapping one end of it with a finger will then demonstrate the propagation of a fluid thrill, as is used clinically in distinguishing between abdominal ascites due to fluid and tympanites due to gas. This experiment, Harvey admitted, raised 'a most powerful objection to the circulation of the blood', though no one seemed to have noticed it. It suggested that there can be a pulse without any fluid being ejected. He was, however, satisfied that there is no comparable state of affairs in the arteries of a living animal. The blood must be continuously moving somewhere, otherwise the system must burst or choke the heart by distending it, as he had shown in the vivisection of an eel. The 'sausage' experiment introduced an interesting reference to the teaching of students 'by demonstration and verbal instruction'. Does this, perhaps, imply that students attended his practice at St. Bartholomew's Hospital? We have no more definite evidence of this.

Harvey's mind then went back to happier days when he could demonstrate his experiments to his late beloved Master:

In the exposed internal jugular vein of a doe (in the presence of many nobles and the most serene King, my Master), divided in two across its length, scarcely more than a few drops of blood came out from the lower portion, rising up from the clavicle. On the other hand, through the other opening of the vein a fairly long way down from the head, a round column of blood came out very copiously in a great rush. You will be able to make the same observation daily during the outflow of blood in phlebotomy. For, if you press on the vein with a finger a little below the opening, the outflow of blood is satisfactorily arrested, but on release of the pressure, it flows out again in abundance as before.

Further ways of demonstrating venous flow are described, with observations on the extent to which the circulation of blood can vary in different parts of the body and under different circumstances. Harvey, in this second letter, seems almost to have forgotten Riolan and his tiresome quibbles. He was enjoying a temporary return to his old style of forceful statement supported by experimental, clinical, and physiological experiences. It is one of his major contributions to medical science, and in the later pages he briefly recapitulated the theme of his former book, *De motu cordis*. Near the end he referred to 'that very acute and ingenious man, René Descartes', and his attempt to deny Harvey's beliefs about the movements of the heart. He could only say that Descartes was wrong, since his own experiments proved that he himself was right, though he managed to prolong the argument through a few more pages. In his concluding paragraph Harvey came back to Riolan, who had been so long in the background, and recommended him to try the simple experiment of ligating the portal vein, when he would find that exactly the same thing happened as when any other vein is tied—it will swell up below the ligature owing to the accumulation of blood flowing towards the liver, showing the absurdity of Riolan's idea of a backward circulation in the portal system.

With this parting shot, based, as always, on direct experiment, Harvey left his opponent. If this did not convince him, he must have thought, nothing would, and indeed it never did. Riolan remained to the end of his life unable to believe the evidence of his senses.

A curious footnote to Riolan's attack on Harvey comes from his reference to a book by Marcus Aurelius Severinus, Professor of Anatomy at Naples, entitled *De recondita abscessuum natura* (second edition, Frankfort, 1643), containing an account of a supposed serpent found in the heart of a young man by Dr. Edward May in 1637.[1] May, a physician extraordinary to Queen Henrietta Maria, but otherwise of little account, described his sensational discovery in a pamphlet with the title: *A Most Certaine and True Relation of a Strange Monster or Serpent Found in the left Ventricle of the heart of John Pennant, Gentleman, of the age of 21 yeares* (London, 1639). This was written in the form of a letter addressed to Sir Theodore de Mayerne and described the details of the autopsy resulting in the discovery of what appeared to May and several other observers to be 'a worme or Serpent' coiled up in the cavity of 'the left ventricle'. The pamphlet contains one of the earliest attacks on Harvey to be printed, for the presence of the Monster in the heart seemed to May to constitute unanswerable evidence against Harvey's doctrine of the circulation of the blood, and so was naturally seized upon by Riolan to support his own attack. Riolan had not seen May's pamphlet, but depended on the description by Severinus. He knew from the book that Severinus had written on 1 March 1639/40 to a friend in England, Dr. John Houghton, asking about the mysterious 'cardiac serpent', suggesting that it was perhaps a plant rather than a worm, and that the matter might be referred 'to your great Harvey, that pillar of England as well as of medicine and anatomy'.[2] Harvey had previously paid Severinus the unusual compliment of giving him a copy of *De motu cordis*.[3] In another letter of 8 August 1640 Severinus thanked Houghton for having consulted Harvey, who was reported to have said that he had often found similar deposits inside the heart. Harvey could not have actually seen May's worm, because the patient's mother had insisted that it

[1] This curious story was fully elucidated in 'Dr. May's Monster' by R. A. Hunter and I. Macalpine, *St. Bartholomew's Hospital Journal* (1957), lxi. 184–93, with reproductions of May's figures and a photograph of a similar 'monster' found at an autopsy in 1957; May's pamphlet was reprinted in *The Somers Collection of Tracts*, 1750.

[2] For the letters from Severinus see J. C. Trent, 'Five Letters of Marcus Aurelius Severinus', *Bulletin of the History of Medicine* (1944), xv. 306–23.

[3] Now in the Houghton Library, Harvard University. It is inscribed on the title-page below the date: *Clarissimo viro Marco Aurelio Severino ab Illustrissimi Autore dono missus cum Libris.*

should be returned to his body before burial, saying: 'As it came with him, so it shall goe with him.' But Harvey had immediately identified it as being nothing more than a post-mortem clot of blood, which had slipped into the heart from the pulmonary trunk, May, in his ignorance, having mistaken the right ventricle for the left. Although Severinus thus knew of Harvey's opinion, with which he really agreed, the story was too good to be spoiled, and he still pretended to give it credence when revising his book for the edition published in 1643 and seen by Riolan. Nevertheless it seems that Harvey had himself likened blood clots to 'worms', for, at a meeting of the Royal Society on 29 June 1664, Dr. Christopher Merrett informed the Fellows 'that Dr. Harvey had sometimes found the blood full of worms in malignant fevers'. This followed a suggestion that 'some physicians, upon occasion, might be appointed to examine the truth of what Kircher affirmed, that little worms were found in the blood of pestiferous persons'.[1]

Dr. George Ent, who delivered the anatomy lectures in April 1665 with the King in his audience (receiving a knighthood on the spot), did his best to discredit the story. In his lecture notes is the passage: 'Dr. May's worm in the heart in a foolish pamphlet of his was a condensed phlegmatic matter, so bifurcated by reason of the vessels it was drawn out of, namely the vena pulmonalis and aorta.'[2] Nevertheless the account of May's 'cardiac serpent' inevitably gained currency in works such as Wanley's *Wonders of the Little World*, 1678, until it was finally disposed of by J. B. Morgagni in his book, *De sedibus et causis morborum* (Venice, 1761).

38

DE GENERATIONE ANIMALIUM (1651)

DURING the time of his prosperity Harvey had published only one book and in the years of trial added but one more on the same theme—the circulation of the blood. It is plain, however, from numerous references in his lecture notes and from his bitter expression of regret at the pillaging of his lodgings at Whitehall in 1641 that he had accumulated a

---

[1] T. Birch, *History of the Royal Society*, 1756, i. 449.
[2] Ent's *Prelectiones*, Royal College of Physicians MS. 110, f. 179, transcribed and translated by Dr. Gweneth Whitteridge.

great quantity of material based on prolonged experiment and observations on other subjects. Reticent as Harvey was, the existence of these materials could not have been unknown to his friends and it was natural that they should expect some evidence of his past activities in the form of another book. Dr. George Ent, an old friend able to address Harvey in candid terms without giving offence, could feel confident that there must be something still in reserve and worthy to be published if he could but break through the older man's habitual unwillingness to court publicity and controversy. Dr. Ent, therefore, trying to rid his own mind of the anxieties engendered by recent political events, set out about Christmas time in 1648, or possibly a year earlier, to visit Harvey in his retreat not far from London, probably, that is, in his nephew Daniel's house near Croydon or at his brother Eliab's at Roehampton. Finding Harvey, as he afterwards said,[1] intent upon the works of Nature, showing a cheerful countenance and a calm spirit, he saluted him with a commonplace inquiry if all were well with him. 'How can it be', came the grave reply, 'while the commonwealth is full of distractions, and I myself am still in the open sea? And truly,' he added, 'did I not find solace in my studies and a balm for my spirit in the memory of my observations of former years, I should feel little desire for longer life.' This gave Ent the opening he needed and he reminded Harvey that he had always consulted Nature herself and had said that he had never yet dissected any animal without finding more than he had expected. 'It is true', Harvey replied:

the examination of the bodies of animals has always been my delight, and I have thought that we might thence not only obtain an insight into the lighter mysteries of nature, but there perceive a kind of image or reflection of the omnipotent Creator himself. And though much has already been made out by the learned men of former times, I have still thought that much more remained behind, hidden by the dusky night of nature, uninterrogated; so that I have oftentimes wondered and even laughed at those who have fancied that everything had been so consummately and absolutely investigated by an Aristotle or a Galen , or some other mighty name, that nothing could possibly be added to their knowledge. Nature, however, is the best and most faithful interpreter of her own secrets, and what she presents either more briefly or obscurely in one department, that she explains more fully and clearly in another. No one indeed has ever rightly ascertained the use or function of a part who has not examined

---

[1] The passages recording this interview are based on Willis's translation of Ent's 'Dedicatory Epistle' in *The Works*, London, 1847.

its structure, situation, connexions by means of vessels and other accidents in various animals, and carefully weighed and considered all he has seen. The ancients, our authorities in science, even as their knowledge of geography was limited by the boundaries of Greece, so neither did their knowledge of animals, vegetables and other natural objects extend beyond the confines of their country. But to us the whole earth lies open, and the zeal of our travellers has made us familiar not only with other countries and the manners and customs of their inhabitants, but also with the animals, vegetables and minerals that are met with in each.

With these advantages Harvey thought that only our own laziness could prevent increase of knowledge. Moreover, 'many persons wholly without experience, from the presumed verisimilitude of a previous opinion, are often led by and by to speak of it boldly, as a matter that is certainly known; whence it comes that not only are they themselves deceived, but that they likewise lead other careless persons into error'.

Ent interrupted the flow of Harvey's discourse with a suggestion that the learned world, knowing of Harvey's industry in the advancement of philosophy, was perhaps expecting from him some further communication regarding his experiments. Harvey smilingly asked his importunate friend if he really wished him to leave the peaceful haven in which he calmly spent his days and to commit himself again to the treacherous ocean. He recalled what troubles his former treatise had raised, adding that it was better to grow wise at home and in private than to stir up storms that might destroy leisure and peacefulness. This was indeed the old Harvey speaking, the researcher who worked for his own satisfaction rather than for notoriety, who knew that he was right, but would not deign to say so when he was attacked. To this Ent agreed, but pointed out that it was no more than the usual reward of virtue; besides, the former winds of controversy had recoiled upon Harvey's critics. At this point Harvey gave way and produced to Ent's delighted gaze his book *De generatione animalium*, a work already, it seems, formed and polished with great labour. Ent at once told Harvey that unless he published these exercises to the world he would be neglecting both his own honour and the enlightenment of others. Moreover, Ent promised that he would assume all responsibility for seeing the book through the press. Harvey produced still further arguments against publication, and protested that the work would be imperfect without the addition of his lost treatise on the 'Generation of Insects'. Finally, however, his opposition was withdrawn (as both of them had no doubt foreseen) and he surrendered the manuscript to Ent with absolute power to publish or suppress as he pleased.

Ent returned home with his prize, feeling himself to be, like Jason, laden with a Golden Fleece, and was amazed, as he perused it, that 'so vast a treasure had remained so long concealed'—implying thereby that the book was no recent production, but had long been completed and revised. It may be doubted, indeed, whether Harvey, now past the age of 70 and broken by misfortune and ill health, could have summoned the strength to compose so weighty a scientific treatise after the year 1647. Probably he had used much of his time at Oxford for adding to his observations on the hen's egg and for completing the manuscript. It is clear also that he still had with him the bulk of his former notes on generation, which did not, therefore, share the fate of his writings on insects, on respiration, and, probably, on other subjects. It was the loss of his work on the generation of insects that hurt him most, and this was because he regarded it as an integral part of the second great contribution to knowledge that he was able to give to the world.

Dr. Ent's account of his interview with Harvey and of its successful outcome was clearly an edited version composed later for the 'Epistle Dedicatory' introducing the book to the President and Fellows of the College of Physicians. Ent declared that he performed merely the office of a midwife in bringing the book to birth, and that he took particular care to oversee the printing, since he knew how much difficulty the compositor would have from the obscurity of Harvey's handwriting. He had noticed the result of this in 'a small treatise not long set forth', that is, in Harvey's *Exercitatio anatomica de circulatione sanguinis* published in 1649.

Ent set about his very considerable task without delay, but it took two years or more to get the book through the press It was published in March 1650/1 under the title *Exercitationes de generatione animalium*, with additions: *De partu, de membranis ac humoribus uteri, & de conceptione*. The book was printed by William Dugard, and it may be that Ent purposely persuaded the publisher, Octavian Pulleyn the elder, to employ him. Not only was Dugard one of the best craftsmen of the time, but was also an educated man likely to deal well with the long Latin treatise; besides being a printer he was Master of the Merchant Taylors' School and had his printing press within the precincts of the school.

Although Ent had undertaken all responsibility for seeing the book through the press, Harvey himself did have some part in the work. In a letter to Paul Slegel of Hamburg dated 26 March 1650/1[1] he explained

---

[1] K. J. Franklin, *The Circulation of the Blood*, 1958, p. 71.

PLATE XXVIII

WILLIAM HARVEY
Aged 72, 1649. Etching attributed to Gaywood

PLATE XXIX

Gulielmus Harveus
de
Generatione Animalium.

FRONTISPIECE TO *DE GENERATIONE ANIMALIUM*, 1·651
Etching attributed to Gaywood

that he had not completed his answer to Riolan's latest arguments because he had been intent on his essays on the generation of animals; this had just been published and he was sending him a copy. Again, writing to Giovanni Nardi of Florence on 15 July 1651,[1] he excused himself for not having written long ago partly on the ground of public trouble and partly because he had been engaged in getting his book ready for the press.

One of the first recipients was Francis Bernard, who inscribed his copy: *Sum Francisci Bernardi Donum Eruditissimi et Perspicacissimi Autoris May 1º 1651*.[2] Bernard was at that time a young man of 24 and it was not until 1698 that he was appointed assistant physician to St. Bartholomew's Hospital, where he had previously been Apothecary. He was no doubt already accumulating the very large medical library sold at his house in Little Britain soon after his death in 1698, and he would have valued Harvey's friendship.

The finished book is a handsome quarto of over 300 pages; it has an allegorical frontispiece, but no further illustrations—a surprising omission, since the text would have gained in clarity by having plates of simple drawings showing the developmental changes described. Highmore's smaller book on the same subject (to be mentioned later) gained considerably by the numerous figures engraved on two folding plates. The first intention was to add to the interest of Harvey's book by including a portrait of the author. He did in fact give sittings to an artist and an etching was made, but in the end this was not used. A few examples of the print have survived, and these present an image of an aged and unhappy-looking man. Not unnaturally this was not regarded with favour by Dr. Ent, or by the author's family, and it was set aside. Its authenticity is established by a passage in a letter from Dr. Caspar Needham to John Evelyn, the diarist, dated from Covent Garden, 5 April 1649:[3] 'Dr. Harvey's picture is etcht by a friend of mine and should have been added to his work, but that resolution altred: however I'l send you a proof with your books that you may bind it up with his book *De Generatione*. I'm sure 'tis exactly like him, for I saw him sit for it. One in this towne is making his statue in white marble.' The date of this letter shows that the preparation of the book was well advanced two years before the date of its publication as given on the title-page, so

[1] Ibid., p. 80.

[2] The book is now in the library of the College of Physicians, Philadelphia. It is not listed in Bernard's auction catalogue, 1698. See W. B. MacDaniel, 'Harvey and Philadelphia,' *Journal of the History of Medicine* (1957), xii. 241–7.

[3] Now in the Evelyn Collection, Christ Church, Oxford.

that Ent's visit to Harvey must have been made not later than December 1648, and not, as has been hitherto supposed, in 1650. Evelyn's copy of the book with the portrait inserted as a frontispiece may be seen today in Oxford at Christ Church, where the bulk of Evelyn's library is housed. It is unfortunate that Needham did not name the artist. It has been conjecturally assigned to Harvey's old friend, Wenceslaus Hollar, but the etching[1] is scarcely good enough to have been done by him. It is possible that he made the drawing, the etching being done by his less accomplished pupil, Richard Gaywood.

The frontispiece of 1651 provides a rather undistinguished figure of Jove seated on a pedestal with his eagle beside him. He holds an egg from which he lifts the upper part with his right hand to allow the escape of a variety of animal forms, including a tiny human being, a bird, a stag, a fish, a lizard, a snake, a grasshopper, a butterfly, and a spider. On the two halves of the egg is the inscription: *Ex ovo omnia*, 'everything from an egg'. This legend must be presumed to have been approved by Harvey, although it is most unlikely that he had any hand in the design of the emblems. The earlier commentators accepted the legend as his dictum; in the middle of the eighteenth century, however, it was quoted as *Omne vivum ex ovo*, 'every living thing comes out of an egg', and during the nineteenth century currency was given by many writers to this 'famous misquotation',[2] which was sometimes repeated in the twentieth, even by the great medical historian Sigerist,[3] who quoted it as *Omne animale ex ovo*. The misquotation gives a more precise meaning to the idea than Harvey ever intended, as will presently be seen.

Harvey's book consists of seventy-two 'Exercises',[4] or chapters, preceded by a long philosophical introduction discussing Aristotle's and Galen's views concerning generation, his own methods of attacking the problem, and how knowledge in general, and of generation in particular, may be acquired. The first thirteen Exercises describe the comparative anatomy of the reproductive organs of a number of animals, with an account of the physiology of reproduction. The twelfth to the twenty-fifth describe the day-to-day development of the chick in the egg.

---

[1] Examples of the etching are to be seen in the Department of Prints and Drawings at the British Museum, the Royal College of Physicians, the Royal College of Surgeons, and the Wellcome Historical Medical Museum. There are two impressions in Evelyn's library at Christ Church and one in my collection. There is at least one in the United States, which I have not located.

[2] F. J. Cole, *Early Theories of Sexual Generation*, 1930, p. 137.   [3] *Grosse Aerzte*, 1932.

[4] The first edition of 1651 appears to contain only seventy-one Exercises, no. 5 being numbered 4 with misnumbering continued to the end.

Exercises 26 to 62 discuss at length various theories and problems of generation. Some of the conclusions reached by Aristotle and Galen Harvey thought were erroneous and hasty, for 'like phantoms of darkness they suddenly vanish before the light of anatomical enquiry'. He adumbrated his newer and better method of ascertaining the truth by ocular investigation, not underestimating the labour involved, but pointing out the sweet compensation provided by the pleasures of discovery. The introduction is greatly lengthened by the discussion of how knowledge is acquired, beginning with Aristotle's insistence that all knowledge is gained primarily through the senses. Harvey's interest in the arts is shown by his pointing out how various are the views of a single object formed in the minds of different poets and painters, illustrated by quotations from Seneca. Artists and philosophers, he says, share the operations of memory to fix experience. The artist then proceeds to fashion something based on memory, whereas the philosopher is content only to know and to record. Harvey therefore recommends each of his readers to confirm what he is told by the evidence of his own senses, since nothing had as yet been sufficiently examined.

Harvey then explains how he proposes to elucidate the facts of generation:

We therefore will explaine first in an Egge and afterwards in other Conceptions of several creatures, what is constituted first and what last in a most miraculous order, & with a most inimitable prudence and wisdome by the great God of nature; and at length we will discover what we have found out concerning the first matter out of which, and the first efficient by which, the fœtus is made, as also of the order and Oeconomy of Generation, that thence we may attain to some infallible knowledge of each faculty of the formative and vegetative Soul, by the effects of it, and of the nature of the Soul itselfe, by the parts or organs of the body and their functions.

The limits of vision, however, determine that 'the larger and more perfect animals' must be used. These include the hen, goose, duck, pigeon; frogs, serpents, and fishes; crustacea, testacea and molluscs; bees, wasps, butterflies, silkworms; sheep, goats, dogs, cats, deer, oxen, and 'lastly we have the most perfect of all animals, Man himself'.[1] Harvey proposed to follow, of the ancients, Aristotle,[2] and of the moderns, his former teacher at Padua, Fabricius of Aquapendente.

[1] This and subsequent quotations are taken from the first English translation of 1653.

[2] 'Harvey cites Aristotle 253 times': Adelman's *Embryological Treatises of Fabricius*, 1942, p. 114.

The sixty-second Exercise, headed, 'That an egg is the Common Original of all Animals', forms a loose link between Harvey's observations on hens' eggs and those on generation in viviparous animals and other classes. Towards the close of the chapter Harvey wrote: 'But hereafter when we treat of the Generation of Insects, and of Spontaneous productions, we shall discover how each of them are either differenced amongst themselves, or else do agree.' This must have been written before the loss of his notes on insects in 1642, the passage being overlooked when the decision was made to print the book in spite of this serious omission. The sixty-third Exercise contains general remarks 'Of the Generation of Viviparous Animals'; the sixty-fourth to the seventy-second describe generation as seen in hinds and does. The last part of the book is almost a separate treatise on generation and obstetrics in mankind, and is not divided into Exercises.

Harvey's argument in this very long book is often difficult to follow, partly for stylistic reasons and partly because of linguistic uncertainties. Harvey wrote in Latin and we do not always know the exact English equivalents of the terms he used: moreover the meaning of the English terms has often changed. Harvey's treatise was translated into English soon after its publication in 1651, the vernacular version being published in 1653, but we do not know who made the translation. It has often been attributed to Dr. Martin Lluelyn (1616–81), who prefixed a poem to the volume. Lluelyn, a graduate of Christ Church, was a versifier rather than a poet, as may be seen in his best-known volume, *Men Miracles and Other Poems*, 1646. After taking his M.A. degree in 1643 he joined the royalist army and later, having been ejected from Oxford by the parliamentary visitors, took up medicine in London and was admitted as a Candidate of the College of Physicians in 1653; he became a Fellow six years later. He was certainly a friend of Harvey and a genuine admirer of his work, but much the greater part of his verses to Harvey celebrate his conquest of the circulation of the blood:

> With Drake and Candish hence thy Bays is curld,
> Fam'd Circulator of the lesser World.

Only the last fourteen lines are devoted to the treatise on generation:

> A Calmer welcome this choice Peice befall,
> Which from fresh Extract hath deduced all,
> And for belief, bids it no longer begg
> That Castor once and Pollux were an Egge:
> That both the Hen and Housewife are so matcht,
> That her Son Born, is only her Son Hatcht;

That when her Teeming hopes have prosp'rous bin,
Yet to Conceive, is but to Lay within.
Experiment, and Truth both take thy part:
If thou canst scape the Women! there's the Art.

Live Modern Wonder, and be read alone,
Thy Brain hath Issue, though thy Loins have none.
Let fraile Succession be the Vulgar care;
Great Generation's selfe is now thy Heire.

Nowhere does Lluelyn give any hint that he had made the translation. Another suggested translator is Dr. George Ent himself; this is more credible than the attribution to Lluelyn, Ent having been so deeply concerned in bringing the book to birth, but there is no direct evidence of his hand. The translator must, however, have been someone with good knowledge of Latin scientific usages in the seventeenth century, and his rendering, if not always perfectly accurate, has a good contemporary style and makes far better reading than the dull excellence of Willis's translation published in 1847. For this reason the text of 1653 has been used here for quotations. Some copies of the English version contain an excellent print of a bust of Harvey engraved by William Faithorne, evidently derived from the large portrait painted for the College of Physicians about 1650 and still to be seen in the College Library.

In Exercise XIV[1] Harvey summed up the views of his predecessors on generation, and this has to be given in full if a just impression is to be formed of his attitude. The example of Dr. Joseph Needham, F.R.S., in his *History of Embryology*, 1959, is followed in reprinting this; he also appreciated the flavour of the contemporary version, but assumed that Lluelyn was responsible for the translation:

Wee have already discovered the Formation and Generation of the Egge; it remains that we now deliver our Observations, concerning the Procreation of the Chicken out of the Egge. An undertaking equally difficult, usefull, and pleasant as the former. For Natures Rudiments and Attempts are involved in obscurity and deep night, and so perplext with subtilties, that they delude the most piercing wit, as well as the sharpest eye.

Nor can we easier discover the secret recesses, and dark principles of Generation, then the method of the fabrick and Composure of the whole world. In this reciprocal interchange of Generation and Corruption consists the Æternity and Duration of mortal creatures. And as the Rising and Setting of the Sun, doth by continued revolutions complete

[1] *Anatomical Exercitations*, 1653, pp. 76–80.

and perfect Time: so doth the alternate vicissitude of Individuums, by a constant repetition of the same species, perpetuate the continuance of fading things.

Those Authors which have delivered any thing touching this subject, do for the most part tread a several Path: for having their Judgements prepossessed with their own private opinions, they proceed to erect and fashion principles proportionable to them.

Aristotle of old, and Hieronymus Fabricius of late, have written so accurately concerning the Formation and Generation of the Fœtus out of the Egge, that they seem to have left litle to the industry of Posterity. And yet Ulysses Aldrovandus hath undertaken the description of the Pullulation or formation of the Chicken out of the Egge, out of his own Observations: wherein he seems rather to have directed and guided his thoughts by the Authority of Aristotle, then his own Experience.

For Volcherus Coiter, living at Bononia at the same time, did by the advice of the said Aldrovandus (whom he calls Tutor) dayly employ himself in the opening of Egges then sat upon by the Hen, and hath discovered many things truer then Aldrovandus himself, of which he also could not be ignorant. Likewise Æmilius Parisanus (a Venetian Doctor), despising other mens opinions, hath fancied a new procreation of the Chicken out of the Egge.

But because somethings (according to our experience) and those of great moment and consequence, are much otherwise, then hath been yet delivered, I shall declare to you what dayly progress is made in the egge, and what parts are altered, especially about the first dayes of Incubation; at which time all things are most intricate, confused, and hard to observe, and about which Authors do chiefly stickle for their own observations, which they accommodate rather to their own preconceived perswasions (which they have entertained concerning the Material and Efficient causes of the generation of Animals) then to truth herself.

What Aristotle relates concerning the Procreation of the Chicken, is most true in it selfe; yet like one who had not experimented the matters himself, but had received them from other experienced persons, he doth not rightly distinguish them by their proper times: and is very much mistaken concerning the place in which the first principle of the Chicken is cast, which he decrees to be in the Acute Angle of the Egge, and is therefore justly reprehended by Fabricius. Nor doth he seem to have observed the beginning of the Pullus in the egge, or to have been able to have found those things there, which he accounts necessary to every Generation. For he would have the White (because nothing can possibly be made of nothing, according to the natural course) to be the Matter constituting the Chicken. Nor did hee sufficiently apprehend how the Efficient cause (namely the Cocks seed) can act without a contact; or how the Egge could of its own accord, without any inherent geniture of the Male, ingender the Fœtus.

Aldrovandus, partaking of the same error with Aristotle, saith moreover (which none but a blind man can subscribe to) that the Yolk doth in the first dayes, arise to the Acute Angle of the Egge: and thinks the Grandines to be the Seed of the Cock; and that the Pullus is framed out of them, but nourished as well by the Yolk as the White: which is clean contrary to Aristotles opinion, who conceived the Grandines to conduce nothing to the fecundity of the Egge.

Volcherus Coiter delivers truer things, and more consonant to Autopsie, yet his three Globuli are meer fables. Nor did he rightly consider the principle from whence the fœtus is derived in the Egg.

Hieronimus Fabricius indeed contends, that the Grandines are not the Seed of the Cock: and yet he will have the body of the Chicken to be framed out of them (as out of its first matter) being made fruitful by the Seed of the Cock. He likewise saw the Original of the Chicken in the Egge; namely the *Macula*, or *Cicatricula* annexed to the membrane of the Yolke, but conceived it to be onely a Relique of the stalk broken off, and an infirmity or blemish onely of the Egge, and not a Principle part of it.

Parisanus hath plentifully confuted Fabricius his opinion concerning the *Chalazæ* or Grandines, and yet himself is evidently at a loss in some certaine circles and points of the Principle parts of the Fœtus (namely the Liver and the Heart): and seems to have observed a *Principium*, or first Principle of the Fœtus, but not to have known which it was, in that he saith, That the *Punctum Album* in the middle of the Circles is the Cocks Seed, out of which the Chicken is made.

So that it comes to pass, that while each of them desire to reduce the manner of the Formation of the Chicken out of the Egge, to their own pre-conceived opinions, they are all wide from the mark.

For some conceive the Seed and Blood to be the Matter which doth constitute the Chicken: Others conceive the Seed to be the Efficient and producing cause, or Artificer that builds the fabrick of it: when yet upon deliberate consideration it appears most infallible, that there is no matter at hand at all, nor no menstruous blood, which the Seed of the Male can fall to work upon, or coagulate: (as Aristotle would have it) nor is the Fœtus made of the Seed of Male or Female, or any commixture of them both.

We have few details of the techniques employed by Harvey in his researches on generation. His failures have been attributed to the limitations of the means at his disposal, particularly to lack of any form of microscope for observation of the initial stages of the development of the embryo in the hen's egg and for the identification of the mammalian ovum and spermatozoon. The first use of a simple lens in embryology is attributed to Riolan the younger, Harvey's contemporary and correspondent. In his *Anthropographia*, published in 1618, Riolan refers to the use of *conspicilia*,[1] or lenses: 'In aborted embryos the structure is damaged and can often not be properly seen, even when you make use of lenses, which make objects so much bigger and more complicated than they ordinarily seem.'[2] Sir Theodore de Mayerne in his dedication of Moufet's *Insectorum theatrum*, 1634, to Sir William Paddy mentions the use of *conspicilia ex crystallo* φακοειδὴ, rendered 'lenticular optick glasses of crystal' by the translator in 1658,[3] which indicates that Harvey's friends in the College of Physicians were familiar with some sort of magnifying instrument—not necessarily a compound microscope. That Harvey used a simple lens is evident from his references to the employment of a *perspicillum*, a variation of Riolan's *conspicilium*. The first translator (1653) rendered the word as 'perspective', a term covering almost any optical instrument from spectacles to a telescope. Harvey's first reference to the *perspicillum* is found in the sixteenth Exercise, where he is describing 'the third inspection of the egg' during the fourth day of incubation:

If you are desirous to make discovery of this observation toward the declining of the third day, you may, if you be extreamly intent, by the assistance of a clear and great light, or by the Sun beam, or a Perspective, make a shift to discerne it. For else this purple streak is so exceeding nice and fine, and the motion of the *Punctum saliens* is so imperceptible, that you will only loose your labour.[4]

Harvey's apologists have, perhaps, been somewhat too ready to stress the limitations of his technical aids. The microscope, that is, the combination of two convex lenses, had been invented in Holland by Zacharias of Middelburg some time between the years 1591 and 1608. One of these instruments, reported to be 2½ feet long and made of gilded brass, was brought to England by Cornelius Drebbel of Alkomaar, mathematician to James I, in 1619.[5] Descartes also described a form of compound microscope in *Dioptrique*,[6] a treatise appended to his *Discours de la méthode*,

[1] Thomas Holyoke's *Large Dictionary*, 1677, gives *conspicilium* and *conspicillum*, 'a spectacle, a prospective glass'.

[2] See Joseph Needham, *A History of Embryology*, 1959, p. 119.

[3] See Topsell's *History of Four-footed Beasts*, with Muffet's *Theater of Insects*, 1658, leaf Ffff3 verso.

[4] *Anatomical Exercitations*, 1653, p. 90.

[5] Needham, loc. cit., p. 233.

[6] See Charles Singer, *Proceedings of the Royal Society of Medicine*, 1914, vii, Section of History of Medicine, pp. 247–79.

1637. Harvey could, therefore, have known of this instrument[1] but perhaps he was too unfamiliar with the science of optics to be able to seize upon the advantages he might have had by its use. It is surprising that Scarburgh, the mathematician, should not have helped him to make this advance. Further evidence that Harvey was somewhat behind his contemporaries in knowledge of possible aids is the fact that Nathaniel Highmore in a small book entitled *The History of Generation* and published in the same year as Harvey's *De generatione* repeatedly refers to the use of a microscope[2] in examining the development of the embryo in a hen's egg. Both observers describe what can be seen day by day. Harvey, speaking of the appearances on the fourth day, says that

you will meet a great Metamorphosis and wonderfull alteration . . . For now the *Limbus* or hemme of the *colliquamentum* beginneth to blush and purple, being encompassed with a slender bloody line: and in the center almost of it, there leapeth a capering bloody point, which is yet so exceeding small, that in its *Diastole*, or Dilatation, it flasheth onely like the most obscure and almost indiscernable spark of fire; and presently upon its *Systole*, or Contraction, it is too subtile for the eye, and quite disappeareth.[3]

In contrast with this, Highmore's description is more precise. By the end of the third day he had seen what Harvey saw on the fourth day; describing the *cicatricula*, or embryonic area, he says that in it,

by the help of Glasses may be discovered the small vessels coming from this dissolved yellow matter from every side to the middle of the white circle, which by a Microscope appears now to be the carina or back and neck of the Chick, and the heart in the midst of it.

On the fourth day he saw the veins and arteries with their anastomoses collecting into four trunks.

Within the white Circle in the middle, which was much dilated too, appeared a red sparkling line encompassing the white spot, now red too, and moving, whose motions plainly shew it was the heart: as afterwards I saw by the help of a Microscope, exactly shewing me the heart perfectly

---

[1] In 1914 Sir D'Arcy Power showed at a meeting of the History Section of the Royal Society of Medicine a painting of Harvey with a compound microscope beside him on a table, but this was obviously a recent forgery. See my *Portraiture of Harvey*, 1949, p. 41.

[2] The earliest use of the word 'microscope' recorded in the *Oxford English Dictionary* is by Thomas Hobbes in a book published in 1656. This requires revision in favour of Highmore. Sir Thomas Browne also refers to 'exquisite microscopes' in his *Pseudodoxia Epidemica*, Book II, chapter 7, but the passage did not appear until the edition of 1672.

[3] *Anatomical Exercitations*, 1653, p. 89.

fashioned, with both his ears, and this red line joyned to it, running quite round in the inside of the white circle. By the help of this Glasse, I saw the motions of the heart and ears for a long time, one anticipating the other, and continuing after the others decay. . . . This glasse shewed me the head too, consisting of three bubbles as it were.[1]

To Harvey the head was not conspicuous until the fifth day.

Harvey had known Highmore for many years, and John Daniel Horst, principal physician at the Court of Hesse-Darmstadt, writing to Harvey in 1655 with a request that he would 'explain to the world the true use of these lymphatic and thoracic ducts', added, 'you have many illustrious scholars, particularly Highmore, with whose assistance it were easy to solve all doubts'. Harvey, replying on 13 July, said: 'Highmore does not live in our neighbourhood, and I have not seen him for a period of some seven years.'[2] Yet Highmore in his textbook, *Corporis humani disquisitio anatomica*, published also in 1651, addressed his dedication to Harvey, and in his description of the heart and circulation gave full credit to Harvey for his work. In the course of the dedication Highmore wrote: 'Eight years have now slipped away since first we had it in mind to expose these lucubrations and our first attempts (by your most ingenious honour's command) to public judgment.' This has sometimes been taken to indicate that Highmore had acted at some period as Harvey's assistant, but it does not seem justifiable to attach this meaning to the words. Highmore had graduated at Trinity College, Oxford, in 1632, taking his M.B. and M.D. degrees in 1641 and 1642; he was still in residence in Oxford in 1642, when Harvey came there, but settled later at Sherborne in Dorset and so had lost touch with Harvey by 1651, when their respective books were published. Harvey's letter to Horst implies that he had not seen Highmore since 1647.

With regard to Harvey's failure to identify the mammalian ovum, it must be remembered that, although blood corpuscles and spermatozoa were first seen with the help of a simple lens, the ovum was not in fact identified (by von Baer) until 1827.

Another technical aid to Harvey's researches might have been the artificial incubation of eggs. This process was not generally known in Europe until the middle of the eighteenth century. Yet the methods used for millennia by the Egyptians for hatching eggs on a large scale were known to Harvey's friend John Greaves, at Merton College. Greaves wrote a description of this, as seen by him at Cairo, at some length,

---

[1] *History of Generation*, 1651, pp. 70–72.
[2] Willis, *Works of Harvey*, London, 1847, p. 615.

though the manuscript was not published until twenty years after Harvey's death. It then appeared in *Philosophical Transactions*, communicated by Sir George Ent.[1] It seems, therefore, that some method of incubation could have been used by Harvey in his workroom at Merton, but he did not make any reference to it, and no doubt it seemed simpler to depend on the services of a broody hen, as was done, according to Aubrey's report already quoted, by Dr. Bathurst at Trinity. On the other hand, Sir Kenelm Digby, who had also carried out some investigations on the development of the chick, certainly did use artificial incubation. In his *Treatise of Bodies*, published in 1644, he recorded that when he wished to observe in hens' eggs 'the course of nature every day and houre, Sir John Heydon, the Lieutenant of his Majesties ordinance, was the first that instructed me how to do this by meanes of a furnace so made as to imitate the warmeth of a sitting henne. In which you may lay severall egges to hatch, and by breaking them at severall ages you may distinctly observe every hourely mutation in them, if you please.'[2] Digby and Harvey were acquainted, as other references show, and, as they were working simultaneously on the same problems, it would be reasonable to suppose that this method of incubation would have been discussed between them. Yet Harvey did not mention it in his book.

Harvey's interest in the problem of generation in viviparous animals was shared by King Charles, and it is made plain in Exercise 64, preliminary to the account of Harvey's researches, how much he owed to the co-operation of his royal master:

Our late Sovereign King Charles, so soon as he became a Man, was wont for Recreation and Health sake, to hunt almost every week, especially the Buck and Doe; no Prince in Europe having greater store, either wandring at liberty in the Woods or Forrests, or inclosed and kept up in Parkes and Chaces. In the three summer moneths the Buck and Stagge, being then fat and in season, were his game, and the Doe and Hind in the Autumne and Winter, so long as the three seasonable moneths continued. Hereupon (for the Rutting time, when the Females are lusty and admit the Males, whereby they conceive and bear their young) I had a daily oportunity of dissecting them, and of making inspection and observation of all their parts, which liberty I chiefly made use of in order to the Genital parts.

We shall therefore disclose the Generation of all Viviparous Animals out of the History of the Hind and Doe, as being the most commodious

[1] See p. 299.
[2] Sir Kenelm Digby, *Two Treatises in the one of which The Nature of Bodies, in the other The Nature of Man's Soule is looked into*, Paris, 1644, p. 220.

Exemplar: treating thereof after the same manner as we have already handled the Generation of all Oviparous productions, out of the History of the Hen-Egge. And this not from any peculiar design of my own, or for the same causes for which I did prefer the Hen-Egge to all other; but because by the favour and bounty of my Royal Master (whose Physitian I was, and who was himself much delighted in this kind of curiosity, being many times pleased to be an eye witness and to assert my new inventions) I had great store of his Deere at my devotion and frequent opportunity and license to dissect and search into them.[1]

Harvey's pleasure at being able to demonstrate to the King the results of his researches is shown by another passage:

I saw long since a fœtus of the magnitude of a Pease-cod, cut out of the uterus of a Doe, which was complete in all its members (so that it was apparently a Male by the parts). I shewed this pretty Spectacle and Rarity of Nature to our late King and Queen. It did swim, trim and perfect, in such a kinde of White, most transparent, and crystalline moysture (as if it had been treasured up in some most clear glass receptacle) about the bigness of a Pigeons egge, and was invested with its proper coat.[2]

The only date mentioned by Harvey is in Exercise 69, where he said: 'I remember indeed, that in the year of our Lord 1633, these signs or rudiments of conception did appear sooner, because it was a cloudy and wet season',[3] so it is likely that the years 1630 and 1635 cover the period when his researches on the King's deer were going on with greatest intensity.

Harvey was concerned to discover how appearances changed in the uterus after impregnation, and had noticed that during the rutting season in September there was an increased vascularity in the uterus, but that no further change was found during the next two months, nor could any trace be found of semen from the stag. By the end of October, however, he would find a substance resembling purulent matter on the inner surface of the uterus, while the tuberculated surface of the lining tended to shrink. These changes Harvey concluded to be indicative of pregnancy, but he could not at first persuade the King's servants that this was true:

This alteration in the Womb when I had often discovered to His Majesties sight (as the first assay towards impregnation) and having likewise plainly shewed that all this while no portion of seed or concep-

---

[1] *Anatomical Exercitations*, 1653, pp. 396–7.   [2] Ibid., p. 88.   [3] Ibid., p. 419.

tion either was to be found in the Womb, and when the King himself had communicated the same as a very wonderful thing to diverse of his followers, a great debate at length arose. The Keepers and the Huntsmen concluded, first, that this did imply that their conception would be late that year, & thereupon accused the drougth; but afterwards when they understood that the rutting time was past and gone, and that I stood stiffly upon that, they peremptorily did affirm that I was first mistaken my selfe, and so had drawn the King into my error, and that it could not possibly be, but that something at least of the Conception must needs appear in the Uterus: untill at last, being confuted by their own eyes, they sate down in a gaze and gave it over for granted. But all the Kings Physitians persisted stiffly, that it could no waies be, that a conception should go forward unless the males seed did remain in the womb, and that there should be nothing at all residing in the Uterus after a fruitful and effectuall Coition; this they ranked amongst their ἀδύνατα [impossibles].

Now that this experiment which is of so great concern might appear the more evident to posterity, His Majestie for tryal-sake (because they have all the same time and manner of conception) did at the beginning of October separate about a dozen Does from the society of the Buck and lock them up in the Course neer Hampton Court. Now lest any one might affirm that doubtlessly these did continue the seed bestowed upon them in Coition (their time of Rutting being then not past) I dissected diverse of them, and discovered no seed at all residing in their Uterus: and yet those whom I dissected not, did conceive by the virtue of their former Coition (as by Contagion) and did Fawn at their appointed time.[1]

This phenomenon of the apparent latent period was described by Harvey to Sir Kenelm Digby, who referred to it in his *Two Treatises*, published in 1644, seven years, that is, before Harvey's description was in print. Digby had described the development of the embryo in hens' eggs, and continued:

In like manner in other creatures, which in Latin are called *Vivipara* (because their young ones are quicke in their mothers wombe) we have, by the relation of that learned and exact searcher into nature, Doctor Harvey, that the seede of the male after his accoupling with the female, doth not remaine in her wombe in any sensible bulke: but (as it seemeth), evaporateth and incorporateth itselfe, eyther into the body of the wombe, or rather into some more interior part, as into the seminary vessels. Which being a solide substance, much resembleth the nature of the females seede, is likely to sucke up, by the mediation of the females seede, the male seede incorporated with it, and by incorporation turned (as it were) into a vapour; in such sort as we have formerly explicated how the

[1] Ibid., pp. 416–17.

body of a scorpion or viper, draweth the poyson out of a wound. And after a certaine time (Doctor Harvey noted the space of sixe weekes or two months in does or hindes) these seedes distill again into the wombe, and by litle and litle do clarify in the middest, and a litle red specke appeareth in the center of the bright clearnesse as we said before of the egge.[1]

Harvey was, not unnaturally, baffled by finding no recognizable embryo in the uterus for seven weeks after he supposed impregnation to have taken place, and it was not until many years later that a full explanation was forthcoming. Harvey was unfortunate in that his special opportunities due to the King's addiction to hunting had led him to use animals whose initial stages of pregnancy are unlike those in several other species used by him. In the deer family and other ungulates the ovum, fertilized soon after leaving the ovary, develops differently from the manner seen in most other mammals. In the fallow and red deer with which Harvey worked the fertilized and developing ovum was surely present during the long period from October until the end of November, when Harvey searched for it, but it was very difficult to recognize. It would be present only as a curious object perhaps twenty centimetres long by a few millimetres wide and very fragile, looking quite unlike the embryos of other animals. Both fallow and red deer normally have but one embryo in each pregnancy and this tiny object lurking in the relatively large cavity of the uterus did not reveal itself to Harvey with his limited techniques. Moreover, even when the developing embryonic tropho-blast did become visible, it was, as mentioned above, a thin elongated object and to Harvey's eyes took the form of 'mucous filaments like spiders' threads',[2] quite unlike the spherical sacs seen in other animals such as the rabbit or dog.

Harvey's painstaking dissections of the King's does and hinds month by month (these amounting to an early example of a 'controlled experiment') are described in the successive Exercises of his book, and he mentions also that he examined the conceptions of ewes during the same intervals,[3] but he failed completely to form any clear idea of the part played by the semen of the male in fecundation of the female. His detailed descriptions of the anatomy of the organs of generation and of the later changes in the development of the embryo and foetus are admirable (though containing a few errors), but the fundamental secret of

[1] Digby, loc. cit., p. 221. He also communicated this story to Highmore, who referred to it in his *History of Generation*, 1651, pp. 100–1.

[2] *Anatomical Exercitations*, 1653, p. 419.

[3] Ibid., p. 444.

the fertilization of the ovum by the spermatozoon remained hidden from him.[1]

The chapters on the hen's egg are filled with detailed studies of every stage of the development of the chick; these form a description which Dr. Joseph Needham in his *History of Embryology* is able to say remains to this day one of the most accurate. Harvey loses no opportunity of refuting the conclusions reached by his predecessors; sometimes it is Aristotle who is regretfully put right, much more often Fabricius is the authority attacked, and Harvey says many hard things of him. The impression is created that Harvey actually enjoyed criticizing and correcting conclusions reached by his old master. Fabricius had, indeed, made the egregious error of disregarding the *cicatricula*, or 'little scar', as of no importance, and believed that the *chalazæ* or grandines, the ligaments holding the yolk sac in place, were the essential elements from which the chick was formed. Harvey corrected this and established the fundamental fact that the *cicatricula* was no scar, but was 'that from which the chick takes its rise'—was, in fact, the embryonic area. Fabricius had undoubtedly advanced the science of embryology, as Harvey recognized, but nevertheless he said in his Preface that Fabricius 'relieth upon probability rather then experience, and layeth aside the verdict of sense, which is grounded upon dissections; he flies to petty reasonings borrowed from mechanicks, which is very unbeseeming so famous an Anatomist'. Harvey's teacher is treated with respect, but his views are firmly rejected whenever Harvey finds himself in disagreement. Often, however, Harvey

---

[1] It has been claimed (Eckstein *et al.*, *Memoirs of the Society for Endocrinology*, no. 6, 1959, p. 6) that Harvey should be given the credit for having first described the phenomenon now known as 'delayed implantation of the ovum', according to which the ovum lies completely dormant in the uterus for several weeks. It has, however, been pointed out to me by Dr. Roger Short that it was shown by Bischoff in 1854 and again recently by himself (Short and Hay, 'Delayed Implantation in Roe Deer', *J. of Reproduction*, ix. 372) that this occurs exclusively in the diminutive roe deer, which Harvey is unlikely to have used. Judging from the breeding seasons mentioned, it was fallow and red deer that he investigated; in these the embryo grows normally, though in the peculiar manner described above. Usually, indeed, there were no roe deer in the south of England in Harvey's time (see F. J. Taylor Page, *Roe Deer*, Animals of Britain, no. 12, London, 1962). In 1618 three specimens were sent to London from Naworth in Cumberland and 32 roe kids were sent to King Charles in 1633—a considerable operation requiring the services of six men and seven horses (see H. A. Macpherson, *A Vertebrate Fauna of Lakeland*, Edinburgh, 1892, pp. 72–73). The animals were liberated in Half Moon Park, Wimbledon, but in 1638 they broke out of the park and the King issued a warrant on 17 January 1638/9 to Sir Henry Hungate for their protection; he was 'to take care that no person hunt, course or use any net or gin within four miles of the said park' (*Domestic State Papers*, 1638–39, ccccix, 1871, p. 323). Evidently he valued them highly, so that it seems most improbable that Harvey would have been allowed to use these animals for his experiments and he makes no mention of them.

is himself unable to reach a conclusion and in spite of his disapproval of speculation expressed in *De motu cordis* he is now able to say:

And therefore being moved by the example and authority of so Gallant a person as Aristotle, least I might seem made up of nothing but the subversion of other mens Doctrines, I have chosen rather to propose a feigned Opinion, then none at all: and have contented my self in this place to play the Phrynis to Timotheus; viz. to shake off the sloth and drowziness of the Age wee live in, and to awaken the wits of Industrious heads, permitting rather that abler men should sport themselves with my proposals, then that any carefull Enquirer into the nature of Things should accuse mee of sluggishness.[1]

References to problems of generation are found often enough in *De motu cordis* to show that these had been in Harvey's mind for a long time before the publication of his first book. Indeed, in Chapter xvi of *De motu cordis*, after mentioning the functions of the umbilical vessels in the chick, he foreshadows the writing of a work on embryology by saying, 'These matters, however, will be more appropriately dealt with in my observations on the formation of the fœtus, in which there can be very many questions of this kind. For example, why is this part made or perfected earlier, and that later? And in respect of the relative importance of members, which of two parts is the cause of the other? And several questions about the heart. . . .' It is impossible, therefore, to put an accurate date to the start of Harvey's work as experimental embryologist. The probability is that the seed sown at Padua began to grow at once, tentative beginnings being made soon after Harvey's return to England. It may even be that parts of *De generatione animalium* were written before the publication of *De motu cordis*.

Harvey's idea of the precise nature of fecundation of the female by the male, with the consequent production of a fertile egg, is not easy to appreciate. He was to the end uncertain of the part played by the semen of the male bird or animal.

It is most certain (he wrote in Exercise 31) that the Fertile Egge cannot be made, but by both Cock and Hen: and yet not in that fashion as Aristotle thought, as if forsooth the Cock alone were the prime Efficient, and the Hen did contribute nothing but the Stuff, or Materials. . . . But the matter is much otherwise in the generation of the Egge. For the Seed (or Geniture rather) proceeding from the Male in Coition, can by no means enter the Womb. Nor hath the Hen after Conception, any excrementitious substance, or purer part of any such substance, or any

---

[1] *Anatomical Exercitations*, 1653, p. 549.

Blood at all in the Cavity of the Womb, which might receive perfection from the Geniture of the Male. . . . For it is a certain truth, that the Egge, be it barren or fertile, is made and formed by the Hen alone: only the fertility indeed is derived from the Cock.

The last statement seems to contradict the first. Never having succeeded in finding semen in the uterus of viviparous animals, he concluded at another time that it was absorbed in the vagina and afterwards distilled into the uterus, where it initiated the formation of the ovum. So difficult did Harvey find it to grasp the idea of conception arising from the direct union of male and female elements that he could even say in Exercise 49 that fertilization was comparable to the contagion which spread infectious diseases.

This is agreed upon by universal consent that all Animals whatsoever, which arise from Male and Female, are generated by the coition of both Sexes, and so begotten as it were *per contagium aliquod*, by a kind of contagion. In like manner as Physitians observe, that contagious diseases (as the Leprosie, the Pox, the Plague and Pthisick) do propagate their infection, and beget themselves in bodies yet sound and untoucht, meerly by an extrinsecal contact: nay sometimes onely by the breath, and *per μίασμα*, by inquination; and that at a distance, through an inanimate medium, and that medium no way sensibly altered.[1]

Thus groping vainly for facts which inevitably evaded him, Harvey finally at the end of his book put forward the startling theory that the uterus could be compared to the brain, where things could be conceived from an immaterial source.

The Conception therefore of the Egge, or Uterus, is (in some sort) like the Conception of the Braine it selfe, and both of them doe alike partake of the End. For the Species, or Forme of the Chicken is in the Uterus, or Egge, without any matter at all: as the Reason of the Work is in the Artificer, and the Reason of the House in the Brain of the Builder.[2]

As late as the year 1685 the Dutch biologist, Anthony van Leeuwenhoeck, wrote in a letter to the Royal Society:

Your Harvey in his Book *de Generatione Animalium* denies that he ever Found in the Uterus Anatomised immediately after conception, the *Semen Masculum*. And our Dr. de Graaf in his Book *de Partibus Muliebribus Generationi inservientibus*, constantly asserts, that the *Semen Masculum* is nothing but a Vehicle of a certain Volatile Salt, or such like spirit, conveying to the Egg of the Female a *Contactum Vitalem*. But though a

[1] *Anatomical Exercitations*, 1653, p. 254. [2] Ibid., p. 555.

late Writer has reckoned up the Authorities of 70 Persons, who have asserted the same Opinion, and that of the *Ovarium*, yet I think they have been all mistaken. As will appear by the following Tryals.

Leeuwenhoeck then described how he proved under the microscope the presence of semen containing live spermatozoa in the cornua of the uterus of a bitch but lately impregnated.[1] He had provided the optical refinement so sorely needed by Harvey.

Harvey continued to be troubled by this insoluble problem, and in his last years made notes about it on the fly-leaves of his copy of *De generatione*.[2] He put the question: *Quod facit semen fecundus?* and then answered it by saying that it is on the analogy of an infection, instancing venereal disease, rabies in dogs, and smallpox, all lying dormant for a time. He then compared it to other imponderables, such as the scent of flowers, fermentation, and the miracles of nature. His mind even went back to something he had seen long before in Paris—'Mr. Boys spainel in Paris lay all the third night and morning in getting dogg. Whelping doggs sent are a stronger sent', with other references to the effect of scent in promoting desire in animals, all examples of action at a distance.

Harvey's views on a variety of other subjects of interest may be found by a careful perusal of his book. In his treatise on the heart he had not touched on one important aspect of the blood—whether or not it was endued with an *animus*, or soul. In Exercise 52 of *De generatione* he made the unequivocal statement that the blood 'is the builder and preserver of the body and principal part wherein the soul hath her Session'.[3] Aristotle, he pointed out, had thought the idea absurd, but Servetus, unknown to Harvey, had argued in favour of it and the doctrine is said to have been current in Padua.[4] Harvey seems to have based his view on the vital function of the blood in maintaining life and health, so that knowledge of the circulation of this precious fluid would induce men to 'be cautious to preserve their blood pure and clean, by commodious diet'. He did not pursue the subject in great detail, meaning 'to treat more fully and exactly of it elsewhere', but later in the book (Exercise 71) returned to it briefly, quoting Virgil (*Aeneid*, x. 487) in support:[5]

[1] *Philosophical Transactions*, vol. xvi, 1686, p. 1121.

[2] The notes were transcribed by Dr. Charles Singer and some were printed in Needham's *History of Embryology*, 1934 (ed. 2, 1959, p. 148). The book is in the medical library formed by Prof. F. C. Pybus of Newcastle-upon-Tyne. It carries the signature of Harvey's nephew Eliab, with the date 1674. The library was given in 1965 to the University of Newcastle.

[3] *Anatomical Exercitations*, 1653, p. 281.

[4] See C. Hill, in *Past and Present* (1964), no. 27, 62–63.

[5] *Anatomical Exercitations*, 1653, p. 455.

Una eademque via sanguisque Animusque sequuntur

Both Soul and Blood
Stream in one Flood

Harvey does not appear to have regarded the doctrine as heretical, though he was inviting criticism from theologians on rather dangerous ground.

Thomas Huxley[1] in 1870 examined *De generatione animalium* to discover, if he could, Harvey's true views on spontaneous generation. In the first Exercise Harvey quoted Fabricius:

The productions of Animals do some of them spring out of Egges, some out of Seed, and some out of Putrifaction; and hence it is, that some are called oviparous, some viviparous, others the issues of putrifaction, or creatures born of their own accord; by the Greeks, αὐτόματα.

This Harvey criticized:

But I dislike this division, because all Animals may in some sort be said to be born out of Egges, and in some sort out of Seed: besides, they are stiled Oviparous, Viviparous, or Vermiparous, rather from the issues themselves bring forth, then from the original matter of which themselves were made; namely, because they produce an Egge, a Worm, or a living Creature. Some of them are also said to be *sponte nascentia*, creatures born of their own accord, not because they quicken out of putrid matter, but because they are begotten by chance, by natures own accord, and by an æquivocal generation (as they call it) and by parents of a different species from themselves.[2]

Harvey does not here seem to make much advance on the opinion of Fabricius. Near the end of the book Huxley found a passage stating Harvey's views in a way meant to be explicit:

All living things do derive their Original from something, which doth contain in it both the matter, and efficient virtue and power: which therefore is that thing, both out of which, and by which, whatsoever is born, doth deduce its beginning. And such an Original or Rudiment in Animals . . . is a certain humour, which is concluded in some certain coat, or shell; namely a similar body, having life actually in it, or *in potentia*: and this, in case it be generated within an Animal, and do there remain, untill it have produced an Univocal Animal, is commonly called a Conception: but if it be exposed without, by being born, or else assume

[1] In an address to the British Association for the Advancement of Science, September 1870; see *Nature* (1870), ii. 400 ff.
[2] *Anatomical Exercitations*, 1653, p. 3.

its beginning elsewhere, it is called either an Egg, or a Worm. But I conceive that both ought alike to be called *Primordium*, the first Rudiment from which an Animal doth spring; as Plants assume their nativity from the Seed: and all these *Primordia* are of one kinde, namely Vital.[1]

Even here the words are somewhat equivocal. What exactly did he mean by *Primordium*? In Exercise 38 he wrote:

And now again some other creatures have a seed provided for them, casually as it were, without any distinction of sex at all; namely those creatures whose Birth is spontaneous,

apparently meaning that the *primordium* had arisen spontaneously. This seems to be confirmed by a passage in Exercise 28:

And though some Animals are born of their own Accord, or (as they commonly say) of Putrefaction. . . .

In other passages it seems to be clear that Harvey did believe in spontaneous generation, as in Exercise 29:

Now the Earth also produceth many things of its own accord, without any seed;

and again in Exercise 38:

For the Sun, or the Heavens (or whatever else is understood to be a common and general Father in the production of living creatures) do produce some things by themselves, by chance, and as it were without employing any intermediate Instrument, by an equivocal generation.

Passages could be multiplied to suggest that Harvey did indeed credit the idea of spontaneous generation, but many others express his conviction that all living things arise from some sort of 'egg', though 'egg' is very far from meaning anything like the egg of a hen enclosed within a shell. Harvey's egg is something much more indeterminate. He even regarded the larva or caterpillar of an insect as a kind of creeping egg from which the perfect imago developed by metamorphosis. In some contexts the egg is another way of expressing a *primordium*, or 'first principle', from which everything arises. Too many quotations will only produce confusion, since Harvey's language is seemingly contradictory owing to his own difficulty in forming an exact expression of his thoughts. Huxley concluded that, like Aristotle, he was an advocate of spontaneous generation; but Meyer in his *Analysis of De generatione*, 1936 (p. 53), seems justified in saying that 'it seems more likely to me that

[1] *Anatomical Exercitations*, 1653, pp. 514-15.

Harvey seriously doubted that the living can arise from the non-living and that he had hoped to demonstrate the untenability of such an assumption, but found himself baffled in all directions'.

Another point at issue is whether Harvey should be given credit for formulating the principle of *Epigenesis* in embryology. In fact, as F. J. Cole has pointed out,[1] Aristotle was the real originator, even though he did not use the word, meaning that the various parts of an organism do not arise simultaneously or are preformed (as the Preformationists held), but are developed in succession as the embryo takes shape. Too much, however, should not be read into the meaning of a scientific term such as *epigenesis*, when used by Harvey, whose notion of it was exceedingly simple. He stated his beliefs on this point very plainly in several passages, of which the following from Exercise 45 is an example:

some [complete animals], having one part made before another, are afterwards nourished, augmented, and formed out of the same matter; that is, they have parts, whereof some are before, and some after other, and at the same time are both formed and grow. Now the Fabrick or constitution of these proceeds from some one part, as from its original, and by the help of that, the other members are produced, and these we say are made *per Epigenesin*, by a post-generation, or after-production; that is to say by degrees, part after part; and this is more properly called a Generation then the former.[2]

Aristotle and Harvey had no conception of the complications now implied by *epigenesis*, introduced by knowledge of cells and cell division, germ layers, and so forth. Harvey rejected the doctrine of the preformationists in favour of a simple form of *epigenesis*, but this does not constitute a major advance, since it was impossible for him to develop the idea any further.

Like all good experimenters, Harvey was not averse to experimenting upon himself. A classic example of this is found in Exercise 57, where he is speaking of the power of the flesh to distinguish a poisonous wound from a harmless one.

I myselfe once, for experiment sake, pricked my hand with a needle; and presently rubbing the same needle upon a Spiders tooth, I pricked my hand in another place, so that I my self could not distinguish between the two pricks. But there was something in my Skin that did distinguish; for in that place where the poisoned prick fell, it presently contracted itself into a pimple, and presently grew red, hot, and inflamed; as if it

---

[1] F. J. Cole, *Early Theories of Sexual Generation*, 1930, p. 132.
[2] *Anatomical Exercitations*, 1653, p. 222.

fortified it self, and stood upon its guard, to oppose and subdue the malice of the venom.

Harvey wished by this to demonstrate the perfection of nature and the presence everywhere of a guiding principle. The result was one of the earliest recorded examples of a controlled observation in toxicology.

In the course of his experiments on eggs he did not shrink from tasting eggs in various stages of development. In Exercise 13 he wrote that

New-layed eggs (if they be whole) being put near the fire will sweat, and are of much pleasanter taste, and more esteemed of, then other. And eggs after two or three dayes incubation are even then sweeter relished then stale ones are; as if the cherishing warmness of the Hen did refresh and restore them to their primitive excellence and integrity. And after full fourteen days (when the Chicken now beginneth to be downey, and extendeth his dominion over half the egge, and the yolke is almost still entire) I have boyled an egg till it was hard . . . and yet the yolke was as sweet and pleasant as that of a new-laid egge, when it is in like manner boyled to an induration.

De generatione animalium contains a wealth of accurate observations and deductions, but it also convicts Harvey of making some remarkable mistakes. In Exercise 65, discussing 'The uterus of hinds and does', he noted the accumulation of semen in the testicles and *vesiculae seminales* of male animals at the time of coition, but because the corresponding glands in the female were not swollen or in any way changed at the same time he concluded that they had no part in generation. Exercise 58 is devoted to a justification of the belief, expressed by Hippocrates, Democritus, and Epicurus, that the fœtus sucks and takes in nutriment by the mouth while in the womb. Harvey was impressed by the fact that the intestine of a fœtus contains excrement and by its being able to suck so effectively immediately it has been born.

Nay, a Newborn Child is more exact at sucking then a grown body, or himself either if he discontinue it but a few days. For the Infant doth not compress the Nipple, and suck at the rate that we do by gulping down: but as if he would devour the Nipple, he still draws it into his mouth, and by the aid of his tongue and palate he sucks the milk as if he chewed it, with far more earnestness and slight, then a grown body. Wherefore he seems to be good at it of old, and to have practised it in the womb.

Harvey noted that Fabricius, quite correctly, ascribed the birth of a fœtus to the action of the womb assisted by the mother's abdominal muscles and diaphragm, but nevertheless chose to believe that the birth is greatly furthered by the activity of the fœtus itself. He illustrated this by relating incidents from his own obstetrical experience in which infants had seemed to be born by their own efforts, and by a story of a white mare belonging to the Queen, which had been delivered of a foal although the genital orifice had been securely closed by an iron ring. Although Harvey had correctly interpreted the movements of the heart as contraction and dilatation of an involuntary muscle, he seems to have been unable to grant that the uterus was another powerful involuntary muscle. Perhaps his opinion was influenced by knowing that the chick was able to escape unassisted from the egg.

Other erroneous opinions could be cited, but they are evidence of the magnitude of the task that Harvey had undertaken and of the courage with which he faced it rather than of any ineptitude on his part or of lack of intellect. It must be admitted that his book is repetitive, confused, and sometimes contradictory. F. J. Cole has called it 'a history of the development of Harvey's thoughts on generation.'[1] Nevertheless it is also packed with acute observation and argument, and in the present context an attempt has been made to show what a large place it occupied in Harvey's life and how worthy it was, in spite of its faults, to receive the full consideration it has been given in Needham's *History of Embryology* after centuries of neglect.

Even so, little attention has been paid to Harvey's literary style, greatly elaborated since the writing of his first book. In *De motu cordis* he studied to be brief and to the point. In *De generatione animalium* he allowed his thoughts to proliferate in many directions, sometimes even to the point of composing passages of conscious literary excitement. The style of Exercise 28, as an example, suggests awareness of the manner of Sir Thomas Browne, though little direct influence can be claimed, since *Pseudodoxia Epidemica* was not published until 1646. Even *Religio Medici*, published in 1642, can hardly have made much impact on Harvey's mind (if he read it then) at a time when he was so much preoccupied with historic events. Exercise 28 is worth giving in full to illustrate the point, though allowance must be made for the passage from Harvey's Latin through the mind of the unknown translator. Credit must to some extent be shared.

That the Egge is not made without a Henne[2]

To omit what ever is in dispute, and to wave all controversies till we

---

[1] Loc. cit., p. 135.   [2] *Anatomical Exercitations*, 1653, pp. 155-8.

come to the General contemplation concerning this subject, we now proceed to things of more certainty, and more obvious.

And first it is manifest that an Egge cannot be made fertile without the help of the Cock and Henne. For without a Cock it cannot be fruitfull, without a Henne it cannot be at all. And this is opposite to that opinion, which deduceth the first rise and fabrick of all living creatures out of the clay of the Earth. For since the several parts of Generation (namely the Testicles and Leading Vessels in the Cock) are formed with such eminent Art, Industry, and Reason, and likewise the Ovary and Uterus in the Henne, together with the Veines and Arteries which are subservient to them, are so skilfully composed, and the situation, figure, and temper of every particular, are disposed in a miraculous method; and all these things are some way or other required to the generation and fecundity of the egge: most certain it is (for nature makes nothing in vain, nor doth she go to work by digressions, where she may be more compendious in her dispatch) that an egge cannot be any other way produced then now it is (namely by a cock and a hen) neither by nature of her own accord, nor by any other means whatever; nor can either cock or hen be produced, but from an Egge. So that the cock and the hen are made for the Eggs sake, and likewise the Egge for the Cock and Hens sake: and you may be justly doubtfull with Plutarch, which of these is first, namely the Egge, or the Henne? For she was first in order of Nature, but the Egge in order of Time. For whatsoever excells, is first in order of Nature; but that from which another is produced, is first in order of Time. Or else we may say, That that Egge from which this or that particular Henne sprung, is of more Antiquity then the Henne: and so on the contrary, That Henne which produceth this particular Egge, is elder then it. For this Vicissitude and Circuite perpetuates the Race of Cockes and Hennes; while now the Chicken, and now the Egge by a constant series and return do continue an Immortal Species, out of the decay and ruines of the Individuals. And after this sort do many sublunary creatures emulate and approach to the Perpetuity of Celestial bodies.

And whether we affirm a soul to be in the egge or not, yet by this circumvolution it appears, that there is some principle of the vicissitude from the Henne to the Egge, and again from the Egge to the Henne, which conferrs a sempiternity unto them. And that very thing (saith Aristotle) beareth an Analogie to the substance of Starres; and causeth the Parents to propagate, and their seed, or eggs, to be prolifical: and is like Proteus, disguised in several formes, ever existent both in the Parents, and in the Egges. For as that Minde or Spirit which rules the world, doth continually reduce the same Rising and Setting Sun from several Quarters and Regions of the Earth; so also in the Progeny of Cocks and Henns, the *Vis Enthea*, or divine Principle, which is now called the Plastical, sometimes the Nutritive, and sometimes the Augmentative Power or Virtue, is also ever conceived to be the Conservative, and Vegetative too: and now putting on the form of the egge, and now of the Chicken, continues for ever. And though some Animals are born of their own Accord, or (as they commonly say) of Putrefaction: and others only produced from a Female (as Pliny notes in some kinde of living creatures there is no Male at all; as in the Ruffes, and the Roches: for they are all taken great with spawn) yet whatsoever is produced from a perfect egge, doth not proceed but from both Sexes.

And therefore, saith Aristotle, The Male and the Female are chiefly to be counted the Principles of Generation. The Cock therefore and the Henne are the two first Principles of the egge; the fruit, or common conception of both which is the egge, containing in it the virtue of both Parents. So that an egge can no more be made without the assistance of the Cock and Henne, then the fruit can be made without the Trees aid. And each particular *Individuum*, both Cock and Henne, seems to be created for the egges sake, that the same Species may be prolonged, though by the ruine and obsequies of the Authors. And it is also clear that when the Parents are no longer youthfull, beautifull, complete and Jovial, then they can generate, or fructifie their eggs, and produce their own like, by the mediation of those eggs. Which work of nature so soon as they have accomplished, as if then they had attained the highest ἀκμὴ, or Pitch of their perfection, and last end for which they were born, they presently wither, grow old and Emerit, and as if God and Nature had forsaken them, they decline speedily, and hasten to their end, like creatures weary of their lives. Whereas on the contrary, the Males when they arm themselves, and are in all respects well appointed for Loves encounter, how strangly doth the potent Cupid heighten their enflamed spirits, how spruce are they, how do they pride it; how vigorous, how testy are they, and prone to conflicts! But when this office and performance ceaseth: oh! how soon doth their force abate, and their late fury coole! how do they hale in all their swelling sails, and check their daring? Nay even while this jocund Sacrifice to Venus is in season, no sooner is the act performed, but they grow tame and pusillanimous; as if it were then deep printed in their thoughts, that while they impart a life to others, they are in full career to their own urnes. Onely our Cock, full fraught with seed and spirits, approves himselfe the onely cheerfull loser, and with the plaudit of his wings and voice, crownes his past triumphs, and lights his wedding Torch at his own Cinders. And yet he also flags after long game, and like an Emerit souldier resignes his Commission. And so the Hens likewise, like Plants worn out, grow decayed Matrons, and fore-go their Nurseries.

This passage could well have formed part of Harvey's projected work announced at the end of Exercise 6 in a discussion of how a male bird knows which of his hens is ready for impregnation. 'But of this elsewhere, in our tract of the *Love, Lust, and act of Generation of Animals*, we shall treat at large.' The title probably represents an unwritten, rather than a lost, work by the author of *De generatione animalium*.

The obstetrical section of *De generatione animalium* has a different character from the preceding Exercises. These are predominantly a record of experiments and observations made in the laboratory and the field; the obstetrical part is more philosophical and reminiscent. Harvey seems to have written it 'out of his head', giving a textbook account of the subject with illustrations derived from remembered incidents in his past practice and general experience. In the last sentences his words suggest that other books were germinating in his brain.

Hereafter when wee shall treat Universally of the Generation of all Animals (even of those also, which are generated by Metamorphosis; namely, of Insects, and Spontaneous Productions, in whose Egges, or first Rudiments there is a plaine Species or Immateriall forme, as being the moving principle in regard of those things which are to be produced, as also in all other Seed whatsoever) and also when we shall discourse of the Soule, and its affections; and also how Arts, Memory, and Experience, are onely the Conceptions of the Brain, wee shall endeavour both largely and perspicuously to explaine.

As already indicated, the Preface contains some discussion of the part played by memory in the arts, and, indeed, the Preface as a whole covers briefly more or less the subjects adumbrated in these last sentences.

It seems reasonable to infer that the seventy-two Exercises had been largely written earlier, probably before 1642, additions perhaps being made in Oxford; that the obstetrical part was added not long before Ent persuaded Harvey to allow publication; and that the Preface was composed last of all, perhaps even after Ent had taken charge of the bulk of the book. Harvey himself said in his letters of 1655 to Horst and Nardi that he was too old 'for the investigation of novel subtleties', but that his mind was still vigorous and capable of serious thought. That this was true is proved by the two letters to Riolan composed in 1648. At that date the power of Harvey's mind was plainly unimpaired.

Dr. Lluelyn's hope that Harvey's book would meet this time with 'a calmer welcome' was fulfilled. The first critic was Alexander Ross. In 1651 Ross had published his *Arcana Microcosmi*, containing a sterile treatise, 'The hid Secrets of Man's Body disclosed, In an Anatomical Duel between Aristotle and Galen concerning the Parts thereof', followed by an attempted 'Refutation of Doctor Brown's Vulgar Errors.' In 1652 this was reprinted with the addition of an Appendix giving further 'Refutations' of Browne followed by criticisms of Harvey's *De genera-tione* and of Bacon's *Natural History (Sylva Sylvarum)*. Ross, born in Scotland and educated at Aberdeen, moved south in later life and was for many years a cleric and schoolmaster in Southampton, eventually being presented to the living of Carisbrooke by Charles I. He was the author of many and tedious books, in which his habit was to attack better men than himself. He did, however, concede that Harvey's book was 'full of excellent learning and observation', and among his criticisms included a not unreasonable objection to the suggestion that 'the Noblest Animals should be conceived without any sensible Corporeall Agent, by mere imagination, not of the brain, but of the Womb'. He also called to his aid Harvey's old opponent Dr. James Primrose, quoting a letter from him on the same point. This, Ross said, showed 'how offensive Dr. Harvey's opinion is to others as well as to myself'. Harvey had admittedly exposed a flank vulnerable to this kind of attack, but, as the foregoing pages have demonstrated, the massive structure of the main part of the book could not be undermined by demolition of a few isolated outworks.

A potential critic was Nathaniel Highmore, who started to write a letter to Harvey, but never completed or published it. An unfinished draft, with the appearance of being a fair copy, is preserved among the Finch-Hatton papers.[1] Highmore courteously posed some obvious difficulties in understanding Harvey's doctrine of fertilization by 'contagion'. He also questioned whether 'the Does & Hindes you observed in dissection that had empty wombes for a month after copulation, may, I suppose, have miscarried in their coition or not then coupled with their males', but, as we have seen, this implied criticism was undeserved. Harvey's experiments were properly controlled and his observations were correct.

Apart from this the only unfavourable notices were by unimportant critics, Matthew Slade and Janus Orcham.[2] Slade published in 1667 his *Dissertatio epistolica*, detecting some purely anatomical errors 'in that golden book on the generation of animals of William Harvey, greatest of physicians and anatomists'. Even these errors were shown not to be errors by Johannes ab Angelis,[3] who wrote at once in Harvey's defence.

[1] British Museum, Add. MSS. 29586, f. 21.

[2] Orcham, *De generatione animalium conjectura observationi cuidam Harveanæ*, Brandenburg, 1667.

[3] ab Angelis, *Vindiciæ ab epistolica Theodori Aldes dissertatione contra Gul. Harveium*, Amsterdam, 1667. Aldes was Slade's pseudonym.

Harvey did not, therefore, have to spend any of the time remaining to him in the kind of argument he so much disliked. On the contrary, his work was soon appraised at its true value by a few later workers in the field of embryology, notably by William Langley, physician of Dordrecht, who published at Amsterdam in 1674 a volume of excerpts from Harvey's book with further observations of his own,[1] and by Andrew Snape, farrier to Charles II, in *The Anatomy of an Horse*, 1683.[2] Meanwhile the Latin text of Harvey's book was being reprinted in Holland and Italy, three editions appearing in 1651 and others in 1662, 1666, and 1680. Harvey's position as an embryologist was established in his lifetime, and he had little to fear from having again challenged the winds of controversy.

39

HARVEY'S CORRESPONDENTS, 1651–1657 *
ATTEMPTED SUICIDE, 1652

It will be remembered that thirty years earlier, in 1621, James Howell, afterwards author of *Epistolæ Ho-Elianæ*, had been under Harvey's care for 'an issue in his left arm'. In 1640 Howell had published the first part of *Dodona's Grove*, a somewhat ponderous fable displaying his knowledge of history and politics, and this Harvey, with his usual courtesy, seems to have read and approved. In 1650 Howell published a second part and sent it to Harvey with the following letter:[3]

To Doctor Harvey, at St. Lawrence Pountney

Sir, I remember well you pleas'd not only to pass a favourable censure, but give a high character of the first part of *Dodona's Grove*; which makes this *Second* to come and wait on you, which, I dare say, for variety of fancy is nothing inferior to the first. It continueth an historical Account of the Occurrences of the Times in an allegorical way, under the shadow of *Trees*; and I believe it omits not any material passage which happen'd as far as it goes. If you please to spend some of the parings of your time,

---

[1] *Observationes et historiæ omnes & singulæ e Guilielmi Harvei libello De Generatione Animalium excerptæ, & in accuratissimum ordinem redactæ. Item Wilhelmi Langly De Generatione Observationes quædam*, Amsterdam, 1674.

[2] Snape, Andrew, *The Anatomy of an Horse . . . Appendix of the Generation of Animals*, London, 1683, References to Harvey's book in the Appendix.

[3] *Epistolæ Ho-Elianæ*, book IV, no. xxxvii.

and fetch a walk in this *Grove*, you may haply find therein some recreation : And if it be true what the Ancients wrote of some Trees, that they are *fatidical*, these come to foretell, at leastwise to wish you, as the season invites me, a good New-year, according to the Italian compliment, *Buon principio, miglier mezzo, ed ottimo fine* : With these wishes of happiness in all the three degrees of comparison, I rest—your devoted Servant,

J. H.

Lond. 2 Jan [1651/2]

Evidently Howell, at this time a prisoner in the Fleet because of his royalist opinions and writings, was still glad to claim acquaintance with the distinguished physician and pleased to regard his opinion on literary matters as of value. We have no other knowledge of Harvey's taste in this kind of reading. Aubrey commented only on his proficiency in mathematics, an interest no doubt fostered by Scarburgh, whose admiration for William Oughtred, the famous Cambridge mathematician, has already been mentioned (p. 304): 'He was pretty well versed in the Mathematiques, and had made himself master of Mr. Oughtred's Clavis Math. in his old age; & I have seen him perusing it, and working problems, not long before he dyed, & that booke was alwayes in his meditating apartment.'

It may be assumed that the publication of Harvey's replies to Riolan in 1649 would stimulate others to try to engage him in correspondence on scientific subjects, particularly the circulation of the blood and the purpose of the lymphatic vessels. One letter of an earlier date from the Danish anatomist, Thomas Bartholin, will be noticed and others from Jan Beverwijk have already been given (pp. 271–3) with Harvey's replies. But on the whole Harvey's customary reluctance to engage in controversy seems to have discouraged foreign anatomists from writing to him, though this may only be because the evidence happens not to have survived. By 1651, however, the number of Harvey's correspondents was growing, and, although he complained from time to time of being impaired by old age and infirmity, his mind was vigorous and he could still compose long and weighty letters in Latin. Most of these letters are well known and have been several times translated.[1]

On 26 March 1621/2 Harvey wrote a long letter to Paul Marquard Slegel of Hamburg, a man twenty-seven years his junior, who in 1631 had visited Holland, England, France, and Italy. He had been a pupil of Caspar Hofmann at Altdorf and has already been mentioned in

[1] The extracts quoted here are taken from Professor K. J. Franklin's translation in *The Circulation of the Blood*, Oxford, 1958.

connexion with Harvey's visit to Hofmann in 1636 (p. 232). When in London, Slegel may have met Harvey, who addresses him as if they were personally acquainted, but there is no direct evidence in confirmation. Slegel was a convinced supporter of Harvey's doctrine and a keen critic of Riolan, and he had sent Harvey a copy of his book, *De sanguinis motu commentatio in qua præcipue in Joannis Riolani sententiam inquiritur* (Hamburg, 1650), in which he attacked in particular Riolan's teaching about the function of the portal vein. In his letter of acknowledgement Harvey warmly praised the book and told Slegel he had demolished Riolan's attacks on himself. In connexion with Riolan's denial of the passage of blood from the lungs to the left ventricle of the heart, Harvey described to Slegel an experiment he had recently made on this point 'in the presence of several colleagues, and from the implications of which there is no escape'. Having ligated the pulmonary artery, the pulmonary vein, and the aorta in the cadaver of a throttled man, he introduced a small tube through the vena cava into the right ventricle, and attached to the tube a bladder, which he filled with water and used as a pump. He then filled the ventricle and auricle with water under pressure and showed that none passed into the left ventricle, which had been opened. He next released the ligatures and introduced the tube into the pulmonary artery, at the same time tying a ligature so that no water could pass back into the right ventricle. The pump then pushed water mixed with blood freely into the lungs, and an equal amount came out through the opening in the left ventricle. 'You can try it as often as you wish', he added, 'and discover that it is so.' The remainder of the letter discussed the question whether the arterial and venous systems are connected by anstomoses or by passage from arterioles to venules, which was Harvey's conception of a capillary system. He had, of course, already expressed his disbelief in the existence of anastomoses.

Another correspondent at this date was Giovanni Nardi of Florence, where they had become friends during Harvey's visit in 1636. Nardi had written various books, including in 1647 an annotated edition of Lucretius, and Harvey thanked him in a short letter of 15 July 1651 for sending copies of his works. Nardi had also been kind to one of Harvey's nephews who had visited Florence. Harvey ended: 'So soon as I learn that you still survive and remain mindful of me, I shall enjoy more often such literary exchange, and see that other books are sent off to you.' Nardi seems to have been slow to answer, for Harvey's next letter was not written until 30 November 1653. He thanked Nardi for a copy of his Lucretius and said: 'It was certainly a cause of rejoicing to me that very learned men here and there were advancing the republic of letters even in this age, in which the crowd of writers devoid of taste is as numerous as a swarm of flies on a very hot day, and we are almost stifled by the stench of their thin and trifling productions.' He then speculated on how plague is spread, comparing it to the difficulty of explaining how 'the idea, or form, or vital principle can be carried across from the genitor to the genetrix and thence into the conceptus or ovum, and thence again into the fœtus', with a production of likeness and chance peculiarities. It was Harvey's old difficulty, discussed at such length in *De generatione animalium*. He concluded:

These are among the more hidden matters, learned Nardi, and they call for your shrewd attention. Nor is there any reason for you to plead advancing years, for I am myself almost an octogenarian and, although my physical powers are tottering with my body broken, yet with my mind active I give myself up most gladly to studies of this sort. I send to you with this letter three books on the subject about which you were asking me. Further, if in my name you will thank the Duke of Tuscany most warmly for the unusual honour which he once did me when I was in Florence, and will offer him my good wishes for his safety and prosperity, you will be doing a most kind thing to

Your devoted and affectionate
William Harvey

Harvey wrote a third short letter to Nardi on 25 October 1655. He had not heard whether Nardi had received the books previously sent, and asked 'how far, pray, you have advanced with your *Noctes geniales* and the other works on which you have resolved. For I am wont to enliven my now rather inactive old age and my spirit which scorns the trifles of everyday, by reading the best books of that kind.' He again thanked Nardi for his former kindness to his nephew and asked for similar favours to another (favourite) nephew who was bringing the letter. This was probably a son of his brother Eliab, perhaps young Eliab, now just 20 years old. It is almost certain, however, that Nardi had died before the young man reached Florence. His book, *Noctes geniales*,[1] had been completed in 1652, but was not printed until 1655 and was then edited by his son, Philip, who referred to his father's death in the dedication. Although Nardi expressed almost fulsome admiration for Harvey, extolling his modesty and other qualities, he nevertheless criticized some of his conclusions and was the first to assert that Cæsalpinus had anticipated his recognition of the circulation. Harvey had not read *Noctes*

[1] *Noctes geniales*, Bologna, 1655; references to Harvey, pp. 273–4, 712–46.

geniales when he wrote his last letter to Nardi, and perhaps he never did. Nardi's criticisms could not, in any event, have caused him any anxiety, for Bayon regarded them as 'so much inane word-spinning'.[1]

Gaspare Aselli, Professor of Anatomy in Padua, had made his observations on the lacteal vessels in 1622, but they were not published until 1627, the year after the author's death. He had erroneously supposed that the lacteals carried the milky chyle, or products of digestion in the alimentary tract, to the liver. A French anatomist, Jean Pecquet, had carried the matter further in 1647 by identifying the thoracic duct and the *receptaculum chyli* with their termination in the left subclavian vein, his results being published in his book *Experimenta nova anatomica*, Paris, 1651. At the same time Olof Rudbeck (1630–72) of Uppsala had made similar observations in 1651, published in his *Nova exercitatio anatomica*, Arosiae, 1653. A dispute then arose between Rudbeck and Thomas Bartholin of Copenhagen concerning priority, Bartholin having described the lymphatic system in two books[2] published in 1652. All these anatomists had added to knowledge of their subject, but Aselli and Pecquet were the major contributors. In this connexion the foreign correspondent next in date was Dr. Robert Morison (1620–83) of Paris. He had studied medicine at Aberdeen, but, after fighting in the Civil War as a Royalist, settled in Paris and did not return to England until the Restoration, when he came back in the King's company. He became a royal physician and spent the latter part of his life in Oxford.[3] He had already written more than one letter to Harvey asking his opinion of Jean Pecquet's book. Harvey had not received it before the end of March 1651/2, and so did not reply until 28 April 1652. He expressed his admiration for Pecquet's work, but confessed that, even before Aselli had announced his discoveries of the lacteal vessels from the intestines, he 'had looked carefully at those little white channels' and could not agree that they carried chyle. The fluid appeared to him to be milk, and he required clear-cut experimental proof that it was actually chyle. He thought the vessels were too variable as demonstrated in different animals and were too small for their supposed function. And the fluid, if really derived from the food, should vary in appearance according to the food eaten. He admitted, however, that if the chyle was indeed conducted from the intestines by the thoracic duct to the subclavian vein, he

---

[1] *Annals of Science* (1939–40), iv. 353.

[2] *Vasa lymphatica nuper Hafniæ in animantibus inventa*, and *De lacteis thoracicis in homine brutisque nuperrime observatis historia anatomica*, Hafniæ, 1652.

[3] *D.N.B.*

would have to agree that it mixed with the blood before reaching the right ventricle of the heart. In fact, however, he believed that the mesenteric veins, being large and numerous, were the real channels by which nourishment was conveyed from the intestines. He was satisfied that embryos were nourished through their circulating blood, and was reluctant to believe that grown animals were nourished by any other route. He concluded his letter by sending his greetings to M. Pecquet and to M. Gayant, presumably another medical acquaintance in Paris.

Thomas Bartholin had been in communication with Harvey ten years earlier, having written him a letter, in default of actually meeting him, on 14 July 1642. He claimed to have long admired Harvey and his work. 'If in my early writings my slender Muse set down anything of value to you and your most sure discoveries, I should wish it approved by the wise. And I have not circumscribed the secrets of your mind in the margins of a single page; I have freely expounded them by word of mouth in all places where I have travelled, perhaps with some success.'[1] Bartholin had, indeed, accepted most of Harvey's views in his anatomical works, as can be seen in Culpeper's translation,[2] though he believed, unlike Harvey, that the blood was 'perfected', that is, endued with warmth, by the heart and its motion. He raised further obscure difficulties in his letter of 1642, but these are now of little value. He again addressed Harvey on 1 May 1652 in a letter of greater interest, which has not previously been quoted:

Of the nourishment of the infant from the chyle[3]

To William Harvey, London.

The everlasting renown of your name and your most high deserts for the republic of literature have been obvious to me heretofore, truly you have deserved the votes of all fair men by your Circulation of the blood, for human industry could discover nothing more elegant, more useful, more true than that. And I must not pass over your clearly inspired Exercises on Animal Generation, in which you have taught the learned world things unheard. What the chorus of the learned who consider the matter fairly may conclude about these great memorials of your wit and marvellous learning I have no wish to elaborate in a long speech, and I set no price on your work, when I do not doubt that you yourself read your great name among all peoples every day.

[1] *Epistolarum medicinalium a doctis vel ad doctos scriptarum centuria I & II*, Hafniæ, 1663, Centuria I, letter 23, pp. 105–7. Translation by W. R. LeFanu.

[2] *Bartholinus Anatomy*, published by Nich. Culpeper and Abdiah Cole, London, 1663, pp. 99–101.

[3] Loc. cit., Centuria II, letter 24, pp. 478–81; translation by W. R. LeFanu.

But I, the least of the learned, though the greatest in affection and love of literature, formerly trained and accustomed to other principles, most willingly embraced in my love of truth the most true discovery of the circulated blood and presage well for the author. This I proposed, not merely once, in public discussions among strangers warmed by another sun and in my native Academy, and already persuaded it of Harvey's most true teaching.

I would have wished that all Anatomy had been reformed by the author and discoverer himself in accord with these principles, but when I saw him busied with greater cares and striving with the difficulties of the times, I took that business upon myself. Would that I had satisfied public wishes and your Excellency's thought. What I have achieved, you have seen perhaps from the third edition, published in Holland, of my 'Anatomy reformed and adapted to the Circulation of the blood'. Whether I have everywhere followed the sense of the discovery you will tell me briefly. I have truly tried with my might, but when I saw that no one had corrected anatomy as a whole at that time, I assumed a greater load than my shoulders perhaps would bear. But thereupon Highmore's elegant and erudite anatomical disquisition, which rolls the same stone, arrived with us.

Now however I am wholly taken up with your experiments concerning the generation of animals and often enter Democritus' cave in your company. First I rejoice in the name of Hippocrates, whom I ever follow, that you have proved that the embryo sucks the chyle by mouth. But we stick at the ways by which the chyle is carried to the womb, since no ways appear beside the arteries and veins conspicuous with blood. In pregnant and milking dogs I have made the venture, but found nothing to satisfy me plainly. But for the future I shall search more diligently. Do the arteries convey it? Yet how will the fluid be separated from the blood or whence will the arteries draw it, since indeed there are none in the mesentery destined to convey the chyle? Here I request your help and infinite experience.

I have tried to make some comment on this matter in my 'Anatomical History of the lately discovered Thoracic Lacteals', which I am sending you. The distinguished youth Wilhelm Worm will take it to you. He is the not unworthy son of Mr. Ole Worm our topmost physician and savant here, and accordingly I introduce him to your favour and friendship. What you think of that lacteal discovery, and why in 'Exercises on the Circulation of the Blood, against Riolan' and lately in 'The Generation of Animals' you hold Aselli's lacteal veins suspect, if your work bears this out, I ask you of your kindness to explain to me, if it be no burden. Finally I intercede with you for the public, no longer to look askance with your different wisdom on nails bitten down in the study of anatomy.

I would not dare to put forward my private interests, unless, as I earnestly desire and request by this letter, you would admit me to your close friendship, so shall I ever be most bound to you and my head will touch the stars.

May God, incomparable Sir, long preserve you to be the glory of the republic of anatomy.

Copenhagen, 1st May 1652.   Your
                                             Thomas Bartholin

It is of interest to know that Harvey probably received a copy of Bartholin's work on the thoracic duct, but by this date he may have been wearied by frequent questions about the lymphatic system and he is not known to have replied. Had he done so Bartholin would surely have printed the letter in his three *Centuries of Medical Letters*. The reference to Bartholin's intended messenger, Wilhelm Worm, is tantalizing, for this young man, son of the learned Ole Worm (or Olaus Wormius) kept a diary written in elegant Latin. The manuscript is now in the University Library at Copenhagen, and from this it appears that Wilhelm did indeed come to England with his father's blessing and under the Ambassador's protection in the summer of 1652. He saw all the proper sights in London and Oxford; yet there is no mention of his having delivered Bartholin's pamphlet and message to Harvey, who was, perhaps, too unwell at the time to receive him. The elder Worm, like all other Danish medical men, was greatly interested in Harvey's theories and would have been eager to make personal contact with him through his son.

Nearly two years later, on 1 February 1654/5, Harvey was answering yet another letter on the same subject received from Johann Daniel Horst (1616–85), Professor at Giessen and court physician at Hesse-Darmstadt. He seems to have had relations at some earlier time with Harvey, who expressed his pleasure at being still remembered. He wished

that it might be given to me to satisfy your request in the way that you would like. But in fact my age denies me that pleasure, partly because I have not many more years to go, partly because I am often unduly distressed by recurrence of ill health. With regard to Riolan's opinion and his view about the circulation of the blood, he has very obviously achieved mighty trifles by great effort and I cannot see that his fictions have brought pleasure to anyone. Schlegel wrote more carefully and modestly and, had the fates permitted, would doubtless have taken the force out of Riolan's arguments and even out of his taunts. But I learn, and that with sorrow, that he shuffled off this mortal coil of ours a few months since. Moreover, the things you ask me about the lacteal veins and the so-called thoracic ducts demand sharp-sighted eyes and a mind free from other cares in order that you can establish anything definite about those very small vessels; to me, however, as I have said, neither of the prerequisites mentioned is any longer available.

Harvey then repeated briefly his objections to admitting Pecquet's views on the lacteals and thoracic duct as already expressed to Dr. Morison, but did not doubt that truth was buried in the well of Democritus and would one day be discovered. Horst was not, however, going to be easily put off by Harvey's pleading his age and ill health. He wrote another letter saying that he was sure from his own observations of the existence of the lacteal vessels and that they contained chyle from the intestines. Horst concluded his letter by a reference to Nathaniel Highmore, already noticed (p. 342), through whom Harvey, 'the most Observant and Excellent Man, would instruct me (nay, the World) in these matters'. Harvey wearily wrote a second letter on 13 July 1655, still protesting that his age and illness had destroyed any wish to 'explore new subtleties, and after long labours my mind is too fond of peace and quiet for me to let myself become too deeply involved in an arduous discussion of recent discoveries. So I am far from setting myself up as a suitable mediator in this dispute.' Highmore, he said, was not living near him and he had not seen him for over seven years.[1]

Harvey's last correspondent was Dr. Jon Vlackfeld of Haarlem, concerning whom little is known. Vlackfeld had written asking for an opinion about an obscure condition in a patient with incontinence, and finally suppresion, of urine. He reported that 'I found the bladder after death so contracted that the whole was not larger than a walnut not yet husked, while the membranaceous part was thicker than the little finger; meanwhile the inner coat had been eaten away by the sharpness of the viscid matter'.[2]

Harvey's reply, written within seven weeks of his, death, is worth reading in full as evidence of his patience, courtesy, and mental acuity even when his waning physical powers were about to be finally extinguished.

---

[1] Harvey's letters and part of Horst's reply are found in Horst's book on the lacteals and lymphatics: *Observationum anatomicarum decas. Additæ sunt epistolæ*, Frankfort, 1656, pp. 61–67.

[2] Extracts from Vlackfeld's letter together with Harvey's reply are given by Akenside in the *Opera omnia*, 1766, p. 634, but there is no indication of the source. The translation of Vlackfeld's report is by W. R. LeFanu.

Learned Sir,

There has come to me your very pleasant letter, in which you show both extreme goodwill towards myself and also exceptional industry in the cultivation of our art.

It is indeed so. Nature is nowhere wont to reveal her innermost secrets more openly than where she shows faint traces of herself away from the beaten track. Nor is there any surer route to the proper practice of medicine than if someone gives his mind over to discerning the customary law of Nature through the careful investigation of diseases that are of rare occurrence. Indeed, in practically all things it is apparently arranged that we scarcely perceive what is useful or most serviceable in them unless some are lacking in these features or have a faulty disposition. The case of the plasterer you mention is certainly an unique instance, in the elucidation of which it is possible for much discussion to arise. But it is useless for you to spur me on and for me to gird myself for some new research when I am not only ripe in years but also—let me admit—a little weary. It seems to me, indeed, that I am entitled to ask for an honourable discharge. On the other hand, it will always be a pleasure to me to see distinguished gentlemen such as yourself engaged in such worthy contest. Farewell, elegant Sir, and whatever you do, continue to hold in affection

Yours respectfully,
William Harvey

London, 24 April 1657

The truth of Harvey's shrewd remark about the importance of rare conditions in the elucidation of medical problems has often been proved by the later history of medical research. Harvey was speaking from personal experience, and had surely earned his 'honourable discharge'.

His references in the earlier letters to his ill health followed by young Worm's failure to deliver his message to Harvey in 1652 suggest that he was indeed in great misery about this time. There is, perhaps, evidence of it in part of the tradition of his having at the end taken his own life with an overdose of laudanum, as will be related in due course (see p. 410). This tradition usually refers only to his last hours, but one source of the story maintains that he had made a previous attempt to end his life when he was 'about 72', that is, about the year 1650, though it seems more likely to have been a year or two later.[1] The story is preserved in the diary of Viscount Perceval, afterwards first Earl of Egmont (1683–1748), and is related under the date 20 June 1740:

My wife's fever abated so much that she began to take the bark, but she had much of the colic. Her physician, Dr. Wilmot, in discoursing of

[1] There was a story current in 1651 that Harvey had somehow voided a stone. See p. 394.

many things, told me an anecdote of the famous Dr. Harvey, the discoverer of the circulation of the blood, namely that he voluntarily killed himself with laudanum, being one of those whom, if he were now living, we should call a free thinker, and who believed it lawful to put an end to his life when tired of it. The first attempt he made to do it was unsuccessful, as Dr. Scarborow, his intimate friend, related it, who agreed in opinion with the other that suicide was lawful. One day, Harvey being in great pain (he was then about 72 years old) sent for Scarborow, and acquainting him with his intention to die by laudanum that night, desired he would come next morning to take care of his papers and affairs. Scarborow, who had long before promised him that friendly office when occasion called on him, did accordingly come next morning, but was surprised to find Harvey alive and well; it seems the laudanum he had taken, instead of killing him, had brought away a considerable number of stones, which effect caused a suspension of his design to destroy himself for some years.[1]

The 'Dr. Wilmot' of this story is to be identified with Dr. Edward Wilmot (1693–1786), admitted a Fellow of the College of Physicians in 1726, appointed a royal physician in 1736, and created baronet in 1759. He delivered the Harveian Oration in 1735 and had married Sarah, the eldest daughter of Dr. Richard Mead,[2] a younger contemporary of Sir Charles Scarburgh, whom he certainly knew well. Moreover, Perceval was himself descended from Daniel Harvey through Sir Edward Dering, Daniel's son-in-law. The story cannot, therefore, be lightly set aside, though it is not corroborated from any other source.

40

LIFE WITH HIS BROTHERS, 1650–1657 * THE CASE OF SIR JOHN BRAMSTON * GIDEON HARVEY

THE foregoing discussion of Harvey's *De generatione* and of his foreign correspondents has made a long interruption in the narrative of his life after the surrender of Oxford. He had joined the King at Newcastle in

---

[1] *Historical Manuscripts Commission, MSS. of the Earl of Egmont*, vol. iii, 1739–49, Stationery Office, 1923, p. 148.

[2] A portrait of Harvey from Dr. Mead's collection was deposited at St. Bartholomew's Hospital on permanent loan by the late Sir Arthur Wilmot, Bt., in 1937. See my *Portraiture of Harvey*, 1949, p. 33.

November, but returned to the south by January 1646/7 to live in retirement at the homes of his brothers, Daniel and Eliab. Daniel had a house
a few miles from London at Croydon in Surrey. Eliab's main seats were
at Roehampton near London and Rolls Park at Chigwell, fifteen miles
to the east in Essex; he did not acquire Cockaine House in Broad Street,
London, until 1654. His property at Hempstead in Essex will be described later; it seems to be improbable that William ever went there. Mrs.
Harvey was alive in 1645; this must be so, since John Harvey by his Will,
made and witnessed in June, left her the sum of £100. How long thereafter she may have lived with her husband we do not know, but the
presumption is that she did not long survive; we hear no word about her
from Aubrey, who says that he first came to know Harvey in 1651.

Although Harvey was living in London or its neighbourhood, he was
taking little part in the affairs of the College of Physicians. It is clear from
later events that the College was still one of his greatest interests, but he
no longer attended Comitia and is hardly mentioned in the Annals
during the years 1645 to 1649. This may have been connected with the
fact that Dr. John Clarke, President through these years, was not a man
that Harvey cared to meet. As we have seen, Clarke had obtained the
reversion of the office of Physician to St. Bartholomew's Hospital in
1634, though he did not officially occupy the post until 1643. In that
year Harvey had been evicted by Parliament as a follower of the party
in arms against the State, and Clarke had at length succeeded him by
favour of those in power—an allegiance such as would not commend him
to Harvey's friendship. In 1650 Dr. Francis Prujean was elected President
of the College, holding office for five years, and it is noticeable that after
that date Harvey's name begins again to occur in the Annals. John
Clarke held no further post in the College after 1649 and died in 1653,
being succeeded at St. Bartholomew's by Dr. John Micklethwaite, who
had married Clarke's eldest daughter and had been nominated by Parliament to have the reversion of Harvey's place at the Hospital. He thus
became assistant physician to Clarke and full physician at his death in
1653.

Aubrey stated that he became acquainted with Harvey in 1651 through
his being 'my she cozen Montague's physitian and friend'. Harvey was,
therefore, still in practice, though probably seeing only a limited number
of patients. Aubrey, in spite of his great regard for him remarked that:
'All his Profession would allowe him to be an excellent Anatomist, but I
never heard of any that admired his therapeutique way. I know several
practisers in the Towne that would not have given 3*d.* for one of his

Bills; and that a man could hardly tell by one of his Bills what he did aime at. He did not care for Chymistrey, and was wont to speake against them with an undervalue.' Aubrey added afterwards that 'his practise was not very great towards his later end; he declined it unlesse to a special friend'. Nevertheless it is plain that Harvey still practised his profession with all the dignity due to his eminence. According to Aubrey 'he rode on horseback with a Foot-cloath to visitt his patients, his man following on foote, as the fashion then was, which was very decent, now quite discontinued'. Judges also rode with foot-cloths and they were always used in ceremonial processions, such as the coronation of a sovereign. The cloth was a broad piece of richly embroidered material laid over the horse's back under the saddle and reaching almost to the ground on either side. Besides giving an air of distinction to the rider, the cloth would protect his legs and feet from the splashing of water and mud from the road. Aubrey stated that he had seen Harvey ride in 1654 or 1655.

On 26 February 1649/50 Parliament had passed an 'Act for Removing all Papists, and all Officers and Soldiers of Fortune, and divers other Delinquents from London and Westminster, and confining them within five miles of their dwellings'.[1] The Parliamentary party had been alarmed by receiving 'certain Information of many Designs now in hand, endeavored to be carried on by Correspondencies with the Son to the late Tyrant, his Agents and Complices, and by the Conspiracies of old and new Malignants'[2]—in other words, the Prince of Wales was thought to be hatching plots with Scottish sympathizers, and so Harvey, already judged to be a 'delinquent', was (at any rate in theory) banished as from 20 March to a distance of not less than twenty miles from London under pain of imprisonment. The Act was to remain in force until 20 March 1650/1. Such 'delinquents' as had been pardoned before 20 March 1649/50 and had 'taken the Engagement to be true and faithful to the Commonwealth of England'[3] could stay in their homes, but it seems that Harvey was not one of these. In certain circumstances, however, a licence to move for a specified time, signed by four Justices of the Peace, could be obtained, and Harvey took advantage of this clause in April 1650.

In December 1637 Harvey had certified that his patient Sir Thomas Thynne was unfit to travel into the country for the winter months. Sir Thomas's widow, the dowager Lady Thynne, was now in need of Harvey's advice and he succeeded in obtaining a licence to visit her in London. The parliamentary Council received on 23 April 1650 a request 'That Doctor Harvey be permitted to move to this Towne to administer

---

[1] *An Act*, etc., London, 1649, p. 713.   [2] Ibid., p. 714.   [3] Ibid., p. 722.

Physick unto the Lady Thynne, she engaging her selfe, that he shall not doe any thing prejudiciall to the Commonwealth, who is to stay here to that purpose for the space of fourteene dayes in case the Lady shall live soe long'.[1]

Two days later the permit was issued:

Whereas there hath beene a desire made to this Councell on the behalfe of the Lady Dowager Thynne, who is at present in a dangerous sicknesse, that leave might be granted to Doctor Harvey (who she hath formerly made use of as her Physitian in the like case with very good successe) to come to this Towne to receive his advice & counsell as to her present disease. These are therefore to will & require you upon sight hereof to permit & suffer the said Doctor Harvey to come to this Towne, & there to stay for the space of 14 days to come from the date hereof in case the said Lady Thynne shall live soe long. Of this you are not to fayle &c.

Given &c. 25 April 1650.

To all whomsoever this may concerne.[2]

Lady Thynne's illness was not immediately fatal and she lingered on, so that on 6 May a request was received that Harvey should be allowed to stay in London for a month longer, if his patient should live so long.[3] Harvey was in London, therefore, from 25 April until about 7 June attending the old lady's death-bed. This is the only positive knowledge we have of Harvey's movements in this year. Aubrey stated that 'about 1649 he travelled again into Italy, Dr. George (now Sir George) Ent then accompanying him'. Nothing whatever is known about any such journey, and this is odd if Aubrey's statement is true. It can be tested, though not quite conclusively, by reference to the Annals of the College of Physicians, where Ent's attendances at Comitia are all recorded. He was not, in fact, absent for any length of time during the period from March 1648 to September 1650. Then, after 30 September, he did not appear again until 23 December, so that a journey to Italy and back could have been undertaken during this period of almost three months. If these two distinguished doctors did really travel together to Italy in 1650 they would surely have left some traces of their presence at various centres of learning on their tour, but hitherto none has been discovered.

According to Aubrey, Harvey left Oxford after the surrender in 1646 and went to live with his brother Eliab at his house on St. Lawrence Pountney Hill in the City of London, or at his country house at

---

[1] Public Record Office, *Domestic State Papers, 1650*, i. 64, f. 237.   [2] Ibid., f. 262.
[3] Ibid., f. 310.

Roehampton. Aubrey also refers to Harvey's having had a house at Coombe in Surrey. As will be seen, Harvey did not himself possess a house at Coombe, but the rest of Aubrey's statements are likely to be true.

Harvey's brothers, Daniel (born 1587) and Eliab (born 1590), were both, at the time of the Civil War, wealthy men with royalist sympathies. In November 1643 they were assessed by the usurping government for forced loans of £5,000 and £2,500 respectively. Daniel refused to pay. In April 1644 his estate was seized and he was imprisoned in Lambeth House until November, when part of the money was paid. By the following February he had discharged the whole of his obligation, and he was free to resume occupation of his estate at Coombe on the southern border of the parish of Croydon, a few miles south of London. He had bought the Coombe estate in October 1641 for £1,200 from his brother-in-law, George Mellish, a London merchant-tailor, he and Mellish having each married a daughter of Henry Kynnersley. Daniel had had connexions with Croydon for many years, the births and deaths of members of his family being registered in the parish.[1] It is certain that he was living, when not at the business house in London, near or in the Coombe estate, where he may have been a tenant. The proof of this is to be found in Lord Clarendon's autobiography, where, under the date 1635, he related that

There was a merchant of the greatest reputation (Daniel Harvey) who, having a country house within the distance of a few miles from Croydon, and understanding the whole business of trade more exactly than most men, was always very welcome to the Archbishop [Laud], who used to ask him many questions upon such matters as he desired to be informed in, and received much satisfaction from him. Upon such an accidental discourse between them what encouragement merchants ought to receive, who brought a great trade into the Kingdom, and paid thereupon great sums of money to the King, Mr. Harvey mentioned the discouragements they had received in the late times by the rigour of the earl of Portland in matters that related nothing to the King's service, but to the profit of private men.[2]

The merchants had reorganized trade so well that substantial duties were paid to the King, but Portland had upset their arrangements by insisting that their goods should be unloaded at the customs-house quay,

---

[1] *Minute Book of Homage Jury, Manor of Croydon, 1582–1722*, p. 254. See Clarence G. Paget, *Croydon Homes of the Past*, Croydon, 1937, p. 70. Paget supplied copies of the original documents concerning Daniel's purchases to the Royal College of Physicians in 1929.

[2] Edward, Earl of Clarendon, *The Life Written by Himself*, new edition, Oxford, 3 vols., 1827, i, pp. 24–30.

pretending that the King would otherwise be defrauded of his dues. Portland was unmoved by their protests, and they regarded his action 'as an ill reward for the service they had done, and a great discouragement to trade'. Laud was much troubled by this information, and next time he was at Croydon sent again for Daniel Harvey and said he wondered the merchants had not petitioned the King. Harvey replied that they had, and believed that the matter was in the hands of Mr. Hyde, a young lawyer of the Middle Temple, who had lately married the daughter of Sir Thomas Aylesbury. Laud thereupon sent for Hyde to find out about the merchants' grievance, and so Harvey was instrumental in introducing the future Lord Clarendon to the Archbishop, this being the start of his distinguished career.

Presumably owing to Daniel Harvey's connexions with Croydon, his younger brother, Matthew (born 1593), also settled there, buying land in the Coombe area in October 1640, before Daniel had actually bought the estate. Matthew, however, did not enjoy it for long, dying at the age of 49 in December 1642. He was buried at Croydon and left his property to his nephew, the younger Daniel, then a boy of 11.

The elder Daniel Harvey did not long survive his persecution, dying on 10 September 1647.[1] He was buried at the church of St. Lawrence Pountney in London. His son Daniel at the age of 16 succeeded to the Croydon estate, with other lands in Kent, Suffolk, Rutland, and Leicestershire. The elder Daniel left £1,000 to his brother William, £10 to the Vicar of Croydon, and £30 to the poor of the parish, with many other bequests to his daughters and poorer relations.

As already mentioned, Aubrey wrote that William Harvey 'had a house heretofore at Coombe in Surrey, a good aire and prospects, where he had caves made in the Earth, in which in summer he delighted to meditate'. There is no other evidence, however, that Harvey ever owned a house at Coombe, though he certainly kept some of his possessions in his brother's, or his nephew's, house, his Will containing a reference to 'all that Linnen houshold stuffe and furniture which I have at Coombe near Croydon'. The house has been identified by the late Clarence G. Paget as the present Coombe Lodge, situated on Coombe Road to the south of Croydon. The late Dr. Mervyn Gordon, of St. Bartholomew's Hospital, attempted in 1929 to find the caves mentioned by Aubrey.[2]

---

[1] Both D'Arcy Power and Herringham give the date of Daniel's death as 1649, but this is wrong, as is shown by the Minute Book of the Manor of Croydon. See Paget, loc. cit., p. 272.

[2] Personal communication, and recorded by Dr. Gordon in a document inserted in a copy of Paget's book now in the College Library at St. Bartholomew's Hospital.

With the help of the late Lord Horder he seached the gardens at Coombe Lodge, but failed to find any trace of the caves. He thought, however, that they might still be there, perhaps in the chalk of the rising ground nearby.

The Act for clearing all 'delinquents' out of London in 1650 laid down that they should not live anywhere within twenty miles of the City. The Harvey house near Croydon was less than ten miles from the City. Eliab's estate, Rolls Park at Chigwell in Essex, was not much more; his other house at Roehampton was much nearer. Of the available Harvey houses only Winslow, or Winchlowe, House at Hempstead, acquired by Eliab Harvey before 1647, was outside the limit set by the Act, and it is possible that William Harvey went there for a time. On the other hand, so obviously harmless a 'delinquent' as the elderly Doctor Harvey might perhaps have been allowed to live within the twenty miles, at Coombe, for instance, though not permitted to enter London without a pass. It seems likely, therefore, that in April 1650 he might have been seen riding into London from Croydon with his foot-cloth and attendant servant to visit his old patient, Lady Thynne, living during his stay in the business house on St. Lawrence Pountney Hill.

We do not know how Harvey divided his time after 1650 between young Daniel's house at Coombe, Eliab's at Roehampton, and the London houses, first at St. Lawrence Pountney and later at Cockaine House in Broad Street. Aubrey refers in his loose way to Harvey's being at Coombe, at Roehampton, and at Cockaine House, after 1654, where he 'was wont to contemplate on the Leads of the house & had his severall stations, in regard of the Sun or wind'. In his Will Harvey left a legacy of £10 'among the servants of my brother Eliab which shall be dwelling with him at the time of my decease', implying thereby a more or less permanent residence with Eliab at Roehampton or Cockaine House, and it is believed that he died at one or other of these places, but details are lacking. The exact situation of Eliab's house at Roehampton has been satisfactorily established by the researches of Dr. J. Tudor Lewis. It was to the west side of Roehampton Lane on the site now occupied by the Convent of the Sacred Heart, and stood there until 1796, when it was destroyed by fire.[1]

It is clear from the evidence that, except for the episode of Lady Thynne's illness, Harvey was not to be seen in London during 1650. We know that he did not attend at the College of Physicians although Dr. Clarke was no longer President. Harvey had written to the College

---

[1] J. Tudor Lewis, 'Harvey: The scene of his Last Years and Hours', *Medical History* (1960), iv. 18–31.

on 31 May 1647 asking for a Letter of Attorney to sue for his stipend as Lumleian Lecturer and this was granted. Otherwise his name does not appear in the Annals until December 1652, when his statue was being placed in the College.

About the year 1651 Sir John Bramston the younger (1611–1700) suffered from a serious illness which led to a consultation with Harvey. Bramston, son of an eminent jurist, was himself a prominent lawyer who took part in public affairs through the reign of Charles I, the Protectorate, and the two succeeding reigns. In his old age he wrote a detailed auto-biography, the account of the earlier years being based on his journal. Throughout his life he was interested in medical matters and recorded particulars of a variety of illnesses that afflicted members of his family and their connexions. He had a wide experience of doctors—indeed, his eldest daughter, Abigail, who died in his house unmarried at the age of 57 in 1694, during her last illness consulted eleven physicians, including Lower, Millington, Scarburgh, Wetherley, Radcliffe, and Lister, and a number of apothecaries. She obtained as many opinions as there were doctors and her father remarked of this: 'All in vaine; for at best they doe but guess, and I am perswaded most of them dissemble their opinions, and comply with the patient's desires, and their owne profit.' Nevertheless in his own illnesses he did not neglect medical advice and was seen by many physicians. He related that in the year 1637, a twelve-month after his marriage:

On a morning when I rose out of my bed, I felt a paine in one of my ancles, and told my wife I had sprained my foote the day before, and felt it not. I had been that day a birding with the sparhawke and stonebow[1] (a sport I much delight in), and caught cold. I dressed me and went out to the parlor, and some gentlemen comeing that day to dine with my father, Mr. Pinchon and Mr. Bernard, I waited on them and we dranck a botle or two of wine. That night the paine removed into my other ancle, and so into my knee, and rested in the hollow of my hamm with great paine. Whereupon Mr. Vuies, a physician, a Dutchman dwellinge at Chelmesford, was sent for; who, comeinge immediately, let me blood and soon after purged me and swet me. But my paines continuinge, and removinge from joint to joint, my father would have a phisitian sent for from London; and Dr. Spicer came, and brought with him an apothe-carie. He blooded me, purged me, and swet me, and stayed four or five days here, and then left me weake and in paine still. But, by God's mercie, after a month or six weekes I was rid of my paines and I came abroad againe.

---

[1] A kind of cross-bow for shooting with stones.

About fifteen years later, that is in 1651, Bramston suffered from a severe recurrence of his symptoms. He was riding from his home in Essex to London, and:

When I alighted from my horse I found a great paine in my hip on the right side, but I tooke litle notice of it to any bodie. Next day both my ancles were sore, and before night both my knees. Then I began to feare my old disease was come againe. And so it did, and rann over every joint of my bodie, even my neck; but I thanck God it neither tooke my head nor my stomack. But, whatsoever the doctors could doe, which were Dr. Leonard and Dr. Prujean, I was confined to my bed, and eate no manner of thinge but water gruel; and tho' purged and blooded and sweated oftentimes, I could stir neither hand nor foote, but was fed by my daughter Abigaile (whom therefore I stiled my nurse) from that time untill March followinge was ended; and for the most part of that time was raised by fower men untill my bed was new made, and so layd down againe. My joints were so benumbed and enfeebled that I could not for a longe time after goe without leadinge, nor could I open or shutt one hand without the help of the other. So that many thought I should be a criple duringe the remainder of my life. And therefore some advised that I should goe to the Bath; and amongst others Mr. William Painter was exceedinge earnest for it, sayinge he had knowne some had receaved the use of theire limbs on the like case. But Dr. Leonard was absolutely against it, and sayd it might petrifie the humor and make me lame all my dayes, but good it could not doe. My father continued doubtfull. I went to Dr. Harvy, then newly come from Oxford, and askt his opinion. He told me the Bath was a fine place, and there was good companie there. I replied, I knew the humor of the Bath and the companie; but my question was, whether the Bath would recover me my limbs againe. He sayd he could not say it would, but it might possiblie harden the humor in my joints, and lame me. But, sayd he, if you would be rid of the gout, you must neither drinck wine nor any stronge drinck; you must eate but once a day, and that very sparingly too. And so I left him and went to Sir William Palmer and Mr. Coppin, with my brother Robert Abdy, unto the Fleece in Cornewell [Cornhill]; who inquiring what Dr. Harvey sayd, I told them. And Mr. Coppin replyed, Dr. Harvey hath starved himselfe these twentie years, neither eating nor drinkinge, but as he hath directed you and yet he hath the gout. To which I returned, If to fast and have gout be all one with eat and have the gout, I will doe as I have done. And from that time to this present I have never had any touch of it untill this Christmas, that I was put in feare of it, as I have sayd. For which I hartily thanck my mercifull God.[1]

[1] *The Autobiography of Sir John Bramston*, K.B., London, Printed for the Camden Society, 1845, pp. 384–5.

It may well be doubted whether Harvey's diagnosis of gout was correct; the history and symptoms seem rather to suggest that the patient had attacks of acute rheumatism, but arthritic complaints are, and no doubt were, notoriously difficult to diagnose with accuracy.

Aubrey's belittlement of Harvey's competence as a doctor may have originated in his habit of listening too much to gossip at drinking parties, where it would have been more fun to retail examples of failure on the part of famous men than to add to their reputations by telling of their successes. A few professional men can always be found who even enjoy taking down what they believe to be the exaggerated reputations of better-known members of their own profession. William Harvey had a detractor of this kind in his namesake, Gideon Harvey, who thought the sport worth while even thirty years after William's death.

Gideon Harvey was born in Holland some time between 1630 and 1640. Having matriculated at Oxford in 1655, he studied medicine first in Leyden and then in Paris, and is said to have taken the degree of M.D. at a small French university. He then returned to Holland, becoming a Fellow of the College of Physicians at The Hague. At various times he had also had instruction in chemistry, surgery, and pharmacy, so that he was well qualified for a medical career in London, where he arrived before the Restoration, but probably too late to have been acquainted with William Harvey. He became physician to King Charles II about 1675, though he was never a Fellow of the London College. He was a copious writer on medical subjects and in his first book, *Archelogia philosophica nova* (London, 1663), even aspired to being known as a philosopher, but he afterwards degenerated into a scurrilous, if amusing, author of attacks on individuals and institutions such as the College of Physicians. In his best-known work, *The Art of Curing Diseases by Expectation*, published in 1689, he introduced a gratuitous attack on William Harvey, whose reputation evidently aroused his jealousy. He had treasured in his memory stories to Harvey's discredit, which do not read like inventions, though they can only have been based on hearsay.

Gideon was not without talent, and, though his wit was rough, he showed a wholesome scepticism concerning the efficacy of conventional drugs and the value of frequent blood-letting, with an appreciation of current fallacies in association of cause and effect. The Art of Expectation, however, consisted in doing nothing, and he derided this also. 'These Expectation Doctors', he truly said, 'are the Safe men, the good Children's Doctors, much in request among some wise Women. They are such, as in difficult Diseases kill by omission, and cure easie Distempers by seeming to do something of no importance.' The greater part of the book is an amusing diatribe against the medical profession in general and the College of Physicians in particular. Naturally William Harvey did not escape, Gideon calling him 'the greatest Anatomist of his time and no extraordinary physician'. He then related (p. 179) that Harvey's 'erroneous Judgment was very remarkable in the prescription of a Purge for Esq; Rainton of Enfield, where the Apothecary refraining to prepare more than half the proportion, notwithstanding gave him fourscore stools, which otherwise according to the Doctor's measures, must unavoidably have scower'd him from the close Stool into the other World'. It is safe to assume that the mistake in this instance was not Harvey's, but the apothecary's, who may have had difficulty in reading the prescription. On another occasion,

The Consult made a great noise, when Dr. Wright, Prudgean, Bates, and others, together with the famed Dr. Harvey were Principles; and one Mr. Farwel, Barrister of the Temple, was Patient and Complainent of a painful Disease in his Belly, that deprived him of the use of his Limbs, Strength, Appetite, and Digestion, &c., the forementioned Dr. Harvey ingrossed to himself the speaking part, by reason of his extraordinary claim to Anatomy, and which here, if anywhere, seemed to be of use; after a long contrectation of all the abdomen, did very magisterially and positively assert all his Symptoms to arise from an Aneurism of an Artery, and therefore incurable, as being too remote to come at, wherein all, except Dr. Bates, very readily concur'd, though it was a most absurd offer in Opinion, as ever I yet heard. The Patient being unwilling to give up his cause so, removed his *Corpus cum causa* to Chelsie, where Sir Theodore Majerne lay Bed-ridden at his Country-house, who upon no long *examen* of the matter told him, he was the second or third Patient he had met with diseased in the same kind, and very boldly expressed, he would cure him, but with this inconvenience, that he could throw the cause of the Disease either into his Arms or Legs, according to the choice he would make of those Limbs, which he could best spare, or which of 'em might be more or less useful to him, without consulting the Will and Pleasure of God Almighty, an Arrogancy unheard of, and favouring more of the Atheist (as too many of 'em are) than a pious Physician, as then especially he ought to have been, being not many stages from his Journey's end. (Mayerne died in 1655.)

The patient's occupation being sedentary, he decided he could best spare the use of his legs, but luckily for him the tumour proved to be solid and due to enlarged mesenteric glands, which presently resolved with disappearance of all the symptoms. Harvey had been deceived, as so many others have been since his time, by transmitted pulsation from the aorta, or, as Gideon called it, 'a Vibration'.

A third patient was a tailor of Fleet Street, complaining of sciatica. Harvey, Gideon said, engaged to cure him if he would 'sequester himself from his Trade for three Months', would pay £50, and would submit to having his leg 'laid open to the bone by cutting or burning'. The patient objected to the third condition, and went off to another physician 'of a much lower form, who advised him to the Bath, where he received a perfect cure in six weeks'. Evidently the cure of a prolapsed intervertebral disc by the Art of Expectation is not so modern as we have thought. On this occasion Gideon Harvey observed that:

No doubt but Dr. Harvey in Anatomy, and happiness of theoretic discoveries might justly pretend the precedency of all his Contemporaries; and others before and since have also arrived to a great proficiency in Cat and Dog cutting, also Calf-head and Sheeps-pluck dissecting; yet few of 'em when concerned in Practice, were gifted with sagacity to know Diseases when offer'd to their view, much less capable of curing them; in which curative particular the Thinking Physician has the advantage, though the Prating Physician by his pretended Anatomy ingrosses the opinion of Mankind.

41

HARVEY'S FRIENDS—AUBREY, SELDEN, HOBBES, BOYLE * THE CASE OF LADY ANNE CONWAY

JOHN AUBREY occupies so important a place in any biographical account of Harvey that it is worth while to examine briefly his antecedents and character, and, most important of all, his credibility.[1] He was born in 1626 at the hamlet of Easton Pierse in Wiltshire. His father came of a good Herefordshire family—'longævous healthy kindred' Aubrey calls them, though he himself was a sickly child. It is characteristic of his biographical method that he was able to recall all his childish ailments.

I think I have heard my mother say I had an Ague shortly after I was

---

[1] The best account of Aubrey's life is to be found in *Aubrey's Brief Lives*, edited with an introduction by Oliver Lawson Dick, London 1949, and in Anthony Powells' *John Aubrey and his Friends*, London, 1948.

born. About 3 or 4 years old I had a grievous ague. I can remember it. I gott not strength till I was 11 or 12 years old, but had sicknesse of vomiting (the Belly-ache: pain in the side) for 12 hours every fortnight, then about monthely, then quarterly, and at last once in half a year. About 12 it ceased. This sickness nipt my strength in the bud. 1633, 8 yeares old, I had an issue (natural) in the coronal suture of my head, which continued running till 21. 1634, October, I had a violent Fever that was like to carry me off. 'Twas the most dangerous sickness that ever I had. About 1639 (or 1640) I had the Measills, but that was nothing. I was hardly sick.

Later, while at Trinity College, Oxford, he survived an attack of small-pox. Three times in after years he was in danger of being killed by sword-thrust and throughout his life was careless of his health, being fond of good living and especially of drinking with his friends. Nevertheless he lived to the age of 71, being finally struck down by an apoplexy in his favourite city of Oxford in 1697.

From a worldly point of view his three score years and ten had been largely misspent. He had lived the first part of his life too much under his father's domination, and he was still a young man when his life was disrupted by the civil wars. The death of his father in 1652 allowed him to manage, or rather to mismanage, his own affairs, but when he came to think of what he could do he could only answer: 'Truly nothing; only Umbrages. If ever I had been good for anything, 'twould have been a Painter, I could fancy a thing so strongly and had so clear an idea of it.' But to be a painter meant hard work, and that he could not face. So he decided—if indeed he ever decided anything—to be a consistent dilettante. He was attracted by all manner of antiquarian pursuits, he was possessed by an insatiable curiosity, and he was fascinated by the study of his fellow men; and so in 1654, while in Wales, 'he began to enter into pocket memorandum books, philosophical and antiquarian remarques'. It was the filling of pocket memorandum books that was to be his life's work—an insecure basis, it might be thought, for the founding of a reputation as an antiquary and historian, if the memoranda were never to be reduced to order and their contents never made to provide the matter for grave treatises such as he always intended to write. But whenever he set out to write in an orderly way of what he knew, his mind would run so fast ahead of his pen and be so easily distracted into following side-issues and irrelevancies that the thread was lost and resolution broke down. Consequently his literary output in print was small, but his disorderly manuscripts were legion. In his own words, he 'wanted patience to go through Knotty Studies', though his industry in recording facts and anecdotes was very great.

Aubrey must have been at once charming and exasperating, as was certainly found by Anthony Wood, the Oxford historian, with whom Aubrey worked for the *Athenæ Oxonienses*, first published in 1691. For our present taste in biography Aubrey provides acceptable fare; his style is informal, his language racy, and he had an unerring instinct for the telling detail. Another virtue was his complete lack of self-consciousness or prudery. 'I here lay down to you', he wrote to Anthony Wood, 'the Trueth, and as neer as I can and that religiously as a Poenitent to his Confessor, nothing but the truth: the naked plaine trueth, which is here exposed so bare that the very pudenda are not covered, and affords many passages that would raise a Blush in a young Virgin's cheeke. So that after your perusall, I must desire you to make a Castration and to sowe-on some Figge-leaves—i.e. to be my Index Expurgatorius.'

Attention is drawn to this aspect of Aubrey's work because he has so often been charged with being a false witness. His most illuminating editor, Oliver Lawson Dick (1949), after emphasizing the importance of Aubrey's *Lives*, complains that Victorian biographers 'made vigorous use of them, usually disparaging Aubrey as they pilfered his work. And research', he adds, 'since their day has often proved Aubrey, and not his critics, to have been in the right.' This estimate of Aubrey follows a claim that the *Brief Lives* are 'of importance if only for the information they give concerning Shakespeare, Milton, Hobbes, and Harvey'. This will give some indication of what Aubrey is worth as a witness. He was curious, credulous, and unmethodical. It is admitted that he was often inaccurate, but he was never untruthful, a distinction of great importance in estimating the value of reportage such as he provides.

When Aubrey met Harvey in 1651 he found him 'very communicative, and willing to instruct any that were modest and respectfull to him'. Aubrey was intending to go to Italy, and Harvey told him 'what to see, what companye to keepe, what Bookes to read, how to manage my Studies. In short he bid me goe to the Fountain Head, and read Aristotle, Cicero, Avicenna.' He then condemned the moderns, or 'Neoteriques', with a very rude word which needs to be concealed beneath a fig-leaf.

Aubrey tells how Harvey made him 'sitt by him 2 or 3 hours together in his meditating apartment discoursing'. Perhaps they sat in darkness, since Harvey had said that 'he did delight to be in the darke, and told me he could then best contemplate'. As we have seen in Aubrey's account of his own childhood, he was greatly interested in all medical matters and this entered into many of the 'strange relations' and anecdotes that he was so fond of recording. A typical example is his story of

A fellow in North-Wales, shrowding of a Tree, fell downe on his head, and his Braine being turned, lay for dead. A Mason being thereby, advised that he should have a good strong coffin made, and his feete to come to the end of it, and his head not to touch the other end by two inches. He layeth the Man in the Coffin on a Table-board, and then with a huge Axe, gave a sound Knock at the feet, to turne by that contrary motion his braine right againe. After the blow was given the fellow gave a groane and spake: and he recovered.

With this kind of discourse he could, no doubt, entertain Harvey by the hour. He was particularly fond of stories of odd births, and among others told of how

Mr. Bonham's wife had two Children at one birth, the first time; and he being troubled at it, travelled; and was absent seven yeares. After his return he got his wife with Child, and she was delivered of seven Children at one Birth.

To this he added:

Dr. Wm. Harvey told me that one Mr. Palmer's Wife in Kent did beare a Child every day for five daies together.

Aubrey capped this with the story of

Mris Hine the Vicar's wife of Kington St. Michael, a very able midwife, who told of a lady who was brought to bed at Dorchester, was delivered first of a Sonne (now living and the Heir) and afterwards for eight days together every day another Child: some whereof had heads and Armes and no lower parts; others had lower, but no upper parts.

This he followed with an anecdote of 'two Children born in the grave'. Harvey was able to counter with the story of

a certain Knight in Kent, who having gott his Wive's Mayd with Child, sent her to London to lie-in under pretence of seeing her friends. She was brought to bed then about Michaelmas; and after some convenient time she returned to her Lady. She found herself not well, and in December following she fell in labour again, and was delivered of another child.

That this story was indeed derived from Harvey is proved by its being found, in different words, in the obstetrical section of *De generatione animalium*, where it is given, more scientifically, as an example of the phenomenon of super-fœtation.[1]

Aubrey also records various remedies which appealed to his fancy, as for example,

To cure the Thrush, Take a living Frog, and hold it in a Cloth that it does not go down into the Child's Mouth; and putt the Head into the Child's Mouth till it is dead, and then take another Frog.

Or again;

To cure the Tooth-ache. Take a new Nail, and make the Gum bleed with it, and then drive it into an Oak. This did Cure William Neal, Sir William Neal's Son, a very stout Gentleman, when he was almost mad with the Pain and had a mind to have Pistoll'd himself.

These remedies make it plain that Aubrey, an inveterate believer in astrology and magic, liked the practice of medicine to border on the supernatural. He preferred to believe that, to cure the toothache, the nail must be driven into an oak rather than to attribute it to having opened an abscess by pricking the gum. This may account for his belittlement of Harvey's practice as a doctor. Even so eminent a contemporary as Dr. Thomas Willis could believe that he cured a haemorrhagic state in a young man by hanging round his neck a little bag, in which was 'a Toad dried in the sun and bruised'.[2] It is not possible to believe that Harvey was deceived by absurdities such as this, though they contented other doctors of his time. His mind was of a different cast, instinctively evincing a *Scepsis Scientifica* in practice. He remained faithful to the conventional pharmacopœia because he had no alternative, but rejected what was irrational. It was this sceptical attitude that made Aubrey think him a bad doctor, and no doubt he found others to agree with him. It is really a tribute to Harvey's honesty in the face of a therapeutic poverty due to no fault of his own.

If further refutation of Aubrey's opinion were needed it can be sought in the evidence of the trust reposed in him by so many people of eminence and sense. A number of examples of this have already been mentioned in the foregoing pages. Although his practice was restricted after he left Oxford, it still included many well-known people, some of whom were friends as well as patients.

---

[1] *Anatomical Exercitations*, London, 1653, p. 479.
[2] Thomas Willis, *Remaining Medical Works*, London, 1681, 'Of fermentations, &c.', p. 145.

Harvey's relations with John Hacket, Bishop of Coventry and Lichfield at the time of King James's death, have already been related (p. 143). Later in Hacket's life Harvey attended him with characteristic sense and tact, showing how real was his appreciation of the place of psychology in medicine. Hacket's contemporary biographer, Thomas Plume, relates that after the defeat of the royalist party

he returned to his rural retirement, to end his old age in continual prayer and study, omitting all exercise of body, whereupon he fell into a great fit of sickness; and upon his recovery the famous Dr. Harvy enjoined him two things—to renew his cheerful conversation, and take moderate walks for exercise, assuring him that in his practise of physic since these times, he observed more people died of grief of mind than of any other disease, and that his studious and sedentary life would contract him frequent sickness, unless he used seasonable exercise. Whereupon afterwards for his health's sake he would every morning before he settled to his study take large walks very early to make him expectorate phlegm and other cloudy and fuligenous vapours, whereby he afterwards continued vegete and healthful to the last.[1]

Harvey's advice was so effective that after the Restoration Hacket resumed preaching at St. Paul's and the administration of his diocese, and did not die until 1670 at the age of 78.

The life of John Selden covered almost the same span as Harvey's. Selden was the greatest lawyer of the reigns of James and Charles I and was deeply immersed in political affairs. He was a very tall man, according to Aubrey, towering over little Harvey, and the two men must have known each other in earlier life at court, though no record connecting them remains. After 1649 Selden took no further part in public affairs, and died in 1654 three years before Harvey. Throughout his career he had been indifferent to popular applause and never sought favour at court, caring only to achieve what was, in his view, right. In the Dedication to his book, *Titles of Honour*, 1614, he summarized mankind: 'So generous, so ingenuous, so proportioned to good, such fosterers of virtue, so industrious, of such mold are the few; so inhuman, so blind, so dissembling, so vain, so justly nothing but what's ill disposition are the most.' This view accords with Harvey's more terse observation that man is but a great mischievous baboon, and it is clear from Aubrey's remarks that Selden, Hobbes, and Harvey formed a friendly triumvirate during these

[1] T. Plume, *The Life and Death of John Hacket*, edited by M. E. C. Walcott, London, 1865, pp. 169–70. Plume's *Life* was originally prefixed to Hacket's *Century of Sermons*, 1675.

last years. Evidence that Selden was Harvey's friend and patient is found in an anecdote in his *Table-Talk*, collected by his secretary, Richard Milward, and published in 1689. At the end of this story Harvey is again seen as psychiatrist and as enjoying Selden's complete confidence. The story, in the section on Devils, is as follows:

A Person of Quality came to my Chamber in the *Temple*, and told me he had two Devils in his Head (I wondered what he meant) and just at that time, one of them bid him kill me; (with that I begun to be afraid, and thought he was mad) he said he knew I could cure him; and therefore entreated me to give him something; for he was resolved he would go to nobody else. I perceiving what an opinion he had of me, and that 'twas only Melancholly that troubl'd him, took him in hand, warranted him, if he would follow my Directions, to cure him in a short time. I desired him to let me be alone about an Hour, and then to come again, which he was very willing to. In the mean time I got a Card, and lap'd it up handsome in a Piece of *Taffata*, and put Strings to the *Taffata*, and when he came gave it to him to hang about his Neck, withal charged him, that he should disorder himself neither with Eating or Drinking, but eat very little of Supper, and say his Prayers duly when he went to Bed, and I made no Question but he would be well in three or four Days. Within that time I went to Dinner to his House, and ask'd him how he did? He said he was much better, but not perfectly well, or in truth he had not dealt clearly with me. He had four Devils in his Head, and he perceiv'd two of them were gone with that which I had given him, but the other two troubled him still. Well, said I, I am glad two of them are gone, I make no doubt but to get away the other two likewise; so I gave him another thing to hang about his Neck. Three Days after he came to me to my Chamber and profest he was now as well as ever he was in his Life, and did extreamly thank me for the great Care I had taken of him. I fearing lest he might relapse into the like Distemper, told him that there was none but my self and one Physician more in the whole Town that could cure the Devils in the Head, and that was Dr. *Harvey* (whom I had prepar'd) and wish'd him if ever he found himself ill in my Absence to go to him, for he could cure his Disease as well as my self. The Gentleman lived many Years and was never troubled after.[1]

The third member of the triumvirate, Thomas Hobbes, ten years younger than Harvey, is shown to have been his close friend in his last years by the clause in the codicil to his Will: 'Item to my good friend Mr. Tho Hobbs to buy something to keepe in remembrance of me tenne pounds', and by Aubrey's statement that: 'In his Will he left his

[1] Selden, *Table-Talk*, second edition, 1696, pp. 49–51.

old friend Mr. Th. Hobbes 10 *li* as a token of his love.' The bequest was also mentioned to Aubrey by Eliab Harvey at his brother's funeral.[1]

It is quite possible that Hobbes and Harvey had met at some time in the years 1621 to 1626, when, according to Aubrey, Hobbes was working as amanuensis to Sir Francis Bacon. For some years both before and after this Hobbes was moving about Europe while in attendance, as friend and tutor, on members of the Cavendish family, though he would certainly have had opportunities of meeting Harvey during intervals spent in London. It was about 1630, while in Paris, that Hobbes was suddenly converted to an interest in geometry by opening a copy of *Euclid's Elements* at the forty-seventh proposition of the first book and realizing that what he had thought impossible could be proved. At an uncertain date, but probably not long after this, while listening to a discussion among some learned friends, he became greatly interested in the physiology of motion and sensation, and in one of his earliest tracts, *De corpore*, not published until 1655, he wrote a statement of his theory of the senses. The views there expressed are very much in accord with Harvey's as they appear in his notes for the treatise, *De motu locali animalium*, begun in 1627. Later, about 1636, Hobbes, when in Florence, became a friend of the aged Galileo, and in Paris moved in society which brought him into contact with Descartes. All these intellectual interests would inevitably lead him to take notice of Harvey's demonstration of the motion of the blood in a circle—if, indeed, he had not already heard about it from Harvey himself. A passage in one of Hobbes's latest tracts, 'Of the Causes and Effects of Heat and Cold', discussing the source of the heat of man and animals, strongly suggests that he had perhaps been present at some of Harvey's dissections of the King's deer. He remarked of '*compounded Motion* within their bodies' that:

> At the breaking up of a Deer I have seen it plainly in his Bowels as long as they were warm. And it is called the *Peristaltique* Motion, and in the Heart of a Beast newly taken out of his Bŏdy; and this Motion is called *Systole* and *Diastole*. But they are both of them this compounded Motion, whereof the former causeth the food to Winde up and down through the guts, and the later makes the Circulation of the Blood.[2]

Moreover in his Dedication of *De corpore* to his patron, the Earl of Devonshire, he said of Harvey that he had written the true science of the

---

[1] It has been said that Selden also left the same sum to Hobbes, but the clause does not appear in his Will or codicil as printed with his *Life* by David Wilkins (prefixed to the *Works*, 1726).

[2] Hobbes, *Decameron Physiologicum*, London, 1678, p. 61.

human body in his two books of the Motion of the Blood and of the Generation of Animals, and was the only man he knew of who, conquering envy, had established a new doctrine in his lifetime.[1]

It was natural, therefore, that the two philosophers should delight in each other's company in their old age, and it would be surprising if Harvey did not sometimes act as medical adviser to Hobbes during these years. Hobbes was not a wealthy man, but, like Harvey, was generous, particularly to his relatives. He regulated his life with a certain austerity and took regular exercise until advanced in years, just as Hacket had done on Harvey's advice. Though sometimes irascible in argument, he was a pleasant companion, fond of paradox and sallies of audacious wit. His views aroused much opposition, in particular the political ideas expressed in his most famous book, *Leviathan*. Clarendon regarded it as 'pernicious to the Soveraign Power of Kings and destructive to the affection and allegiance of Subjects'.[2] Hobbes, however, was not a party man, his views being founded on a rational conception of human affairs rather than political bias. Harvey's regard for Hobbes may reflect some light on the older man's views on life and science, if not on religion, for he would not have felt so close to Hobbes unless there had been some measure of agreement. As we have had occasion to notice, Harvey was a Royalist by personal devotion rather than political conviction, and his analytical mind would have appreciated Hobbes's philosophical attitude. Hobbes was accused of being the arch-atheist and materialist, but Harvey would be able to discount this exaggerated idea of his friend's views and would enjoy his intellect and wit, stimulated, perhaps, by cups of his favourite beverage brewed from coffee beans.

The reputed atheism of Hobbes may have given rise to Aubrey's story of a curious scene at Selden's death-bed;

When he was neer death, the minister (Mr. Johnson) was comeing to him to assoile him: Mr. Hobbes happened to be there; sayd he, 'What, will you that have wrote like a man, now dye like a woman?' So the minister was not let in.[3]

On the other hand a later manuscript in the Bodleian Library has quite a different version:

---

[1] *Postremo, Scientiam Humani Corporis, Physicæ partem utilissimam, in libris suis de Motu Sanguinis, & de Generatione Animalium, mirabili sagacitate detexit & demonstravit Gulielmus Harveus; solus (quod sciam) qui doctrinam novam superata invidia vivens stabilivit.*

[2] Clarendon, *A Brief View of the Dangerous and pernicious Errors to Church and State in Mr. Hobbes's Book entitled Leviathan*, Oxford, 1676, Dedication.

[3] Aubrey's *Brief Lives*, Oxford, 1898, ii. 221.

Mr. Selden upon his death-bed disclaimed all Hobbisme and the like wicked and Atheistical opinions, commanded that neither Mr. Hobbs nor Capt. Rossingham should be admitted to him, confessed his sins, and desired absolution, which was given him by Archbp. Usher.[1]

Perhaps both accounts are true, the one incident preceding the other. Would that we could have Harvey's considered opinion on this contradiction.

Robert Boyle was another of Harvey's later acquaintances and, by Boyle's own account, one of his patients. Boyle's main scientific interest was chemistry, but his mind had a wide range, and his question to Harvey about how his conception of the circulation of the blood first arose has already been noted (p. 28). There is no indication of the date when this conversation took place. Boyle had been abroad for some years before returning to England in 1644, and he did not settle down to his scientific work in Oxford until 1654; it may, therefore, not have been until Harvey's last years that they met for the first and only time. The occasion was a wish on the part of the rather hypochondriacal Boyle to get Harvey's advice about his eyes. Boyle was writing about the possible saving of human lives by compiling an accurate register of 'Cures of such Persons as have recovered after having been judg'd irrecoverable by the Doctors', adding that 'the Cures that seem performed by Nature her self, need not be left out of such a Collection'. This led on to a reminiscence of 'such an observation I receiv'd from our most experienced *Harvy*, when, having consulted him about my weak Eyes, he told me among other things (as a very remarkable one) that he had once a Patient . . . that had a confirm'd Cataract in his Eye, and yet upon the use of Physick, to which he could not ascribe so wonderful an effect, that Cataract was perfectly dissipated, and the Eye restored to its wonted Function'.

Boyle then related the case of the girl with hysterical symptoms visited by Harvey in St. Thomas's Hospital already noticed above together with that of the malingerer Anne Gunter, referred by King James to Dr. Edward Jorden (p. 211). Jorden had been present when Harvey was admitted as a Fellow of the College in 1607, and attended meetings until December 1611, but soon after this removed to Bath. He had published in 1603 a book on hysteria (so-called from ὑστέρα, the womb), and its numerous manifestations called *A Briefe Discourse on a Disease called the Suffocation of the Mother*, 'mother' being another name for the uterus. Harvey was familiar with these conditions and described in the

[1] Rawlinson MS. B. clviii, f. 75, in W. D. Macray, *Annals of the Bodleian Library*, London, 1868, p. 77 n.

obstetrical part of *De Generatione animalium* two patients suffering for many years from 'Uterine Melancholy' and 'Hysterical symptoms' until they each developed a prolapse of the uterus. Harvey believed that the prolapse would cure their troubles (or persuaded them to believe that it would do so) with happy results. He afterwards replaced the prolapsed organs and both patients remained well.[1]

Harvey also gave vivid descriptions of two examples of the hysterical condition known as 'false conception', or *pseudocyesis*.

I know a young Woman, who was the Daughter of a Physitian, who was of my neer acquaintance, which being Big, felt all the Symptomes incident to Women in that condition; and continuing healthy and sprightly, after the fourteenth week she perceived the motions of a Fœtus in her Womb; and having finished her time for going with Child, conceiving the hour of her delivery to be nigh at hand, she had her Bed furnished, her Cradle ready, and all the implements appertaining to the purpose laid out for use. But all these preparations came to nothing, and *Lucina* was cross to her wishes; for her customary paines quite left her, and her Belly as it rose by degrees, so it sunk againe, and shee remained barren ever after.

I also knew a noble Matron, who had borne above ten Children, and whose *Courses* were never suppressed unless she were with Child. But being afterwards married to another Husband, besides other usual signes, she apprehended her self to be with Child, by the stirring of it (which both she her self, and her Sister also, who then lay with her in bed, did many times in the night perceive) and all the Arguments I could suggest, could not remove that perswasion from her: till at the last, all her hopes vanished into *flatulency* and *fatness*.[2]

The second example even illustrates the rare and curious condition of 'shared delusions', or *folie à deux*.

Further evidence of Harvey's interest in psychological disorders is found in one of the few surviving books from his library. This is a copy of Galen's *Opuscula varia*, 1640, edited by Harvey's friend Theodore Goulston, in which he has annotated the tract on mental disturbances (*De cognoscendis et corrigendis cujusque animi perturbationibus*).

An earlier example of Harvey's interest in neurology, as distinguished from neuroses, is to be found in Sir Kenelm Digby's *Two Treatises of the Nature of Bodies and of Man's Soule*, Paris, 1644 (p. 282), where the name of Descartes is connected with Harvey's in describing an instance of loss of sensation in the skin, now recognizable as *syringomyelia*, a

[1] *Anatomical Exercitations*, 1653, pp. 502–3.   [2] Ibid., pp. 480–1.

condition due to degeneration of certain tracts in the spinal cord. Digby was arguing against Descartes' ideas on the conduction of movement and sensation by the 'sinews', or nerves, and continued as follows:

To this we may answere by producing examples of the contrary in some men, who have had the motion of their limbes intire and no wayes prejudiced, but have had no feeling at all, quite over their whole case of skin and flesh: as particularly a servant in the colledge of Physitians in London, whom the learned Harvey (one of his Masters) hath told me, was exceeding strong to labour, and very able to carry any necessary burthen, and to remove things dexterously, according to the occasion: and yet he was so voyde of feeling that he used to grind his handes against the walles, and against course lumber, when he was employed to rummage any; in so much, that they would runne with bloud, through grating of the skinne, without his feeling of what occasioned it.[1]

Further light on Harvey's practice at this time may be had from his relations with the Finch and Conway families. He was connected with the Finches through the marriage of his niece Elizabeth, daughter of Daniel Harvey, to Heneage Finch, the future Lord Chancellor and Earl of Nottingham. Finch, then practising as a lawyer, consulted his wife's uncle soon after his marriage in 1646, presumably for rheumatic pains, by which he was said to have been much troubled as a young man.[2] The remedies prescribed were of a general nature designed to 'cleer his body' by purges, clysters and bleeding, followed by massage of the body, regular exercise, and temperance in food and drink. The patient copied out Harvey's prescriptions[3] and instructions in his commonplace book, and it may be presumed profited by them, afterwards living a long and strenuous life in the service of his country and becoming father of a numerous family. In 1652 he helped Harvey in drafting his Will, which he witnessed together with his brother, Francis Finch, and Edward Dering, who married his wife's sister, Mary Harvey.

Harvey's further connexion with the Conways arose from the marriage of Heneage Finch's half-sister, Anne, in 1651 to Edward Conway, son of the second Viscount Conway; indeed, Anne was already before her marriage Harvey's patient on account of an inveterate headache, which tormented her until her death in 1679. Her father-in-law in a letter to her

---

[1] This reference was first noticed by J. F. Fulton in *Sir Kenelm Digby*, New York, 1937, p. 62.

[2] This was stated by Thomas Henshaw in a letter to Sir Robert Southwell dated 16 May 1682. See S. Weir Mitchell's *Some Memoranda in regard to William Harvey*, New York, 1907, p. 15.

[3] These will be found printed in full in Appendix II among Harvey's prescriptions.

dated 1 July 1651 from Petworth confirmed Aubrey's statement about Harvey's loss of practice after the publication of his scientific treatises.

Daughter

I am very glad of your health which you have recovered, and although the Toothache be commonly a paine for which every one is a Physitian yet it doth many times grow to that excesse that it will require the advice of a very good Physitian; I heare that you have a great opinion of Doctor Harvey. I thinke you doe well to love and respect a person of his merite for I thinke he hath deserved extreamely well of all learned men, for what he hath found out, or offered to the world to enquire farther into: he is a most exelent Anatomist, and I conceive that to be his Masterpiece, which knowledge is many times of very great use in consultations, but in the practicke of Physicke I conceive him to be to mutch, many times, governed by his Phantasy, the excellency and strength whereof did produce his two workes to the world, and he is not the only man that hath produced workes in that nature, De Cartes and Campanella, but the first espetially have written as theire phantasy did perswade, and done as a man must doe that goes on hunting in a thicke enclosed country, leave his horse behind him and scramble over hedge and ditch and teare his cloaths, so doe they leave the antient rules, and set up new opinions for the maintenance of which, they are forced to great inconveniencies, in their reason, when they are brought to the Practice; to have a Physitian abound in phantasie is a very perilous thing, occations in diseases are very often suddaine, therefore one ought to have a Physitian that should be governed only by his judgment, as one puts the best man to the Helme in a storme least he should mistake for the turning of the Helme either to the right or left hand unduly [and] may sommetimes cast away the Ship. If I had not a great desire to keepe you I would not write anything against Doctor Harvey whitch might in any kind seeme to prejudice him, for I doe greatly esteeme and value him, but I thinke this is trueth as it is that I beleave that my sonne would not know where to find such a wife nor I sutch a daughter, therefore I pray preserve yourselfe for your owne sake and then if there be any place left for

Your most affectionate father,
Conway and Kilulta.[1]

A few days after giving this solemn warning against the dangers of too much science, Conway again referred to Harvey in slightly derogatory terms:

I perceive that Doctor Harvey is very mutch in your good opinion therefore I shall pray that his Physicke may have good successe with you,

---

[1] *Conway Letters*, edited by M. H. Nicolson, London, 1930, pp. 29–30.

what doth now disease you is not soe unknowne in his cause but that one may assuredly expect your health. Doctor Prudian [Prujean] is one of the learnedest Physitians about London, and his judgment I aprove very much of but his expression in his approbation of Doctor Harvey his bookes puts me in minde of one in the like kinde of Scaliger, who sayd that he had rather be author of those verses in Horace *Donec gratus eram tibi* then be King of France.[1]

After admitting that 'to have a good opinion of the Physitian doth contribute mutch to the cure', the anxious father-in-law indulged in a long discourse on New Books and their Dangers.

In December 1651 Anne Conway's brother, John Finch, writing to her from Paris, retailed a ridiculous story about Harvey, which he rightly discounted:

I was on Saturday with Sir Kenelm Digby where I had some philoso-phicall discourse: and he had heard of your marriage, but wondered with me at your story of Dr. Harvey. I must confesse I have scarce faith enough to believe he would cutt himself but rather believe he voyded that stone you speake of then cutt it out; for I doe not see it was possible for him in two days to be able to goe abroad otherwise.[2]

In August 1652 Anne was still being attended by Harvey, and John wrote:

I grieve much Dearest you are not yet out of Doctor Harveys hands, for though he [be] as able a person as any I know yet I had rather you had no reason for him to exercise his skill which I wonder hath beene so long with so little successe.[3]. . . . Dearest would I could take your headache from you, or could buy it of you: I would purchase it at a high rate though it be not worth the desiring. The opening of an Artery is a thing præscribed by all Physitians. I thinke no man is able to administer the operation so well as Dr. Harvey, though I had rather he might not stand in need to putt it in practise.[4]

On 26 January 1652/3 Anne wrote to her friend and mentor Henry More, the Platonist poet and philosopher, that she was thinking of trans-ferring herself from Harvey, who was himself becoming very sick, to a Dr. Ridsley, 'for I have heard him much commended, and they say he knowes very many secrets in physicke unknown to other physisians'.[5] This practitioner, recommended by John Finch, was not a Fellow of the

---

[1] *Conway Letters*, pp. 30–31.   [2] Ibid., p. 60.   [3] Ibid., p. 65.
[4] Ibid., p. 66.   [5] Ibid., p. 71.

College, and probably Dr. Thomas Ridgley is meant, an eminent physician who died in 1656.

Dr. Ridsley is said to be one will trouble himselfe with very few patients. I have no acquaintance with him (nor his sonne) but I shall the willinger make tryall of him, for your interest in them; when once I have ended my tryalles of Dr. Harvey which I thinke will be very shortly. He is very ill himselfe of the gowt almost continually, and that must needs indispose him to the minding of such things as relates not to his owne perticuler (yet he pretends very much to study and lay my case to heart).[1]

Eventually Harvey persuaded Lady Anne to consider submitting herself to the operation of trepanning, that is opening her skull, in Paris, as was afterwards related by Dr. Thomas Willis.[2] In April the pain was so great that Anne made the journey accompanied by Henry More and a physician[3]—though this was certainly not Harvey. In the end even the French surgeons dared not take the risk, though we are told 'they opened her jugular arteries',[4] that is, she had a phlebotomy done in a vein of the neck. Anne Conway was an exceedingly intellectual lady, an accomplished linguist and philosopher, but it must not be assumed on this account that her troubles were due to a neurosis. Harvey evidently did not think so. Her headaches persisted and in 1666 the famous quack, Valentine Greatraks, the 'stroker', was summoned from Ireland at great expense to try his skill. A distinguished company assembled at Lord Conway's seat, Ragley Hall in Warwickshire, to witness the trial. Although Greatraks successfully stroked many other patients in the district, he failed with Lady Anne Conway.[5]

Robert Boyle is responsible for having suggested that William Harvey also practised 'stroking', though of a different kind. In a book published in 1685 Boyle wrote:

Having one day given a visit to one of the skilfullest and candidest physicians of the famous college of London, I observed in his chamber a fine new fashioned clock; and having taken notice of it to him, as a thing I had not seen there before, he desired me not to think he was rich and vain enough to purchase so dear a rarity; but that it belonged to a courtier, whom he named to me, of whose daughter he told me this story: this young lady had a great tumor in her neck or throat, which being apprehended to be of a scrophulous nature, made her father fear

---

[1] Ibid., p. 73. [2] Will. *Two Discourses*, London, 1683, p. 119.
[3] *Conway Letters*, p. 117.
[4] Richard Ward, *The Life of Dr. Henry More*, edited by M. F. Howard, London, 1911, p. 210. [5] *Conway Letters*, p. 248.

it would oblige him to increase her portion more than his estate could conveniently bear: wherefore at length he addressed himself to my relator, who judging the case to be difficult, and being unwilling to torment the lady with a long course of physic, told the courtier, that if he could animate her to suffer a remedy he would propose, and would assist him to procure it, he hoped to remove this tumor, without weakening her, or putting her to pain. Soon after, all parties being agreed, and the desired conveniency procured, the patient was brought into a room, where there was yet in bed the body of a man, that had died of a lingering disease; this man's hand the doctor took, and laid it upon the patient's tumor, Keeping it there till she either complained or confessed, that she felt the coldness of it penetrate to the innermost parts of her tumor. This application was afterwards repeated more than once, whilst the body continued without smelling; and by this course the tumor was dispelled, and the patient so relieved, that her father, by way of gratitude, knowing how much the physician was a lover of curiosities, made him a present of that clock.

The learned doctor ascribed this odd remedy to *Helmont*.[1]

The learned doctor is not identified in this passage, and he was not Harvey, for twenty years earlier Boyle had written a letter to Dr. Henry Stubbe of Warwick containing a shorter version of the same story, but adding: 'And such another cure of a wen, or some such tumor, I remember our famous *Harvey* related to me as performed (if I very much mistake not) by himself, by stroking the wen, as *Helmont* prescribes, with a dead man's hand.'[2]

It will be recalled that when Boyle told of Harvey's reply to his question about how he came to think of the principle of the circulation, he called the occasion 'the only time I had discourse with him'. In his letter of 1665 Boyle was evidently unsure of whether Harvey had himself directed the repetition of Van Helmont's experiment, so that there are discrepancies in the story. In yet another reference to it Boyle expressed surprise that Harvey, 'who, *as a rigid naturalist as he is*, scrupled not often to try the experiment mentioned by Helmont',[3] and we may share Boyle's surprise to the point of not believing that Harvey in fact used a dead man's hand in this way. It would have been entirely out of character in the practice of the 'rigid naturalist', recognized to be such by Boyle as well as by ourselves.

[1] R. Boyle, *Of the Reconcileableness of Specific Medicines to the Corpuscular Philosophy*, London, 1685, p. 322.
[2] R. Boyle, *Works*, 1744, i. 51.   [3] Ibid., i. 532.

42

THE COLLEGE OF PHYSICIANS, 1651–1656

WE have seen that Dr. George Ent was the agent who in 1647 or 1648 procured the manuscript of Harvey's book on generation for publication. Ent shared with his friend a love of books and libraries, and the Annals record that on 25 June 1651 the library was put in charge of two Fellows, Ent and John King. This was the preliminary step before a sensational announcement made by the President, Dr. Prujean, who read at Comitia on 4 July the following statement and ordered that it should be inserted in the Annals: 'If I can procure one that will build us a Library and a Repository for Simples and Rarities such a one as shall be sutable and honorable to the College; will ye assent to have it done, or no, and give me Leave and such others, as I shall desire to be the designers and over-lookers of the worke, both for conveniency and ornament?' No name was given, but the Fellows were delighted to accept the offer made by their anonymous benefactor. The building seems to have been put in hand at once and it soon became known that Harvey was the donor, for a statue was also commissioned, which was carved, according to Aubrey, in white marble and was almost completed by Christmas 1652. On 22 December the President informed Comitia that the following inscrip-tion[1] was to be added to the statue:

GULIELMO HARVEO,
Viro monumentis suis immortali,
hoc insuper Collegium Medicorum Londinense
posuit.
Qui enim sanguinis motum
ut et
Animalibus ortum dedit, meruit esse
stator perpetuus.

Aubrey further recorded that Harvey was represented 'in his Doctoral Robes', and that above the statue (perhaps on a tablet on the wall) was the further inscription:

GUL. HARVEUS, natus A.D. 1578, Apr. 2 Folkston, in Com. Cantii, Primogenitus Tho. Harvei et Joannæ Halk: Fratr. Germani, Tho. Jo. Dan. Eliab. Mich. Mat.: sorores, Sarah, Amey.

[1] Said by Keevil (*The Stranger's Son*, 1953, p. 120) to have been composed by Baldwin Hamey, but this is not recorded in the Annals.

The sculptor was not named, but it is tempting to conjecture that it was Edward Marshall of Fetter Lane, known to have been the artist who fashioned the marble bust placed after Harvey's death in Hempstead Church. The suggestion is made on a later page that the bust and the statue may have been made at the same time by the same hand. If this was so we can be sure that the statue in the College was a lifelike image, since the bust conveys a great sense of vitality. Although the bust has survived, the *stator perpetuus* has perished, having been destroyed in the Great Fire of 1666, thus illustrating the truth of Sir Thomas Browne's epigram that 'There is nothing strictly immortal but immortality'.[1]

Loss of the statue of Harvey leads to consideration of an important surviving image of him still to be seen in his College. This is the large painting formerly attributed to Cornelius Johnson, but now acknowledged to be by some other, unknown, hand.[2] The size and formality of the picture suggest that it was intended as the official portrait to be kept in the College, but there is no mention of it in the Annals, so that its date remains uncertain. Harvey appears as a younger man than is portrayed in the engraving made for his book *De generatione animalium*, in 1649 (see p. 333), but this may be due to a deliberate idealization of his subject by the artist. Harvey is shown seated in a chair wearing a plum-coloured velvet doublet under a black gown with gold-braided loops on the half-sleeves. His left hand holds his round black doctor's bonnet, which rests on his knees. His right hand and forearm are supported on a table; the gloved hand, with improbably long and slender fingers, is held in a peculiar position, but this is thought to be the result of repainting, done in 1765, over extensive damage, the sum of £3. 10s. having been paid to a restorer, Mr. Cellivoe, on 3 January 1766. A coat of arms painted on the base of a pillar behind the sitter appears to have the Harvey arms quartered with those of Sir Walter Hervey, the Pepperer, but the details are indistinct; it is possible that the coat was added at a later date. The picture was the source of many later images, notably the engraving by William Faithorne the elder found in some copies of the English version of *De generatione animalium*. This, however, is of no value as evidence of the date of the painting, as the print was probably added only to part of the edition at some date after its publication in 1653.

According to tradition the picture is the canvas rescued by Dr. Christopher Merrett, the Harveian Librarian, from the Great Fire on

[1] *Hydriotaphia*, 1658, p. 79.
[2] *Portraits at the Royal College of Physicians of England*, edited by Gordon Wolstenholme and David Piper, London, 1964, p. 204.

4 September 1666; but having rescued it Merrett refused to surrender it to the College, claiming also the other objects he had saved at the same time. Ultimately, in 1681, he was sued by the President and forced to give up all these effects, which consisted, according to his sworn statement, of two pictures (Simeon Fox and Harvey), a mace, a Persian carpet, a collection of surgical instruments, a ballot box, a vellum volume containing the names of benefactors, and 148 books, including the first four volumes of the Annals.[1] The two pictures he had cut from their frames, and they may have been badly damaged. The portrait of Fox has disappeared, and perhaps was discarded. Harvey's picture could conceivably have been repainted for the new College in Warwick Lane, and would then have to be dated after 1681, but this must remain for the present in the realm of conjecture.

Not long after Harvey's death it was decided to place beneath the portrait a copper tablet with an immensely long Latin inscription engraved on it recording his life and achievements.[2]

Harvey's statue had vanished with the building at Amen Corner containing it; of this Aubrey said that the donor's munificence had provided 'a noble building of Roman Architecture (of Rustique worke with Corinthian pillasters) at the Physitians' College aforesaid, viz. a great parlour (a kind of Convocation house) for the Fellowes to meet in belowe; and a Library above. On the outside on the Freeze in letters 3 inches long is this inscription:

SUASU ET CURA FRAN PRUJEANI PRAESIDIS ET EDMUNDI SMITH ELECT INCHOATA ET PERFECTA EST HÆC FABRICA AN MIƆCLIII.'

The building, close to the present site of Stationers' Hall, was opened with suitable ceremony on 2 February 1653/4. First Dr. Prujean, the President, and Dr. Smith, an Elect, who had together supervised the actual building operations and whose names were inscribed on the frieze, invited the Fellows to attend a meeting with the donor, 'the most munificent old man', as he was called in the Annals. In a few words Harvey spoke of the readiness with which he had provided the money to pay for the Museum and its furnishings. The President then expressed his thanks in the name of all the Fellows, and mentioned also Dr. Hamey, who had given the site for the building. Dr. Ent followed with an eloquent speech in praise of the benefactors, who were then honoured at a banquet. The

[1] Sir Charles Dodds, 'Christopher Merrett, F.R.C.P., First Harveian Librarian', *Proceedings of the Royal Society of Medicine* (1954), xlvii. 1053–6.

[2] This does not add anything not already known and will be found printed in Charles Goodall's *Historical Account*, 1684, leaves Ss 2–3.

writer of the Annals observed that it was fitting that Harvey should be splendidly entertained as their guest at least once in surroundings provided by his munificence for the future benefit of the Fellows.

When the feast was over, as the Annals relate, the tables were cleared away and a Comitia was convened in the same room to elect the Professors of Anatomy and Surgery, positions which Harvey had asked to be allowed to relinquish. Dr. Francis Glisson, now known as the distinguished author of classical works on rickets and the anatomy of the liver, was appointed Lecturer in Anatomy; the care of the old library was given to Dr. Christopher Merrett, who was also granted the lease of part of the College house. On 26 June Merrett, as a reward for looking after the details of the new library, was released from any obligation to pay rent for his premises. The President, at Harvey's request, asked for names of Fellows to administer the Statutes of the library as soon as they had been promulgated. Hamey, Ent, Bates, and Merrett were appointed.

A Comitia of special importance was held on 30 September 1654, when Dr. Prujean resigned the Presidency and proposed that Dr. Alston should succeed him. Alston having 'modestly and rightly excused himself from election for the present', Harvey, although absent, was nominated. This was an act of piety, since several of the Fellows present knew that he would not accept it. Nevertheless, Alston and Hamey were commissioned to approach him, and the meeting was prorogued until the next day. Harvey himself then attended and made a speech recorded in the Annals. The writer at this period often allowed himself to use somewhat extravagant language which he evidently thought was likely to enhance the prestige of the College in the eyes of posterity, but on this occasion we seem to get a true idea of Harvey's feelings on what was to him a moving experience. When the Fellows were assembled,

Harvey with a calm brow gave thanks for the new dignity conferred upon him, in which he most gratefully acknowledged that he renounced not more being President of this College than prince of all the doctors in England: that he desired to be excused from this office because of infirmity and principally of age; and he earnestly requested that if the ex-President could be entreated to it, they should again elect him President.

So Prujean was re-elected and Harvey took his place as Consiliarius with Dr. Laurence Wright, a somewhat younger man, though he had first been made Consiliarius in 1647.

Harvey seldom attended meetings at the College after this date, but he was there on 1 October 1655 and took the chair. Although he had declined the Presidency a year before on the grounds of age and infirmity, he now witnessed the elevation of Dr. Alston to the Presidential chair, and himself, 'after giving good counsels, briskly brought the proceedings to an end'. Some of the old clear-cut mental activity could still be summoned up, even though his physical frame was suffering from decrepitude.

Harvey's chief physical affliction at this time was gout, and Aubrey described the rather drastic treatment the sufferer would give himself.

He was much and often troubled with the Gowte, and his way of cure was thus; he would then sitt with his Legges bare, if it were Frost, on the leads of Cockaine-house, putt them into a payle of water, till he was almost dead with Cold, and betake himselfe to his Stove, and so 'twas gonne.

He was hott-headed, and his thoughts working would many times keepe him from sleepinge; he told me that his way was to rise out of his Bed and walke about his Chamber in his Shirt till he was pretty coole, i.e. till he began to have a horror [shivering fit], and then returne to bed, and sleepe very comfortably.

This account is confirmed by Mrs. Harvey, his great-niece, in her memories collected by Dr. Heberden in the mid-eighteenth century, saying, 'that if the gout was very painful to him in the night, he would rise and put his feet in cold water'. Heberden, a distinguished successor of Harvey at the College of Physicians, remarked in his *Commentarii* (*de arthritide*), 1802: 'I neither recommend Harvey's example nor propose it to others for imitation, although he lived to his eightieth year, and died not so much from disease as from old age.'

Harvey's library and museum were safeguarded against ordinary hazards by the special Statutes agreed at Comitia on 19 June 1656. The Librarian and Custodians were instructed as follows:

Let the Librarian collect all the books, whether published or in manuscript, and the rest of the objects entrusted to him in store-houses; and arrange each author in alphabetical order, and let him write on the backs of the books the name of the author, the title of the work, the format of the volume and finally the place and year of publication.

Let the Custodian of the Museum survey at least once every year all the books and other objects committed to his trust, and make up an exact catalogue of the same to be shown to the Curators, where they may have met for that purpose. If he should know that some book or other object is missing, let him make the matter known to the Curators within three days, and take great pains so that that book or other missing object may be restored once more. If he should do otherwise and be guilty of bad faith, let him be fined either by the sum of money involved, or by the loss of his salary.

If any fit person should desire a book belonging to this Museum, let the Librarian immediately assign the book to his use [and] let him enrol the title.

Let him take care that the dirt of the books, tables, bookcases, chairs, windows, etc. be carefully wiped off at least every month.

Let the same follow the advice of the Curators in books to be bought.

Let the names of books and of all other objects be inscribed by the Librarian in a special book, in the same order in which they are placed in the Museum, and let each of the Curators have a copy of the same, signed with the names of the Librarian and of the Curators, so that on any day when they should visit this Museum, they may diligently take care lest the prescribed order of either the books or other objects be disturbed without authorisation, or anything at all be lost by error.

At the same time anyone using the Museum had to give solemn assurances that he would not be guilty of damaging the books by any sort of carelessness and that he would keep a sharp eye on other visitors. We do not know what books Harvey himself contributed, though it is probable that they were by no means strictly medical. Comitia decided that: 'Besides medical books, we consider those to be especially useful and suitable for this Museum, which deal with Geometry, or Geography, or Cosmography, or Astronomy, or Music, or Optics, or Natural History, or Natural Philosophy, or Mechanics, or include voyages to the more remote regions of the earth.' The Fellows knew that this catholicity would meet with the donor's approval.

Harvey had made his Will in 1652 while his new library was still building, for, in case he died before it was finished, he bequeathed 'so much money to be raised and laid out upon that building which I have already begun to erect with the Colledge of Physicians in London as will serve to furnish the same according to the design already made'. At the same time he enjoined his friends Ent and Scarburgh 'to looke over those scattered remnants of my poore Librarie and what bookes papers or rare collections they shall thinke fit to present to the Colledge'. But later, having lived to see the completion of the building, he probably himself deposited these books and papers in the College, and so, unwittingly, ensured their destruction. The library was certainly not so 'poor' as he modestly pretended, for he possessed 'presses and shelves' extensive enough to be worth leaving to his close friend Dr. Ent, who was given at the same time 'five pounds to buy him a ring to keepe or weare in remembrance of me'—a mark of affection not awarded to anyone else.

A few of Harvey's books were perhaps among those rescued by Merrett from the fire. The College still possesses the *Opera* of Fallopius, Frankfort, 1584, with the signature and annotations of Harvey's father-in-law, Dr. Lancelot Browne, and his own annotations in the margins. In the British Museum is Goulston's edition of Galen's *Opuscula varia*, London, 1640, annotated by Harvey. The library of the late Dr. Erik Waller at Uppsala has Sylvius's *De febribus commentarius*, Venice, 1555, with the signatures of Fabricius, of Harvey dated 1621, and of Dr. Mead. Another book presumably from Harvey's library is the *Opera anatomica* of Fabricius, Padua, 1625. This has marginal notes in Harvey's hand on two pages. It belonged formerly to Dr. James Murphy of the Glasgow Veterinary College, but cannot now be traced. Photographs of the notes are preserved at the Royal College of Physicians.

Harvey's benefactions to the College were not yet complete, for on 24 July 1656, according to the Annals written four days later:

The munificent old man, Dr. Harvey, always to be honourably commemorated in our Annals, having first made an elegant speech, made over for the use of the College in perpetuity the ancestral estate (which had come to him by inheritance), public deeds having been presented for the purpose. He also handed over the office of Lecturer (which he had for many years fulfilled with the greatest honour) to Dr. Scarburgh and, moreover, he entertained all the Fellows, together with some other friends, to a magnificent banquet. On that account, the proceedings were brought to an end by elegant and vigorous speeches in his praise by the President, Dr. Alston, and also Dr. Emily and Dr. Scarburgh.

So Harvey at length resigned his office as Lumleian Lecturer, held for forty years, and ensured that it would be carried on in the right tradition by publicly choosing Scarburgh as his successor. The gift of land was the patrimonial estate at Burmarsh in Kent, then valued at £56 a year.

The Trust Deed conveying Harvey's gift to the College is dated 21 June 1656, the parties to it including, besides Harvey himself and his brother Eliab, his nephew-in-law, Heneage Finch, twelve Fellows of the College, and several younger members of the family. The Deed stated that Harvey, out of his great affection for the College and his desire for its advancement, had at his own charge 'erected a building within the said Colledge, wherein he hath placed Bookes, sett upp Statues, and hath furnished the same with Pictures, Presses and receptacles for Bookes, Carpetts and other utensills, and intends the same for a Library for the said Colledge'. The Deed then proceeded to detail the properties at Burmarsh made over to the College for various specific purposes, these being, to pay for a Library Keeper, whose duties were laid down, to encourage friendship among members of the College by a monthly meeting with 'a small collation', and to institute a yearly Feast and Oration at which benefactors of the College should be commemorated by name. At the same time there should be

an Exhortacion to the ffellowes and members of the said Colledge to search and studdy out the secrett of Nature by way of Experiment, And also for the honour of the Profession to continue mutuall love and affeccion amongst themselves without which neither the dignity of the Colledge can bee preserved nor yet perticuler men receave that benefitt by their admission into the Colledge which els they might expect, Ever remembering that *Concordia res parvæ crescunt, Discordia magnæ dilabuntur*.

In these clauses Harvey's most treasured beliefs found expression—his insistence on the paramount importance of the experimental method in research, and of good feeling among the members of a corporate body such as the College of Physicians.

The distribution of the revenue from the estate was carefully apportioned—£20 for the Library Keeper, £6 for the monthly collations, £15 for the annual Feast, £5 for the Orator, and any residue to be applied, if necessary, for the upkeep of the building, or otherwise for 'the honour, ornament and benefit' of the College. Fifteen months later, however, the tenant of the estate was complaining that his rent was too high and that he would give it up unless it was reduced by £10. Decision was deferred, and a year later he was again threatening to throw up his lease unless the College would accept £40 per annum; this reduction was conceded.

The land is still vested in the College and provides an annual income of £233 used for meeting part of the cost of the Harveian Oration and dinner. A discordant note, however, had been introduced by Dr. Emily in his speech at Harvey's banquet. The sympathies of the College were still predominantly royalist. A testimonial letter given to a William Jackson on 22 December 1655 was granted 'by the authority conceded to us by the highest powers', and a marginal note explains that this refers to 'the King in exile'. These feelings were naturally not paraded in public, and at the Comitia held four days after the feast Dr. Emily was accused of having declaimed more bitterly than was proper against military matters, and also of having disparaged the present rule of the Commonwealth.

Emily defended himself, saying that he had spoken in good faith and not in a bad spirit, but his colleagues decided that no such speech should be delivered in future unless it had been read and approved by the Censors at least a month in advance.

Harvey felt able to attend Comitia again on 11 and 30 September 1656, on the second occasion going through the ceremony of receiving the caduceus from the retiring President, Dr. Alston, and giving it up to him again when he was reappointed to the chair. The President then again made Harvey Consiliarius, and 'decided that if he should happen to be absent at any time because of age and poor health Dr. Prujean should take his place'. Harvey did not in fact attend Comitia again after this date.

One of Harvey's last acts at the College about this time was joining with some other Fellows in an invitation to Henry Pierrepont, first Marquis of Dorchester, to become a member of the College.[1] Dorchester was a distinguished Royalist and also a serious student of philosophy, medicine, and law. He readily accepted the invitation and became a Fellow in 1658; at his death in 1680 he bequeathed to the College his magnificent library, which carried on the Harveian tradition of catholicity and today forms the nucleus of the wonderful collection of books owned by the College. Dorchester had come into intimate relations with Harvey in 1649, when he was his patient. A sedentary life and mental anxiety caused by the Civil War had brought him to a low state of health, from which he was restored by the attentions of Harvey, Scarburgh, and others.[2] This experience set him on to a study of medicine and so led to his joining his former doctors as their colleague. It also led to dosing himself with medicines, by which he nearly lost his life, having taken by mistake an overdose of opium. Though treatment rescued him from immediate death, he was afterwards physically impaired and the incident was thought to have hastened his death, which took place soon afterwards from gangrene of the leg.

In spite of the fact that Harvey attended Comitia on 30 September 1656, as already related, it seems to be clear that he had been suffering before this from serious illness. On, or shortly before, 28 December of this year he had made a codicil to his Will, containing a clause: 'Item what money shalbe due to me and Alice Garth my servant on a pawne now in the hands of Mr Prestwood I will after my decease shall all be given my said servant for her diligence about me in my siknesse and service both interest and principall'. No indication is given of the amount of the 'pawne', or security, held for some unknown debt by Mr. Prestwood.

[1] Munk's *Roll*, 1861, p. 263.   [2] Ibid., p. 268.

A previous clause in the codicil mentioned 'what moneys shalbe due to me from Mr. Hen Thompson his fees being discharged I give to my friend Mr. Prestwood'. Already in his main Will of 1652 he had left £100 to the same friend, who seems to have been more than a business acquaintance; probably he was both friend and lawyer, who could be trusted to look after the interests of Alice Garth, to whom Harvey was so grateful. He had already bequeathed to her in his first Will 'during her natural life a yearly rent or summe of twentie pounds'. Aubrey dropped a characteristic aside on Alice, throwing in a sly suggestion as to the way which she served her master: 'I remember he kept a pretty wench to wayte on him, which I guesse he made use of for warmeth-sake as King David did, & tooke care of her in his Will, as also of his man servant.' Aubrey could hardly have known that Harvey, in his Lumleian Lecture notes, speaking of the warmth provided in the abdomen by certain organs, 'like the warmth of kittens', had added, 'So an old man has a cat and David his maidservant'. The idea presented itself naturally to Aubrey's mind, which was not, as we often have occasion to notice, too refined an instrument. Harvey's care for the welfare of his maid and of his servant, John Raby, was characteristic of his generous regard for individuals of all kinds and classes, and need not be attributed to any other motive.

43

HARVEY'S USE OF COFFEE

I t is probable that Harvey was one of the first Englishmen to become addicted to the newfangled beverage made from the coffee bean. It is uncertain who was actually the first person to introduce coffee to England; its use in Turkey had been known to Europeans since 1583, when the traveller Rauwolf mentioned it in his *Itinerarium Orientis*,[1] and Sir Francis Bacon wrote of it in 1624 in his *Sylva Sylvarum*: 'They have in *Turkey*, a *Drinke* called *Coffa*, made of a *Berry* of the same Name, as Blacke as *Soot*, and of a *Strong Sent*, but not *Aromaticall*, which they take, beaten into Powder, in *Water*, as Hot as they can Drinke it: And they take it, and sit at it, in their *Coffa-Houses*, which are like our *Tavernes*. This *Drinke* comforteth the *Braine*, and *Heart*, and helpeth *Digestion*.'[2]

---

[1] See John Ray's *Collection of Curious Travels & Voyages*, London, 1693, pt. I, p. 92.
[2] *Sylva Sylvarum*, London, 1627, Century VIII, p. 191.

John Evelyn wrote in his Diary under the date 29 May—2 July 1637: 'There came in my tyme to the Coll: [Balliol] one Nathaniel Conopios out of Greece, . . . who returning many yeares after, was made (as I understand) Bishop of Smyrna. He was the first I ever saw drink Coffè which custome came not into England til 30 years after.'[1] Yet, as Evelyn indicates, coffee was not in general use in England before about 1650. A coffee-house is known to have been opened in Oxford in, or shortly before, 1655, and after this date such houses became popular in London and the Universities.[2] It is said that the first coffee-house opened in London was due to a Turkey merchant, Daniel Edwards, who brought with him to England in 1652 a Ragusan Greek servant skilled at brewing coffee. This brought him so many callers that, according to John Houghton's 'Discourse of Coffee, read at a Meeting of the Royal Society', he 'got a Shed in the Church-yard of St. Michael Cornhil, where he had great Custom, insomuch that the Ale-house keepers fearing it should spoil their Trade, Petitioned the Lord Mayor against him, alledging his not being a Freeman'.[3]

Aubrey is the primary authority for believing that Harvey often drank coffee. 'I remember', he wrote, 'he was wont to drinke coffee; which he and his brother Eliab did, before Coffee-houses were in fashion in London.' Corroboration of Aubrey's statement is found in Harvey's Will, drawn up in 1652: 'Item I give unto my Niece Mary West and her daughter Amy West halfe the Linnen I shall leave at London in my chests and Chambers together with all my plate excepting my Coffey pot.' Evidently Harvey set a special value on this utensil and perhaps intended that it should pass at his death to his brother Eliab—indeed, this is likely to have been arranged beforehand by verbal promise, since there is no further mention of the coffee-pot in the Will. Harvey no doubt enjoyed drinking coffee as a pleasant beverage and for the sake of the gentle stimulus to the faculties following its use. He is likely to have known about it at an early date because his brothers, as Turkey merchants, would have been able to import supplies of coffee beans into England at any time after 1616, when Thomas and Daniel Harvey were admitted to the Levant Company.

When coffee came into general use much notice was taken of its medicinal properties, another aspect of undoubted interest to Harvey.

[1] *Evelyn's Diary*, edited by E. S. de Beer, 1955, ii. 18. The editor thinks that Evelyn added his statement about coffee at a later date.

[2] See E. F. Robinson, *The Early History of Coffee Houses in England*, London, 1893.

[3] *Philosophical Transactions*, xxi. 1700, p. 312. See also Benjamin Morley, *A Treatise concerning the Properties and Effects of Coffee*, fifth edition, London, 1792, pp. 14–15.

Bacon had mentioned its beneficial effect on the digestion, but it was not until 1657 that coffee was recommended in a book. Judge Walter Rumsey then enlarged on Bacon's encomium in a work entitled: *Organon Salutis. An Instrument to cleanse the Stomach, As also divers New Experiments of the Virtues of Tobacco and Coffee: How much they conduce to preserve humane health*, London, 1657. Coffee in Rumsey's opinion was a valuable adjuvant to the use of a 'provang', or 'probang', in procuring a comfortable vomit. This instrument, invented by Rumsey, consisted of a piece of whalebone two feet in length with a button fixed at one end and a piece of string at the other. Being flexible, the probang could be introduced down the oesophagus, button-end first, and, being long enough to reach well down into the stomach, would stir up the contents for a satisfactory vomit. It was then pulled up again by the attached string. The patient was to prepare his stomach for this operation by taking beforehand a lump (the size of a nutmeg) of an 'electuary' made by adding powder of Turkish coffee to a thick mixture of butter, sallet oil, and honey. The same electuary was strongly recommended for the treatment and cure of the stone, and, taken first thing in the morning, it was also thought to be good for the gout, though for this it was to be accompanied by sucking a piece of the stalk of a tobacco leaf, well dried, the taste being disguised by cinnamon. There is no reason to think that Harvey used a coffee electuary for treating his own gout; but could coffee, perhaps, have been the 'secret remedy' so unsuccessfully used many years before for his unfortunate patient, Sir William Smith, suffering from a stone in the bladder? In 1620 coffee would certainly not have been generally known as an active therapeutic agent. Thomas Willis, who wrote about coffee in his *Pharmaceutice Rationalis* in 1674, dwelt chiefly on its action as an anti-hypnotic. He believed that if it were drunk every day it would clarify and purge the brain, and, indeed, sometimes sent his patients to a coffee-house rather than to an apothecary. He does not seem to have noticed its diuretic effect. Willis had previously recommended drinking coffee for somnolency and 'lethargy of the brain' in his *De Anima Brutorum*, 1672.[1] If Harvey was aware of the properties of coffee used as a beverage before the time of his residence in Oxford he may well have talked of it to Willis, who speaks, however, rather from his own experience than from the opinion of others.[2]

[1] See Willis, *Two Discourses, concerning the Soul of Brutes*, London, 1683, pp. 134–5.

[2] An extremely improbable anecdote concerning Harvey's attitude to coffee has been retailed in recent years, but its source remains undiscovered beyond its appearance in a German work on the history of coffee published in 1934. The English version (see H. E. Jacob, *The Saga of Coffee*, London, 1935, p. 128) relates that

Harvey's generally abstemious habits are known from more than one source, and he certainly did not frequently indulge in stimulation by any kind of wine. We have, however, the testimony of Sir Kenelm Digby that he was fond of drinking a mildly alcoholic beverage made from apples. Among Digby's collection of medical and other recipes, printed in *The Closet of Sir Kenelme Digby Opened* in 1671, is found a description of how to make 'Dr. Harvey's pleasant Water-Cider, whereof he used to drink much, making it his ordinary Drink'. After the apples had been boiled in water for some hours, the fluid was strained and set to ferment with sugar and yeast for forty-eight hours. The full description will be found in Appendix II among Harvey's other prescriptions and recipes.

44

DEATH AND BURIAL, 1657

ON 29 May 1761 the eminent physician Dr. Heberden made a note of having been told that Harvey's great-niece, Mrs. Harvey,[1] had said that the Doctor lived at his brother's at Roehampton the latter part of his life. That he used to walk out in a morning combing his hair in the fields.

That he was humoursome, and would sit down exactly at the time he had appointed for dinner whether the company were come or not.

That his salt-seller was always filled with sugar, which he used to eat instead of salt.[2]

'When William Harvey was nearing his latter end, he summoned a solicitor and showed the man of law a coffee-bean. Thrusting his finger-nail caressingly into the groove of the bean, he said with a smile: "This little fruit is the source of happiness and wit!" In his will, he bequeathed to the London College of Physicians the greatest treasure in his laboratory, fifty-six pounds of coffee, directing that his colleagues, so long as the supply lasted, should assemble month by month, to commemorate the day of his death by drinking coffee together . . . Harvey never dreamed that twenty years after his death London would be full of coffee houses; or that coffee, of which he had procured a sack from Venice at great cost, would by then be brought to England in shiploads, to fill the warehouses at the docks.'

Most of this story is so obviously untrue that the whole is likely to be a fabrication. There is no mention in Harvey's will of a bequest of coffee to the College of Physicians. His niece's husband, Heneage Finch, was his lawyer, but it has not been possible to connect him in any way with the story, and there is no evidence that Harvey ever procured a sack of coffee from Venice.

[1] Mrs. Elizabeth Harvey, daughter of Sir Eliab Harvey and wife of Edward Harvey of Coombe, Surrey; died 15 January 1695, aged 35.

[2] Dr. Heberden's notes are among the papers at the Royal College of Physicians collected by Dr. Macmichael, author of *The Gold-headed Cane*, London, 1827.

If these reminiscences are true, it appears that in his old age Harvey was becoming somewhat eccentric, though his foibles were harmless enough. We believe that, in fact, his last days were divided between his brother Eliab's two houses, Cockaine House in London, and the country residence at Roehampton. There is some uncertainty as to which of these houses was the scene of his death on 3 June 1657. Though nearing the age of 80, his mental faculties were unimpaired and he was still active; yet, being enlightened by a lifetime's practice of medicine, he would be well aware that he could not expect to live very much longer. He did not possess the knowledge we now have of arterial degeneration and high blood pressure, but he was accustomed to noting the symptoms in his patients foretelling the likelihood of a cerebral castastrophe, or 'stroke' as it is called, and he may even have noticed his own distended temporal arteries (discernible on his marble portrait bust) as a visible warning of such an event.

Aubrey stated that 'his chamber [in Cockaine House] was that roome that is now the office of Elias Ashmole Esq.; where he dyed, being taken with the dead palsye, which took away his speech', and he afterwards elaborated this statement. There are two possible reasons for doubting Aubrey's accuracy, though neither is convincing. One is the reference in the grant of administration of Harvey's Will—'The Last Will and Testament of William Harvey late of the parish of St. Peters the poores in London but att Roehampton in Surrey Doctor in Physicke Deceased';[1] but the Will was proved in May 1659, nearly two years after Harvey's death, and may not give an exact statement. The other hint is a passage in a letter from Bishop Brian Duppa to Sir Justinian Isham (see p. 414) saying that he had seen Harvey 'the day before he died'; Duppa was living at Richmond and his remark suggests that he had seen Harvey at Roehampton, only a mile or two distant, but the statement is not necessarily exact, and may have meant 'a few days before he died'.

Writing further of the manner of Harvey's death, Aubrey added details (such as saying that Harvey sent for his apothecary from Blackfriars), which seem to confirm his statement that Harvey died at Cockaine House. Aubrey then retailed a scandalous rumour of a kind that he himself would have enjoyed, though he tried very positively to discredit the truth of it.

It is now fitt, and but just, that I should endeavour to undecieve the world in a scandall that I find strongly runnes of him, which I have mett

[1] F. N. L. Poynter, 'William Harvey's Last Will and Testament', *Journal of the History of Medicine* (1957), xii. 165.

amongst some learned young men: viz. that he made himself a way to putt himselfe out of his paine, by opium; not but that, had he laboured under great paines, he had been readie enough to have donne it; I doe not deny that it was not according to his principles upon certain occasions to . . .: but the manner of his dyeing was really, and *bona fide*, thus, viz. the morning of his death about 10 a'clock, he went to speake, and found he had the dead palsey in his tongue; then he sawe what was to become of him, he knew there was then no hopes of his recovery, so presently sends for his young nephewes[1] to come-up to him, to whom he gives one his watch ('twas a minute watch with which he made his experiments); to another, another remembrance, etc.; made signe to . . . Sambroke, his apothecary (in Black-Fryars), to lett him blood in the tongue, which did little or no good; and so he ended his dayes.

Later Aubrey added:

The scandall afore said is from Sir Charles Scarborough's saying that he had, towards his latter end, a preparation of opium and I know not what, which he kept in his study to take, if occasion should serve, to putt him out of his paine, and which Sir Charles promised to give him; this I believe to be true; but doe not at all beleeve that he really did give it him. The palsey did give him an easie passe-port.

We may believe with Aubrey that Harvey would not have hesitated to ease his passage with opium, had the pains of death been very great. Euthanasia would have appealed to him as sensible and he would not have needed any sophistry to justify it morally. He was not sentimental or conspicuously religious. He had always looked facts in the face and would not have dropped his gaze in the presence of death. It must be admitted in addition that Aubrey had a good authority for the story, Sir Charles Scarburgh having been, as we know, a close friend of Harvey of many years standing. Moreover, there is evidence that a belief in the fatal potion had persisted in the family at least until the end of the eighteenth century, as may be seen from the narrative found in Edward Hasted's work on the history of the county of Kent, published in 1790.[2] Here Hasted wrote:

The following circumstantial account of the death of this eminent man, I believe, is little known beyond his family, but is related on the authority of a clergyman of this county who was assured of the fact of it by the late Eliab Harvey Esq., barrister at law, a descendant of the

---

[1] Probably Eliab's two younger sons, Matthew and William, aged 18 and 17. Eliab junior, the eldest of the three, was 22 and more likely than the others to have been absent.

[2] Edward Hasted, *History and Topographical Survey of Kent*, Canterbury, 1790, ii. 382 n.

Doctor's younger brother of that name. Dr. Harvey was ever afraid of becoming blind. Early one morning, for he always rose early, his house-keeper coming into his chamber to call him, opened the window shutters, told him the hour, and asked him if he would not rise, upon which he asked if she had opened the shutters; she replied yes—then shut them again—she did so—then open them again. But still the effect was the same to him, for he had awaked stone blind. Upon which he told her to fetch him a bottle (which she herself had observed to stand on a shelf in his chamber for a long time), out of which he drank a large draught, and it being a strong poison, which it is supposed he had long before prepared and set there for this purpose, he expired within three hours after.[1]

It may be that the story was embroidered in the telling from one generation to another through nearly a century and a half and so we may justifiably disbelieve with Aubrey that Harvey actually took the draught, particularly in view of the circumstantial details about his actions just before his death.

A pleasant confirmation of this view is suggested by the correspondence that passed shortly after Harvey's death between Bishop Duppa and his old friend Sir Justinian Isham of Lamport Hall near Northampton. Brian Duppa, son of a brewer, born at Lewisham in Kent in 1588 and therefore Harvey's junior by only ten years, had certainly known him very well. Educated at Westminster School under Lancelot Andrewes and at Christ Church, Oxford, he was a cultivated and scholarly man. After being a Fellow of All Souls and Dean of Christ Church he was later tutor to Charles II as Prince of Wales, with whom he lived for a time at Richmond Palace. He became successively Bishop of Chichester, Salisbury, and Winchester. Throughout the reign of Charles I Duppa was very close to him, and, with Bishop Juxon was allowed to act as his spiritual adviser in the last days before his execution. He had been made Bishop of Salisbury in 1641, but after the death of the King, whom he had attended, just as Harvey had done, throughout his stay in Oxford, he retired to Richmond, a place for which he had a particular affection. He was, therefore, living very near Harvey during his last days at Roehampton, and may have paid him many visits. In 1660, three years after

---

[1] The tradition has also been preserved in an inscription on the reverse of a small pencil drawing made by Jonathan Richardson, senior, after the portrait of Harvey now in the Hunterian collection at Glasgow University. The picture had belonged to Dr. Richard Mead (1673–1754). Richardson wrote on his drawing: 'Dr. Harvey dy'd 1657. ag. 80. Finding his Eyes quite Extinct Himself went out (his Own Phrase) by Opium. From a Pict^r Dr. Mead has 29 July 1738'. The drawing was sold at Christie's, 16 July 1963, lot 89. It is now in the United States of America.

Harvey's death, he became Bishop of Winchester, but died in 1662. His funeral sermon was preached by his intimate friend Henry King, his successor as Bishop of Chichester and, in earlier days, the close friend of Dr. John Donne. Duppa's correspondent, Sir Justinian Isham, was much younger, having been born in 1610. His interests were in the main those of a country squire, but he did not neglect to cultivate his mind. He was at Christ's College, Cambridge, with Milton and became a friend of an older poet, Gabriel Harvey. He was admitted to the Middle Temple in 1628, was a Member of Parliament for Northampton in 1661–74, and was elected F.R.S. in 1673, two years before his death, but he lived most of his life at Lamport Hall, where he formed an important library. Among the books still at Lamport is King Charles's Bible, given by him to Duppa, who passed it on to Isham. The surviving letters[1] between the two friends cover the decade 1650–60. The passages referring to William Harvey begin with an endorsement by Sir Justinian on a letter from Duppa dated 16 June [1657]:

My Lord, I hope the infirmitie lately ceas'd on your Lordship is but temporary, and being a goutish humour tending to the outward parts may less indanger the vitalls. I heare that Dr. Hervey, the physician, also Sir Mat. Leistor, both very learned men and praeservers of others' healths are lately dead. Surely I take the greatest benefitt to be had by their art is rather in the freeing or mitigating of paine then in the prolongation of life, which cannot but be miserable where the organs are decay'd.

Duppa replied on 8 July:

The conversation I have with you by letters is so much contentment to me, that though it cannot cure those infirmityes which age hath brought upon me, yet is so much pleasure to my mind, that my infirme bodie by copartnership is the better for it. And possibly it doth more then this, for since I heard from you (*post hoc*, I am sure, and whether *propter hoc* or no I cannot determine), my gout hath so farr left me that I have nothing to complain of the relicks of it but only a tenderness of my feet, which, though without pain, keeps me from renewing of my walk and the prospect of the Hill [at Richmond], which for these 3 months I have not had the sight of.

And because you mention the death of Dr. Harvey, and that the best effect of phisick is the mitigation of pain, I shall so far agree with you, that the mitigation which you speak of is a high commendation to that

---

[1] *Northamptonshire Record Society*, xvii. [1955]. The Correspondence of Bishop Brian Duppa and Sir Justinian Isham 1650–60, edited by Sir Gyles Isham, Bt., Lamport Hall.

art, but certainly the worth of it goes farther, and reacheth to the prolongation of life. And the person which we now speak of (with whom I
was the day before he died) was to me a great example of it, who had no
pain to complain of, but being of a dry sear body, he praeserved it so
long by the rules of art and diet, that his life went out like a spark, without any violence or noise at all.

There wer a triumvirate of excellent phisitians belonging all to the
Court, whom for som yeares last past, I had an ey upon, not onely out
of freindship to them, but out of som curiosity. For having observed
that they wer all three of a severall course of diet, I watched which of
them would fall first, their age there was som difference in but not much.
Mayern was the first that fell but maturely enough (for he was above
four score), whose diet was somthing more then liberall; Lister followed
him, who, though not abstemious, yet kept himselfe in more reasonable
bounds, and lived to outreach seven yeares beyond the other. Harvey
closed it up, who would somtimes fast two dayes together, but at last
fell with the rest. And if you should ask, which of these diets might conferr most to longaevity, I should subscribe to that of Lister's. But when
all else is said, there is an higher Providence, that lengthens and contracts
our dayes not onely without, but against the rules of art.

If William Harvey died at Roehampton, his body would soon have been
taken to Cockaine House. If he died in London, it could remain where it
was in the room occupied later, as Aubrey said, by Elias Ashmole,
Comptroller for the Excise, Cockaine House having been taken for the
Excise Office after Eliab's death in 1661. There Harvey's body must have
been embalmed, since it lay in the house for more than three weeks,
awaiting completion of the arrangements for the funeral at Hempstead
in Essex.

Eliab Harvey had a large house, Rolls Park, at Chigwell in Essex and
many properties elsewhere, but he chose to make Hempstead, a small
village near the Essex–Suffolk border, the family centre. He had bought
this property, together with lands at Great Samford, Radwinter, and
Finchingfield, from a member of the Mordaunt family before 1647.[1] It

---

[1] See Philip Morant's *History of Essex*, London, 1768, ii. 365: 'Sir Robert Mordaunt sold it
[the Hempstead estate] to Eliab Harvey Esq., brother of the most learned Physician Dr.
William Harvey, and in the said Eliab's posterity seated at Chigwell it hath continued ever
since. The Court for this maner is kept at Wynslow-hall in Hemsted.' Also p. 529: 'Sir Charles
Mordaunt succeeded his father [Sir Robert], dwelt chiefly at Massingham and dyed at London
10 July 1647. Before his decease he sold this estate either to Dr. Harvey, or his brother Eliab
Harvey Esq., and in that family, seated at Chigwell, it hath remained ever since . . . Sir
Robert Mordaunt did homage for his maner of Wynselow's &c. 5 July 1630. He resided
chiefly at Hemsted and was buried here in 1638.'

PLATE XXX

WINSLOW HALL, HEMPSTEAD
From a drawing made in 1809

PLATE XXXI

BUST OF WILLIAM HARVEY IN HEMPSTEAD CHURCH
By Edward Marshall

has been suggested[1] that Eliab Harvey fixed on Hempstead because of its proximity to the manor of Spains-hall, held by Hervey de Ispania under Count Alan 'at the time of the General Survey', that is, of Domesday Book, this family continuing there from the Conquest until the reign of Edward II. If the Harveys owned a Spanish ancestor, this might account for William's swarthy complexion, but there is no evidence whatever of any such ancestry. Another possible connexion is suggested by the occurrence of the name Hempsted in the sixteenth-century Wills of Thomas and John Harvey mentioned on p. 2. Eliab, knowing that some of his forebears had come from this place, may have been attracted by the idea of returning to an old family centre.

The manorial house at Hempstead, formerly known as Crockman's, was called Winslow, Wynselow, or Wynchlow Hall, and was situated about half a mile from Hempstead Church.

In 1655 Eliab Harvey built a chapel on the north side of Hempstead Church with a vault below. Here the bodies of his family and their descendants could lie together, with their commemorative monuments on the walls of the chapel above. Winslow Hall was a fine Tudor mansion, where so wealthy a man as Eliab Harvey could live in comfort, but it is some fifty miles from London and not easy of access, since it was seven miles from the nearest town, Saffron Walden, and not, therefore, on any main route. There is no evidence that William Harvey ever went there until Eliab, his brother and executor, decided that his last journey should take him by country roads and lanes to Hempstead, now known to fame only as the burial place of Harvey and the birth place, in 1706, of the famous highwayman, Dick Turpin. Winslow Hall was situated on high ground to the north-west of the village, facing south-east and surrounded by a very wide moat. The house fell into disrepair in the nineteenth century and was demolished, leaving only a small portion, now converted into a gardener's cottage.

On 25 June at the College of Physicians 'the Fellows were reminded that they attend the solemnities of Dr. Harvey's funeral to be held next day, in their gowns'; Harvey's pre-eminence among his fellows is attested by the fact that this is the only entry of the kind to be made in the College Annals during the seventeenth century. Next day the funeral procession started from London. The route, it may be guessed, would be northwards through Epping Forest to Bishop's Stortford, and so to Newport and Saffron Walden, then turning east to Hempstead—unless the coaches branched off at Stansted Mountfitchet to Thaxted and so by narrow

---

[1] *The Times*, 19 October 1883.

roads to their goal. The journey must have taken at least two days, a night being spent perhaps at Bishop's Stortford. The funeral service at Hempstead cannot, therefore, have taken place before 28 June.[1] Many of the Fellows of the College doubtless rode with the cortège for some miles beyond the City walls; how many of them went on as far as Hempstead we do not know. Aubrey says that he was there and helped to carry the body into the vault, but only mentions in addition 'Dr. Alsop', who remarked that Harvey 'was 80 wanting one', adding inaccurately, unless he was including the sisters, 'that he was the eldest of 9 brethren'. The name of Dr. Alsop does not appear in Munk's Roll of the Fellows of the College, and it seems certain that Aubrey meant to name Dr. Edward Alston, President of the College from 1655 to 1666, and knighted at the Restoration. Dr. Alston had been very active in reorganizing the affairs of the College after the confusion created by the political conditions and must often have consulted Harvey in this connexion. His family would have profited indirectly from Harvey funds a few years later, when his youngest daughter married a son of Sir Harbottle Grimston, to whom John Harvey had left most of his fortune. Other Fellows who were present at the College Comitia on 25 June and would certainly have gone to Hempstead, were Dr. Prujean, Dr. Baldwin Hamey, Dr. Scarburgh, Dr. Christopher Merrett, and Dr. Edmund Wilson, who delivered the second Harveian Oration on the 16th of the next month. Wilson himself died shortly afterwards, the Annals recording on 17 August that 'In the dead of night of this day Dr. Wilson, who very recently elegantly and vigorously sang the praise of Dr. Harvey (removed from human affairs on 3rd June of this year), himself laid aside mortality'.

The Harvey Chapel at Hempstead can be seen today almost unchanged since it was built in 1655. It is a plain rectangular brick structure with a tiled roof of high pitch opening on the south side into the body of the Church. It had already been used in 1655 and 1656 when Eliab Harvey had deposited the bodies of two of his daughters, children aged 12 and 9. It was not the custom of the Harveys to provide coffins for their dead. Instead, they were, as Aubrey said of William Harvey, 'lapt in lead', the metal case being roughly shaped and tapered towards the feet to look like a human form, with a face crudely engraved on the surface. The case containing Harvey's body provided no guide to his stature. He is known to have been very short, whereas the case measures $6\frac{1}{4}$ feet in length. On the breast is an inscription in large raised letters:

[1] No record of the actual date remains, the parish registers having been lost and probably destroyed.

DOCTOR
WILLIAM+HARVEY+
DECEASED+THE+3+
OF+JUNE+1657+
AGED+79+YEARS

The entrance to the Harvey vault is now outside the Church, where a sloped door, normally padlocked, leads down a few steep steps to the floor on which the rows of bodies rest. The floor of the chapel above is high enough for normal people to stand upright in the vault, and Aubrey with the other pallbearers would have had no difficulty in carrying the heavy leaden case down to the floor, where it was placed with the feet towards a barred, but unglazed, window in the east wall.

The Harvey Chapel today has on its walls memorials of many later members of the family, most of them of the eighteenth century, one of them signed by the sculptor Roubiliac (1695–1792). The vault became so crowded with bodies by 1766 that an inner vault was constructed beneath the floor of the Church. Visitors were allowed to enter the vault in the summer of 1928 during the celebration of the tercentenary of the publication of *De motu cordis*. A macabre spectacle then greeted our eyes, when we saw the close-packed rows of leaden shells and more recent coffins with crimson velvet coverings, all containing the mortal remains of members of the Harvey family, including those of Admiral Sir Eliab Harvey, commander of the *Temeraire* at the battle of Trafalgar. Many of the leaden cases with the passage of centuries had sagged around the limbs of their occupants clearly outlining the bones of the skeletons within.

The memorial to William Harvey is on the north wall of the transept, just outside the Chapel, having presumably been placed there by Eliab Harvey soon after the funeral. It consists of a life-size bust in white marble standing in a niche with the Harvey coat of arms above and a long Latin inscription below describing Harvey's qualities and works. The whole monument was executed, as Aubrey recorded, 'by Mr. Marshall, the stone cutter', that is, Edward Marshall (1598–1674), a celebrated London statuary and master-mason, whose yard and shop were in Fetter Lane. Marshall is recognized today[1] as having been one of the foremost sculptors of his time; he executed the monuments of many well-known people, including that of the poet Michael Drayton in

[1] See Katherine Esdaile's *English Church Monuments*, London, 1946.

Westminster Abbey. It has been suggested that the face of the Harvey bust was copied from a death-mask,[1] but it seems unlikely that so lively and convincing an image could have been done from anything but the living face of the subject, and the bust, indeed, is now to be regarded as probably the best representation of Harvey in his old age that we possess. The rather too luxuriant hair and the mantle covering the shoulders are conventionalized according to the custom of the time, but the features and details, such as the folds of the cheeks and the distended temporal arteries, are sensitively rendered. Harvey looks out from his niche with the steadfast and unruffled gaze of a great seeker after truth. His face is full of character and more like the man we should expect to see than are any of the existing portaits in oils. It may well be that the bust was made a few years before Harvey's death at the same time as the statue placed in the library at the College of Physicians in 1652, for it was not unusual in the seventeenth century to make commemorative sculptured portraits during the subjects' lifetime. Harvey would have known that he was not likely to survive for many years, and no false modesty would have made him object to this anticipation of the inevitable event. Eliab Harvey had already built his chapel, and the brothers would naturally talk together of how it was to be used.

Dr. George Ent, when speaking at the inauguration of the hall where the marble statue of Harvey was standing, said of it, 'Look on that living and almost breathing image, which shines with happy countenance. . . . Look on it as the familiar genius and Patron of this place, and mark how fixedly it watches us all. It seems to advise us to grow in virtue and diligence.'[2] The same might be said of the Hempstead bust with the Latin lines below it supposed to have been composed by Ent himself.

A visitor to Hempstead Church at the present time will notice that a large part of the space in the Harvey chapel is occupied by a massive marble sarcophagus, containing, as the inscription on it states, the remains of William Harvey. His body had lain in the vault for 226 years before it was transferred in 1883 to the chapel above. It had been known for some time that the leaden shell containing Harvey's body had been falling into disrepair. The vault was visited in 1847 by Dr. (later Sir) Benjamin Ward Richardson, an eminent Fellow of the College of Physicians; he was the first medical man to go there for many years, and

---

[1] The opinion of Thomas Woolner, R.A., recorded by Dr. B. W. Richardson in *The Lancet* (1878), ii. 776–8.

[2] From a manuscript copy of Ent's speech preserved at the Royal College of Physicians translated by W. R. LeFanu

he found that the shell, lying beneath the east window of the vault, was exposed to injury by the weather and by stones thrown at it though the grating by the village boys. The lead had cracked for part of its length and the upper surface had sagged so that water accumulated in the resulting depression. The vault was repaired after a later visit by two other physicians in 1868, but the case was found to be further damaged and was open widely enough to admit a frog, which jumped out when it was disturbed. Ten years later, in 1878, Dr. Richardson paid another visit and saw that the lead had collapsed still further, so closing the opening reported in 1868. He was unable to determine how much of Harvey's remains were still undecayed, but noted that the shell was filled with a dark fluid, 'thick as melted pitch and having a peculiar organic odour'[1]—evidence, perhaps, of the substances used to embalm the body in 1657. Dr. Richardson suggested that the shell and its contents should be decently interred in Westminster Abbey, otherwise after another century had passed nothing recognizable would remain. Dr. Stanley, then Dean of Westminster, favoured the idea, but owing to his failing health and subsequent death the project was not carried out. Final catastrophe almost overwhelmed Harvey's resting-place when the whole tower of the Church and part of the nave collapsed into the churchyard towards the south-west on 28 January 1882. Being now thoroughly alarmed, the College of Physicians made another examination of the vault and found that the shell had further deteriorated and was full of water. It was then decided to keep Harvey's remains at Hempstead, but to transfer them to a marble sarcophagus in the chapel. The weight of this necessitated the building of a pillar in the vault to support the floor. When this had been done, a ceremony took place on St. Luke's Day (18 October) 1883, at which the leaden case was carried from the vault by eight Fellows of the College and deposited in the sarcophagus in the presence of the College officials and many Fellows, with four members of the Harvey family. Another leaden case was added, containing the 1766 edition of Harvey's *Works* together with a sealed bottle enclosing a scroll recording the event and the reasons for which it was done.[2]

With the help of the College the ruined nave and the lower part of the tower were afterwards partly rebuilt; another effort to complete the work was made in 1933, but much of the materials originally forming the upper part of the tower lay heaped in the churchyard for eighty years, together with the bells. Ultimately enough money was collected by the

[1] Described in *The Lancet*, loc. cit.
[2] The ceremony was described in detail in *The Times*, 19 October 1883.

Harveian Society of London, stimulated by their President, Arthur Dickson Wright, F.R.C.S., to finish the rebuilding of the tower exactly in its original form, the work being carried out under the supervision of Colonel S. A. Smith, resident in Hempstead. Colonel Smith also arranged for the rehanging of the six bells, with the exception of the large tenor, which provided metal for two smaller bells, the casting being done at the same foundry as had cast the original bell in Whitechapel in 1664. The whole building was consecrated by the Bishop of Colchester on 3 June 1962 in the presence of many distinguished members of the medical profession and a large congregation of parishioners. One admirer of Harvey's merits had even flown over from Texas to attend the ceremony, thus acknowledging the reverence felt for Harvey's personality and achievement all over the world.

45

EPILOGUE * COWLEY'S *ODE UPON DR. HARVEY*

It is easy for those following Harvey in the profession of medicine 300 years after his death to be dazzled by his achievement, so universally acclaimed, often so lavishly praised. We may naturally wonder whether perhaps the sense of proportion has been lost, and Harvey, the human being, become obscured by the meed of praise now so fixed by convention as to be almost without meaning.

The term 'immortal' was so often applied to Harvey by his contemporaries that there can be no doubt of the impact made by his personality. Cooler appraisement at a later date has seldom shown any disposition to belittle either the man or his achievement, except when nationalistic enthusiasm has created some bias in favour of supposed rivals in the field of discovery.

The facts of Harvey's life as we know them have now been passed in review, and it is certainly impossible to doubt his pre-eminence in his own environment. He possessed the intellect and the courage to assume the leading place in biological advance in Europe during the first half of the seventeenth century, even though he still emphasized his allegiance in many things to the views of Aristotle and Galen. 'I have still prized

PLATE XXXII

WILLIAM HARVEY
Detail from the official portrait in the Royal College of Physicians. By an unknown painter

Aristotle's judgement so highly', he wrote, 'that I never would recede from his Oracles without premeditation.'[1] Aristotelian ideas and methodology are continually found to be reflected in his writings, but he was aware, too, that his investigations might profoundly influence and alter medical practice, though he was uncertain of how far this could go in the particular circumstances of his time. As a doctor he was still bound, for want of anything better, to current views on the value of innumerable remedies which we now know to have been virtually without pharmacological action. We have enough evidence of Harvey's relations with his patients to enable us to see that he was not deceived by the fantastic, semi-magical ideas still possessing an interest for clinicians who succeeded him, such as the acute observer Thomas Willis and the philosophical John Locke. Harvey seems to have regulated his clinical attitude by sheer good sense, though sometimes, like any other practitioner, making mistakes liable to give a handle to malicious critics.

Harvey's relations with his colleagues were always correct and it is plain that he enjoyed the warm regard of the other Fellows of the College of Physicians. The welfare of the College was one of his chief interests through the fifty years covering the time from his admission as a Fellow to the day of his death, and the Annals of the College have provided ample evidence of how the others always turned to him as intellectual leader in their day-to-day affairs. Dr. Samuel Garth in his Harveian Oration delivered forty years after Harvey's death said that he 'was approved for a facetious courteousness'.[2] The term *facetious* is not to be taken in its modern sense of 'jocose', but was understood rather as 'pleasant' or 'witty', meaning that Harvey's courtesy showed warmth rather than formality. Garth also said, comparing Harvey with Baldwin Hamey, that 'Harvey was in repute for bounty, Hamey for his plain integritye'. Garth was thinking of Harvey's generous gifts to the College, these having made his last days especially memorable. He could not have meant to imply that Harvey lacked integrity. Everything that we know about him testifies to his invariable honesty and plain-dealing. His ethical standards were high; he was generous and courteous even when replying to unreasonable attacks on his doctrines. Garth's tribute to Harvey's nature was confirmed by Sir Charles Scarburgh, who said in his Oration of 1662 that 'he was adorned above all things by singular candour of mind, charm of character, and politeness joined with sweetest affability', adding that anyone who talked with him in his old age came

[1] *Anatomical Exercitations*, 1653, p. 52.
[2] F. H. Ellis, 'Garth's Harveian Oration', *Journal of the History of Medicine* (1963), xviii. 8.

away not only instructed, but also feeling more cheerful. Harvey, he said, had, to the end, an alert mind and a perpetual air of youthfulness.

In private conversation, as we know from Aubrey's reports, Harvey could be cynical, or even bitter. 'He would say that we Europeans knew not how to order or governe our Woemen and that the Turkes were the only people used them wisely', Aubrey wrote, but then added, 'He was far from bigotry', and attributed to him the statement that, 'A blessing goes with a marriage upon a strong impulse'. In another passage Aubrey enlarged on Harvey's friendliness and liberal-mindedness—'Ah! my old friend Dr. Harvey—I knew him right well—he made me sitt by him 2 or 3 hours together discoursing. Why! had he been stiffe, proud, starcht & retired, as other formal Doctors are, he had known no more than they. From the meanest person, in some way or other, the learnedst may learn something. Pride has been one of the greatest stoppers of the Advancement of Learning.' When Harvey contemplated the stupidity and prejudice with which his work was at first received, or the political events which destroyed the happiness of so much of his later years, he could hardly avoid some bitterness, but his essential humanity would become evident when helping younger people or trying to break down the superstitions and cruelty of his times.

Harvey was reticent concerning his religious beliefs. Passages in *De generatione animalium*, 1651, express a profound consciousness of a Divine Providence watching over man's affairs and forming the laws of Nature. Clauses in his Will relating to his hopes of a future life are in the conventional phraseology of the time and reveal nothing of his real beliefs. It has sometimes been conjectured that Harvey may have secretly acknowledged the Catholic religion, perhaps because of his close relations with the formerly Catholic Earl of Arundel,[1] but there does not seem to be any justification for believing this. Outwardly he lived a sober life consistent with the Protestant faith, but nowhere did he express any feelings of fervent Christianity. His intimate friend Charles Scarburgh said that although it was not apparent to all, Harvey always cherished that philosophy which had a reverence for divine authority and uprightness of character so that he might regulate his life with integrity. This agrees with the general impression created by his life and writings.

Details of Harvey's domestic life are completely unknown. There is no reason for supposing that it was anything but happy. His relations with his six brothers were always close and he clearly had warm family

---

[1] Though brought up as a strict Catholic by his mother, Arundel repudiated his faith by joining the Church of England in 1616. See Hervey, loc. cit., p. 112.

feelings with a sense of responsibility for the welfare of all his numerous relations. Aubrey's remark that 'for 20 yeares before he dyed he tooke no manner of care about his worldly concernes', and that he depended on his brother Eliab for ordering his affairs is not consistent with what we know of his attitude to his possessions. The story of his lawsuit with the family of his patient Sir William Smith shows that early in his career he could even be hard in exacting his just dues. In later years he was willing to take great trouble to obtain money due to him for his lectures or from any other source, although his medical practice was extensive and must have brought in a considerable income. Harvey's father, certainly a hard-headed man, made him the sole executor of his Will. Two of his brothers, Matthew and Daniel, bequeathed to him substantial sums of money, and Thomas, who died in 1622, entrusted his son John, then a minor, to William's care. Harvey himself acquired large landed properties in his last years, and Aubrey estimated the value of his estate at £20,000. Harvey was generous both publicly in his benefactions to the College of Physicians and privately, as can be seen from the terms of his Will. Nowhere do we find signs of negligence in worldly concerns. Although Harvey was a wealthy man he lived abstemiously, as we know from more than one source. Scarburgh said in his Harveian Oration that his tastes in dress and food, and in the other necessities of life, were of the simplest, this simplicity being imposed on him by the demands of his personal philosophy. In another Oration, delivered immediately after Harvey's death, Dr. Edmund Wilson said that Harvey 'had led his life with the utmost temperance and according to the strict rule of medicine'.[1]

Dr. Samuel Garth in his Oration already quoted characterized Harvey as one 'whose Sharpnesse of Wit and brightnesse of mind, as a light darted from Heaven, has illuminated the whole learned world'. The truth of this has been abundantly illustrated by the narrative of his life. From this it should have been possible to form a mental image of a small, swarthy man with an alert and eager manner, interested in everything around him, observant, impatient, but with a natural dignity permitting no liberties and an intelligence commending him to the company and friendship of many of the best minds of his day. His professional eminence brought him the confidence of two Kings and the close friendship of one, to whom he gave his affection and a loyalty not to be lessened by political adversity, or to be for one moment forgotten after events had reached their tragic climax. Politics played no part in determining Harvey's

---

[1] Wilson's Oration has not been printed; a copy (MS. 109) is in the library of the Royal College of Physicians.

motives or actions. Personal loyalty was the touchstone, and it cost him the Presidency of the College which he served with equal devotion throughout his professional life. When eventually circumstances allowed the offer of the Presidential Chair to be made, it found him broken by ill health and the weariness of old age, so that he could only refuse it with his customary grace. Although politics did not affect Harvey's actions, it may well be that they did engage his interest and attention—indeed, it could hardly be otherwise. This belief seems to have been current in the latter part of the seventeenth century, for the political writer Henry Neville (1620–94) told Walter Moyle (1672–1721), another politician, that the Physician, a character in Neville's *Plato Redivivus*, 1681, was intended to represent Harvey, 'who relieved his abstruser studies by conversations in politics'.[1] No doubt in his later years talk with Hobbes and Selden sometimes turned from philosophy to current affairs.

Even if we wished to do so, it would be difficult, from the evidence in our possession, to find any serious flaw in Harvey's character. Above all let it never be forgotten 'that he is the first Englishman of whom we know enough to say that he was definitely what we now mean by "a scientific man". He viewed the problems of life as we view them, he observed the facts as we observe them, he experimented as we experiment, and he reasoned as we reason.'[2] This was said in 1928 by Sir Wilmot Herringham, one of Harvey's successors on the staff of St. Bartholomew's Hospital, and the words embody the mainspring of Harvey's active life. It was his delight to pursue the secrets of Nature to the limit of what could be achieved by the means at his disposal. This was more important to him than any consideration of monetary gain. Ambition, as far as it concerned his professional advancement, had been quickly satisfied. It remained to use his opportunities for scientific research as fruitfully as he was able; his reward has been that he is remembered not only as the founder of the great school of physiology in his own country, but also as having laid down the pattern of scientific method to be followed for ever after by the civilized world.

This assessment of Harvey's character as a man of science seems plain enough now, and it is unlikely to be assailed in the future. Yet it has not always been regarded in this light, for even so distinguished an anatomist as William Hunter thought fit to belittle Harvey's achievement in one of his last lectures, given in 1783. Hunter grouped together as three of the

[1] See Moyle's *Works*, London, 1727, pp. 26–27.
[2] Herringham, 'William Harvey at St. Bartholomew's', *St. Bartholomew's Hospital Journal* (1928), xxxv. 13–16.

great 'discoverers' the names of Christopher Columbus, Copernicus, and Harvey but commented that

In merit Harvey's rank must be comparatively low indeed. So much had been discovered by others, that little more was left for him to do than to dress it up into a system; and *that*, every judge in such matters will allow, required no extraordinary talents. Yet, easy as it was, it made him *immortal*. But none of his writings shew him to have been a man of uncommon abilities. It were easy to quote many passages which bring him nearly to a level with the rest of mankind. He lived almost thirty years after Asellius published the Lacteals, yet, to the last, seemed most inclined to think that no such vessels existed. Thirty hours at any time, should have been sufficient to remove all his doubts.[1]

Hunter thought that Realdus Columbus, followed by Cæsalpinus, had 'clearly given the circulation of the blood through the lungs, which we may reckon, at least, three quarters of the discovery'. He had failed to appreciate the difference between a mind that had formulated an *hypothesis* containing a half-truth and the larger intellect able to *prove* the whole truth by methods so new that they could initiate a train of investigation leading to the scientific knowledge of the present day.[2] Many a fundamental discovery has seemed obvious once it has been made.

Surprise has sometimes been expressed that Harvey was not given a knighthood by King Charles. Doctors were frequently honoured in this way, and Harvey's genuine devotion to the King would have marked him as a suitable recipient of royal favours. His friend Baldwin Hamey is known to have been offered a knighthood by Charles II, but Hamey's modesty and unworldliness led him to refuse both that and the appointment of physician-in-ordinary, even after he had given the King a very valuable diamond ring formerly worn by Charles I.[3] Harvey must certainly have been offered the same honour by his royal Master, but also refused it because it was not part of his character to attach any value to worldly titles of that kind. In his copy of Galen's *Opuscula varia* he approved a passage exalting the value of learning over rank with the

[1] William Hunter, *Two Introductory Lectures to his last course of Anatomical Lectures*, London, 1784, p. 47.

[2] An elaborate and very learned attempt to belittle Harvey's achievement on the same grounds was published fifty years later by John Redman Coxe, M.D., with the title: *An Inquiry into the Claims of Doctor William Harvey to the Discovery of the Circulation of the Blood; with a more Equitable Retrospect of the Event*, Philadelphia, 1834. Coxe in 245 closely printed pages contrived, like Hunter, to miss the point.

[3] John Keevil, *The Stranger's Son*, London, 1953, p. 130.

contemptuous remark, 'wooden leggs',[1] meaning that he despised such artificial props as worthless. Scarburgh confirmed this attitude by saying in his Oration that when Harvey saw that titles and decorations tended rather to Titles of Honour than to integrity of character, 'he passed all these things by'.

Constantly throughout his writings Harvey insisted on the value and importance of experiment. It was John Hunter who, trying to encourage Jenner to find things out for himself, wrote to him, 'Why think? Why not try the experiment?'[2] But Harvey's example had anticipated Hunter by more than a century and a half. When Galen said that treatment of a patient was merely a matter of applying the remedies known to be effective for certain symptoms, Harvey asked, *quomodo nisi experimentum?* 'how can this be except by experiment?'[3] He undoubtedly admired Galen as a great teacher and physician, and agreed with his statement that 'the first and greatest of all errors is to make a rash pronouncement out of self-love, or of ostentation of knowledge', but when Galen in his *Opuscula varia* seemed to belie this by boasting of certain things he could do pointing the way to truth, Harvey exclaimed several times in the margin of the book, 'Arrogant'.[3] Small private notes like this, not meant to be seen by any eye except his own, reveal to us the true greatness of Harvey's character.

Of Harvey's contemporaries none perceived more clearly than Abraham Cowley the main motive actuating his passion for research. Harvey had written in *De generatione animalium*: 'But as in the greater world, we say, *Jovis omnia plena*, All things are full of the Deity, so also in the little edifice of a Chicken and all its actions and operations, *Digitus Dei*, the Finger of God, or the God of Nature, doth reveal himself.'[4] So Cowley saw how Harvey had 'sought for truth in truth's own Book', and predicted the consequences of his discoveries to the progress of biological science and the art of medicine. He whimsically called him 'Physic's own physician', but admitted that at last his own body must succumb to Time's onslaught, so providing Nature with her revenge for his relentless pursuit of her secrets. Cowley's 'Ode', though written during Harvey's lifetime, is an eloquent epitaph fit to conclude this attempt to define his character and achievement by placing him in his proper setting as far

---

[1] Sir Norman Moore, *The History of the Study of Medicine in the British Isles*, Oxford, 1908, pp. 184–5.

[2] Hunter's autograph letter at the Royal College of Surgeons, first printed in Baron's *Life of Jenner*, London, 1827, p. 33.

[3] Gweneth Whitteridge, 'Harvey's Galen', *St. Bartholomew's Hospital Journal* (1957), lxi. 175.

[4] *Anatomical Exercitations*, 1653, p. 310.

as the evidence allows. Harvey's modesty is not in question, and he would have been astonished at the avidity shown by his successors for knowledge of his life. 'Anything about Harvey sounds like music'— these words recently expressed the feelings of one of his many admirers in the younger generation of medical historians.

ODE

Upon Dr. Harvey.

I

Coy Nature, (which remain'd, though Aged grown,
   A Beauteous virgin still, injoyd by none,
     Nor seen unveil'ed by any one)
When Harvey's violent passion she did see,
Began to tremble and to flee,
Took Santuary like *Daphne* in a tree:
There Daphne's lover stop't, and thought it much
    The very Leaves of her to touch,
But *Harvey* our *Apollo*, stopt not so,
Into the Bark, and root he after her did goe:
    No smallest Fibres of a Plant,
For which the eiebeams Point doth sharpness want,
    His passage after her withstood.
What should she do? through all the moving wood
Of Lives indow'd with sense she tooke her flight,
Harvey persues, and keeps her still in sight.
But as the Deer long-hunted takes a flood,
She leap't at last into the winding streams of blood;
Of man's *Meander* all the Purple reaches made,
    Till at the heart she stay'd,
    Where turning head, and at a Bay,
Thus, by well-purged ears, was she o're-heard to say.

2

Here sure shall I be safe (sayd shee)
None will be able sure to see
   This my retreat, but only Hee
   Who made both it and mee.
The heart of Man what Art can e're reveal?
   A wall Impervious between
   Divides the very Parts within,
And doth the Heart of man ev'n from its self conceal.
   She spoke, but e're she was aware,
   Harvey was with her there,
And held this slippery *Proteus* in a chain,
Till all her mighty Mysteries she descry'd,
Which from his wit the attempt before to hide
Was the first Thing that Nature did in vain.

3

He the young Practise of New life did see,
   Whil'st to conceal its toylsome Poverty,
It for a Living wrought, both hard, and privately.
    Before the Liver understood
   The noble Scarlet Dye of Blood,
   Before one drop was by it made,
Or brought into it, to set up the Trade;
Before the untaught Heart began to beat
The tunefull March to vital Heat,
From all the Souls that living Buildings rear,
Whether implyd for earth, or sea, or air,
Whether it in the womb or egg be wrought,
A strict account to him is hourly brought,
   How the Great Fabric do's proceed,
What time and what materials it do's need,
He so exactly do's the work survey,
As if he hir'd the workers by the day.

4

Thus *Harvey* sought for truth in truth's own Book
   The creatures, which by God himself was writ;
   And wisely thought 'twas fit,

Not to read Comments only upon it,
But on th'original it self to look.
Methinks in Art's great Circle others stand
  Lock't up together, Hand in Hand,
  Every one leads as he is led,
  The same bare path they tread,
And Dance like Fairies a Fantastick round,
But neither change their motion, nor their ground:
Had *Harvy* to this Road confind his wit,
His noble Circle of the Blood, had been untroden yet.
Great Doctor! Th'art of Curing's cur'd by thee,
  We now thy Patient Physick see,
From all inveterate diseases free,
  Purg'd of old errors by thy care,
New dieted, put forth to clearer ayr,
  It now will strong, and healthfull prove,
It self before Lethargick lay, and could not move.

5

These Usefull secrets to his Pen we owe,
And thousands more 'twas ready to bestow;
Of which a Barba'rous Wars unlearned Rage
  Has robb'd the Ruin'd Age;
O cruell loss! as if the Golden Fleece,
 With so much cost, and labour bought,
And from a farr by a Great *Hero* Brought,
 Had sunk eve'n in the Ports of *Greece*.
O Cursed Warre! who can forgive thee this?
  Houses and towns may rise again,
  And ten times easier it is
To rebuild *Pauls*, than any work of his.
That mighty task none but himself can doe.
  Nay scarse himself too now,
For though his Wit the force of Age withstand,
His Body alas! and Time it must command,
And Nature now, so long by him surpass't,
Will sure have her revenge on him at last.[1]

[1] A. Cowley, *Verses written upon Several Occasions*, London, 1663, pp. 18–21.

The core of the matter has been expressed more succinctly by Dr. Walter Pagel,[1] a perceptive student of Harvey's philosophy and of the conception of circular motion as exemplified by the circulation of the blood: 'Harvey, the Aristotelian, died in 1657, while Harvey, the discoverer and physiologist, was to remain immortal.'

[1] W. Pagel, 'The Philosophy of Circles', *Journal of the History of Medicine* (1957), xii. 156.

APPENDIXES I–VIII

I. *Account of William Harvey*

BY JOHN AUBREY

(Transcribed from the Aubrey manuscripts in the Bodleian Library, Oxford)

* William Harvey M.D. natus at Folkestone in Kent:

† borne at the house which is now the Post-house, a faire stone-built house which he gave to Caius Coll: in Cambr: with some lands there: vide his Will. His brother Eliab would have given any money or exchange for it, because 'twas his father's, and they all borne there; but the Dr (truly) thought his memory would better be preserved this way, for his brother has left noble seates & about 3000 *li* p. annum at least.

‡ Hemsted in Essex towards Audeley End: ibi sepultus Dr Harvey.

† Quaere Mr Marshall, the stone-cutter for the IS in the Church there.

§ Quaere Mr Marshall in Fetterlane for the copie of the IS on his monument in Essex.

|| Dr W. Harvey: [ask his] epitaph [from] Mr Marshall.—Quaere Anthony Wood if there is a MS in bibl. Bodleiana that speakes of the Circulation of the Bloud: Dr [Luke] Ridgeley and Dr Trowtbec can enforme from Meredith Lloyd.—Memorandum, Mr. Parker tells me that Mr. [John] Oliver the City surveyor, had his father Marshall's inscriptions and papers; ergo vide there for the Doctor's inscription & also for the ISS of Inigo Jones.

Dr William Harvey—ex libro meo B[1]

Over Dr Harvey's Picture in the great Parlour under the Library at the Physitians' College at Amen-corner (burnt):

Gul. Harveus, an. aetat 10 in Schola Cantuar. primis doctrinae rudimentis imbutus; 14 Col. Gonvil. et Caii alumnus; 19 peragavit Galliam et Italiam; 23 Patavii praeceptores habuit Eust. Rudium, Tho. Minad, H. Fab. ab Aquapend.; Consul Anglor. 16 fit; 24 Doctor Med. et Chirurg. Reversus Lond. praxin exercuit et uxorem duxit; 25 Coll. Med. Socius; 37 Anatom. et Chirurg. Professor; 54 Medicus Regius factus. Scripsit de Motu Sanguinis et de Gen. Animal. Obiit 30 Jun. MDCLVII. Aetat. 80.

—(But I well remember that Dr Alsop in his Funerall sayd that he was 80 wanting one; and that he was the eldest of 9 Brethren.)

---

* MS. Aubr. 23, fol. 121ᵛ. † MS. Aubr. 6, fol. 64. ‡ MS. Aubr. 23, fol. 108ᵛ.
§ MS. Aubr. 6, fol. 66ᵛ. || MS. Aubr. 8, fol. 18.

[1] Vol. B of Aubrey's antiquarian collections, now lost.

He lies buried in a Vault at Hempsted in Essex, which his Brother Eliab Harvey built; he is lapt in lead and on his brest in great letters

DR WILLIAM HARVEY

I was at his Funerall & helpt to carry him into the vault.

In the library at the Physitians' Colledge was this following IS above his statue (which was in his Doctorall Robes):

GUL. HARVEUS, natus A.D. 1578 Apr. 2. Folkston in Com Cantii, Primogenitus Thom: Harvei et Joannae Halk: Fratres Germani, Tho. Jo. Dan. Eliab. Mich. Mat.: sorores Sarah, Amey.

Under his white marble statue on the Pedestall thus

GULIELMO HARVEO

Viro

Monumentis suis immortali

Hoc insuper

Coll. Med. Lond.

Posuit.

Qui enim SANGUIN. MOTUM

(ut et ANIMAL. ORTUM) dedit

meruit esse

STATOR Perpetuus

*Dr Harvey added (or was very bountifull in contributing to) a noble building of Roman Architecture (of Rustique worke with Corinthian pillasters) at the Physitians' College aforesaid, viz. a great parlour (a kind of Convocation house) for the Fellowes to meet in belowe; and a Library above. On the outside on the Freeze in letters 3 inches long is this inscription:

SUASA ET CURA FRAN. PRUJEANI PRAESIDIS ET EDMUNDI SMITH ELECT. INCHOATA ET PERFECTA EST HÆC FABRICA. AN. MIƆCLIII.

All these Remembrances & Building was destroyed by the generall fire.

He was always very contemplative & the first that I heare of that was curious in Anatomie in England. He had made Dissections of Frogges, Toades & a number of other Animals and had curious observations on them, which papers together with his goods in his lodgings at Whitehall were plundered at the beginning of the Rebellion, he being for the king & with him at Oxon; but he often sayd that of all the losses he sustained no greife was so crucifying to him as the losse of these papers, which for love nor money he could never retrive or obtaine. When the king Charles I by reason of the Tumults left London, he attended him & was at the fight of Edge-hill with him; & during the fight

* MS. Aubr. 6, fol. 64.

the Prince & D. of Yorke were committed to his care. He told me that he withdrew with them under a hedge & tooke out of his pockett a booke and read;
but he had not read very long before a Bullet of a great Gun grazed on the
ground neare them, which made him remove his station; he told me that Sir
Adrian Scrope was dangerously wounded there & left for dead amongst the
dead men stript; which happened to be the saving of his Life. It was cold cleer
weather & a frost that night; which staunched his bleeding and about midnight,
or some houres after his hurt, he awaked and was faine to drawe a dead body
upon him for warmeth-sake.

After Oxford was surrendred, which was 24 July [June] 1646 he came to
London & lived with his brother Eliab a [great *del.*] rich merchant in London
on . . . hill opposite to St. Lawrence (Poultry) church [St. Dunstan's church in
the *del.*], where was then a high leaden steeple (there were but two viz. this and
St. Dunstan's in the East) and at his brother's Country house at Roe-hampton.

His brother Eliab bought about 1654 Cockaine-house now (1680) the Excise-
Office, a noble house, where the Doctor was wont to contemplate on the
Leads of the house & had his severall stations in regard of the Sun or wind; he
did delight to be in the darke & told me he could then best contemplate. He
had a house heretofore at Combe in Surrey, a good aire & prospects where he
had Caves made in the Earth in which in sumer time he delighted to meditate.
He was pretty well versed in the Mathematiques and had made himselfe master
of Mr Oughtred's Clavis Math. in his old age; & I have seen him perusing it
and working problems not long before he dyed & that booke was alwayes in
his meditating apartment.

his chamber was that roome that is now the office of Elias Ashmole Esq.,
where he dyed, being taken with the dead palsye, which tooke away his speech.
As soone as he sawe he was attaqued he presently sent for his brother & nephews
& gave one a watch, another another thing etc. as remembrances of him. He
dyed worth 20,000 *li.* which he left to his brother Eliab. In his Will he left his
old friend Mr Th: Hobbes 10 *li.* as a token of his Love.

His sayings: He was wont to say that man was but a great miscievous Baboon.

He would say that we Europeans knew not how to order or governe our
Woemen and that the Turkes were the only people used them wisely.

He was far from bigotry.

He had been Physitian to the Ld Ch. Bacon, whom he esteemed much for his
witt & style, but would not allow him to be a great Philosopher. 'He writes
Philosophy like a Lord Chancellor,' said he to me, speaking in derision, 'I have
cured him'.

About 1649 he travelled again into Italy, Dr George (now Sir George) Ent
then accompanying him.

At Oxford he grew acquainted with Dr Charles Scarborough, then a young
Physitian (since by king Charles II knighted), in whose conversation he much
delighted; & whereas before he marched up and downe with the Army, he

tooke to him & made him ly in his Chamber & said to him, 'prithee leave off thy gunning & stay here; I will bring thee into Practise'.

I remember he kept a pretty young wench to wayte on him, which I guesse he made use of for warmth-sake as King David did, & tooke care of her in his Will, as also of his man servant.

For 20 yeares before he dyed he tooke no manner of care about his worldly concernes, but his brother Eliab, who was a very wise & prudent manager, ordered all not only faithfully, but·better then he could have donne himselfe.

He was, as all the rest of the Brothers, very Cholerique; & in his younge days wore a dagger (as the fashion then was, nay I remember my old schoolemaster, [old *del.*] Mr Latimer at 70 wore a Dudgeon with a knife & bodkin, as also my old grandfather Lyte & Alderman Whitson of Bristowe, which I suppose was the common fashion in their young dayes), but this Dr would be to apt to draw-out his dagger upon every slight occasion.

He was not tall, but of the lowest stature, round faced, olivaster like wainscott in complexion, little eie, round, very black, full of spirit; his hair was black as a Raven, but quite white 20 yeares before he dyed.

I first sawe him at Oxford, 1642, after Edgehill fight, but was then too young to be acquainted with so great a Doctor. I remember he came severall times to our Trin. Coll. to George Bathurst B.D., who had a Hen to hatch Egges in his chamber, which they dayly opened to discerne [*duplicated with* see] the progres & way of Generation. I had not the honour to be acquainted with him [to know him *del.*] till 1651, being my she cos. Montague's physitian & friend. I was at that time bound for Italy (but to my great griefe disswaded by my mother's importunity). He was very communicative & willing to instruct any that were modest & respectfull to him. And in order to my journey gave me, i.e. dictated to me, what company to keepe, what bookes to read, how to manage my studies: in short, he bid me goe to the fountain head & read Aristotle, Cicero, Avicen., & did call the neoteriques shitt-breeches. He wrot a very bad hand, which (with use) I could pretty well read.

Elsewhere (Aubrey MS. 6, fol. 61) he noted other parts of this conversation:

Vesalius
Bauhinus Anthocologia
J. Riolani
_____
de oculo
_____
Julius Placentinus: *de oculo et*
auditu
de oculo et visione
Fabricius Aquapendente

Ad legendos hosce bonos autores cohortatus sum a doctore Gulielmo Harveo.

I have heard him say that after his Booke of the Circulation of the Blood came-out, that he fell mightly in his Practize and that 'twas beleeved by the vulgar that he was crack-brained; and all the Physitians were against his Opinion and envyed him; many wrote against him, as Dr Primrose, Paracisanus, etc. (vide Sir George Ent's booke); with much adoe at last, in about 20 or 30 yeares time, it was receivd in all the Universities in the world, &, as Mr Hobbes sayes in his book *de Corpore*, he is the only man, perhaps, that ever lived to see his owne Doctrine established in his life-time.

He understood Greek & Latin pretty well, but was no Critique and he wrote very bad Latin. The Circuit. Sang. was, as I take it, donne into Latin by Sir George Ent (quaere), as also his Booke de Generatione Animalium, but a little book in 12° against Riolani (I thinke), wherein he makes-out his doctrine clearer, was writt by him selfe, & that, as I take it, at Oxford.

His majestie King Ch. I gave him Wardenship of Merton Colledge in Oxford as a reward for his service, but the Times suffred him not to receive or injoy any benefitt by it.

He was Physitian and a great Favorite of the Lord High Marshall of England, Tho. [William *del.*] Howard, Earle of Arundel and Surrey, with whom he travelled as his Physitian in his Ambassade to the Emperor . . . at Vienna A° Dm̄ 163–. Mr W. Hollar (who was then one of his Excellencie's Gentlemen) told me that in his Voyage he would still be making of excursions into the Woods makeing Observations of strange Trees and plants, earths etc. naturalls and sometimes like to be lost, So that my Lᵈ Ambassador would be really angry with him, for there was not only danger of Thieves, but also of wild beasts.

He was much and often troubled with the Gowte and his way of Cure was thus: he would then sitt with his Legges bare, if it were Frost, on the leads of Cockaine-house, putt them into a payle of water till he was almost dead with Cold and betake himselfe to his Stove, and so 'twas gonne.

He was hott-headed, and his thoughts working would many times keepe him from sleepinge; he told me that then his way was to rise out of his Bed and walke about his Chamber in his Shirt till he was pretty coole, i.e. till he began to have a horror, and then returne to bed and sleepe very comfortably.

I remember he was wont to drinke Coffee, which he and his brother Eliab did before Coffee-houses were in fashion in London.

All his Profession would allowe him to be an excellent Anatomist, but I never heard of any that admired his therapeutique way. I knew severall practisers in this Towne London that would not have given 3ᵈ for one of his Bills and that a man could hardly tell by one of his Bills what he did aime at.

He did not care for Chymistrey and was wont to speake against them with an undervalue.

It is now fitt and but just that I should endeavour to undecieve the World in a Scandall that I find strongly runnes of him, which I have mett amongst some learned young men: viz. that he made himselfe a way to putt himselfe out of his paine, by opium; not but that, had he laboured under great paines, he had been readie enough to have donne it; I doe not deny that it was not according to his Principles upon certain occasions to . . .: but the manner of his dyeing was really, and *bona fide*, thus, viz. the morning of his death about 10 a clock he went to speake and found he had the dead palsey in his Tongue; then he sawe what was to become of him, he knew there was then no hopes of his recovery, so presently sends for his young nephewes to come-up to him, to whom he gives one his Watch ('twas a minute watch with which he made his experiments); to another, another remembrance, etc.; made signe to . . . Sambroke, his Apothecary (in Black-Fryars), to lett him blood in the tongue, which did little or no good; and so he ended his dayes. His practise was not very great towards his later end; he declined it unlesse to a speciall friend—e.g. my lady Howland, who had a cancer in her Breast, which he did cutt-off & seared, but at last she dyed of it.

He rode on horseback with a Foot-cloath to visitt his Patients,* his man following on foote, as the fashion then was, which was very decent, now quite discontinued. The Judges rode also with their Foote-cloathes to Westminster-hall, which ended at the death of Sir Rob. Hyde, L^d. Ch. Justice. Anthony Earl of Shafton would have revived, but severall of the judges being old & ill horsemen would not agree to it.

Lettres on naturalls: [quaere] Mr Samb[roke].

The scandall aforesaid is from Sir Charles Scarborough's saying that he had, towards his latter end, a preparation of Opium and I know not what, which he kept in his study to take, if occasion should serve, to putt him out of his paine, & which Sir Charles promised to give him; This I beleeve to be true; but doe not at all beleeve that he really did give it him. The Palsey did give him an easie Passe-port.

I remember I have heard him say he wrote a booke de insectis, which he had been many yeares about, & had made curious researches and anatomicall observations on them; this booke was lost when his lodgings at Whitehall were plundered in the time of the Rebellion: he could never for love nor money retrive them or heare what became of them and sayed *'twas the greatest crucifying to him that ever he had in all his life.*

†Dr Harvy told me & any one if he examines himself will find it to be true, That a man could not fancy—truthfully—that he is imperfect in any part that he has, v.g. teeth, eie, tongue, spina dorsi, etc. Natura tends to perfection and in matters of generation we ought to consult more with our sense & instinct then our reason & prudence, fashion of the Country and Interest. We see what contemptible [despicable *del.*] products are of the prudent politiques, weake fooles

---

* I have seen him ride in 1654 or 5.

† MS. Aubr. 21, fol. 12. These passages are from Aubrey's projected comedy, *The Country Revel.* The sowgelder is dissuading Sir John Fitz-ale from marrying a widow.

& ricketty children, scandalls to nature & their country. The Heralds are fooles
—tota errant via. A blessing goes with a marriage for love upon a strong
impulse.

Sowgelder. To see, Sir John, how much you are mistaken; he that marries a
widdowe makes himself cuckold. Exempli gratia, to speake experimentally and
in my trade, if a good bitch is first warded with a curre, let her ever after be
warded with a dog of a good straine and yet she will bring curres as at first, her
wombe being first infected with a curre. So the children will be like the first
husband (like raysing up children to your brother). So the adulterer, though a
crime in law, the children are like the husband.

Sir John. Thou dost talke me thinks more understandingly of these matters
then any one I have mett with.

Sowgelder. Ah! my old friend Dr Harvey—I knew him right well—he made
me sitt by him 2 or 3 hours together discoursing. Why! had he been stiffe,
proud, starcht & retired, as other formall Doctors are, he had known no more
then they. From the meanest person in some way or other the learnedst man
may learn something. Pride has been one of the greatest stoppers [retarders *del.*]
of the Advancement of Learning.

II. *Prescriptions for Mrs. Lucia Troute (aet. 14), 1652*

(*Transcribed and annotated by Dr. Gweneth Whitteridge*)

Dr Harvey's direction for a dyett drinke for Mistress Lucia Troute February
1652, for the Kings Evill, not the malignant Evil but the white Evill.

$\frac{m}{\overset{\text{i}}{m}}$ Take the wood of Guiacum 3 oz. infuse it for 24 howers in 6 pints of springe
water afterwards boyle it to the consumpcion of halfe addinge to it of the leaves
of Bittany 3 handfulls, Tamaris one handfull, Coriander seeds 2 scruples, the
leaves of Scenna 4 oz., Rhubarb one oz., sweete fennell seeds one oz. Lett it be
boyled to the halfe addinge to it the fruite of Tamarinds ½ an oz., the best
manna 3 oz. and of clarified honey 3 oz. Then straine it and take 3 or 4 oz. at a
tyme for a dose every morninge. If for a child then the halfe quantity to be made.

After The Dr directed the swellinge to be opened by a Chirurgion in the
nature of an issue and a pease to be put therein and a plaster to kepe the same
in it, but the soare beinge ripe, which . . .[1] broake it selfe next day, but the
directions was followed.

April 53. after the soare was broke and had rune, then in Apr.[2] 56. direct the
dyet drinke followinge:

1 Take a handfull of Bugle and a handfull of Bittany and a sprigg of tyme,
  boyle these in water and whitwyne and lett her drinke morninge and in the
  afternoone at 4 of the clocke.

[1] Three more words here above the line inserted over a caret are illegible.
[2] The reading seems to be right, but the meaning is not clear.

2 This plaister to be applyed to the soare:

Take a handfull of Redd sage, boyle it in a pinte of Smithes water to halfe a pint then straine the liquor and add it to that underwritten which the Appothecary makes and then wett soe much lint therein as will cover the soare and soe apply it and cover it with a plaister to make it sticke.

That which the Dr appointed the Appothecary to make and was to be mingled with the smiths water was as followeth:

3 Take burn't vitriol, verdigrease, burn't Allum, of each 2 drams, fine bolalminacke[1] one drame, soe mingle it with an oz. of honey of roses and keep it for your use.

The plaister wich covered the lynt and soare was spred with cerat diachilon simple.

[British Museum, MS. Sloane 206A f. 138.]

Febr. 1653. Dr. Harvey prescribed Mistress Lucia Troute she beinge weake this followinge Electuary:

R fol. sennae pulv.,[2]
   radicum rusci, sarsaparillae,
   radicum scrophulariae, ana ℥ j.
   radicis jalappae ℨ j.
   trochisci de viperis optimi[3] ℥ ij.
   electuarii lenitivi[4] q.s.
   cum conserva rosarum damascenarum.[5]
   Elect. cap. singulo mane q.[6] nucis moschatae vel juglantis . . .[7]

The plaister for the soare, for after one was healed it brake out in another place:

R diachyl. simpl. ℥ iij.
   matanstur[8] cum pinguedine hominis q.s. et
   unguento à floribus Aurantiorum ℨ j.
   Fiat ceratum pro summit.

After the child have a could and cough and a swellinge under her Arme the Dr prescribed as followeth, first for a broth she being in a consumpcion speene[1] and the scurvey:

To a pint of water infuse 1 oz. of china thyn sliced. After 12 howers infusion maker broth thereof and put in scabious, mayden haire and folefoote, fresh water cresses which byte the tongue and a sprige of winter savery and French barley first scalded in other water, raisins stoned, currants and one slice of Spanish liquorice scraped.

---

[1] So written, but not understood.   [2] *Pharmacopoeia Londinensis*, 1638, p. 70.
[3] Ibid., p. 115.   [4] Ibid., p. 93.   [5] Ibid., p. 53.
[6] Seems to be a *q*; but *cum* would have been expected. Perhaps this *q* stands for *quum*?
[7] The last two words uncertain; it should be the amount of nutmeg and walnut.
[8] This seems to be what is written. Probably a mistake for *miscetur*.

1 July 1655. Dr Harvey prescribed another Electuary:

[*The receipt is not given and the remainder of the folio is blank except for a note written across the bottom which reads*:

I shall endeavour to supply you with the Recipes here intended as soone as I finde them which at present are mislayde.]

[British Museum, MS. Sloane 206A, f. 138 verso]

Another Electuary of Dr Harvey's for Mistress Lucia Trout the 20 of March 1655 when the greate soare under her chynn brake:

Take of diaphaenicon one ounce, of the trochiske of vipers 2 drams, of sarsa-parilla and of China rootes in powder and of scena of each 2 drams, of Rubarb and Agaricke of each one dram, of Jalop 2 scruples, of Cassia newly drawne 3 drams, of the species of diacodion abbatis and of the trochiske of Alkakengi[1] in powder of each one scruple. Make this accordinge to Arte with the forme of an Electuary whereof take every newe and full moone the quantity of a Chesnutt at a tyme. If it worke not well and answerable to desire the next tyme Augment the quantity of as much more. (*In the margin*: After this directe her to drinke swete wyne.)

13 March 1659 (Dr Harvey then dead) Dr Pruieans prescription for Mistress Lucy Troute (14 ans) he seeinge some of Dr Harveys Recipes. Take etc.

[British Museum, MS. Sloane 206A, f. 139]

Prescriptions for John Aubrey, 1653–5

(*Transcribed and annotated by Dr. Gweneth Whitteridge*)

Mr Aubrye Ap. 23 1653

R̸ fol. sennae ℥ ſs.[2]
 Rhubarbari, Agarici,
 Radicis Hellebori nigri,
 Seminarum anisi,
  foeniculi, ana ʒ i.
 liquoris hissopi magistralis ʒ i ſs.
 passularum P.[3] i.

---

[1] See *Pharmacopoeia Londinensis*, p. 116.

[2] Of the purgatives listed in this prescription rhubarb and the syrup of red roses were considered effective against yellow bile, senna and hellebore against black bile, agaric against phlegm. Fernel puts rhubarb, agaric, and senna half-way between the violent and the mild purgatives. Aniseed and fennel are included for their carminative properties.

[3] i.e. a pinch of dried grapes, currants, raisins, or perhaps more probably here prunes. P = *pugillus* and is equal to half a *manipulus* (M), a handful; it is defined as the amount that can be picked up with the thumb and two fingers. Prunes were classified by Fernel among the 'benign' purgatives.

Fiat decoctio in aquae et vini albi ana q. s. ad colaturae ℥ iiij ſs.
Adde syrupi magistralis purgantis ad Melancholiam,[1]
> syrupi rosacei solutivi,[2] ana. ℥ i.
> aquae cinnamomi[3] guttae vj.

Misce.
Capiat cum custodia.

Postera die emittatur sanguis ex vena hepatica dextri brachii ad ℥ ij.

℞ radicorum 5 communium aperientivorum[4] ana ℥ i.
> radicis lappae[5] ℨ i.

---

[1] According to the *Pharmacopoeia Londinensis* of 1638, p. 36, this syrup was compounded in the following manner:

> ℞ Succi Pomorum odoriferorum (vulgò *Pearemaynes*) sesquilibram.
> > Borraginis, Buglossi, ana uncias novem.
> Fol: Sennae orientalis mundatae semilibram.
> Semin: Anisi, Foeniculi dulcis, ana drachmas tres.
> > Epithymi Cretensis uncias duas.
> > Agarici albissimi, Rhabarbari optimi, ana semunciam.
> > Zingiberis, Macis, ana scrupulos quatuor.
> > Cinnamomi scrupulos duos.
> > Croci semidrachmam.
>
> Agaricus et Senna concisa cum seminibus, Zingibere, atque Mace crassiusculè contusis, macerentur cum Epithymo in succis praescriptis, horas viginti quatuor. Bulliant deinde lento igne, usque ad despumationem, et per manicam Hippoc: colentur. Colaturae jam factae adjiciatur Sacchari albissimi sesquilibra, et coquantur s. a. nec sine despumatione, ad consistentiam Syrupi, modò inter coquendum, Crocus panno lineo ligatus infricetur. Tum demùm admisceatur Infusio Rhabarbari concisi, cum Cinnamomo crassiusculè contuso, in Vini albi, et succi Pomorum, ana unciis duabus, interim facta, et fortiter expressa. Denuò ferveant parùm commista ad ignem pro syrupo.

[2] The recipe for its preparation is given in the *Pharmacopoeia Londinensis*, p. 29:

> ℞ Infusionis Rosarum ex Rosis pallidis Damascenis recentibus novies infusis (infusio fiat eâ proportione ut pro qualibet libra Rosarum sumantur aquae librae quatuor in quibus, rejectis prioribus floribus, recentes infundantur) libras sex. Sacchari libras quatuor.
> > fiat decoctio s. a. in syrupum.

From the same source it appears that this preparation was attributed to Mesue, the ninth-century Arabian pharmacologist Iachiâ Ibn Masawâch, whose works were first printed in Venice in 1471 and appeared in nineteen different editions before the sixteenth century.

[3] See *Pharmacopoeia Londinensis*, p. 6:

> ℞ Cinnamomi contusi libram unam semis.
> Vini Hispanici libras duodecim.
> Macerentur et distillentur per Alembicum. Extrahendo fortioris lib. iij. tenuioris q. s. Stillatitio liquori addatur Sacchari purissimi in tenuissimum pollinem redacti, quantum satis.

[4] These were: *apium, asparagus, foeniculum, petroselinum,* and *ruscum.*
[5] Probably *Lappa minor,* which is *xanthium* or burweed.

corticis radicis tamariski ℥ iij.

florium borradginis, violarum recentium, ana P. i.

passularum ℥ fs.

seminarum nula : concris : ℥ i fs.[1]

fiat decoctio in aquae hordei q. s. ad lib. i fs.

cui adde aquae cichorii, endivae, borradginis, ana ℥ ij.

      vini Rhenani ℥ iij.

      oxymellis julianisantis ℥[2] ij.

misce.

Capiat bis in die ℥ iiij.

Et quinto quoque die repetitur purgatio.

℞ Unguenti citrini optimi ℥ ij.

Cerussae praeparatae Ɖ ij.

Aquae cinnamomi parum, viz : guttae vj.

Olei terebinthinae[3] guttae iij.

Olei ligni Rhodii Citrinini[4] guttae iij.

Misce.

Pro litu.

At the foot is added:

This is Dr Wm. Harvey's owne Writing.

---

[1] The second and third words, although apparently legible, have not been deciphered. The first word is almost certainly an abbreviation for *seminarum*. The second word looks as though it reads *nula*, which could be an abbreviation *nummulariarum*, i.e. 'of pennyworts', but the seeds of this plant do not seem to have been used medicinally, only the leaves or the whole plant (see Gerarde, 1633, p. 529). The last word looks as though it should be *cancris*, but *cancri* is the genitive of *cancer*, a crab, and Harvey would not make a mistake of this kind. It could read *concris* and be an abbreviation for *concrispus*, or something similar with the right ending, in which case it would mean 'curled', but this is not found used with *nummularia*, so that these seeds are not identified. Harvey is not here prescribing any part of the anatomy of a crab.

[2] See *Pharmacopoeia Londinensis*, p. 44 :

    ℞ Corticum radicum Capparum,

      Radic : Ireos, Foeniculi, Petroselini, Řusci, Cichorii, Asparagi, Cyperi, ana unciam dimidiam.

      Herb : Scolopendriae, Scoenanthûs, Tamaricis, ana manipul. medium.

      Semin : Foeniculi dulcis unciam dimidiam.

    Coquantur post debitam infusionem in Poscae* acidioris libris tribus ad libram unam semis : ex colatura cum

      Mellis optimi, et Sacchari despumatorum, ana libra dimidia.

    Fiat decoctio ad syrupi consistentiam.

(* Posca fit ex Aqua et Aceto, idque ex re praesenti, vel acidior, vel dilutior, pro intentione Medici.)

[3] See ibid., p. 178.

[4] Presumably that kind of rosewood called by Gerarde *Aspalathus albicans torculo citreo*, White Rose-wood (1633, p. 1624).

Dr. Harveys bill for my purge to prevent an Impostumation.

November 19. 1655.

℞ fol. sennae ℈ ſs.
   et ℥ ij Rhubarbari, Agarici.
   Seminarum feniculi, coriandri, ana ℈ j.
   Tamarindi ℥ iij.
   Liquoris hiſſopi ℥ j ſs.
   Paſſularum, florium Borraginis, violarum, ana P. j.
   Fiat decoctio in aquae vel vini albi ad q. s. ad colaturae ℥ iiij.
   Syrupi rosacei solutivi, Mannae, elebori, ana ℥ ſs.
   Misce
   Capiat cum custodia.

For Mr Jo: Aubrey.
from his honoured friend Dr Harvey.

Added at the foot:

The ℞ is Dr Harveys own handwriting.

Harvey's Water-Cider Drink

Sir Kenelme Digby: *The Closet Opened*, London, 1671 (third edition, 1677), pp. 95–96: Dr. Harvey's pleasant Water-Cider, whereof he used to drink much, making it his ordinary Drink.

Take one bushel of Pippins, cut them into slices with the parings and cores; boil them in twelve gallons of water, till the goodness of them be in the water; and that consumed about three gallons. Then put it into an Hippo-cras-bag, made of Cotton; and when it is clear run out, and almost cold, sweeten it with five pounds of brown Sugar, and put a point of Ale-yeast to it, and set it a working two nights and days: Then skim off the yeast clean, and put it into bottles, and let it stand two or three days, till the yeast fall dead at the top: then take it off with a clean knife, and fill it up a little within the neck (that is to say, that a little about a finger's breadth of the neck be empty, between the superficies of the liqour and the bottom of the stopple) and then stop them up and tye them, or else it will drive out the Corks. Within a fortnight you may drink of it. It will keep five or six weeks.

Prescriptions Preserved by Dr. John Hall

Dr. John Hall, Shakespeare's son-in-law, quoted two prescriptions by Harvey in his book: *Select Observations on English Bodies of Eminent Persons in desperate Diseases. First written in Latin by Mr. John Hall, Physician: After Englished by James Cook, Author of the Marrow of Chirurgery.* London. 8°. 1679.

Second century Observation xliii. 131:

One of Northampton . . . now being vexed with a virulent Gonorhea, he took the following pouder for ten days . . . and by this he became well. But after riding to London (by what occasion I know not) it broke forth again, where he had the advice of Doctor Harvy, who prescribed what follows:

> ℞ Troch. Rhasis alb. ʒ ſs Troch. Gord. Э i Aloes opt. ʒ ii ſs Penidior ʒ i ſs Aq. Plantag. lb. ſs. Inject.

The following Electuary he used at night; the quantity of a Bean, when he went to bed:

> ℞ Troch. Alkekerg. cum Opio ʒ ſs Syr. Limon. q. s. Gum Tragacanth, Mastich, Crystal præp. Coral præp. ā Э i f. Elect.

By these he was again restored. After he went to St. Vincent's Well, and was better by their use. After this, being hurt with the forcing in a Pipe to remove a Caruncle by a Chirurgeon, he again relapsed, and never was cured.

Prescriptions and Instructions for Heneage Finch

Harvey's prescriptions and instructions for Heneage Finch were copied by Finch into his commonplace book, which is now in the library of the College of Physicians of Philadelphia. The book remained in the possession of the Finch family until about 1867. Later it belonged to Edward Almack, F.S.A., and in 1906 was bought by Dr. S. Weir Mitchell of Philadelphia, who bequeathed it to the College of Physicians. The book was described by Weir Mitchell in *Some Memoranda in regard to William Harvey*, New York, 1907, pp. 13–17. The relevant pages of the manuscript have been supposed to be in Harvey's hand, but it is clear that they are copies of the original.

Let Mr Finch first take his clyster about fore of the clock in the afternoone, and after take his purge early in the next morning so as Hee may sleepe after it untill it worke, but after it beginneth to worke let Him not sleepe and keepe his chamber.

The next day About eight or nine of the clock let Him bleed out of the arme eight or nine ounce of blood; afterwards continue to take his Apozem for three weekes or a moneth twice in the day, A draft early in the morning and at fower in the afternoon, and walke abroad and use moderate exercise.

And while Hee taketh this once in five or six dayes take his purge againe or if that worke much take two or three pills as big as pease either an howre before supper, or going to bed, if taking them before supper worke in the night, before next morning.

When Hee taketh his pills He needeth not much observance of keeping in, but may drinke a draft of his Apozem after them.

But that day Hee taketh his Apozem let Him keepe in and drinke after them a little thin broth.

After Hee hath continued in this course of cleering his body 14 or 15 dayes let Him every morning before Hee arise out of his bed have his belly and sides rubbed and chaffed in with a soft hand for all most an howre together, and then taking his drinke, arise and walke abroad early. All this while Hee taketh this physicke let his dyet bee temperate, of on[e] dish, rise early, walke much, abstaine from wine, strong drinke and all salt meates.

Harvey

℞ Decoct: Commis emollient lb i. Mellis ros. sol. Mellis Anthosal. ana ʒ i ſs spec: Hieræ ʒ i ſ Olei Chamomel violac: ana ʒi misce: capiat hora quarta pomerid: pro clyst: et die sequente

℞ Fol. senæ ʒ v Rhabarb: Agari: ana ʒ i. Semen fæniculi dulcis et flor: violar: ana Ə iiii Radi: Hellebor niger Ə ii Liqueris Hispan: ras ʒ i ſs fiat decoctio in aqua et vino albo q.s. ad colatur: ʒ iii adde syrup: ros. sol. ʒ i vel ʒ ii aquæ cinnamom. guttæ v misce: capiat summo mane cum custod: dosis miniatur et augmentatur prout operabitur.

Post emittatur sanguis e brach: dext: ad ʒ 9

℞ Radic: 5 Comm: in Aceto macerat: ana ʒ i flores violar. recentium m ſs Tamaris virid: m i ſs Cicor: capilli veneris ana m: i Cortex radicis capparis ʒ ii Radic polypod: recentis ʒ i et ʒ ii fumariæ recentis m :i fiat decoctio in aqua optima fontana lb iii et Acet: parte octava et decoquat: ad medias in fine addendo vini albi lb ſs Colaturiae adde Oxymel: Julia: ʒ iii: syrup: Aceto: simpl: ʒ i. misce, capiat bis in die ʒ iiii vell 5 et continuatur per mensem.

Interim sing: quarto vel sexto die, repetatur purgans potio, prius script: vel si plurimam potio operabitur repetatur duntaxat singulo duodecimo die, et capiat quarto die ex pillulis infra scriptis pilllu: iii per horam ante cænam vel hora somni.

℞ : pill: ʒ ... ʒ i pillul: ex Aloe Rasal: ʒ ii olei Absyn: Chymic: gutt. iii misc: fiat mass: pillulæ

Unguentum ex succis Aperetiv: Foesis: ʒ iii: olei Absinth: Chymic: Gutt: 12 olei cappo: ʒ ſs: misce fiat lineamen:

Harvey

The Art of Glass. Written in Italian by Antonio Neri and Translated into English [by Christopher Merrett] *with some observations on the Author*. London. 8°. 1662.

In his *Observations* Merrett described (p. 300) the smelting of brass, made, he said, from copper and *Lapis Calaminaris* (carbonate of zinc) found in Somerset and North Wales. This ore was to be calcined for about five hours in a furnace and then mixed with the copper. It would be found that during the smelting 'half the *calamie* flies away in flour and sticks to the mouth of the furnace . . . I could easily prove these flours to be the true *pompholix* of the ancients, and to be used in the ointment that hath its denomination thence. 'Tis an excellent dryer, and applied to Gleeting Nerves and Tendons without pain, it soon exciteth them. This powder I communicated to the eternal glory of our nation and Anatomy, & an excellent Chirurgion, and never to be by me forgotten, the incomparable Dr. Harvey, a man most curious in all natural things, who confessed he thought this to be the said Pompholix, and with most happy results frequently used it.'

Pompholyx, or 'flowers of zinc', that is, zinc oxide, is a powerful astringent, and was a component of the *Unguentum Diapompholigos* in the *Pharmacopœia* of the College of Physicians.

III. *Harvey's Anatomical Observations*

A paper by William Harvey obtained by Thomas Hollier, lithotomist to St. Thomas's and St. Bartholomew's Hospitals. Read to the Royal Society by Dr. Gale on 4 May 1687 and preserved in their Archives (*Register*, vii. 88). First printed in Birch's *History of the Royal Society*, 1757, vol. iv, pp. 535–7.

'1. All the blood in the body paffeth twice within one hour through the heart, and through the lungs: through the heart to receive vivacity, and new fpirits; through the lungs to receive a temperament of heat.

'2. The panting of the heart is but the pumping about of the blood, in the expanfion receiving, and in the contraction fending it out; and it receives fo much at every expanfion, that confidering the great proportion, and the many beatings of the heart in half an hour, it muft of neceffity come round about.

'3. All the blood comes to the heart by the veins, and is fent from it to the arteries; for there are many little valvulæ in every vein, which open to the heart, but none from it, which is a demonftration to the fenfe of this pofition.

'4. The paffing of the blood through the artery upon the contraction of the heart is the caufe of the pulfe, together with the fpirits, that come with it.

'5. The veins in the body have feveral names, yet have they a general connexion, as if they were truly but one; for blow the umbilical vein of a dead child born, and all the veins in the body will prefently fwell, and be filled with wind.

'6. Every artery runs at laft into a vein, and fo fends back the blood into the heart.

'7. The reafon we find little or no blood in the arteries after men's death, is becaufe they have no valvulæ to retain it, and fo it flides through in the veins.

'8. The reafon our bladders hold wind after our death, which let in water before, is, becaufe thofe various meanders, like the top of a young vein, that run between the two membranes are fhut up, and contracted by death.

'9. The kidney is full of little teats, by which the water drops into the ureters, and when the ftone begins to increafe, then thofe teats begin to excoriate, and being very fenfible parts, are the chief caufe of the pain in the body of the kidney.

'10. It was a cuftom at their antient matches of drinking, to take every one an egg in his hand, and not to ftir, untill they could hatch their eggs in their hands by the extraordinary heat.

'11. The liver doth not give tincture unto the blood, but rather blood difcolours the liver, for we find it blood in the meferaic veins before it comes to the liver. And I have feen perfect blood in an egg, before there hath been any liver.

'12. The liver and fpleen do not differ in fubftance; only the great quantity of blood in the fpleen, and more corrupt blood, makes it to look fomewhat bluer.

'13. As the firft concoction comes to the liver, fo what is left of that concoction in the ftomach, as yet crude, and what hath paffed beyond the firft concoction into the upper part of the gut, is laboured by the fpleen, and by it prepared for the liver.

'14. I have feen a goofe, that hath had the cœcum almoft full of chylus, and yet beyond all that chylus nothing but excrement; which how fhe can eject without defiling the chylus is to me a miracle.

'15. The pancreas or fweet-bread is as a foft pillow to the veins and arteries, and keeps them from twifting, and intorting one about another.

'16. All arteries are ftronger than veins, and every artery hath its greateft ftrength nigh the heart, becaufe there it fuffers the force and impulfion of the heart, in the emiffion from the blood, in a great remiffion from the heart. An artery cannot be diftinguifhed from a vein, but by the valvulæ.

'17. The heart, that hangs in its lunula almoft juft in the midft of the body, hath two veffels. One receives the blood from the veins, and fends it to the lungs; the other receives it from the lungs, and fends it to the arteries.

'18. In fears and forrow, phyfic; becaufe the mind works ftronger upon the body, than the phyfic.

'19. The diaphragma is that, which caufeth the hiccough, vomitings, fternutations, and fneezings; laughter is but a convulfion.

'20. The diaphragma is fo exceeding fenfible, and of fo different a fenfe from the reft, that I am almoft induced to think it the organ of the fixth fenfe.

'21. The fame mufcles, that ferve for expelling excrements, are alfo caufes of parturition, and fending out the fœtus.

'22. Cut a vein, and the blood will run out; cut an artery, and it will fpurt out; which is another demonftration, that it flows from the impulfion of the heart.

'23. The caufe of fleep is this, that when the foporiferous veins are full, and grow heavy, they fall upon the arteries of the fenfes, and fo by little and little ftop up their paffage, and at laft hinder their operation; and as the foporiferous begins to rife, fo men begin to wake.

'24. The brain and the marrow are the fame fubftance, and one receives nutriment from the other.

'25. Children's kidneys are like thofe of veal, full of little rundles, and they grow into a compact intire fubftance afterwards.

'26. Blood comes originally from the heart; firft becaufe there is no life without blood, and the heart lives firft; fecondly becaufe all the veins are greater, nigher the heart, than the liver.

'27. Many men die backward, for wind enters at the fundament, and fills the guts; the guts beginning to fwell blow up the liver and the heart; there the lungs, and fo the party is fuffocated. Or cut the navel, that by many ligaments holds down thefe parts, and the man is prefently ftrangled.

'28. All the fibræ have a natural contraction in themfelves; for take one of them in a party dead; and ftretch it in your hand, and it will contract of itfelf.

'29. The prefent information and intelligence from our firft part to another, is very admirable; for when one makes a blow at my hand, my eye is the fentinel, and firft difcovers it, and that informs my common fenfe my reafon, my reafon my will, my will the fpirits, the fpirits the arteries, thefe my mufcles, thofe my hand to arife to my general defence, and all this almoft in an inftant.

'30. The brain is divided juft in the middle with a membrane, which they call futh:[1] no part of the body is fo full of veins, as the brain.

'31. The membrances about the brain both dura and pia are called matres, becaufe all other membranes in the body are derived from them.

'32. The omentum or caul is to keep the guts in due order, when we ride, or ftir, left they fhould twift, or knit, and fo there could be no paffage for the excrement, which would be prefent death.

'33. I have feen a man's fpleen on the right fide removed with the hand, with much art and labour, in his proper place.

'34. No creatures in proportion have fo great a fpleen and brain, as a man.'

IV. *The Reception of Harvey's Doctrine during his Lifetime, 1628–1657*

(Based, with permission, on Dr. E. Weil's 'Echo of Harvey', *Journal of the History of Medicine* (1957), xii. 167–74)

1628

GASSENDI, Pierre (1592–1655), *Viri illustris N. C. F. de Peiresc vita*, The Hague, 1655. See the English translation, *The Mirrour of True Nobility and Gentility*, London, 1657, pp. 28–29, under the date 1628: 'When I had given him notice that Dr William Harvey, an English Phyfitian, had set out an excellent Book of the passage of the blood out of the Veins into the Arteries, and back out of the

---

[1] That is, the *sythe*, or *falx cerebri*.

Arteries into the Veins, by secret Anastomoses; and that among other Arguments, he confirmed the same by the valves of the Veins, touching which he had heard somewhat from *Aquapendens*, and whose Inventer he was wont to say was Father *Paul Sarpi* of *Venice*, he would thereupon needs both have the Book and search out those valves and know other things, as those winding passages in the Septum of the heart which *Harvey* denied, but I made appear unto him.' See below under 1650.

1629

FLUDD, Robert (1574–1637), *Medicina Catholica. V. Pulsus seu nova et arcana pulsum historia*, Frankfort, 1631, p. 11: Harvey's doctrine is accepted. Dated at the end: 19 October 1629. (See p. 135.)

1630

GASSENDI, Pierre (1592–1655), *Epistolica exercitatio in qua principia philosophiæ Rob. Fluddi reteguntur*, Paris, 1630. Chiefly criticizing Fludd's book and suggesting that he accepted the circulation only in a mystical way; but on p. 132 he said Fludd should have listened to Harvey, his countryman (*Denique nisi Fluddio comminis explicatio ratio placeret, audiendus forte fuerat Harveus ejus conterraneus*).

See also Gassendi, *Opera*, Florence, 1727, iii. 218–20, where, in a discourse addressed to Mersenne he discussed Harvey's doctrine in the course of *Examen Philosophiæ Roberti Fluddi*.

PRIMROSE, James (*c.* 1598–1659), *Exercitationes et animadversiones in librum G. Harveii de motu cordis et circulatione sanguinis*, London, 1630. The first attack on Harvey to appear in print. Reprinted in 1639. (See p. 320.)

1631

SCHWABE, Jacob, *Wormii Olai et ad eum doctorum virorum epistolæ*, Hafniæ, 1751, i. 460. Schwabe, a Danish student, wrote to Worm after reading Harvey's book. (See p. 321.)

1632

WORM, Ole (1588–1654), *Controversiarum medicarum exercitatio sexta. Controv. v*, Copenhagen, 1632. Worm, a good Galenist, presented a series of careful arguments against Harvey's work here and in later books. (See p. 321.)

1633

DAWSON, Edward (*c.* 1600–35) at the Oxford Act of July 1633 defended for the degree of M.D. the affirmative reply to the question *An circulatio sanguinis sit probabilis*. (See Christopher Hill, 'William Harvey and the idea of Monarchy', *Past and Present* (1964), no. 27, 56–72.)

1634

MERSENNE, P. Marin (1588–1658), *Questiones théologiques et philosophiques*, 1634. Mersenne accepts the idea of the circulation. He had sent a copy of *De motu cordis*, 1628, to Gassendi (Mersenne, *Correspondence*, 1932–55, ii. 181).

1635

GASSENDI, Pierre (1592–1655), *De septo cordis pervio observatio*, in: Severinus, Pinæus, *Opusculum physiologum et anatomicum in duos libellos distinctum*, Leyden, 1650, p. 261: Gassendi's letter to Peiresc on Primrose's *Animadversiones*, 1630, was written 27 October 1635 in defence of Harvey.

PARISANUS, Emilius (1567–1643), *Nobilium exercitationum de subtilitate pars altera de cordis et sanguinis motu singularis certaminis. Ad G. Harveum*, Venice, 1635. Parisanus printed the greater part of Harvey's book in paragraphs alternately with his refutations. Reprinted in 1639. See Keynes, *Bibliography of Harvey*, 1957, pp. 8–9. (See p. 243.)

1636

HOFMANN, Caspar (1572–1648). His letters to Harvey are in *G. Richteri J. C. ejusque familiarum epistolæ selectiores*, Nuremberg, 1662. See Poynter and Franklin in *Journal of the History of Medicine* (1960), xv. 17. (See p. 237.)

RHODE, Johannes (*c.* 1587–1659). In *Laureæ Apollinari*, Padua, 1636. Verses addressed to George Ent when he received his M.D. at Padua, with references to Harvey and the circulation.

1637

DESCARTES, René (1596–1677), *Discours de la méthode pour bien conduire sa raison*, Leyden, 1637, p. 51: Descartes accepted the main part of Harvey's doctrine, though with important reservations. (See p. 321.)

YESLING, Johann (1598–1649), in *Observationes anatomicæ et epistolæ medicæ ex schedis posthumis*, ed. T. Bartholinus, The Hague, 1640. Reprinted Copenhagen, 1644. Vesling's letters to Harvey were first printed here, dated 1637. (See p. 270. Also Vesling's *Responsio* in Licetus, *De motu sanguinis: origine nervorum*, Udine, 1647, pt. vii.)

1638

BEVERWIJK, Jan van (1594–1647), *Exercitatio in Hippocratis aphorismum de calculo. Accedunt doctorum epistolæ*, Leyden, 1641, pp. 190–9: two letters to Harvey with his reply, 1637–8. (See p. 271.)

1639

BOË, Franz de le [SYLVIUS] (1614–72), *Disputationes medicæ*, Amsterdam, 1663. These lectures, recognizing Harvey's work, were given in 1639.

DRAKE, Roger (1608–69), *Disputatio medica de circulatione naturali seu cordis et sanguinis motu circulari pro cl. Harveio*, Leyden, 1640. Drake's thesis was read at Leyden in 1639 in the presence of Jan de Wale. Reprinted in *Vindiciæ contra animadversiones D. D. Primrosii*, London, 1641. (See p. 282.)

FOLLI, Cecilio (1615–60), *Sanguinis à dextro in sinistrum cordis ventriculum defluentis facilis reperta via*, Venice, 1639. In this treatise on the *foramen ovale* Folli praised Harvey for reviving Galen's recognition of the circulation, which had fallen into oblivion, but held that the occurrence of a patent *foramen ovale* refuted Harvey's disbelief in the permeability of the septum.

PRIMROSE, James (*c.* 1598–1659), *Animadversiones in Walæi disputationem quam pro circulatione sanguinis proposuit*, Leyden, 1639. Written against Drake's thesis of the same year. Printed in a composite volume with a reprint of Parisanus and Primrose's tract of 1630. (See p. 320.)

1640

CONRING, Hermann (1606–81), *De sanguinis generatione et motu naturali*, Helmstadt, 1643. The first German recognition of Harvey. The dissertations were read by Conring in 1640. Reprinted at Leyden, 1646.

DU ROY, Henri [REGIUS] (1598–1679), *Spongia, qua eluuntur sordes animadversiorum, quas Jacobus Primirosius adversus theses pro circulatione sanguinis in Academia Ultra-jectina disputatas nuper edidit*, Leyden, 1640. Written in defence of theses by Joan. Haymann and others.

PRIMROSE, James (*c.* 1598–1659), *Antidotum adversus Spongiam*, Leyden, 1640. An attack on Du Roy's *Spongia*, 1640. Reprinted 1644.

WALE, Jan de [WALÆUS] (1604–49), *Epistola: de motu sanguinis ad Thomam Bartholinum*, 1640, pp. 385, 409. In C. Bartholin's *Institutiones anatomicæ*, ed. T. Bartholinus, Leyden, 1641. Reprinted with Harvey's *De motu cordis*, Padua, 1643, and in a longer form, London, 1660. See Keynes, *Bibliography of Harvey*, 1957, nos. 4 and 10.

1641

ENT, George (1604–89), *Apologia pro circulatione sanguinis, qua respondetur Aemilio Parisano, medico Veneto*, London, 1641. Reprinted 1685. (See p. 174.) Ent's original manuscript is in the R.C.P. Library. He said that Sir Henry Wotton took a copy of Harvey's book to Venice and gave it to Sarpi (Father Paul), who transcribed much of the contents for his own use; Sarpi had died, however, in 1623, so that there is some confusion in Ent's version of the story.

ROLFINK, Werner (1599–1673), *Epistolæ duæ ad Th. Bartholinum de motu chyli et sanguinis*, Leyden, 1641. Written in support of Harvey.

WALLIS, John (1616–1703), in *Philosophical Transactions*, 1700–1, xxii. 76. Letter to Edward Tyson, 3 February 1699/1700: 'Dr Glisson hath since told me that I was the First of all his Sons that did (in a public Disputation) maintain Dr Harvey's Circulation of the Blood in the year 1641 (when it was but a new doctrine).' Glisson was Regius Professor of Physic at Cambridge.

1642

BARTHOLIN, Thomas (1616–80), *Epistolæ*, xxiii. 105–7, his letter to Harvey, 14 July 1642, '*Dubia quædam contra circulationem sanguinis*'. (See p. 365.)

The same, pp. 113–15, his letter to Jan de Wale, 30 October 1642, on Harvey and his forerunners.

FORBERGER, Jacobus (1620–82), *Disputatio medica de pulsu et ejus usu*, Prague, 1642. The only copy of this book is in the Prague University Library. In this thesis, defended before Marcus Marci, Forberger summarized the contents of *De motu cordis*, though he did not mention Harvey by name. See V. Kruta, *Physiologia Bohemoslovenica* (1957), vi. 433.

TRULLIUS, Giovanni (1598–1661), In Sinnibaldi's *Geneanthropeia sive de hominis generatione*, Rome, 1642, where Harvey was first openly defended in Italy by Trullius. Reprinted at Frankfort, 1669.

1643

BARTHOLIN, Thomas (1616–80), *Epistolæ*, xxxiv. 132–6, his letter to Severinus, 8 May 1643, defending Harvey, '*De pustulis lucentibus, & viperis*'.

The same, *Epistolæ*, xxx. 124–6, his letter to Ole Worm, 18 June 1643, '*De lucis origine et circulatione nova Liceti*'.

The same, *Epistolæ*, xxxix. 175–7, his letter to Ole Worm, 13 August 1643, '*Dubia de luce & circulatione soluta*'.

BERIGARDO, Claudio (1591–1664), *Circulus Pisanus . . . De veteri et peripatetica philosophia. In tres libros Aristotelis de anima*, Utini, 1643. Circ. v, pp. 28–29, reference to Harvey and Wale. See Pagel and Poynter, *Bulletin of the History of Medicine* (1960), xxxiv. 420.

DESCARTES, René (1596–1677), in Beverwijk's *Epistolicæ quæstiones, cum doctorum responsis*, Rotterdam, 1644, pp. 118–49. Three letters from Descartes on the circulation, the first dated 1643, giving his views very fully and clearly. The letters were translated for Sir William Osler by L. A. Post, whose manuscript is now in the Osler Library, McGill University, Montreal.

LICETUS, Fortunius (1577–1657), in T. Bartholin, *Epistolæ*, xxxvii. 149–72, letter to Bartholin, 13 July 1643, '*De duplici sanguinis euripo*', with an absurd alternative theory of two circulations, venous and arterial, blood being transmitted through the coronary veins.

SEVERINUS, Marcus Aurelius (1580–1656), in T. Bartholin, *Epistolæ*, xxxi. 127–8, letter to Bartholin, 15 April 1643, '*De Harveio judicium*', criticizing Harvey. (See p. 329.)

WORM, Ole (1588–1654), in T. Bartholin, *Epistolæ*, xxxvii. 172–4, letter to Bartholin, 7 July 1643, '*De circulatione dubia*'.

1644

ARGOLI, Andrea (1570–1653), *Pandosion Sphæricum*, Padua, 1644. Contains *De circulatione*, abridged from Harvey without acknowledgement.

BEVERWIJK, Jan van (1594–1647), *De calculo renum et vesicæ. Cum epistolis et consultationibus magnorum virorum*, Leyden, 1644, pp. 20–24. He accepts Harvey's doctrine of the circulation.

DIGBY, Sir Kenelm (1603–65), *Two Treatises*, Paris, 1644, pp. 235, 238, answering Descartes' objections to Harvey. (See p. 322.)

PLEMP, Vopiscus Fortunatus (1601–71), *Fundamenta medicinæ libri VI*, Louvain, 1644, p. 126. He had been an opponent of Harvey, but now acknowledged he was right.

1645

LEICHNER, Eckard (1612–90), *De motu sanguinis: exercitatio anti-Harveiana.* Arnstadt, 1645. Reprinted Jena 1653, Arnstadt, 1665.

1646

HOGELANDE, Cornelius ab (b. 1590), *Cogitationes . . . Nec non, brevis historia œconomiæ corporis animalis*, Amsterdam, 1646, pp. 73–288, giving an account of the heart and circulation based on Harvey, who is acknowledged on p. 195: *cujus benignæ liberalitati hanc cognitionem debemus.*

1647

BACK, Jacobus de (*fl.* 1617), *Dissertatio de corde*, in Harvey's *Exercitatio anatomica de motu cordis et sanguinis*, Rotterdam, 1648. Reprinted with later editions and translated into English 1653. Written in support of Harvey about 1647.

BONACCORSI, Bartholomao, *Della natura de polsi*, Bologna, 1647. Argoli's *Pandosion*, 1644, is criticized, but without mentioning Harvey except erroneously as 'the Pisan Harvey' in connexion with the lacteal vessels (see Pagel and Poynter, *Bulletin of the History of Medicine* (1960), xxxiv. 426–8).

LICETUS, Fortunius (1577–1657), in T. Bartholin, *Epistolarum medicinalium centuria I & II*, Copenhagen, 1663. Letter to Bartholin disagreeing with Harvey. See also under Vesling, 1637.

S., S. *Discours sceptique sur le passage du chyle, et le mouvement de coeur. Ou sont touchées quelques difficultés sur les opinions des veines lactées, et de la circulation du sang*, Leyden, 1648. Dated at the end from Leyden, 15 October 1647. Author not identified.

1648

RIOLAN, Jean, *fils* (1580–1657), *Enchiridium anatomicum*, Paris, 1648. Criticizing Harvey, who replied in his *Exercitationes duæ*, 1649. (See p. 323.)

WOOD, Zachariah [SYLVIUS] (*fl.* 1648), Preface to Harvey's *Exercitatio anatomica de motu cordis et sanguinis*, Rotterdam, 1648. Reprinted with later editions and translated into English 1653. See Keynes, *Bibliography of Harvey*, 1957, nos. 7–11 and 19.

1649

BRAVO DE SOBREMONTE, Gaspar (1610–83), *Resolutione et consultationum medicarum universam totius philosophiæ doctrina*, Valladolid, 1649. The first Spanish recognition of Harvey. See J. J. Izquierdo, *Harvey: iniciator del metodo experimental*, Mexico, 1936, pp. 207 ff., and his paper, 'On Spanish neglect of Harvey's *De motu cordis*', *Journal of the History of Medicine* (1948), iii. 105–24.

RIOLAN, Jean, *fils* (1580–1657), *Opuscula anatomica nova . . . de motu circulatorio sanguinis in corde*, London, 1649. (See p. 328.)

1650

GASSENDI, Pierre (1592–1655), *De septo cordis pervio, observatio*, Leyden, 1650. Gassendi's tract, disagreeing with Harvey about the permeability of the septum, is printed with four others by Severinus and others. See *Bibliotheca Osleriana*, 3680, and under 1628 above.

SLEGEL, Paul Marquart (1605–83), *De sanguinis motu commentatio*, Hamburg, 1650. He tells in the Preface how he unsuccessfully attempted to persuade Caspar Hofmann to admit Harvey's doctrine of the circulation in 1638. (See p. 237.)

1651

BARTHOLIN, Thomas (1616–80), *Anatomia, ex Caspari Bartholini parentis institutionibus . . . tertium ad sanguinis circulationem reformata*, Leyden, 1651. (See p. 365.)

BIRKENHEAD, Sir John (1616–79), in William Cartwright's *Comedies, Tragicomedies, with other Poems*, London, 1651. Contains a commendatory poem by Birkenhead with references to Harvey. (See p. 309.)

HIGHMORE, Nathaniel (1613–85), *Corporis humani disquisitio anatomica*, The Hague, 1651. Full credit is given to Harvey for his work. See the Dedication to him and pp. 140–63. (See p. 342.)

PECQUET, Jean (1622–74), *Experimenta nova anotomica . . . Dissertatio anatomica de circulatione sanguinis et chyli motu*, Paris, 1651. Harvey's doctrine is accepted.

RUTGERS (*fl.* 1651), in *Exercitationum anatomicarum de motu chyli et sanguinis . . . sub praesidio Dn. Joannis van Horne publice defendere conabitur*, Leyden, 1651. Rutgers defended Harvey against Riolan.

1652

FRANCOSIUS, Hieronimus, Veronensis, *De motu cordis et sanguinis in animalibus*, Verona, 1652. Harvey is quoted. Two small woodcuts of valves on p. 165.

MARCHETTI, Domenico (1626–88), *Anatomia: cui responsiones ad Riolanum contra Veslingium additæ sunt*, Padua, 1652. Folli is corrected concerning the *foramen ovale*.

POWER, Henry (1623–68), *Circulatio sanguinis. Inventio Harveiana*, 1652. A manuscript treatise (British Museum, Sloane MS. 1343) supporting Harvey. Printed by F. J. Cole, *Journal of the History of Medicine* (1957), xii. 291–324. (See p. 319.)

RIOLAN, Jean, *fils* (1580–1657), *Opuscula anatomica, varia et nova. Imprimis de motu sanguinis . . . Responsio ad duas exercitationes postremas*, Paris, 1652. An answer to Harvey's *Exercitationes duæ*, 1649.

RUDBECK, Olaf (1630–1702), *De circulatione sanguinis*, Uppsala, 1652. Supporting Harvey.

1653

PAPIN, Nicolas (d. 1653), *Cordis diastole, adversus, Harveianam innovationem, defensa*, Alençon, 1653. Papin accepts Harvey's circulation but does not agree with his conception of the functions of the heart.

RIOLAN, Jean, *fils* (1580–1657), *Manuel anatomique et pathologique de toute l'anatomie. Augmentée de la sixième partie, sur la circulation du sang*, Paris, 1653. Pp. 696–738 give Riolan's last word in the dispute with Harvey.

ROLFINK, Werner (1599–1673), *Dissertatio de hepate . . . ad circulationem accommodata*, Jena, 1653. His views, in support of Harvey, are repeated in his *Dissertationes anatomicæ*, Nuremberg, 1656.

1654

BAUSNER, Bartholomaeus (1629–83), *Disputatio philosophica de cordis humani actionibus*, Leyden, 1654. Bausner, a Transylvanian, wrote in defence of Harvey's doctrine. See also his *De consensu partium*, Libri III, Amsterdam, 1656, pp. 133–7, Lib. II, cap. vi, *De corde*, though Harvey is not mentioned by name.

GLISSON, Francis (1597–1677), *Anatomia hepatis*, London, 1654. References to Harvey by the Regius Professor of Physic at Cambridge accepting his doctrine.

KYPER, Albert (1605?–55), *Institutiones medicæ ad hypotesin de circulari sanguinis motu compositæ*, Amsterdam, 1654. Kyper was associated with Riolan, and is shown in the frontispiece to Riolan's *Encheiridion anatomicum*, 1649, performing a dissection.

WEBSTER, John (*fl.* 1654), *Academiarum examen*, London, 1654. Harvey's discovery is acknowledged.

1655

ANONYMOUS. *Anthropologie Abstracted: or the Idea of Humane Nature Reflected in briefe Philosophicall, and Anatomicall Collections*, London, 1655. On p. 83 Harvey is mentioned as disagreeing with other authorities on the porosity of the interventricular septum, but the whole description of the heart and its functions is pre-Harveian.

BARTHOLIN, Thomas (1616–80), *Defensio vasorum lacteorum . . . Accedit cl. v. Gulielmi Harvei de venis lacteis sententia expensa ab eodem Th. Bartholino*, Copenhagen, 1655. On p. 179 Harvey is praised for the discovery of the circulation, but blamed for neglecting '*chyliferarum venarum pretium*'.

DIETERICH, Helvius (1601–55), *Vindiciæ adversus Otthonem Tachenium*, Hamburg, 1655. Harvey's doctrine was accepted in this public disputation, when Dieterich was a pupil of Hofmann. (See Ferrario, Poynter, and Franklin, *Journal of the History of Medicine* (1960), xv. 11.)

NARDI, Giovanni (d. 1655), *Noctes geniales, annus primus*, Bologna, 1655. Harvey's discovery is discussed at pp. 712–46. (See p. 363.)

PEIRESC, Nicholas Claude Fabri de (1580–1637), see under Gassendi, 1628.

WINSTON, Thomas (1575–1655), *Anatomy Lectures at Gresham College*, London, 1659. Winston lectured at Gresham College in 1615–42 and 1652–5, and must have known Harvey very well, but ignored his work in the lectures. The editor, F. P., mentions Harvey's name in the preface as occurring next to Winston's in the London *Pharmacopoeia*.

1656

COLLOP, John (*fl.* 1630–60), *Poesis Rediviva: or, Poesie Reviv'd*, London, 1656. Pp. 57–59, 'On Dr. Harvey', a poem of thirty-eight lines in praise of Harvey, followed by one 'On Dr. George Ent,' also mentioning Harvey. There are also references to the circulation in a poem, 'Of the Blood', on pp. 46–47.

HARRINGTON, James (1611–77) *The Commonwealth of Oceana*, London, 1656. P. 2 (writing against Hobbes)—'Which is as if a man should tell famous Harvey, that he transcribed his Circulation of the bloud, not out of the Principles of Nature, but out of the Anatomy of this or that body.'

SHORT, Richard (*fl.* 1656), περι ψύχροποσιας *Of Drinking Water, Against our Novelists, that prescribed it in England*, London, 1656. Reference on A8: 'peradventure the opinion so highly cried up is not new, though it be made more manifest by Doctor Harvie. For Plato in his Times seems to make mention of the circular motion of the blood [περιφερομένου σφοδρῶς]. And thus much for novelties.'

V. *The Will of Thomas Harvey*

Proved in the Prerogative Court of Canterbury, 16 July 1623, folio 77

In the name of God, Amen. The 12th daie of June Anno Domini 1623. I Thomas Harvey of the parishe of Hackney doe make this my will and testament. And first I do humbly commend my soule to God that gave ytt, by whose free mercie in the merites of Jesus Christ I hope to be saved. And my bodie to the earth to be buried with the rest of the families of God.

Touchinge my goods and chattells, I wish to be distributed in legacies to the poore of the parish of Newington five pounds; to the poore of Foulkstone five pounds; to Mr. Paterson, minister of Foulkstone, fortie shilllings; to Patience Penny twentie shillings; to the poore of Hackney fortie shillings; to Mr. Dalbyn twentie-two shillings; to Mr. Partridge twentie-two shillings; to Mr. Jacob, minister, twentie shillings; to James Adwicke, my servant, fortie shillings; to Henry Brockman twentie-two shillings; to Joseph Denn, twentie-two shillings. To every one of my brothers and sisters sonnes, viz. to Thomas Harvey, to Thomas Nott, to Thomas Denn, to Vincent Denn, to every one of them twentie-two shillings. Also to my sisters daughters, viz. Jone, Elizabeth, and Maria Harvey; and to my sister Rolfe's daughters, viz. to Margerie, to Eden, and Em–; and to my sister Wood's daughters, viz. to Cicely, Amey, Joan, and Sara; and to my sister Dennis' daughters, viz. to Mary, Martha, Elizabeth, and Sara; to every one of the last recited eleaven shillings. Also to Richard Haulke and his children, and to Thomas Haulke's and William Haulke's children, to every one of them eleaven shillings apiece. To Mr. William Somner eleaven shillings; to Nicholas Marks twentie shillings; to George Smeede the some of twelve pounds; to Mary Godwyn, widowe, the some of fortie pounds; to Bartholomew Godwyn tenn pounds. Also I doe give unto my twoe grand-children John Harvey and to Daniell Harvey the some of fiftie poundes apiece. And if either of them shall dye before they come to age, that then the survivor of my grandchildren to have the whole hundred pounds. Item I doe give unto uy son John Harvey my capitall messuage and lande in the parishe of Newing-ton and Foulkstone or elsewhere, knowne by the name or names of West Dane or Arpinge, now in the occupation of John Pilchard and Nicholas Marke or their assignes, to be houlden to the said John and his assignes for ever. Also to Mary Foake, my grandchilde, thirtye-three shillings; to William Foake and to Maria Foake to either of them fiftie pounds, and in case one of them should dye, to the over liver of the said William and Maria Foake. Item I doe give unto my three youngest sonnes the some of one hundred pounds already in their hande, to be equally divided between them. Also I give to my daughter Julian the some of fortie pounds; to her eldest sonne Thomas Cullen the some of fortie punds; to Marie Cullen the some of thirtie pounds, to be paide into her at the age of eighteen yeares; to William and John Cullen tenn pounds apiece, to be paide at the age of twentie and one yeares. Item I will one hundred pounds to be spent on my funeral rites. All these petty legacies herein mentioned with some others named by me on my death-bed, I desire may be accepted to buy some small thinge by every one of them to be worne in remebrance of me.

Lastly, I doe make and ordaine my sonne *William Harvey* my sole executor of this my last will and testament, commending him and all the rest of them to the blessings of Almightie God, desireing them to live in his fear and unite with one another fast knitt together, as they may be evermore an helpe one to another.

This his last will.

Witness hereunto

THOMAS HARVEY

DA. DOLBEN Vi of Hackney

Probatum fuit testament^m suprascriptum apud London: decimo sexto die mensis Iulii A.D. 1623 juramento *Wll^i Harvey* filii dicti defuncti et execut.

VI. *The Will of John Harvey*

Proved in the Prerogative Court of Canterbury, 28 July 1645

In the name of God Amen. I John Harvey the elder of London Esq. doe make and ordaine this to be my last will and testam^t revoking all former wills. First I bequeathe my soule to allmightie god believing that thorough the merrits of Christ my Saviour I shall have everlasting life. And as concerning my wordly estate I doe hereby give demise and bequeath all my landes tenements and hereditaments & all my goodes Chittles money plate Jewells debtes offices and leases with all securities and evidences concerning the same to Harbottle Grimston of Bradfield hall in the Countie of Essex Esqu. whoe I make my executor and to his heires & assignes for ever nevertheless upon this trust & confidence that my said executor shall within six monthes after my decease by good and sufficient assurance in law convey and assure upon William Fowcke my nephue or upon his Uncles William Harvey and Eliab Harvey for the use and benefit of the said William and dureing his said life the yearly rent or summe of Fyftie pounde per annum to be yssueing out of all my lande payable half yearly the first payment to begin at the feast of St. Michael th' archangel or th' annunciacion of our blessed lady St Mary the Virgin which shall first happen after my death with such clause of distresse, penalties for non payment of the said rent and other covenants as my said executor in his discrecion shalle thinke fitt: And further upon this Condicion yf the said William Fowcke or any other person or persons in his name or to his use or claymeing by from or under him shall clayme or demande any thing of my executor pretending that anye part of the estate of the said William Fowcke doth still remaine in my handes which I have fully and truly satisfied as may plainly appeare by my accompt touching the estate of the said William that then and from thensforth the grant of the said rent of Fyfty poundes per annum shall cease and be voyd and that the said William his executor administrator and assignes shall repay to my said executor so much as he or they shall hereafter receave by vertue of the said graunt. And also that my said executor shall convey and dispose of the residue & remainder of my estate or any part thereof in manner and forme following or as shall hereafter be limitted & appointed by any writeing under my hande and seale. That is to saye I give and bequeath to the poore of Foulkstone twentie pounds To the poore of Newington neere Hith in the Countie of Kent ten pounds To the poore of the parrish where I shall be buried fyve pounds To my neece Mary the wife of Robert West one hundred pounds To my nephue Thomas Cullen Fyftie pounds To my kinsman William Cullen and his sister Mary Pratt and to her husband fyve pounds a peece To William Halke my kinsman twenty pounds To Elizabeth the wife of John Trowte five pounds To her sisters Luce Katherine and Mary fortie shillings a peece To my cosen John Halke fortie shillings To Michaell Halke fortie shillings To every one of my owne brothers twentie shillings and to their wives five pounds a peece To my sister Harvey the wife of Doctor Harvey one hundred pounds To Ellen Fountayne one hundred pounds To William Jenkins of Foulkstone in the Countie of Kent gent one hundred pounds To Thomas South fortie shillings To my cosen Tomes and his wife Fortie shillings a peece To every one of my poore kindred twentie shillings a peece To my servant George Lowe twenty pounds To Thomas Hunt fourtie shillings To Mary Ellis the wife of Henry Ellis fyve pounds to buy her a mourning gowne To John Skynner & his wife Fourtie shillings a peece and to their servantes twentie shillings a peece Item I will that my said executor shall bestowe one hundred pounds upon my whole funerall and noe more In witness whereof I have hereunto set my hand & seale this six & twentieth day of June Anno Dom 1645 Joh Harvey published and delivered as my last will and testament in the presence of us Jordan Fairfax Richard Nilward Robert Beadle Henry Ellis.

Probatum fuit testamentum suprascriptum apud London coram delecto subdito nostro Roberto Aylet legum doctore subdito delecti subditi nostri Nathanealis Brent militis legum etiam doctoris curiae nostrae praerogativae Londinarum magistri Sive custodis legitime constituti vicesimo octavo die Mensis Julii Anno domini Millesimo sex quadragesimo quinto Juramento Harbottle Grimston Armigeri executoris in hujus modi testamento nominati cui commissa fuit administracio omnium et singulorum bonorum jurium et creditorum dicti defuncti de bene et fideliter administrando eadem Ad sancta dei evangelica Jurati.

VII. *The Will of William Harvey, M.D.*

Proved in the Prerogative Court of Canterbury, 2 May 1659

In the name of the Almighty and Eternal God Amen I WILLIAM HARVEY of
London Doctor of Physicke doe by these presents make and ordaine this my
last Will and testament in manner and forme following Revoking hereby all
former and other wills and testaments whatsoever Imprimis I doe most humbly
render my soule to Him that gave it and to my blessed Lord and Saviour Christ
Jesus and my bodie to the Earth to be buried at the discretion of my executor
herein after named The personall estate which at the time of my decease I shalbe
in any way possessed of either in Law or equitie be it in goods householdstuffe
readie moneys debts duties arrearages of rents or any other wayes whatsoever
and whereof I shall not by this present will or by some Codicill to be hereunto
annexed make a particular gift and disposition I doe after my debts Funeralls
and Legacies paid and discharged give and bequeath the same vnto my loving
brother Mr. Eliab Harvey merchant of London whome I make Executor of this
my last will and testament And whereas I have lately purchased certaine lands
in Northamptonshire or thereabouts commonly knowne by the name of Oxon
grounds and formally belonging vnto the Earl of Manchester and certaine other
grounds in Leicestershire commonly called or knowne by the name of Baron
Parke and sometime heretofore belonging vnto Sir Henry Hastings Knight both
which purchases were made in the name of several persons nominated and trusted
by me and by two severall deeds of declaracon vnder the hands and seales of all
persons any waye parties or privies to the said trusts are declared to be first vpon
trust and to the intent that I should be permitted to enioye all the rents and profits and the benefit of the collaterall securitie during my life and from and after
my decease Then upon trust and for the benefit of such person and persons and
of and for such estate and estates and Interests And for raysing and payment of
such summe and summes of Money Rents Charges Annuities and yearly pay-
ménts to and for such purposes as from time to time by any writing or writings to
be by me signed and sealed in the presence of Two or more credible witnesses
or by my last will and testament in writing should declare limit direct or appoint
And further in trust that the said Mannors and lands and everie part thereof
together with the Collaterall securitie should be assigned conveyed and assured
vnto such persons and for suche Estates as the same should by me be limited
and directed charged and chargeable nevertheleles with all Annuities rents
and summes of money by me limited and appointed if any such shalbe And
in default of such appointment then to Eliab Harvey his heires executors and
Assignes or to such as he or they shall nominate as by the said two deeds of
declaracon both of them bearing date the tenth day of July in the year of
our Lord God one Thousand six hundred Fiftie and one more at large it
both appeare I doe now hereby declare limit direct and appoint that with all

convenient speed after my decease there shalbe raised satisfied and paid these severall summes of money Rents Charges and Annuities herein after expressed and likewise all such other summes of Money Rents Charges or Annuities which at any time hereafter in any Codicill to be hereunto annexed shall happen to be limited or expressed And first I appoint so much money to be raised and laid out vpon that building which I have already begun to erect within the Colledge of Physicians in London as will serve to finish the same according to the designe already made   Item I give and bequeath vnto my lo sister in Law Mrs Eliab Harvey one hundred pounds to buy something to keepe in remembrance of me Item I give to my Niece Mary Pratt all that Linnen householdstuffe and furniture which I have at Coome neere Croydon for the vse of Will Foulkes and to whome his keeping shalbe assigned after her death or before me at any time Item I give vnto my Niece Mary West and her daughter Amy West halfe the Linnen I shall leave at London in my chests and Chambers together with all my plate excepting my Coffey pot   Item I give to my lo sister Eliab all the other halfe of my Linnen which I shall leave behind me   Item I give to my lo sister Daniell at Lambeth and to everie one of her children severally the summe of fiftie pounds Item I give to my lo Coosin Mr Heneage Finch for his paines counsell and advice about the contriving of this my will one hundred pounds Item I give to all my little Godchildren Nieces and Nephews severally to everie one Fiftie pounds Item I give and bequeath to the towne of Foulkestone where I was borne two hundred pounds to be bestowed by the advice of the Mayor thereof and my Executor for the best vse of the poore Item I give to the poore of Christ hospitall in Smithfield thirtie pounds   Item I give to Will Harvey my godsonne the sonne of my brother Mich Harvey deceased one hundred pounds and to his brother Michaell Fiftie pounds Item I give to my Nephew Tho Cullen and his children one hundred pounds and to his brother my godsonne Will Cullen one hundred pounds   Item I give to my Nephew Jhon Harvey the sonne of my lo brother Tho Harvey deceased two hundred pounds   Item I give to my Servant John Raby for his diligence in my service and sicknesse twentie pounds And to Alice Garth my Servant Tenne pounds over and above what I am already owing vnto her by my bill which was her mistresses legacie Item I give among the poor children of Amy Rigdon daughter of my lo vncle Mr Tho Halke twentie pounds Item among other my poorest kindred one hundred pounds to be distributed at the appointment of my Executor   Item I give among the servants of my sister Dan at my Funeralls Five pounds And likewise among the servants of my Nephew Dan Harvey at Coome as much Item I give to my Cousin Mary Tomes Fifty pounds   Item I give to my lo Friend Mr Prestwood one hundred pounds   Item I give to everie one of my lo brother Eliab his sonnes and daughters severally Fiftie pounds apiece All which legacies and gifts aforesaid are chiefly to buy something to keepe in remembrance of me Item I give among the servants of my brother Eliab which shalbe dwelling with him at the time of my decease tenne pounds   Furthermore I give and bequeath vnto my Sister Eliabs Sister Mrs Coventrey a widowe during her natural life the yearly rent or summe of twentie pounds Item I give to my Niece Mary West during her naturall life the yearly rent or summe of Fortie pounds Item I give for the vse and behoofe and better ordering of Will Foulkes for and during the term of his life vnto my Niece Mary Pratt the yearly rent of tenne pounds which summe if it happen my said Niece shall dye before him I desire may be paid to them to whome his keeping shalbe appointed Item I will that the twentie pounds which I yearly allowe him my brother Galen Browne may be continued as a legacie from his sister during his naturall life Item I will that the payments to Mr Samuel Fentons children out of the profits of Buckholt Lease be orderly performed as my deere deceased lo wife gave order so long as that lease shall stand good Item I give vnto Alice Garth during her naturall life the yearly rent or summe of twentie pounds Item To John Raby during his naturall life sixteene pounds yearly rent All which yearly rents or summes to be paid halfe yearly at the two most vsuall feasts in the yeare viz Michaelmas and our Lady day without any deduction for or by reason of any manner of taxes to be any way hereafter imposed The first payment of all the said rents or Annuities respectively to beginne at such of those feasts which shall first happen next after my decease Thus I give the remainder of my lands vnto my lo brother Eliab and his heires All my legacies and gifts &c. being performed and discharged Touching my bookes and householdstuffe Pictures and apparell of which I have not already disposed I give to the Colledge of Physicians all my bookes and papers and my best Persia long Carpet and my blue sattin imbroyedyed Cushion one paire of brasse Andirons with fireshovell and tongues of brasse for the ornament of the meeting roome I have erected for that purpose Item I give my velvet gowne to my lo friend Mr Doctor Scarbrough desiring him and my lo friend Mr Doctor Ent to looke over those scattered remnant of my poore Librarie and what bookes papers or rare collections they shall thinke fit to present to the Colledge and the rest to be Sold and with the money buy better And for their paines I give to Mr Doctor Ent all the presses and shelves he please to make use of and five pounds to buy him a ring to keepe or weare in remembrance of me And to Doctor Scarbrough All my little silver instruments of surgerie Item I give all my Chamber furniture tables bed bedding hangings which I have at Lambeth to my Sister Dan and her daughter Sarah And all that at London to my lo Sister Eliab and her daughter or my godsonne Eliab as she shall appoint Lastly I desire my executor to assigne over the custode of Will Fowkes after the death of my Niece Mary Pratt if she happen to dye before him vnto the Sister of the said William my Niece Mary West Thus I have finished my last Will in three pages two of them written with own hand and my name subscribed to everie one with my hand and seal to the last

WILL HARVEY.

Signed sealed and published as the last will and testament of me William Harvey In the presence of us Edward Dering Henneage Finch Richard Flud Francis Finche Item I have since written a Codicill with my owne hand in a sheet of paper to be added hereto with my name thereto subscribed and my seale.

ITEM I will that the sumes and charges here specified be added and annexed vnto my last will and testament published heretofore in the presence of Sir Edward Dering and Mr Henneage Finch and others and as a Codicill by my Executor in like manner to be performed whereby I will and bequeath to John Denn sonne of Vincent Denne the summe of thirtie pounds. Item to my good friend Mr Tho Hobbs to buy something to keepe in remembrance of me tenne pounds and to Mr Kennersley in like manner twentie pounds Item what moneys shalbe due to me from Mr Hen Thompson his fees being discharged I give to my friend Mr Prestwood Item what money is of mine viz one hundred pounds in the hands of my Cosin Rigdon I give halfe thereof to him towards the marriage of his niece and the other halfe to be given to Mrs Coventrey for her sonne Walter when he shall come of yeares and for vse my Cosin Rigdon giving securitie I would he should pay none Item what money shalbe due to me and Alice Garth my servant on a pawne now in the hands of Mr Prestwood I will after my decease shall be given my said servant for her diligence about me in my siknesse and service both interest and principall Item if in case it so fall out that my good friend Mrs Coventrey during her widowhood shall not dyet on freecost with my brother or Sister Eliab Harvey Then I will and bequeath to her one hundred marke yearly during her widowhood Item I will and bequeath to my loving Cosin Mr Henneage Finch (more than heretofore) to be for my godsonne Will Finche one hundred pounds Item I will and bequeath yearly during her life a rent of thirtie pounds vnto Mrs Jane Nevison Widdowe in case she shall not preferre her selfe in marriage to be paid quarterly by even porcons the first to beginn at Christmas Michaelmas or Lady day or Midsummer which first happens after my decease Item I give to my Goddaughter Mrs Eliz Glover daughter of my Cosin Toomes the yearly rent of tenne pounds from my decease vnto the end of five years Item to her brother Mr Rich Toomes thirty pounds as a legacie Item I give to John Cullen sonne of Tho Cullen deceased all what I have formerly given his father and more one hundred pounds Item I will that what I have bequeathed to my Niece Mary West be given to her husband my Cosin Rob West for his daughter Amy West Item what should have bene to my Sister Dan deceased I will be given my lo Niece her daughter in Law Item I give my Cosin Mrs Mary Ranton fortie pounds to buy something to keep in remembrance of me Item to my nephews Michaell and Will the sonnes of my brother Mich one hundred pounds to either of them Item all the furniture of my chamber and all the hangings I give to my godsonne Mr Eliab Harvey at his marriage and all my red damaske furniture and plate to my Cosin Mary Harvey Item I give my best velvet gowne to Doctor Scarbrowe. WILL HARVEY

Memorandum that upon Sunday the twentie eighth day of December in the yeare of our Lord one thousand six hundred fiftie six I did againe peruse my last will which formerly conteined three pages and hath now this fourth page added to it And I doe now this present Sunday December 28 1656 publish and declare these foure pages whereof the three last are written with my owne hand to be my last will In the presence of Henneage Finch John Raby.

THIS WILL with the Codicill annexed was proved at London on the second day of May In the yeare of our Lord God one Thousand six hundred fiftie nine before the Judge for probate of wills and granting Adcons lawfully authorized By the oath of Eliab Harvey the Brother and sole executor therein named To whom Administracon of all and singular the goods Chattells and debts of the said deceased was granted and committed He being first sworne truely to administer.

CHAS. DYNELEY
JOHN IGGULDEN   } *Deputy*
W. F. GOSTLING   } *Registers.*

The will of Harvey is without date. But was almost certainly made some time in the course of 1652. He speaks of certain deeds of declaration bearing date the 10th of July, 1651; and he provides money for the completion of the buildings which he has 'already begun to erect within the College of Physicians.' Now these structures were finished in the early part of 1653. The will was, therefore, written between July 1651, and February 1653. The codicil is also undated: but we may presume that it was added shortly before Sunday the 28th of December 1656, the day on which Harvey reads over the whole document and formally declares and publishes it as his last will and testament in the presence of his friend Henneage Finch, and his faithful servant John Raby (*The Works of Harvey*, translated by Robert Willis, London, 1847, p. xcvi).

Another grant of administration dated 1659 has been found to accompany an official copy of the Will now in the Wellcome Historical Medical Library as follows (see F. N. L. Poynter, *Journal of the History of Medicine* (1957), xii. 165–6):

'Richard Lord Protector of yᵉ ComonWealth of England Scotland & Ireland and the Dominions & Territories thereto belonging To all persons to whome theise presents shall come Greeting Know yee yᵗ uppon yᵉ second day of May in the yeare of our Lord God one Thousand six hundred fifty Nine, before yᵉ Judges for probate of Wills & granting Administrations lawfully authorized The Last Will & Testament of William Harvey late of yᵉ parish of Sᵗ Peters yᵉ poores in London, but att Roehampton in Surrey Doctor in Phisicke Deceased was at London in Comon forme proved which Will is to theise presents annexed and Administration of all & singular yᵉ goods chattels & debts of yᵉ said deceased which any manner of way concerne him or his said Will was granted & Comitted to Eleab Harvey his brother the sole and only Executor named in yᵉ said Will hee having first taken his oath well & truly to Administer yᵉ said goods chattels & debts according to yᵉ tenor & effect of yᵉ same Will and to make or cause to be made a true & perfect Inventory of all & singuler yᵉ goods chattels & debts of yᵉ said deceased which have shall or may any way whatsoever come to his hands possession or knowledge and alsoe a true & just accompte in & Concerninge his said Administration when hee shalbe assigned or Lawfully called soe to doe which touching an Inventorie hee was presently assigned to performe at or before yᵉ last day of June next Enseuinge Given at London under yᵉ Seale of yᵉ Court for probate of Wills & granting Administrations The day & yeare aforesayd

Mark Cottle Regʳ   R. Sankey   Wm. Hobbs.

VIII. *A Letter from Harvey to Lord Denbigh, 20 March 1636/7*[1]

Too late for inclusion in the body of the book, a letter from Harvey, hitherto unrecorded, has appeared in the London sale rooms (Newberry Library sale, Sotheby's 9 November 1965, lot 363). Though the recipient is not named, he was evidently Basil Feilding, Viscount Denbigh. The 'injurious affront' received by Denbigh's house no doubt refers to his strong protest against the arrest of two men in a house rented by him and adjoining his own dwelling. One man had been wounded and the Ambassador's gondolier had been beaten. The *Collegio* of Venice replied that the prisoners had been guilty of high treason and were justifiably arrested (*Calendar of State Papers. Venice, 1636–9*. London, 1923, xxiv, pp. 137–8). The mention of the birth of a Princess must refer to the Princess Anne, born 17 March 1636/7, although Harvey, contrary to custom, dated his letter 20 March 1637 instead of 1636. The text of the letter, transcribed by Dr. Gweneth Whitteridge, is as follows:

Right Honᵇˡᵉ & Eccell.

Although there be very little I can write to yʳ Eccel. that ye will not have more fully from a better hand, yett I cannot perswade my selfe, to lett soe convenient a messenger depart wᵗʰout presenting to yʳ Eccel. att the least my thankes for soe greate & soe many favours receyved, & as youʳ humble affectionat servant condole that iniurious affront youʳ howse receyved, not dowting but, as I perceyve heare yoʳ proceedinges are thought descreet & iust, soe you will receyve therin honor & satisfaction, wʰ as I hartely wish soe I am, & ever, wilbe ready with the best of my poore endeavours, to promote. We are heare contriving & proiecting for the sea & plantations, butt what will follow or how succeede is uncerteyne. The plauge we hope this weeke will declin, although it be as nothing & her Mᵉʸ safe brought a bed of a princes lyeth in att S James. The springe begineth heare very early it being now very fayer & pleasant dry weather. These lines I pray pardon wʰ are rather to begg yʳ commands then any performance of the duty of

yʳ Eccell.

Sᵗ James London   obliged servant
    March 20   Will Harvey
      1637

1 Acquired in 1974 by the Pierpont Morgan Library, New York.

INDEX